PRINCIPLES AND PRACTICE OF
ELECTRICAL ENGINEERING

Principles and Practice of
ELECTRICAL ENGINEERING

ALEXANDER GRAY, Whit.Sch., M.Sc.

Late Professor of Electrical Engineering, Cornell University
Author of "Electrical Machine Design"

Revised by

G. A. WALLACE, M.Sc.

Professor of Electrical Engineering
McGill University

SEVENTH EDITION

McGRAW-HILL BOOK COMPANY, INC.

New York   Toronto   London

1955

THE MAPLE PRESS COMPANY, YORK, PA.

PREFACE

This electrical-engineering textbook has been written primarily for students who are specializing in other branches of engineering. However, it is also suitable as a first book for students who are specializing in electrical engineering because it has been written with the basic idea in mind that in this age of rapid scientific development, even nonelectrical students will derive more benefit from a clear understanding of the fundamental principles of electrical circuits and machines than from the accumulation of much ephemeral and half-understood information and of rule-of-thumb methods.

In the current revision the general character and purpose of the book have not been changed. It remains an elementary textbook. But the treatments of certain topics have been made more precise, especially those dealing with a-c machinery and electronics. It is hoped that these increases in precision are all in the interest of greater clarity and ease of understanding. The most elementary textbook is not necessarily the one that is most easily understood.

The revision has been fairly thorough. Twenty per cent of the articles are either new or completely rewritten, many others have been modified, and there are ninety-nine new figures. The major portion of the additions and improvements is to be found in the chapters dealing with thermionic tubes, induction motors, synchronous motors, and transformers. The major additions include the following: Kirchhoff's laws; current limiting by amplidyne control; automobile-battery charging; the polyphase wattmeter; basic design of a transformer; three-phase power measurement with instrument transformers; equations for rotor current, torque, power factor, and slip of an induction motor; vector diagrams, locked test, and circle diagram for an induction motor; equivalent circuits for transformers and induction motors; dynamic braking of induction motors; an improved treatment of the operation of synchronous motors; a revised and extended treatment of single-phase motors; demonstration and calculation of the performance of amplifiers; distortion and power limits; negative feedback; impedance matching in the output stage; grid-controlled thyratron rectifier and speed control of a d-c motor; and the cathode-ray oscilloscope.

Problems marked with an asterisk are not provided with answers.

G. A. WALLACE

CONTENTS

power factor.   Resistance, inductance, and capacity in series and in parallel.
Impedances in parallel.   Single-phase transmission line.   Complex-quantity
method of solving alternating-current circuits.   Circuit constants.

Single-phase, two-phase, and three-phase generators.   Voltage, current, and
power in Y- and Δ-connected machines.   The three-phase three-wire system.
Three-phase versus two-phase.   Power measurements in three-phase circuits.
Watt-radio power-factor chart.   Generator construction.   Kilovolt-ampere
rating of generators.   Equivalent Y and Δ loads.   Power-factor correction
three-phase.   Unbalanced three-phase loads.

General theory of the transformer.   Leakage reactance.   Emf equation.
Losses and efficiency.   Equivalent resistance and reactance.   Percentage
reactance.   Cooling of transformers.   Core-type and shell-type transformers.
Autotransformer.   Induction voltage regulator.   The induction furnace.
The constant-current transformer.   Saturable reactor.

Polarity of transformers.   Connections to two-phase and three-phase lines.
Open-delta or V connection.   Relative advantages of the Y and delta connections.   The Scott connection.   Instrument transformers.

The rotating field.   Multipolar machines.   Running and starting torque.
Squirrel-cage rotors and wound rotors.   Running conditions.   Adjustable-
speed operation.   The double squirrel-cage rotor for high starting torque.
Vector diagrams.   Equivalent circuit of an induction motor.   Starting induction motors.   The induction generator.   Brush-shifting polyphase induction
motor.

Armature reaction.   Vector diagram.   Voltage characteristic curves.   Measurement of synchronous reactance.   Automatic voltage regulators.   Rating.
Efficiency.   Short-circuit current.

Principle of operation of the synchronous motor.   Vector diagrams.   Maximum output.   Underexcited and overexcited operation.   Power-factor correction by means of the synchronous motor.   Parallel operation of alternating-
current generators.   Synchronizing.   Hunting.

The synchronous motor.   The induction motor.   Adjustable-speed operation
of induction motors.   The brush-shifting polyphase induction motor.   Starting compensators.   Starter for wound-rotor motor.   Starting synchronous
motors.   Dynamic braking of induction motors.

PRINCIPLES AND PRACTICE OF ELECTRICAL ENGINEERING

1

MATTER AND ELECTRICITY

1. The Constituents of Matter. The number of substances that exist in the world today is extremely large and is continually increasing as scientists and engineers evolve new chemical processes. These different substances are the result of different combinations of a relatively small number of chemical elements, and according to modern theory the elements themselves are all composed of the same constituents.

For a time it was believed that these constituents were only two in number, namely, *protons* and *electrons*. Further research produced evidence to indicate that there are more than two constituents, but, since the electrical and chemical properties of an atom appear to be determined entirely by its protons and electrons, the other ingredients may be practically ignored in a textbook on electrical engineering.

The AIEE Standard Definitions of Electrical Terms define the proton as *the natural, elementary quantity of positive electricity* and the electron as *the natural, elementary quantity of negative electricity*. If these two definitions are accepted, it follows that the two principal ingredients of matter are positive and negative electricity.

2. Properties of Protons and Electrons. It requires approximately 6.02×10^{23} protons to make up a mass of 1 g, and the mass of a proton is 1,847 times the mass of an electron.

Protons repel each other, through apparently empty space, and so do electrons, but between protons and electrons there is attraction. These forces of repulsion and attraction between protons and electrons are presumably the most fundamental forces of the material universe. They lie behind all chemical and electrical action and the structure of all matter. They also lie outside the present range of human understanding, and for the time being we must accept them as blindly as we accept the force of gravity.

3. Structure of the Atom. An atom may be regarded as the smallest particle of an element that can exist. If an atom of any element is split into two parts, the result is the creation of two new atoms of some element, or elements, of lower atomic weight.   For example, if an atom of oxygen were split into four equal parts, the result would presumably be four helium atoms, or it might be split unequally to produce one carbon atom and one helium atom.

An atom is composed of two parts, namely, the central *nucleus* and the *surrounding*, or *orbital, electrons*.   The nucleus contains all the protons and all the other ingredients, if any, of the atom, except the orbital electrons.   The electrons are generally considered to be traveling around the nucleus in much the same way that the planets of the solar system travel around the sun.

Normally every atom contains protons and electrons in equal numbers. A hydrogen atom consists of 1 orbital electron and 1 proton.   A helium atom consists of 2 orbital electrons and a nucleus that contains 2 protons.

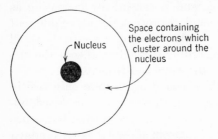

A carbon atom has 6 orbital electrons and its nucleus contains 6 protons.   A gold atom has 79 orbital electrons and its nucleus contains 79 protons.

If the nuclei contained nothing but protons, the atomic weights would be proportional to the numbers of protons in the various atoms; but this proportionality does not hold, and in the case of all the elements except hydrogen the atomic weight is usually at least double the number of known protons in the atom.   Consequently, the nuclei must contain something else besides protons in order to make up the correct masses.   The additional constituent, or constituents, that make up the correct masses appear to have no effect upon the chemical or electrical properties of the atoms; in fact they usually appear in different amounts in different atoms of the same element, thus giving rise to what are called *isotopes*. The isotopes of an element have different atomic weights but cannot be distinguished from one another chemically.

FIG. 1. Highly conventionalized diagram of an atom.   NOTE: The boundaries of the two spaces are drawn here as the surfaces of spheres because a drawing must have a definite shape, but the drawing should not be interpreted as definitely asserting that the spaces are spherical.   The ratio of the diameters of the two spheres also has no significance.

4. Electric Charges.   Normally, every body contains equal numbers of protons and electrons, but it is possible to remove electrons from a body or add electrons to it.   A body that contains unequal numbers of electrons and protons is said to be **electrically charged.**

A body that contains more than its normal number of electrons is said to be **negatively charged.**

A body that contains less than its normal number of electrons is said to be **positively charged.**

In practice, the charging is almost invariably accomplished by the addition or removal of electrons; for example, if a glass rod is rubbed with a piece of silk, the silk will rub electrons off the surface of the glass and therefore leave it positively charged. The silk will be negatively charged, since it carries the electrons that it removed from the glass.

Two pieces of silk treated in this way will repel each other and so will two pieces of glass, but between the glass and the silk there is attraction. That is, like charges repel each other and unlike charges attract each other. The repulsion between like charges and the attraction between unlike charges are, of course, made up of the repulsions and attractions between the individual excess protons and electrons. Bodies which are not electrically charged, that is, which contain equal numbers of protons and electrons, neither attract nor repel each other in this way, because the forces of attraction and repulsion are in equilibrium.

The nucleus of an atom, since it contains all the protons of the atom, is always positively charged. The cluster of electrons surrounding the nucleus constitutes a negative charge of electricity and is presumably held in place by the force of attraction between itself and the positively charged nucleus.

Although an atom may contain any number of orbital electrons from 1, in the case of hydrogen, to 92, in the case of uranium, it is generally not possible to remove more than one electron from any one atom. In fact, no one has ever succeeded in removing as many electrons from a body as there are atoms in that body. The greater the number of electrons removed from a body, the greater the number of excess protons in that body, and the greater the force with which these excess protons resist the removal of additional electrons. The activities of the one removable electron per atom constitute the main basis for the whole field of electrical engineering.

5. Electric Current. *A moving stream of electrons constitutes an electric current.* To produce currents of the order of magnitude met with in engineering practice requires the flow of billions of billions of electrons per second. For example, the current flowing in the filament of an ordinary incandescent lamp is about 10^{19} electrons per sec.

A moving stream of positive charges also constitutes an electric current, and in the case of flow through ionized gases and electrolytes the current consists partly of positively charged particles moving in one direction and partly of negatively charged particles moving in the opposite direction. In all other cases the electric current consists solely of moving electrons.

6. Insulators, Conductors, and Resistors.   An insulator is a material which offers a very high resistance to the passage through it of an electric current, and which is used to confine a current of electricity to a particular path.   In many cases the insulator also performs the additional function of acting as a mechanical support for the conductor.   A conductor is a material which offers a comparatively very low resistance to the passage of an electric current, and which is used to provide a path for an electric current.

A perfect insulator would offer an infinite resistance to the passage of an electric current, and a perfect conductor would offer no resistance. No perfect insulators or conductors are available in engineering practice, but the best insulators, such as air, glass, mica, porcelain, rubber, oil, and varnish, have an electric resistance at room temperatures of more than a million million times that of copper or aluminum.

A resistor is a material that is used to oppose the flow of an electric current, either for the purpose of controlling that current, as in the case of rheostats, or for the purpose of converting electrical energy into heat, as in the case of electric stoves and lamps.

The enormous variation in electric resistance among the various substances is, of course, due to differences in structure of the substances.   A current of electricity through a body is merely a continuous drift of electrons through that body.   If every molecule in a given body held fast to every electron belonging to it, there could be no drift of the electrons, and the body would be a perfect insulator.   In order that a body may be a conductor, there must be a certain amount of fluidity of the constituent electrons.   Even in the best conductors, however, the great majority of the electrons are definitely attached to particular atoms and are not free to drift from atom to atom.

Inasmuch as the forces holding the electrons in place in an insulator are presumably not infinite, it follows that, if a force tending to drive a current through the insulator is made sufficiently great, the electrons can be forced away from their atoms and made to flow through the body. When this happens, the insulator is said to be ruptured or punctured. In most cases the rupture is accompanied by a certain amount of chemical action or by a mechanical fracture, and the insulator, if it is a solid, is ruined.

7. Velocity of Flow of Electric Current.   It is frequently stated, in a rather loose way, that the velocity of electricity is approximately 187,000 miles per sec.   This does not mean that the electrons flow at that speed. It merely means that if we suddenly introduce a flow of electrons into one end of a copper wire, which is 187,000 miles long, electrons will begin to come out at the other end—or attempt to come out—1 sec later. Similarly, if we suddenly introduce a flow of air into one end of a pipe, which is 1,100 ft long and is already filled with air, there will be an interval of 1 sec before air begins to flow out at the other end.   That is, a pressure wave travels in air at the rate of 1,100 ft per sec.   The copper wire is full of electrons, just as the pipe is full of molecules of air, and the electrical pressure wave travels through the array of electrons at the rate of 187,000 miles per sec.   The velocity of a pressure wave depends upon the physical constants of the medium and is independent of the magnitude of the pressure.   The sustained flow of the medium under a steady pressure is a phenomenon quite distinct from the traveling of a pressure wave through that medium.   The velocity of the sustained flow depends upon the magnitude of the pressure and upon the resistance offered by the path.

The average velocity of the flow of electrons through wires in ordinary engineering practice is surprisingly low.   For example, in an ordinary incandescent lamp the electrons flow along the tungsten filament with an average velocity of slightly less than 1 in. per sec, and this velocity is great enough to heat the filament to a white heat.   The copper conductors leading to the lamp are very much larger in cross section and the velocity of flow is correspondingly less.   It should be realized, however, that an inch is an enormous distance in comparison with the dimensions of an atom.

8. Electric Currents from Friction. Prior to the discovery of the voltaic cell the only known method of producing electric charges and electric currents was the friction method.   The friction machines constructed during that period are rarely used now, but unfortunately the method still functions in our factories and has been the cause of many fires.   Manufacturing companies that use inflammable materials are careful to install extensive grounding systems on their apparatus in order to provide paths through which the electric charges produced by friction may leak away without doing any damage.

9. Electric Currents from Chemical Action. One of the biggest steps in the development of our electrical knowledge was the discovery that electric currents may be produced by chemical action.

If a sheet of zinc and a sheet of copper are partially immersed in dilute sulfuric acid and are connected together by a conducting wire, as shown in Fig. 2, an electric current will flow continuously through the connecting wire, the zinc will be gradually converted into soluble zinc sulfate, and hydrogen gas will collect on the surface of the copper plate and escape in bubbles to the atmosphere.

The chemical action will cease immediately if the connecting wire is removed, showing that the electric current is necessary to the chemical action.   The copper plate remains unaffected by the chemical action. Its only function is to complete the electric circuit and any other good conductor that is chemically inert with respect to sulfuric acid would do equally well.

The zinc and copper plates are called the *electrodes*, the sulfuric acid solution is called the *electrolyte*, and the assembly of electrodes, electrolyte, and container is called a *voltaic cell*, or a *primary battery cell*.

10. Theory of the Voltaic Cell. When H_2SO_4 (sulfuric acid) is dissolved in water, some of the H_2SO_4 molecules become dissociated, or split up, into three component parts, namely, H^+, H^+, and $SO_4^=$. These component parts are electrically charged and are called *ions*. The two minus signs on the $SO_4^=$ ion indicate that it carries two more than its normal number of electrons. The plus sign on each hydrogen ion indicates that it carries one less than its normal number of electrons, the plus and minus signs being used in accordance with the definition of positive and negative

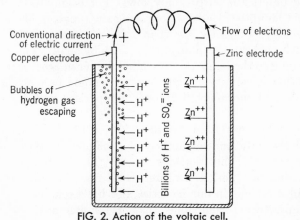

FIG. 2. Action of the voltaic cell.

charges. The minus charges are equal to the positive charges, so that the liquid as a whole is not electrically charged.

When a plate of pure zinc is immersed in the sulfuric acid solution, zinc ions (Zn^{++}) tend to leave the plate and go into solution to form zinc sulfate. Therefore every time an atom of zinc leaves the plate it gives the plate a negative charge of 2 excess electrons. As the negative charge accumulates on the zinc plate, the force with which this charge opposes the leaving of Zn^{++} ions increases and in a very short time becomes great enough to stop the chemical action. A condition of chemical and electrical equilibrium is thus arrived at and no further action takes place. The zinc plate carries a definite negative charge, and the electrolyte an exactly equal positive charge.

If now we insert a copper plate in the electrolyte and connect the two plates together with a wire, as shown in Fig. 2, the negative charge will expand through the connecting wire into the copper plate, in the same way that gas will flow from a higher-pressure tank into a lower-pressure tank if the two are connected by a tube. Electrons repel each other just as gas molecules do—though not for the same reason—and the flow of electricity is in many ways closely analogous to the flow of a gas. The negative charge that flows over into the copper plate attracts the positively charged hydrogen ions, and, as each hydrogen ion touches the copper, it acquires one of the excess electrons from the copper plate and becomes a normal hydrogen atom. The atoms unite in twos to form hydrogen molecules, and the hydrogen molecules form bubbles and pass off into the air. As the negative charge on the zinc plate leaks away through the connecting wire, the state of chemical and electrical equilibrium at the surface of the zinc plate is upset, and additional Zn^{++} ions leave the zinc plate and thus provide additional excess electrons to maintain the negative charge. Thus the action is continuous until either the acid or the zinc is entirely consumed.

This theory of the voltaic cell is decidedly sketchy but it does describe what actually takes place. A more complete explanation of the why and wherefore of the actions could be based only upon an extensive knowledge of physical chemistry.

11. Direction of the Current. The original investigators of the action of voltaic cells were familiar with positive and negative charges of electricity, as obtained by friction, and soon discovered that in the cell described above the zinc plate was negatively charged and the copper plate positively charged. They were also familiar with the fact that, if two insulated conductors, carrying electric charges equal in magnitude but opposite in sign, were connected together by means of a conducting wire, the electric charges disappeared. They did not know whether the negative charge flowed over to neutralize the positive charge, or the positive charge flowed over to neutralize the negative charge, or both charges flowed over to neutralize each other. They did, however, recognize that the flow had directional sense, and for convenience they adopted an arbitrary convention as to the direction and decided that the direction of the current should be identified by the direction of flow of the positive charge. They were unfortunate in their choice, because in all conducting paths except ionized gases and electrolytes the electric current is simply a flow of electrons, that is, of negative electricity. The convention has never been changed. Consequently, when we say that the current is flowing in one direction in a wire, we know that the only actual flow of electricity is in the opposite direction. If this convention becomes too confusing in any particular case, the term *electric current* is dropped, and the phrase *flow of electrons* is used instead.

12. Electromotive Force and Potential. Electromotive force is the force that causes a current of electricity to flow. If we have two compressed-air storage tanks, one of which is at a higher pressure than the other, and we connect the two tanks together by means of a pipe, air will flow along this pipe from the high-pressure tank to the low-pressure tank. The force that causes this current of air to flow is the pressure difference between the two tanks. Similarly, in the zinc-copper voltaic cell described above, the zinc and copper electrodes both contain vast quantities of electrons, but owing to the chemical action the zinc electrode is charged to a greater *electron pressure* than the copper electrode. The *electron-pressure difference* is the electromotive force that causes the flow of electrons from the zinc electrode to the copper electrode through the external connecting circuit.

The term *electron pressure*, although descriptive, has no social standing. The word *potential* had been used to express the same idea for many years before the development of the electron theory.

Two conducting bodies are said to be at the same *potential* if there is no flow of electric current between them when they are joined together by a conducting wire. The two electrodes of a voltaic cell are said to be at different potentials, and the *difference in potential* between the two electrodes is the electromotive force available to cause a current to flow.

13. Parallel and Series Connections of Voltaic Cells. A group of voltaic cells connected together is called a battery. Figure 3 is a conventional diagram representing three voltaic cells connected in parallel. The difference in potential between the two terminals A and B of Fig. 3

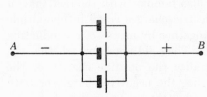

is independent of the number of cells, because connecting together a number of points that are all at the same potential does not affect the potential. The quantity of zinc and of sulfuric acid is proportional to the number of cells, and, since 1 atom of zinc and 1 molecule of acid are consumed for every 2 electrons that pass through the external circuit, it follows that the capacity of the group of cells, measured in current strength times time, is proportional to the number of cells connected in parallel. Similarly, if we connect a number of pumps or air compressors in parallel, the pressure obtainable is independent of the number of pumps or compressors, but the capacity is directly proportional to the number of pumps or compressors.

FIG. 3. Three cells in parallel.

Figure 4 represents three voltaic cells connected in series. If the potential difference between the terminals C and D is measured, it will be found to be three times the potential difference across the terminals of a single cell.

In the theory of the action of the voltaic cell given in Art. 10, it was tacitly assumed that none of the constituent parts of the cell was electrically charged before the cell was assembled, so that the cell as a whole remained uncharged, the negative charge which developed on the zinc electrode being equal in magnitude and opposite in sign to the positive charge carried by the electrolyte and copper electrode. The only condition for chemical and electrical equilibrium in the cell, however, is that there should be a certain definite potential difference between the zinc electrode and the surrounding electrolyte. Raising or lowering the potentials of both the zinc and the electrolyte by equal amounts does not affect the condition of equilibrium. Consequently, the potential difference between the terminals of a battery consisting of a group of voltaic

FIG. 4. Three cells in series.

cells connected in series is equal to the potential difference across a single cell multiplied by the number of cells. The capacity, measured in current strength times time, is independent of the number of cells connected in series, since each cell must carry the total current. Similarly, three pumps connected in series will develop three times as much pressure as a single pump.

Therefore if we wish to increase the electromotive force of a battery, we connect more cells in series; while if we wish to increase the current capacity, we connect more cells in parallel or else use larger cells. The current carried by each cell of N similar cells connected in parallel is equal to $1/N$ times the total current delivered by the battery.

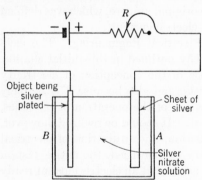

FIG. 5. Electroplating.

14. Electroplating and Refining. In the zinc-copper voltaic cell we have an example of chemical action driving an electric current. The reverse effect is obtained in electroplating and refining. A current is driven through a cell by an external electromotive force, and chemical actions take place in the cell that would not take place of their own accord.

For example, Fig. 5 shows a possible arrangement for silver plating. A voltaic cell V drives an electric current through the cell, the amount of the current being controlled by the variable resistance R. In a solution of silver nitrate in water the silver nitrate is always partially dissociated or split up into Ag^+ and NO_3^- ions. The voltaic battery maintains a positive charge on electrode A, and a negative charge on electrode B. Therefore, since unlike charges attract each other, the positively charged silver ions are attracted to electrode B and on touching it receive 1 electron from it and become ordinary silver atoms. These silver atoms adhere closely to the electrode and form on it a silver film that increases steadily in thickness as the process continues. Additional Ag^+ ions go into solution from the silver sheet A to restore the condition of chemical and electrical equilibrium, and thus the concentration of the silver nitrate in the electrolyte does not change, and the net result is that silver is transferred from A to B. Each atom of silver transferred leaves one of its electrons behind it in electrode A and absorbs 1 electron from electrode B. Consequently, the number of silver atoms transferred during a given time interval is equal to the number of electrons that pass any given point in the connecting wires during that time interval, provided that no other chemical actions are taking place in the cell. Note that the silver does not desire to be transferred but, if the electric current is driven through the cell in the proper direction by some external means, the action is forced to take place.

15. Unit Electric Current—the International Ampere. Since the rate of the chemical action in an electroplating cell is directly proportional to the rate of flow of the electrons, we may measure current in terms of chemical action. In the International system of electrical units the *ampere* is the unit of current and is defined as being that flow of current which, if maintained constant, will deposit silver from a silver nitrate solution at the rate of 1.118 milligrams per second. The quantity 1.118 was chosen so as to make the International ampere equal, within the limits of experimental accuracy, to the original ampere, which was defined in terms of the magnetic effects of an electric current.

16. Status of Electron Theory in Electrical Engineering. The electron theory of electricity has been briefly outlined in this initial chapter in order to give the student a glimpse of the conception of electricity now generally held by modern scientists, and also because it is scarcely possible to give an intelligible explanation of the operation of batteries, thermionic tubes, or rectifiers without it. It should be realized, however, that as far as the generation, transmission, and utilization of electrical energy by means of rotating machinery is concerned, the entire system was developed without any knowledge as to what an electric current really is. Just as a hydraulic engineer may design, construct, and operate a water-power plant, without any knowledge of the molecular structure of water, so an electrical engineer may design, construct, and operate an electric-power system, without any knowledge of the electron theory of electricity. In both cases the engineer is working with general fundamental laws that are based on a firm foundation of experimental facts. The facts may often be beyond our understanding but the laws are simple and may be relied upon.

In the following chapters the fundamental physical laws, used in the design and operation of electric-power systems, will be given, together with the experimental facts upon which they are based.

2

MAGNETS AND MAGNETISM

17. Magnets. Any body which possesses the power to attract pieces of iron is called a magnet, and the condition of a body by virtue of which this attraction takes place is called magnetism. Magnetite iron ore (Fe_3O_4) is a natural magnet, and practically all samples of iron and its alloys show traces of magnetism. If a magnet is dipped in iron filings and withdrawn, it will be found that the iron filings adhere to the magnet in two patches of dense tufts, showing that the power to attract is largely concentrated in two areas. These two areas are called the poles of the magnet. Although both poles attract iron filings, the two poles are not alike. If we take two bar magnets, with the poles located at the ends of the bars, and suspend them at a considerable distance from each other and from any other magnets in such a manner that they are free to turn in a horizontal plane, as, for example, two magnetic-compass needles, they will both turn until they are pointing north and south. If then the two bar magnets are brought near to each other, it may be observed that the north-seeking poles repel each other and that the south-seeking poles also repel each other, but between the north-seeking poles and the south-seeking poles there is attraction. That is, like poles repel each other and unlike poles attract each other.

The north-seeking pole of a magnet is called its north pole, and the south-seeking pole its south pole. The earth itself is a huge magnet, with its magnetic poles located within the Arctic and Antarctic Circles, though not coincident with the ends of the axis of rotation. It may be noted that the earth's geographic north magnetic pole is actually a south magnetic pole when the earth is treated as a magnet. This is not a paradox. It is merely a slight confusion between geographical and electrical conventions.

It should be clearly understood that we have as yet no conception of the nature of these magnetic forces of attraction and repulsion. They are fundamental, like the force of gravity and the forces of attraction and repulsion between electric charges. We do not understand these forces but we do know the laws which govern their actions and we can therefore use them.

18. Magnetic Fields and Magnetic Lines of Force. The space surrounding a magnet, through which its influence extends, is called the magnetic field of that magnet. In practice the term is limited to the space within which the force of the magnet is perceptible. The boundaries of this space are indefinite and depend on the sensitivity of the detecting apparatus.

A north magnetic pole placed at any point in a magnetic field is acted upon by a force tending to move it in a particular direction. A south magnetic pole, placed at the same point, is acted upon by a force tending to move it in exactly the opposite direction. Consequently, if a small

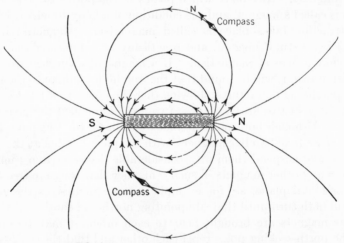

FIG. 6. Magnetic field of a bar magnet.

magnetic compass is placed in the field of an isolated bar magnet, as in Fig. 6, it will line itself up with the field, its north pole pointing in the direction in which a free north pole would move, and its south pole pointing in the direction in which a free south pole would move. If the compass is then moved in such a way that the direction of its motion is always the direction in which its north pole is pointing, its path will be a smooth curve terminating on the south pole of the bar magnet. The curve may be completed by returning the compass to its original position and moving it in the direction in which the south pole is pointing. It will be found in this case that the path terminates on the north pole. A line traced in this way from pole to pole of a magnet is called a *magnetic line of force.* By repeating this process for various initial positions of the compass, the magnetic field of a magnet may be mapped out, as shown in Fig. 6. The lines of force shown on such a map merely show the direction of the magnetic force at any point and there is no limit to the number of lines that can be drawn for any one magnet by this method. Very frequently, however, the line of force is given a quantitative significance, the number of lines per square centimeter of cross section of the field being made proportional to the magnetic force, as will be explained in Art. 20.

The direction of the magnetic field is arbitrarily stated to be the direction in which a free north pole would move.

19. Unit Magnetic Pole. The principle of introducing an idealized physical agent to assist in deducing a mathematical relationship is very widely utilized in science. For example, in mechanics we have the frictionless plane, the rigid body, the body with its mass concentrated at a point, etc. We may idealize a physical agent in any way we please, as long as we do not evade the logical consequences of our assumptions or misapply our conclusions.

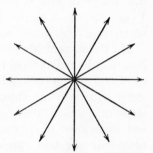

FIG. 7. Magnetic field in any plane through an isolated unit magnetic pole. The lines indicate the direction and the uniformity of the field, but the total number of lines drawn is not intended to have any significance.

The unit magnetic pole is an idealized physical agent. It may be visualized as being the north pole of a cylindrical bar magnet of infinitesimal cross section and of infinite length, with the pole concentrated at the end of the bar, so that all the lines of force emerge from a common point. The field about the pole is assumed to be symmetrically uniform in all directions throughout the limited space under consideration in any given application of this idealized pole.

Thus a unit magnetic pole is visualized as a point source from which straight lines of magnetic force diverge uniformly in all directions, as indicated in Fig. 7. The strength of this idealized unit magnetic pole is fixed by requiring that two identically equal unit magnetic poles, placed 1 cm apart, shall repel each other with a force of 1 dyne.

20. Magnetic Intensity—Symbol H—Oersted. The magnetic intensity, or strength, of a magnetic field at any point in space is defined as being equal to the force in dynes which that field would exert upon a unit magnetic pole placed at that point. In the cgs system of units the unit of magnetic intensity is the *oersted*. **At any point in space the value of the magnetic intensity in oersteds is equal to the force in dynes exerted on a unit magnetic pole placed at that point.** Thus the magnetic intensity of a field at any point may be expressed as either H oersteds or H dynes on unit pole.

A map of a magnetic field constructed by the method described in Art. 18 shows only the direction of the magnetic force and does not indicate its magnitude. When it is desired to indicate the strength of a field as well as its direction, the "line" is sometimes given a quantitative significance. In that case the number of lines, drawn or imagined, per square centimeter of cross section of the field, is made equal to the strength of the field.

Since a unit magnetic pole, placed in a magnetic field of 1 line per sq cm, is acted upon by a force of 1 dyne, and since a unit magnetic pole, placed 1 cm distant from another unit magnetic pole, is also acted upon by a force of 1 dyne, it follows that the magnetic field 1 cm distant from a unit magnetic pole is 1 line per sq cm; and since the area of a sphere of 1 cm radius is 4π sq cm, it follows that the total number of lines of force emanating from a unit magnetic pole is equal to 4π.

21. Permanent Magnets. It will be shown in Chap. 8 how a piece of iron may be magnetized by winding a coil of insulated wire around it and passing a current through the wire. The various magnetic alloys of iron differ widely in the amount of opposition that they offer to changes in their magnetic states. Annealed mild steel is very easily magnetized but loses most of its magnetism as soon as the magnetizing current is removed. Certain special hard steels, however, such as cobalt steel, require many ampere-turns for their magnetization, but retain their magnetism with great tenacity when the current is removed. Magnets made of such special steels are called *permanent magnets*, and are used for a great variety of purposes. For example they are used to provide magnetic fields in meters, telephone receivers, and some small generators. They are also used as compass needles. For illustrations, see Figs. 6, 9, 13, 15, and 16.

3

MAGNETIC PROPERTIES OF AN ELECTRIC CURRENT

22. Magnetic Field about a Conductor Carrying Current. A conductor carrying an electric current is surrounded by a magnetic field, which may be represented by lines of magnetic force, as shown in Fig. 8.

It is a general convention to draw a cross, representing the tail of an arrow, on the cross section of a conductor to indicate a current going away from the observer and to draw a dot, representing the point of an arrow, to indicate a current coming toward the observer.

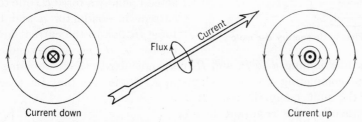

Current down   Current up

FIG. 8. Magnetic field surrounding a conductor carrying current.

The direction of the current and the direction of the resulting magnetic field are related to one another as the forward travel and the twist of a corkscrew.

The lines of force indicate that an isolated free magnetic pole would rotate continuously about a conductor carrying current if placed within its field. That this is so may be easily shown by experiment. It is, of course, impossible to construct a magnet with only one pole, but it is possible to arrange that one of its poles becomes inoperative. Figure 9 shows how this may be done. N and S are the poles of a bar magnet, bent as shown and balanced on a supporting pivot. A is a mercury cup, carried by the bar magnet, into which the stationary conductor D dips. B is a stationary annular trough filled with mercury into which the rotating arm C dips to complete the electric circuit through the battery.

As long as the current flows, the north pole N of the magnet tends to rotate continuously about the conductor D. Reversing either the direction of the current or the polarity of the magnet will reverse the direction of rotation. This is probably the most primitive type of electric motor that can be constructed. The possible power per pound of material or per cubic foot of space is very small.

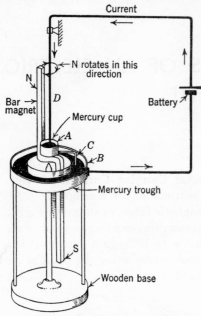

FIG. 9. Elementary d-c motor.

23. Magnetic Field about Two Parallel Conductors. Figure 10 may be constructed by taking the two conductors of Fig. 8, placing them the desired distance apart, and adding their superimposed magnetic fields by means of the parallelogram of forces. For example, a unit magnetic pole placed at the point P in Fig. 10 would be acted upon by a force H_a due to the current in conductor a and by a force H_b due to the current in conductor b, H_a being perpendicular to the line joining a to P, and H_b perpendicular to the line joining b to P. On completing the parallelogram, H is the resultant force acting upon the unit magnetic pole at P. Consequently, the resultant line of force through P must be tangent to the vector H at P. In order to perform such an addition in practice, it is, of course, necessary to know the magnitudes as well as the directions of H_a and H_b. Figure 8 shows directions only.

24. Magnetic Field of a Solenoid. A coil of wire wound in the form of a helix or tube is called a solenoid. The word *solenoid* is derived from two Greek words meaning "tubelike."

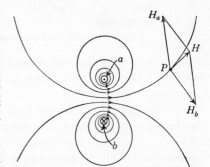

FIG. 10. Magnetic field produced by two parallel conductors carrying equal currents in opposite directions.

Figure 11 is a cross section of a solenoid through its axis. When an electric current is passed through such a coil, it acts as a magnet, and the direction of its magnetic field may be found by the corkscrew rule, Art. 22.

Comparing Fig. 11 with Fig. 6, we see that the magnetic field of a solenoid is practically identical with that of a bar magnet of the same dimensions.

25. Force on a Conductor Carrying Current in a Magnetic Field. When a conductor is carrying current and is in a magnetic field, as in Fig. 12c, it is acted upon by a force tending to move it sideways, in a direction at right angles to the directions of the current and of the magnetic lines. The force is proportional to the current and to the strength

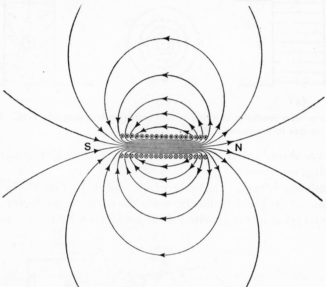

FIG. 11. Magnetic field produced by a solenoid.   (To be compared with Fig. 6.)

of the magnetic field. The direction of this force may be determined as follows:

Figure 12a shows the magnetic field between the poles of a magnet when the conductor either is not present or is carrying no current.

Figure 12b shows the magnetic field produced by the current in the conductor alone.

Figure 12c shows the resultant field when the conductor carrying current is placed between the poles of the magnet. This resultant field may be plotted by adding the two component magnetic fields of Fig. 12a and b, by means of the parallelogram of forces, Art. 23.

If the magnetic lines of Fig. 12c were filaments of stretched elastic, they would tend to straighten and exert a force F upon the conductor in the direction shown. This is not offered as an explanation of the production of the force F, and we do not in fact know how or why the force is produced, but it does provide a means of remembering the direction of the force.

When it is desired to determine the direction of the force on a conductor in any given case, Fig. 12c should be constructed mentally.   After a little practice this can be done in a second or two and there is very little chance of making an error.   The "left-hand rule," sometimes used to determine the direction of the force, is awkward, takes much longer, and

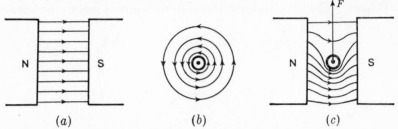

FIG. 12. Force on a conductor carrying current and lying in a magnetic field.   *F*, force on the conductor due to the distorted field.

is subject to error in that it is difficult to remember which quantities the various fingers represent.

26. Barlow's Wheel.   Barlow's wheel, shown in Fig. 13, is a simple electric motor designed to illustrate the fact that a conductor carrying current and lying in a magnetic field is acted upon by a force tending to

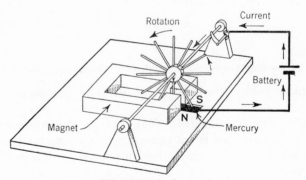

FIG. 13. Barlow's wheel.

move it sideways.   The entire wheel and shaft are made of conducting material such as brass.   The base is made of insulating material.   The spokes of the wheel dip in a trough of mercury cut in the base.   The current from the battery flows along the shaft and down a spoke into the mercury trough and back to the battery.   *N* and *S* are the poles of a magnet, and, since the spoke that is carrying the current is in the field of this magnet, it moves to the right.   The amount of the mercury in the trough is adjusted so that the following spoke makes contact with the mercury before the spoke that is carrying the current breaks contact;

thus there is always at least one spoke carrying current and tending to drive the motor.

Reversing either the direction of the current (by reversing the battery) or the polarity of the magnet (by turning it over) will reverse the direction of rotation. The two motors shown in Figs. 9 and 13 work on the same fundamental principle. Action and reaction are equal. If a conductor carrying current and lying in a magnetic field is acted upon by a force tending to move it in one direction, the magnet must be acted upon by an equal force tending to move it in the opposite direction. In Fig. 9 the conductor is fixed in position and the magnet is allowed to move. In Fig. 13 the magnet is fixed in position and the conductor is allowed to move.

Practically all electric motors work on the same fundamental principle as the motors of Figs. 9 and 13.

27. Unit Electric Current—the Abampere and the Ampere. In the cgs system of units the unit of electric current is defined in terms of the magnetic intensity produced by the current.

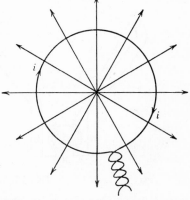

FIG. 14. Current *i* flowing in a circle with a unit pole at the center.

An abampere is that current which when flowing in a circle of one centimeter radius will exert a force of one dyne per centimeter of arc on unit pole placed at the center of the circle. The current is said to be *i* abamp if the force on the unit pole is *i* dynes per centimeter of arc.

The direction of the force is perpendicular to the plane of the circle. Now the force is a repulsion between the circle and the unit pole. Therefore there is a force acting on the circle equal and opposite to the force on the unit pole. Also the circle is lying in the field of the unit pole, at a distance of 1 cm from the pole, at which distance the field of the pole is of unit strength (Art. 20), and at every point on the circle the direction of the current is at right angles to that field, as shown in Fig. 14. Therefore the definition of the abampere might equally well be worded as follows: An abampere is that current which, when flowing in a conductor that is lying in a magnetic field of unit strength at right angles to the lines of force, causes each centimeter length of the conductor to be acted upon by a force of one dyne, assuming that the conductor is not immersed in a magnetic medium. For all practical purposes air is nonmagnetic.

The practical unit of current, called the **ampere (amp)**, is defined as being one-tenth of an abampere. The **milliampere (ma)**, equal to one-thousandth of an ampere, and the **microampere** (μa), equal to one-millionth of an ampere, are used for measuring small currents.

28. Moving-coil Direct-current Ammeters.   The standard d-c ammeter, shown in Fig. 15, is designed to measure current in accordance with the above definition. M is a permanent horseshoe magnet with its pole faces bored out cylindrically, and E is a cylindrical soft-iron core concentric with the pole faces.   Magnetic lines of force therefore pass as shown in Fig. 15A and the flux density in the air gaps is uniform.   In this magnetic field a coil C is placed and is supported on jeweled bearings.

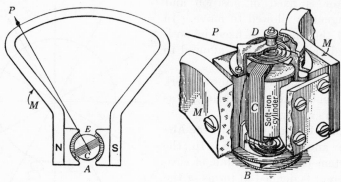

FIG. 15. Moving-coil ammeter.

The coil consists of a number of turns of fine insulated wire wound on a light aluminum frame, and the current to be measured enters the coil through one of the two spiral springs DD, Fig. 15B, and leaves it through the other spiral spring.   Since current is flowing *up* in the conductors on one side of the coil and *down* in the conductors on the other side of the coil, and both coil sides are in the same magnetic field, it follows that the two coil sides tend to move in opposite directions, and the coil is turned through an angle against the torsion of the spiral springs DD.   The restraining force of a spring is proportional to its deflection, and the actuating torque is proportional to the current; consequently the deflection of the pointer that is attached to the coil is proportional to the current.   A blank scale is placed under the pointer and the instrument is then calibrated by passing known currents through the coil and marking the corresponding positions of the pointer on the blank scale.

The current required for full-scale deflection depends upon the number of turns on the coil and upon the stiffness of the spiral springs.   Both of these factors can be varied, and this type of instrument is manufactured in a variety of ranges.

It is not economically feasible or desirable to construct the moving coil to carry large currents; consequently when it is desired to measure currents larger than about 20 ma, a low resistance, called a shunt, is connected in parallel with the moving coil, so that the moving coil carries a small but constant percentage of the total current. This shunt is considered to be part of the meter and the scale is generally marked to read the total current.

When it is desired to design the instrument to measure currents less than about 10 μa, it is necessary to eliminate the friction at the jeweled bearings, since the actuating torque is necessarily very small with such small currents. This is accomplished by suspending the coil at the end of a fine phosphor bronze wire or ribbon. The instrument is then called a D'Arsonval galvanometer. In its more sensitive ranges it uses a beam of light for a pointer.

29. Summary of the Properties of an Electric Current. *a. Electrochemical Properties.* *A current of electricity may permit or cause a chemical action.*

The electrochemical properties of an electric current give rise to the electrochemical industries, such as electroplating, electrolytic refining and smelting, the battery industry, and the manufacture of various synthetic products.

b. Heating Properties. *In general a current of electricity heats any body through which it passes.*

The heating properties of an electric current are utilized in a great variety of electric heating devices, such as stoves, radiators, water heaters, and electric steam boilers, in welding, smelting, tempering, and annealing, and in electric lighting, etc.

c. Magnetic Properties. *A current of electricity produces a magnetic field,* as explained in detail in Arts. 22 to 26.

It is the magnetic properties of an electric current that are utilized in our great power systems to convert mechanical energy into electrical energy in hydroelectric and steam-electric powerhouses, and to convert the electrical energy back into mechanical energy again, in motors, after the electrical energy has been transmitted to the desired location. In such power systems the current of electricity fulfills the same function as a belt or rope drive or a line of shafting; but whereas the distance of economical transmission of energy with rope drives or lines of shafting is limited to a few hundred feet, electric currents have provided economical transmission over distances up to 300 miles, and this distance will probably be increased considerably in the future. Even where the distances are small, the electric drive is often preferable, either because of its greatly superior possibilities of control or because of space considerations.

4

ELECTROMOTIVE FORCE

Electromotive force, generally abbreviated to emf, is the force, or electron-pressure difference, that causes a current of electricity to flow.

30. The Abvolt and the Volt. In the cgs system of units an abvolt of electromotive force is defined as being the emf acting in a circuit when, with one abampere of current flowing, the power is one erg per second. The practical unit of emf, called the volt, is defined as being equal to 10^8 abvolts.

31. Methods of Producing an Electromotive Force. There are three commercial methods of producing an emf: (1) by chemical action; (2) by thermal action; (3) by electromagnetic induction. All the great hydro-electric and steam-electric power plants develop emf by electromagnetic induction. Where large amounts of energy are required, the cost of electrical energy obtained from power plants working on the electro-magnetic-induction principle is very much less than the cost of electrical energy obtained from chemical action in any batteries that have been developed to date.

An emf is produced by thermal action when the junction of two dis-similar metals is heated; and a device that develops an emf in this manner is called a thermocouple. The emf that can be produced by a thermo-couple is too small to be of any use for general power purposes, but thermocouples have proved very useful in certain types of metering equipment.

32. Electromagnetic Induction. When a conductor is moved side-ways through a magnetic field, in such a direction as to cut the lines of force, an emf is generated or induced in the conductor. This is illus-trated in Fig. 16. N and S are the poles of a magnet and V is any device for indicating the existence of an emf or current, as, for example, the moving-coil ammeter described in Art. 28. A deflection of the pointer indicates that a current is flowing and thereby proves the existence of an emf, since current will not flow without an emf to drive it. If the current is reversed, the pointer moves in the opposite direction so that the meter indicates direction as well as magnitude.

If the conductor in Fig. 16 is moved down through the magnetic field, emf is generated in the conductor in the direction shown. If the conductor is moved up through the field, the emf generated is in the opposite direction. If the conductor is moved in a direction parallel to the lines of force, no emf is generated in it.

It is an experimental fact that the emf generated is proportional to the rate at which the lines of force are cut.

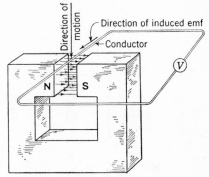

FIG. 16. Generation of emf.

The phenomena of Figs. 12 and 16 are both manifestations of the same fundamental principle, namely, that *when either an electron or a proton is moved through a magnetic field in a direction perpendicular to the field it is acted upon by a force perpendicular to the directions of both its motion and the field*. The conductor of Fig. 16 contains billions of protons and electrons. When this conductor is moved down through the field, the electrons experience a force tending to move them along the conductor in one direction, while the protons experience a force tending to move them along the conductor in the opposite direction. The protons are fixed in position in the conductor, but some at least of the electrons are free to move and are therefore crowded toward one end of the conductor. If the conductor were replaced by an insulator, neither protons nor electrons would move, but the forces would be there just the same.

No explanation is available as to why these forces act on the electrons and protons when they are moved through a field.

Note that it is an emf that is generated and not a current. Whether a current flows or not depends upon whether or not the circuit is completed, and the magnitude of the current, if any, depends upon the resistance of the circuit; but the emf is there whether current is allowed to flow or not.

Barlow's wheel, Fig. 13, can be used as a generator. If the battery is replaced by a meter for measuring emf, and the wheel is rotated by some mechanical means at various constant speeds, the meter will show that an emf is generated whose magnitude is proportional to the speed of the wheel, and whose direction is reversed if the direction of rotation is reversed, or if the direction of the magnetic field is reversed.

33. Direction of the Induced Electromotive Force. The direction may be determined by the right-hand rule, which states that if the thumb, the forefinger, and the middle finger of the right hand were placed at right angles to one another so as to form three coordinates in space, with the thumb pointing in the direction of motion of the conductor relative to the magnetic field, and the forefinger in the direction of the lines of magnetic force, then the middle finger will point in the direction of the induced emf.

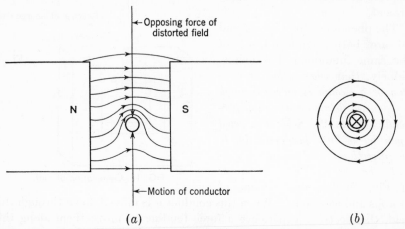

(a)   (b)

FIG. 17. Direction of induced emf as required by the principle of the conservation of energy. (a) Field opposing a conductor that is being forced through a magnetic field, when the circuit is complete, so that current is flowing in the direction of the induced emf.   (b) Magnetic field which the current must produce in order to cause the distortion shown in diagram (a).   Also, direction of the current to produce that field and direction of the induced emf to produce that current.

This rule has the virtue of simplicity but it is awkward to apply and easy to forget. A better method is to visualize the magnetic field as shown in Fig. 17. If a conductor is moved sideways through a magnetic field, an emf is generated in it, as described in Art. 32, and if an external return path is provided to complete the circuit through this conductor, current will flow. This current will distort the magnetic field, as explained in Art. 25, and the distorted field will exert a force upon the conductor to oppose its motion, as shown in Fig. 17a. That the force will oppose the motion, and not assist it, is required by the principle of the conservation of energy. If the force did assist the motion, then once a generator was started it would drive itself and moreover would accelerate itself very rapidly until it flew to pieces, at the same time driving current through an external circuit and doing work there.

The line of reasoning is therefore as follows: When a conductor which is part of a closed circuit is forced sideways through a magnetic field, the field must be distorted in such a way as to oppose the motion of the conductor, as in Fig. 17a. The direction that the current must have in order to create this distortion is readily visualized for any given case as in Fig. 17b, if we remember that magnetic fields add vectorially, and this must also be the direction of the induced emf that drives the current. After a little practice one can visualize the sketches of Fig. 17 in a second or two.

Note that if no current is allowed to flow, the field is not distorted and there is no force opposing the motion of the conductor, but the emf is generated just the same. Motion is required to generate emf but no mechanical force is required to maintain that motion unless current is allowed to flow.

34. Magnetic Induction—Symbol B—the Gauss. The magnetic induction of a field at any point is the measure of the ability of that field to induce emf in a conductor that is moving through the field at that point. In the cgs system the unit of magnetic induction is the *gauss*.

The magnetic induction of a uniform field is said to be one gauss if a straight conductor one centimeter long, moving sideways through the field with a velocity of one centimeter per second, has an emf of one abvolt induced in it, the conductor, velocity, and lines of magnetic force being all three mutually perpendicular.

If the field is not uniform, it is necessary to consider a conductor of infinitesimal length. Then, extending the definition to include non-uniform fields and fields of strengths other than unity, **the magnetic induction at any point, in gauss, is equal to the abvolts induced per centimeter length of the conductor at that point, the velocity of the conductor being one centimeter per second, and the conductor, velocity, and lines of magnetic force being all three mutually perpendicular.**

It is an experimental fact that the emf induced in the conductor is directly proportional to its velocity. Therefore, in the case of a uniform field, the emf induced in a straight conductor of length l cm moving with a velocity of v cm per sec in a direction perpendicular to itself and to the field is given by the equation

$$e = Blv \qquad \text{abvolts} \tag{1}$$

where B is the magnetic induction of the field in gauss.

Another method of expressing the strength of the magnetic induction of a field is in lines per square centimeter. In Arts. 18, 20, and 24, lines were used to map out the H property of a magnetic field. Lines can equally well be used to map out the B property. In fact, in a vacuum the same lines can be used to represent both properties. It will be shown in Art. 50 that in a vacuum H and B are numerically equal in the cgs system of units. They are not equal in the mks system of units. It is considered correct to express the magnetic induction of a field either as B gauss or as B lines per sq cm, or even in lines per square inch.

35. Magnetic Flux—Symbol ϕ—the Maxwell—the Weber. When the field is uniform, the magnetic flux is the product of the field strength in gauss by the cross-sectional area in square centimeters. When the field is not uniform, the cross section can be divided into an infinite number of elemental areas dA, and the magnetic flux is the sum of the products of each area by the average value of B over that area, or in calculus notation $\phi = \int B \, dA$.

In the cgs system the unit of magnetic flux is the **maxwell. It may be defined as the amount of flux through one square centimeter of cross section when the magnetic induction is one gauss.** The term **gauss** may seem somewhat superfluous since the magnetic induction can be expressed equally well as B maxwells per sq cm, B gauss, or B lines per sq cm. It is evident that the maxwell and the line of magnetic flux are identical.

In Eq. (1) the product lv is the area in square centimeters swept through by the conductor in 1 sec, and B is the flux density in lines per square centimeter. Therefore Blv is the flux cut per second. Hence Eq. (1) can be rewritten

$$e = \text{flux cut per second} \qquad (2)$$

where e is in abvolts and the flux is in lines or maxwells.

The abvolt and the maxwell are both very small units. The volt, equal to 10^8 abvolts, has been in general use for a long time. Its use introduces a factor of 10^{-8} in Eq. (2). In order to eliminate this factor a new unit of magnetic flux, called the **weber**, was adopted in 1935. **The weber is of course equal to 10^8 maxwells**, and therefore Eq. (2) is true for volts and webers as well as for abvolts and lines.

Problems

4-1. If the permanent magnet of Fig. 16 is to have a flux of 1 weber, and the maximum flux density obtainable with the material used is 7,000 gauss, what must be the area of the pole face?

4-2. The rotor of a generator is turning at 1,200 rpm. The conductors carried by the rotor, as shown in Fig. 63, are arranged in a circle of 20 cm radius. The axial dimension of the pole face is 30 cm and the flux density in the air gap is 8,000 gauss. What is the emf generated in each conductor as it is passing across a pole face?

5

ELECTRIC CIRCUITS AND RESISTANCE

36. Flow of an Electric Current through a Conductor. This is similar in many ways to the flow of air or gas through a pipe. The similarity would be somewhat increased if the pipe were filled with steel wool or any very porous material. The atoms of which the conductor is composed obstruct the flow of the electrons as the steel wool obstructs the flow of the gas molecules. In order to maintain a steady flow of a gas or liquid along a horizontal length of pipe, the pressure at one end of the length of pipe must be greater than the pressure at the other end. The difference in pressure is the force that causes the fluid to flow against the frictional resistance offered by the pipe. The work done by this force is all converted into heat. Similarly, in order to maintain a steady electric current through a length of wire, there must be an electric-pressure difference between the two ends of the wire. This pressure difference is the emf that causes the current of electricity to flow against the frictional resistance offered by the wire.

37. Ohm's Law. Ohm discovered that the steady rate of flow of an electric current produced by a constant emf is directly proportional to the emf. That is, in any circuit

$$E = IR \qquad (3)$$

where E = constant emf impressed on the circuit

I = sustained current

R = a constant, called the *resistance* of the circuit

In the cgs system the abampere is the unit of current, the abvolt is the unit of emf, and the abohm is the unit of resistance. If we define any two of these units, Ohm's law will serve as a definition of the third one. Since the abampere and the abvolt have already been defined, *the abohm may be defined as the resistance of a conductor when, with an unvarying current of one abampere flowing through it, the potential difference between the ends of the conductor is one abvolt.*

38. Definitions of Ampere, Volt, and Ohm. In the practical system of units, which is based on the cgs system, the definitions are as follows:

An ampere is defined as being equal to one-tenth abampere.

A volt is defined as being equal to 10^8 abvolts.

An ohm is, by Ohm's law, defined as being the resistance of a circuit through which an emf of one volt will drive a current of one ampere. This makes an ohm equal to 10^9 abohms.

39. The International System of Electrical Units. In the International system of units the definitions are as follows:

An *ampere* is defined as being that rate of flow of electric current which will deposit silver from a standard silver nitrate solution at the rate of 1.118 milligrams per second.

An *ohm* is defined as being the resistance offered to a constant electric current by a column of mercury, at 0°C, of length equal to 106.3 centimeters, of mass equal to 14.4521 grams, and of constant cross-sectional area.

A *volt* is, by Ohm's law, defined as being the amount of emf that will drive a current of one ampere through a resistance of one ohm.

The International units were developed with the idea that they would be simpler and capable of more accurate reproduction than the practical units based upon the cgs system, and they were adopted by an international congress in 1893. However, as the art developed, it became possible to reproduce the cgs units with greater accuracy than the International units, and the International Electrotechnical Commission decided to discard the International System of Electrical Units on Jan. 1, 1940. The Second World War delayed the change until Jan. 1, 1948, on which date the U.S. National Bureau of Standards officially revalued their primary standards in terms of the practical units based on the cgs system. This revaluation involved changes of less than one-twentieth of 1 per cent in the magnitudes of the units, and therefore affected very few people.

40. Specific Resistance. It has been determined experimentally that the resistance of a conductor is directly proportional to its length and is inversely proportional to its cross-sectional area. That is,

$$R = \rho \frac{l}{A} \qquad (4)$$

where R = resistance of wire, ohms
  l = length of wire
  A = cross-sectional area of wire
  ρ = a constant, called specific resistance

The specific resistance depends upon the material and upon the units of length and area chosen. If centimeter units are used, the specific resistance is the resistance between the opposite parallel faces of a centi-meter cube of the material. In practice the unit of cross-sectional area most generally used is the *circular mil*, which is defined as being the area of a circle 1 mil (1/1,000 in.) in diameter. The advantage of using the circular mil is that it eliminates the factor $\pi/4$ from the calculation of the cross section of cylindrical conductors. The area of a circle in circular mils is equal to the square of the diameter in mils. Thus the area of a circle 1 in. in diameter is equal to 10^6 cir mils. The area of a 1-in. square is $4/\pi \times 10^6$ cir mils.

When the circular mil is used as the unit of cross-sectional area, the foot is generally used as the unit of length. The specific resistance of standard pure annealed copper[1] is 1.724×10^{-6} ohm per cu cm or 10.371 ohms per cir mil-ft, at 20°C. A circular mil-foot is a cylinder 1 mil in diameter and 1 ft long.

41. Conductivity. The reciprocal of the specific resistance of a mate-rial is called its conductivity. In practice, conductivities are used chiefly to compare one conductor material with another. It is therefore convenient to choose one material as the standard and to compare the others with it. Accordingly, pure annealed copper has been chosen as the standard and its conductivity is taken as being 100 per cent.

Conductor materials may be compared on either an equal-volume basis or an equal-mass basis. If the resistance per circular mil-foot of a given material is four times that of copper, at the same temperature, its volume conductivity is said to be 25 per cent, and the cross-sectional area of a conductor made of this material would need to be four times as great as it would be if made of copper, in order to have as low a resist-ance. Where space is the prime consideration, as in the slots of a generator or motor, volume conductivities are useful. In the case of transmission lines, however, the space is not limited, and, as conductors are bought by the pound, the conductor materials are compared on an equal-mass basis. If the resistance of a uniform wire, of a given material, 1 m long and weighing 1 g is twice the resistance of a uniform wire of standard pure annealed copper 1 m long and weighing 1 g, at the same temperature, its mass conductivity is said to be 50 per cent; and it is necessary to buy twice as many pounds of that material as of copper in order to have as low a resistance in the transmission line.

The volume conductivity and the mass conductivity of a material are given by the following formulas:

$$\text{Volume conductivity} = \frac{10.371}{\rho_1} \times 100\% \qquad (5)$$

[1] See Table 10 in the Appendix for specific resistance of other materials.

where 10.371 = resistance of a circular mil-foot of standard annealed copper at 20°C

ρ_1 = resistance of a circular mil-foot of given material at 20°C

$$\text{Mass conductivity} = \frac{0.15328}{\rho_2} \times 100\% \qquad (6)$$

where 0.15328 = resistance at 20°C of a uniform wire of standard annealed copper 1 m long and weighing 1 g

ρ_2 = resistance at 20°C of a uniform wire of given material 1 m long and weighing 1 g

Example. Hard-drawn aluminum has a resistance of 17.00 ohms per cir mil-ft or 0.0764 ohm per meter-gram, at 20°C. Calculate the volume conductivity and the mass conductivity.

$$\text{Volume conductivity} = \frac{10.371}{17.0} \times 100\% = 61.0\%$$

$$\text{Mass conductivity} = \frac{0.15328}{0.0764} \times 100\% = 200.7\%$$

This means that, as a conductor of electricity, 1 lb of aluminum is equivalent to 2.007 lb of copper, and 1 cu in. of aluminum is equivalent to 0.61 cu in. of copper.

The main application of conductivities, however, is in the writing of specifications for conductor materials. In order to have 100 per cent conductivity, a copper sample must be at least 99.9 per cent pure copper, and even minute amounts of impurities reduce the conductivity very considerably. Aluminum is affected in the same way. The purchaser protects himself against low-grade conductor material by specifying the conductivity.

The conductivity of hard-drawn copper or aluminum wire is roughly 2 per cent less than when annealed, but where tensile strength is required the gain in tensile strength due to hard drawing is much more important than the loss in conductivity.

42. Variation of Resistance with Temperature. In general, the electric resistance of a material changes with its temperature. The resistance of insulators and other nonmetallic materials generally decreases with increase of temperature. In fact, some materials, such as glass, for example, that are excellent insulators at room temperatures become very poor insulators if heated to a red heat.

For all pure metals the resistance increases with the temperature. If the resistance of any pure metal is plotted on a temperature base, it is found that over the range of temperatures from 0 to 100°C the graph is practically a straight line, as shown in Fig. 18. If this straight line is produced, it cuts the temperature axis at some temperature $-T_0$°C. This does not mean that the resistance of the metal is actually zero at that temperature, but $-T_0°\text{C}$ is the temperature at which the resistance would be zero if the rate of decrease between 100 and 0°C were maintained constant at all temperatures.   From the similarity of the triangles in Fig. 18,

$$\frac{R_{t_2}}{R_{t_1}} = \frac{T_0 + t_2}{T_0 + t_1} \tag{7}$$

where t_1 and t_2 are any two temperatures in degrees centigrade and R_{t_1} and R_{t_2} are the resistances at those temperatures.   Therefore if the resistance R_{t_1} is known for any one temperature t_1, it can be calculated for any other temperature t_2 by means of Eq. (7), provided that the T_0 for that particular material is known. For copper, $T_0 = 234.5$, for aluminum, $T_0 = 236.4$.

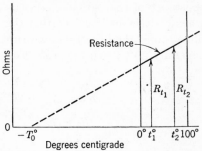

FIG. 18. Variation of resistance of pure metals with temperature.

Equation (7) may be used for temperatures outside the range of 0 to 100°C but becomes inaccurate if the temperatures are either very high or very low.   In this connection it is of interest to note that the resistance of many pure metals drops to zero at temperatures slightly above absolute zero.

Example. A coil of copper wire has a resistance of 12.7 ohms at 18°C.   What will its resistance be at 50°C?

$$\frac{R_{50}}{12.7} = \frac{234.5 + 50}{234.5 + 18}$$

Therefore the resistance at 50°C is

$$\frac{12.7 \times 284.5}{252.5} = 14.3 \text{ ohms}$$

The variation of resistance with temperature is often utilized to measure temperature changes.   For example, in testing various types of electric machines, the resistance of the coils is measured both before and after the test run, and the increase of resistance is a measure of the rise of temperature.   An excessive rise of temperature would damage the insulation.   For measurements of temperature rise, Eq. (7) may be transposed to the following form:

$$t_2 - t_1 = \frac{R_{t_2} - R_{t_1}}{R_{t_1}} (T_0 + t_1) \tag{8}$$

Example. The resistance of the copper field coils of a generator was 35.3 ohms at 19°C. After the test run the resistance was 41.9 ohms. What was the average temperature rise of the coils?

$$\text{Temperature rise} = t_2 - t_1 = \frac{41.9 - 35.3}{35.3} (234.5 + 19) = 47.4°C$$

A temperature of 20°C has been adopted as the standard reference temperature for resistance measurements, and the handbooks give the resistance of the various materials at that temperature. Consequently, when a designer is calculating the resistance of any conductor from its dimensions, the initial temperature t_1 at which the resistance is known is generally 20°C. In that case Eq. (7) is often transposed as follows:

$$\frac{R_t}{R_{20}} = \frac{T_0 + t}{T_0 + 20}$$

$$R_t = R_{20} \frac{(T_0 + 20) + (t - 20)}{T_0 + 20}$$

$$= R_{20} \left[1 + \frac{1}{T_0 + 20} (t - 20) \right]$$

$$= R_{20}[1 + \alpha(t - 20)] \tag{9}$$

where $\alpha = 1/(T_0 + 20)$ and is called the temperature coefficient of resistance of the material corresponding to a reference temperature of 20°C.

For copper, $\alpha = 0.00393$; for aluminum, $\alpha = 0.00390$.

Example. A coil has 1,000 turns of copper wire. The cross-sectional area of the wire is 1,288 cir mils. The length of the mean turn is 15 in. What will be the resistance of the coil at 60°C?

The resistance of 1 cir mil-ft at 20°C is 10.371 ohms, and the resistance of the coil at 20°C is

$$\frac{10.371 \times 1,000 \times 15}{1,288 \times 12} = 10.065 \text{ ohms}$$

The resistance of the coil at 60°C is given by

$$R_{60} = 10.065[1 + 0.00393(60 - 20)] = 11.65 \text{ ohms}$$

43. Kirchhoff's Laws. These two laws are the most fundamental and widely applied laws of electric circuits. They may be stated as follows:

First law: The algebraic sum of the instantaneous currents flowing toward any junction point in a network is zero.

This law applies not only to electricity but also to everything else that flows, provided that the points at which the flows are measured are close enough to the junction point so that the storage capacities of the intervening conducting paths are negligible. If the flows are constant this proviso is not required. Kirchhoff's first law follows directly from the law of conservation of matter.

Second law: The algebraic sum of the products of the current and resistance in each of the conductors in any closed path in a network is equal to the algebraic sum of the electromotive forces in that path.

Note that if some of the emfs in a closed path are clockwise, while others are counterclockwise, it is necessary to choose which direction shall be regarded as positive, and to assign negative signs to emfs that are in the opposite direction. Similarly a current in the negative direction

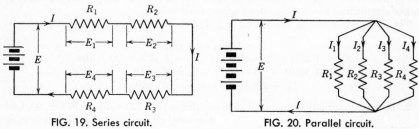

FIG. 19. Series circuit.　　　FIG. 20. Parallel circuit.

must be regarded as negative, in which case an IR drop due to that current will also be negative. Note also that if we are dealing with a transient condition in which the current is changing, the emf of self-induction, if any, must be included. Self-induction is discussed in Chap. 11.

The following cases illustrate the application of Kirchhoff's laws to the steady-state solution of direct-current circuits:

Series Circuit. If several resistances are connected in series, as in Fig. 19, then the current I is the same in all parts of the circuit, and the single emf E is equal to the sum of the four voltage drops E_1, E_2, E_3, and E_4, where $E_1 = IR_1$, $E_2 = IR_2$, $E_3 = IR_3$, and $E_4 = IR_4$, so that

$$E = IR_1 + IR_2 + IR_3 + IR_4 \qquad \text{(Kirchhoff's second law)}$$
$$= I(R_1 + R_2 + R_3 + R_4)$$

Therefore the total resistance of the circuit is $R_1 + R_2 + R_3 + R_4$.

Parallel Circuit. If several conductors are connected in parallel as shown in Fig. 20, then the voltage across each length of conductor is the same, while the total current is the sum of the currents in the different paths, so that

$$I = I_1 + I_2 + I_3 + I_4 \qquad \text{(Kirchhoff's first law)}$$
$$= \frac{E}{R_1} + \frac{E}{R_2} + \frac{E}{R_3} + \frac{E}{R_4}$$
$$= E\left(\frac{1}{R_1} + \frac{1}{R_2} + \frac{1}{R_3} + \frac{1}{R_4}\right)$$

It has been found convenient in problems on parallel circuits to use a quantity called the *conductance* of the circuit, where the conductance G is, in d-c circuits, the reciprocal of the resistance R, and then the above expression becomes

$$I = E(G_1 + G_2 + G_3 + G_4)$$

and the total resistance of the circuit consisting of the four paths in parallel is $1/(G_1 + G_2 + G_3 + G_4)$.

Examples. 1. Four coils having resistances of 3, 5, 10, and 12 ohms, respectively, are connected in series across 120 volts, as in Fig. 19. Find the current in the circuit and the voltage drop across each coil.

The total resistance of the circuit is $3 + 5 + 10 + 12 = 30$ ohms. Therefore

$$I = {}^{120}\!/_{30} = 4 \text{ amp}$$
$$E_1 = 4 \times 3 = 12 \text{ volts} \qquad E_2 = 4 \times 5 = 20 \text{ volts}$$
$$E_3 = 4 \times 10 = 40 \text{ volts} \qquad E_4 = 4 \times 12 = 48 \text{ volts}$$
$$12 + 20 + 40 + 48 = 120 \text{ volts}$$

2. If these four coils are connected in parallel across 120 volts, as in Fig. 20, find the total current and the current in each coil.

$$I_1 = {}^{120}\!/_3 \ = 40 \text{ amp}$$
$$I_2 = {}^{120}\!/_5 \ = 24 \text{ amp}$$
$$I_3 = {}^{120}\!/_{10} = 12 \text{ amp}$$
$$I_4 = {}^{120}\!/_{12} = 10 \text{ amp}$$
$$\text{Total } I = \qquad \overline{86 \text{ amp}}$$

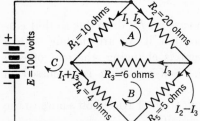

FIG. 21. A typical d-c network.

3. An emf of 100 volts is impressed on the network shown in Fig. 21. It is required to find the current in each part of the circuit.

Let I_1 = current through R_1
I_2 = current through R_2
I_3 = current through R_3

The directions of I_1 and I_2 are obvious, but the direction of I_3 is assumed at random, and we may find that I_3 is negative. By Kirchhoff's first law, $I_4 = I_1 + I_3$ and $I_5 = I_2 - I_3$. In traveling around the closed path A, through R_1, R_2, and R_3, we do not pass through any source of emf, and therefore, by Kirchhoff's second law, the algebraic sum of the IR products must be zero. Therefore, taking clockwise as the positive direction, we have

$$I_2 R_2 + I_3 R_3 - I_1 R_1 = 0$$
or $$20 I_2 + 6 I_3 - 10 I_1 = 0 \qquad (a)$$

Similarly for the closed path B,

$$5(I_2 - I_3) - 4(I_1 + I_3) - 6 I_3 = 0$$
or $$5 I_2 - 15 I_3 - 4 I_1 = 0 \qquad (b)$$

and for the closed path C,

$$10 I_1 + 4(I_1 + I_3) = 100$$
or $$14 I_1 + 4 I_3 = 100 \qquad (c)$$

Solving the three simultaneous equations (a), (b), and (c), we obtain $I_1 = 7.333$, $I_2 = 3.866$, $I_3 = -0.667$, $I_4 = 6.667$, $I_5 = 4.533$.

The method employed in solving the network of Fig. 21 is effective and widely used but it is not the only method.   More advanced methods will sometimes give greater accuracy with less effort.

44. Voltage Drop in a Distribution Circuit

Three floodlighting units drawing 17 amp each are spaced 100 ft apart and are connected as shown in Fig. 22.   The connecting wires are No. 6 B & S copper

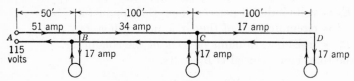

FIG. 22. Distribution circuit.

having a resistance of 0.4 ohm per 1,000 ft.   The voltage at the point of supply A is 115 volts.   Calculate the voltage across each lighting unit.

Each of the two wires running from A to B has a resistance of

$$\frac{0.4 \times 50}{1,000} = 0.02 \text{ ohm}$$

and the voltage required to drive 51 amp through 0.02 ohm is

$$51 \times 0.02 = 1.02 \text{ volts}$$

Therefore there is a voltage drop of 1.02 volts in each wire from A to B, and the voltage across the lamp at B is

$$115 - (2 \times 1.02) = 112.96 \text{ volts}$$

Similarly each wire running from B to C has a resistance of

$$\frac{0.4 \times 100}{1,000} = 0.04 \text{ ohm}$$

and the voltage drop in each wire is

$$34 \times 0.04 = 1.36 \text{ volts}$$

Therefore the voltage across the lamp at C is

$$112.96 - (2 \times 1.36) = 110.24 \text{ volts}$$

and the voltage across the lamp at D is

$$110.24 - (2 \times 17 \times 0.04) = 108.88 \text{ volts}$$

Note that, although these lighting units are rated at 17 amp and each is assumed to be drawing that current in the calculation, the unit at D with 108.88 volts impressed across its terminals will not actually draw so much current as the unit at B with 112.96 volts impressed, nor will it produce so much light.   A more accurate solution could be obtained if the resistances of the three loads were known, but in the case of lamps the resistance varies so widely with the voltage, because of temperature changes, that a more accurate solution is not considered feasible.

45. Relationship between Electromotive Force and Difference of Potential. Consider Fig. 23, which shows a conductor bent into a circle, with a magnetic pole passing through the center in a direction perpendicular to the plane of the circle. Every centimeter of the conductor is cutting magnetic flux at the same rate, and therefore the emf induced per centimeter in this conductor is everywhere the same.

Let E_c = volts induced per centimeter of conductor.

$\quad l$ = circumference of the circle in centimeters.

$\quad R_c$ = resistance in ohms of 1 cm of the conductor.

Then the total emf induced is $E_c l$ volts.

$$\text{Total resistance} = R_c l \quad \text{ohms}$$

$$I = \frac{E_c l}{R_c l} = \frac{E_c}{R_c} \quad \text{amp}$$

rearranging $\qquad\qquad E_c = I R_c$

or in words, the emf induced per centimeter is equal to the IR drop per centimeter. Thus the emf induced in

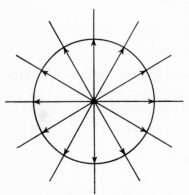

each centimeter of conductor is consumed in that centimeter and there is no difference of potential to be found anywhere on the circle. If, however, we stop the current by making a thin cut through the conductor, the IR drop will then be zero, and a difference of potential equal to $E_c l$ volts will appear across the cut.

Consider a generator supplying current to a load, as in Fig. 29. The maximum difference of potential is that across the terminals of the generator, but the emf generated in the generator must be larger than this by the amount of the emf required to drive the current through the internal resistance of the generator itself. A voltmeter can measure an emf only if that emf can be made to appear as a difference of potential. It is impossible to measure directly the emf acting in a circuit in which current is flowing. The usual method of determining the emf is to measure the difference of potential across the terminals of the source of the emf and to add to this the value of the IR drop inside the source.

FIG. 23. Showing a conductor bent into a circle, with a magnetic pole passing through the center.

46. Voltmeter Series Resistance—Multipliers. The standard d-c volt-meter consists of a low-range ammeter (described in Art. 28) with a high resistance connected in series with it, as in Fig. 24.

If the terminals TT are connected to any two points between which an emf E exists, as, for example, the two terminals of a battery, a current I will flow through the series resistance and the moving coil. By Ohm's law, $I = E/R$, where R = total resistance of voltmeter. Therefore, since the current is proportional to the emf, the deflection of the pointer is also proportional to the emf, and the scale can be calibrated to read volts. The current that flows through the meter does no useful work, other than deflecting the pointer, and the electric-power in-put to the meter, represented by this flow of current, is all wasted, the electrical energy being converted into heat in the resistance of the meter. The moving-coil system is usually designed to give full-scale deflection of the pointer with a cur-rent of 10 ma flowing through it, and the series resistance is designed to pass this amount of current when the meter is connected to the maxi-mum voltage which it is designed to

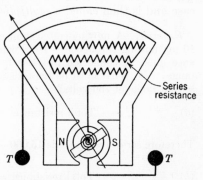

FIG. 24. Direct-current voltmeter. The series resistance consists of fine manganin wire wound on mica cards. See Art. 28 for a description of the moving system.

measure. While 10 ma is only about one-sixtieth of the current that flows through an ordinary reading lamp and while a current drain of 10 ma may be an entirely negligible trickle when drawn from a power system, it is a substantial load when drawn from such a tiny source of electrical energy as a radio B battery, and a voltmeter should not be left connected continuously to such a source.

As a general rule, pressure gauges do not allow any flow through themselves, but the d-c voltmeter is an example of a pressure gauge which allows a small trickle to flow and uses that trickle to measure the magni-tude of the pressure.

In order that the readings of a voltmeter should not be affected by the temperature, the series resistance must be made of a material whose temperature coefficient of resistance is practically zero. Manganin, an alloy of copper, manganese, nickel, and iron, has a specific resistance about thirty times that of copper at 20°C, and its temperature coefficient is practically zero over a range of temperatures from 10 to 35°C, which covers the temperature range usually encountered in metering. Even outside this range the temperature coefficient is very small. The series resistance of voltmeters is made of fine manganin wire. The moving coil is made of copper but it constitutes such a small part of the total resistance that the change in its resistance due to temperature changes is negligible when expressed as a percentage of the total resistance.

A single voltmeter may be given several voltage ranges by simply tapping the series resistance at the proper points and providing additional terminals for these taps.

For the lower-voltage ranges the series resistance is always enclosed in the same case with the moving coil, as indicated in Fig. 24, but for the higher-voltage ranges part of the resistance is often enclosed in a separate case and is then called a *multiplier*.

Example. A moving-coil system gives full-scale deflection with a current of 10 ma flowing through it. Its resistance is 5 ohms. (*a*) What value of resistance must be connected in series to convert it into a voltmeter of 150 volts' range? (*b*) What must be the resistance of a multiplier to give this voltmeter a second range of 750 volts?

(*a*) $$\text{Total resistance} = \frac{E}{I} = \frac{150}{0.01} = 15{,}000 \text{ ohms}$$

Therefore series resistance is $15{,}000 - 5 = 14{,}995$ ohms.

(*b*) $$\text{Total resistance} = \frac{E}{I} = \frac{750}{0.01} = 75{,}000 \text{ ohms}$$

Therefore multiplier resistance is $75{,}000 - 15{,}000 = 60{,}000$ ohms.

47. Ammeter Shunts. The moving-coil d-c ammeter was described in Art. 28, and in this article it was stated that it was not economically feasible to construct the moving coil to carry large currents, and therefore, when it was desired to measure currents larger than about 20 ma, a low resistance, called a shunt, was connected in parallel with the moving-coil system, so that the moving coil carried a small but fixed percentage of the total current.

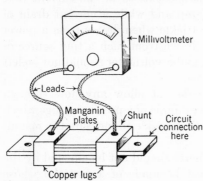

FIG. 25. Direct-current ammeter.

The ammeter shunt is made of manganin so that its resistance is practically independent of the temperature over the range of room temperatures. In order to avoid temperature errors, it is necessary that the resistance of the moving-coil system should also be practically independent of the temperature. This is accomplished by connecting special alloy resistance wire in series with the moving coil and actually converting it into a low-range voltmeter, called a millivoltmeter. The standard d-c ammeter therefore consists of a millivoltmeter and a shunt, as shown in Fig. 25, and the millivoltmeter measures the voltage drop across the shunt, which is proportional to the current. The scale, however, is calibrated to read amperes.

In low-range ammeters the shunt is small and is often enclosed in the millivoltmeter case, but for the higher ranges the shunt is quite heavy and is separate from the millivoltmeter. In that case it is important that the leads used to connect the millivoltmeter to the shunt should be the ones provided by the manufacturer, as they constitute part of the resistance of the millivoltmeter, and if this resistance is changed an error is introduced. Ammeters are usually designed to give full-scale deflection with a 50-millivolt (mv) drop across the terminals, but with precision instruments the drop is often 100 mv.

Example. A millivoltmeter has a resistance of 20 ohms and gives full-scale deflection when connected across an emf of 100 mv. What must be the resistance of the shunt to make the meter give full-scale deflection when measuring a current of 50 amp?

The current through the millivoltmeter with full-scale deflection is

$$\frac{0.100}{20} = 0.005 \text{ amp}$$

Therefore the current through the shunt is

$$50 - 0.005 = 49.995 \text{ amp}$$

and the resistance of the shunt is

$$\frac{0.100}{49.995} = 0.0020002 \text{ ohm}$$

48. Measurement of Resistance Using a Voltmeter and an Ammeter.
Since the resistance of a circuit is the ratio of the impressed volts to the resulting amperes, the most obvious method of measuring the resistance of a circuit is to connect the circuit to a source of emf, such as a battery, and to measure the emf and current by means of a voltmeter and an ammeter. A practical difficulty arises, however. There are two possible ways of connecting in the two meters, namely, those shown in Figs. 26 and 27. When connected as in Fig. 26, the voltmeter reads the voltage across the resistance but the ammeter does not read the current through the resistance; it reads the sum of the currents through the resistance and the voltmeter. When the meters are connected as in Fig. 27, the ammeter reads the current through the resistance but the voltmeter does not read the voltage across the resistance; it reads the voltage across the ammeter, resistance, and connecting wire.

The ammeter reading of Fig. 26 may be corrected to give the true current through the resistance by subtracting the current through the voltmeter, which is equal to the voltmeter reading divided by the resistance of the voltmeter.   The resistance of the voltmeter is generally given by the manufacturer.   If R is less than one four-hundredth of the resistance of the voltmeter, the correction to the ammeter reading will be less than one-fourth of 1 per cent, which is within the limits of accuracy of high-grade portable meters; consequently no correction need be applied to the ammeter reading if the resistance being measured is less than one four-hundredth of the resistance of the voltmeter.

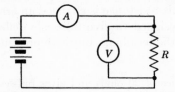

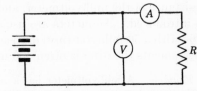

FIG. 26. Correct arrangement of meters for measuring a low resistance.   A = ammeter; V = voltmeter.

FIG. 27. Correct arrangement of meters for measuring a high resistance.

The voltmeter reading of Fig. 27 may be corrected to give the true voltage across the resistance by subtracting the voltage drop in the ammeter and the connecting wire, if that is known.   If R is larger than 400 times the resistance of the ammeter, the correction to the voltmeter reading will be less than one-fourth of 1 per cent and may therefore be neglected.

In general, it will be found that the two ranges of resistance referred to in the two preceding paragraphs overlap, so that for any given resistance one of the two arrangements shown in Figs. 26 and 27 will give sufficient accuracy for ordinary purposes without applying any correction. It is impossible, however, to draw a definite dividing line and say that all resistances below a certain value should be measured with connections as in Fig. 26, and all those above that value with connections as in Fig. 27, because the best location of the dividing line depends upon the magnitude of the applied emf and upon the types of meters used.   When in doubt, apply the correction.

Note that if the arrangement of Fig. 26 is used to measure very high resistances, or the arrangement of Fig. 27 for very low resistances, and the meter readings are not corrected, errors up to 100 per cent or more may be obtained.   There is always the possibility of momentarily disconnecting the voltmeter of Fig. 26 while the ammeter is being read, which automatically corrects the ammeter reading, but this prevents the two meters from being read simultaneously and may lead to considerable error if the source of emf is not constant; or if the source of emf is a dry battery, the disconnecting of the voltmeter decreases the current drain on the battery and results in a greater emf being impressed on the resistance than was present when the voltmeter measured it.   Consequently, this method must be used with discretion.

Problems[1]

5-1. An aluminum bar with an average cross section of 0.185 sq in. and a length of 2.956 ft has a resistance of 207 μohms at 20°C.   What is the resistance of the aluminum in ohms per circular mil-foot at this temperature?   What are the mass conductivity and the volume conductivity of this sample of aluminum?

***5-2.** An 8-ft sample cut from a long coil of nichrome wire (used for heaters) has an average diameter of 0.161 in.   Its resistance is found to be 0.186 ohm. What is the resistance in ohms per circular mil-foot of this wire at the same temperature?

5-3. A No. 14 wire (the smallest allowed in house wiring) has a diameter of 0.064 in.   Find the sectional area of the wire in circular mils.   Find the resistance per 1,000 ft of wire at 25°C.   Resistivity of copper = 9.7 ohms per cir mil-ft at 0°C.

5-4. The resistance of the field circuit of a shunt generator is measured at 25°C. After a load run its resistance is found to be 20 per cent higher.   What is the average temperature of the field coil?

5-5. The resistance of a conductor increases by 31 per cent from 23 to 75°C. What is the temperature coefficient of the metal?

***5-6.** The resistance of the coils of an electromagnet at room temperature of 20°C is 20 ohms.   After the current has been on for an hour the resistance becomes 24 ohms.   What is the cause of the increase in resistance and what is the average temperature of the winding?   If the applied voltage is 110, what is the current in the coil at the beginning and at the end of the hour?

5-7. Three resistances, R_a = 10 ohms, R_b = 15 ohms, R_c = 20 ohms, are connected in series across 110 volts.   Find the current flowing and the voltage drop across each resistance.   The same resistances are connected in parallel across 110 volts.   Find the current through each branch and the total current drawn from the line.

5-8. Two resistances of 6 and 8 ohms are connected in parallel across a line of unknown voltage.   If the total current is 40 amp, what is the current through each and what is the voltage of the line?

***5-9.** A total current of 42 amp divides between three branches in parallel, of resistance r_1 = 6 ohms, r_2 = 10 ohms, and r_3 = 12 ohms.   Determine the current in each branch.

5-10. In Fig. 22, if the resistance of each load were 5 ohms, and the voltage at D were 110 volts, what would the voltages be at C, B, and A, when the conductors of the feeder line have a resistance of 0.25 ohm per 1,000 ft of wire?

***5-11.** In the laboratory circuit shown, find the voltages at points a, b, c, and d, if the resistance of the feeder is 0.4 ohm per 1,000 ft of wire.

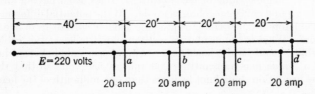

5-12. Three streetcars a, b, and c are $\frac{1}{2}$, 1, and 2 miles, respectively, from the power station. Cars a and b are drawing 50 amp and car c is drawing 200 amp. Find the voltages at each car, given that the station voltage is 600, the trolley resistance 0.42 ohm per mile of wire, and the return track resistance 0.03 ohm per mile of track.

*5-13. The resistance of each wire of a two-wire transmission line is 0.6 ohm. What voltage is necessary at the generating end in order to produce a current of 75 amp: (*a*) when the line is short-circuited at the receiving end; (*b*) when a pressure of 500 volts must be maintained at the receiving end?

5-14. A Weston d-c voltmeter has a resistance of approximately 100 ohms per volt of scale division. What current will a 150-volt voltmeter take when placed across 125 volts?

*5-15. Why should a voltmeter have a high resistance and an ammeter a low resistance? What would happen to the instruments if the voltmeter and ammeter in Fig. 27 were interchanged, E being 110 volts?

5-16. Two voltmeters, A of 10,000 ohms resistance and B of 5,000 ohms resistance, are connected in series across 150 volts. What will be the reading of each?

5-17. A 150-range voltmeter has a resistance of 10,000 ohms. What additional resistance must be placed in series with the instrument so that 450 volts will give a full-scale deflection?

5-18. A 25-amp meter has a resistance of 0.002 ohm. What is the voltage drop across the instrument for a full-scale deflection?

*5-19. What would happen if by accident an ammeter were used to measure the voltage of a 150-volt line? What would happen if by accident a voltmeter were placed in a line to measure the current flow?

5-20. A high resistance R is measured with a milliammeter I and a voltmeter V as shown in Fig. 26. The resistances of the meters are 1.0 and 17,500 ohms, respectively. If the ammeter reads 42.1 ma and the voltmeter 138 volts, what is the value of R? What is the percentage error in saying that $R = V/I$?

5-21. If the applied voltage E and the resistance R are the same as in the preceding problem, what will be the readings of the instruments in Fig. 27? What would be the percentage error made in this case by saying that $R = V/I$?

5-22. The coil of a well-known type of moving-coil instrument has a resistance of 1.5 ohms and will give a full-scale deflection with 50 mv across the terminals.

a. How can this meter be used as a 50-amp range ammeter? Specify the shunt (resistance and current capacity).

b. How can it be used as a 150-scale voltmeter? Specify the series resistance (resistance and current capacity).

*5-23. In order to determine the value of an unknown high resistance, a 150-scale voltmeter whose resistance is 17,000 ohms is connected in series with it across 220-volt mains. If the voltmeter reads 40 volts, what is the value of the unknown resistance?

5-24. A two-conductor line 5 miles long is laid in underground conduit. The conductors are single-conductor lead-sheathed cables, each having an insulation resistance to ground of 200 megohms per mile. If the potential difference between the line conductors is 2,000 volts, what is the leakage current from one conductor to the other? What is the insulation resistance of 4 miles of this cable?

*5-25. What should be the insulation resistance per mile between the two conductors of a 2-mile line transmitting 200 amp at 550 volts so that the leakage through the insulation should not be more than one-millionth of the load current?

5-26. In Fig. 5-26 B_1, B_2, and B_3 are three batteries producing emfs. E_1 = 10 volts; $E_2 = 2$ volts; $E_3 = 6$ volts. $R_1 = 25$ ohms; $R_2 = 45$ ohms; $R_3 = 20$ ohms.   Neglecting the internal resistance of the batteries and connecting

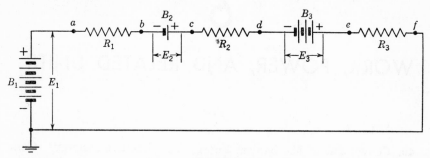

FIG. 5-26

wires, determine the current and the potential differences between ground and each of the six points, a, b, c, d, e, and f.   Plot a graph to show these potential differences.

5-27. Find the currents through the three resistances of Fig. 5-27, assuming that the resistances of the batteries and connecting wires are negligible.

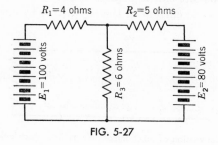

FIG. 5-27

6

WORK, POWER, AND RELATED UNITS

49. Conversion of Mechanical Energy into Electrical Energy. Consider Fig. 28, which represents a conductor XY being moved at constant velocity across the face of a north magnetic pole whose field is uniform. The magnetic lines of force are perpendicular to the paper and are therefore represented by dots.

The conductor XY is cutting the magnetic field at a constant rate, and therefore a constant emf is being generated in it. This emf maintains a constant electric current in the circuit. The current distorts the

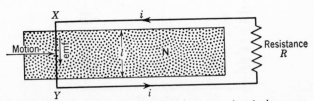

FIG. 28. Conversion of mechanical energy into electrical energy.

magnetic field, as explained in Art. 25, and causes the conductor to be acted upon by a force that opposes the motion of the conductor. A mechanical force equal and opposite to this force is therefore required to push the conductor through the field. This mechanical force does work, and, as there is no friction or acceleration, all this mechanical work or energy is converted into electrical energy. In this particular illustration the electrical energy is all converted into heat in the resistance R (where R is considered to be the total resistance of the circuit) but we are here concerned only with the conversion of mechanical energy into electrical energy and not with the ultimate fate of the electrical energy. As there are no mechanical losses in this elementary generator, the efficiency of conversion is 100 per cent, and the electric-power output is equal to the mechanical-power input. Let us proceed to write down expressions for these two powers and to equate them.

Let B = magnetic flux density, lines per sq cm

$\quad\quad l$ = length of that part of the conductor that is cutting magnetic field, cm

$\quad\quad v$ = velocity of conductor, cm per sec

$\quad\quad e$ = emf generated by conductor cutting magnetic flux, abvolts

$\quad\quad i$ = current produced by the emf e, abamp

$\quad\quad F$ = force required to push conductor through field at constant velocity v, dynes

From the definition of an abvolt, Art. 30, it follows that the electric-power output is ei ergs per sec.

The mechanical-power input is Fv ergs per sec.   Therefore

$$Fv = ei$$

but $\quad\quad\quad\quad\quad\quad e = Blv \quad\quad$ (Art. 34)

therefore $\quad\quad\quad\quad Fv = Blvi$

or $\quad\quad\quad\quad\quad\quad F = Bli \quad\quad$ dynes $\quad\quad\quad\quad\quad\quad$ (10)

Equation (10) is the basic equation for calculating the forces on conductors in all types of electric equipment.

50. Relationship between B and H. In Art. 27 it was shown that when a conductor carrying 1 abamp is lying in a vacuum in a field of unit strength ($H = 1$), a force of 1 dyne is exerted on each centimeter of its length, or, numerically, force = Hli dynes.   But Eq. (10) shows that force = Bli dynes.   Therefore in a vacuum B is numerically equal to H.

In Art. 20 it was shown that 4π lines emanate from unit magnetic pole in empty space when the lines are drawn to represent the H property of the field.   It has just been shown that in empty space B is numerically equal to H.   Therefore, when the lines are drawn to represent the B property of the field, there are still 4π lines emanating from unit pole.

51. Units of Work and Power. When used with their scientific meanings, work and energy are synonymous terms.   The potential energy which a body possesses owing to its having been raised to a certain elevation is the work done in raising it to that elevation.   The kinetic energy which a body possesses because of its velocity is the work done by the force that accelerated it to that velocity.   It is merely custom that decides which term we use in a given case.   "Potential work" has the same meaning and descriptive force as "potential energy."   Work is done when a force moves through a distance.   The cgs unit of work is the *erg*.   **An erg is the work done when a force of one dyne moves through a distance of one centimeter.**

From the definition of an abvolt, Art. 30, it follows that when a constant emf of e abvolts maintains a constant current of i abamp for t sec the power is ei ergs per sec, and the work done is eit ergs.

Now 1 volt = 10^8 abvolts, and 1 amp = $\frac{1}{10}$ abamp. Therefore if the emf is E volts and the current is I amp, the power = $EI \times 10^7$ ergs per sec = EI joules per sec = EI watts, where the joule is defined as being 10^7 ergs and the watt is a power unit defined as being 10^7 ergs per sec, or 1 joule per sec.

TABLE 1. Conversion Factors

Quantity	Cgs unit	Other units
Length.............	centimeter (cm)	1 inch (in.) = 2.54 cm
Mass..............	gram (g)	1 pound (lb) = 453.6 g
Time..............	second (sec)	
Force.............	dyne	1 g = 981 dynes
		1 lb = 453.6 g
Work, or energy....	erg, or dyne-cm	1 joule = 10^7 ergs
		= 1 watt-sec
		1 foot-pound (ft-lb) = 1.356 joules
		1 watthour (whr) = 3,600 joules
		1 kilowatthour (kwhr) = 1,000 watthours
		1 gram-calorie (g-cal) = 4.184 joules
		1 pound-calorie (lb-cal) = 1,900 joules
		1 Btu = 1,054 joules
Power.............	erg per sec	1 watt = 10^7 ergs per sec
		= 1 joule per sec
		1 kilowatt (kw) = 1,000 watts
		1 milliwatt (mw) = 0.001 watt
		1 microwatt (μw) = 0.000,001 watt
		1 megawatt = 1,000,000 watts
		1 horsepower (hp) = 550 ft-lb per sec
		= 746 watts

A **British thermal unit (Btu)** is the energy required to raise the temperature of one pound of water by one degree Fahrenheit.

A **gram-calorie (g-cal)** is the energy required to raise the temperature of one gram of water by one degree centigrade.

52. Power Expended in a Resistance—Joule's Experiments. To force a current of I amp through a circuit that has a resistance of R ohms, a voltage $E = IR$ is required.

$$\begin{aligned} \text{Power} &= EI &&\text{watts} \\ &= (IR)I &&\text{watts} \\ &= I^2R &&\text{watts} \end{aligned}$$

All the electrical energy is converted into heat.

Joule carried out some experiments to support the theoretical proof that the rate at which electrical energy is converted into heat in a resistance is I^2R watts. He took coils of wire of fairly high resistance, immersed them in water, and connected them across the terminals of batteries of voltaic cells. He measured the emf and current and also the rate at which the heat was produced. By repeating the process for various values of resistance and for various values of current, he verified the statement that the rate at which electrical energy is converted into heat in a resistance is I^2R watts.

The equation "power $= EI$ watts" is a general one and applies to all possible circuits, but the equation "power $= I^2R$ watts" is a particular one and applies only to resistances. For example, when a battery is being charged, as in Fig. 29, the generator drives current through the battery against the emf E_b of the battery and reverses the chemical action that takes place when the battery is discharging. The greater part of the electrical-energy output of the generator is con-

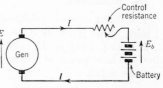

FIG. 29. Charging a battery.

verted into chemical potential energy and is stored in the battery, but some of the electrical energy is converted into heat as a result of the current being driven through the resistance of the circuit.

If R equals the combined resistance of control resistance, battery, and the connecting wires, then, by Ohm's law,

$$I = \frac{E - E_b}{R} \tag{11}$$

where $E - E_b$ is the total emf acting in the circuit. Equation (11) may be transposed to the form

$$EI = I^2R + E_bI \tag{12}$$

where EI = power output from generator, watts

I^2R = rate at which electrical energy is being converted into heat (and therefore wasted), watts

E_bI = rate at which electrical energy is being absorbed by chemical action, watts

53. Electric Generators and Motors. An electric generator is a device that converts mechanical energy into electrical energy.

An electric motor is a device that converts electrical energy into mechanical energy.

In general, the same piece of apparatus will function either as a generator or as a motor, as desired. Barlow's wheel is the best example of an electric motor given so far in this book, and it operates either as a motor, as explained in Art. 26, or as a generator, as explained in Art. 32.

Motors and generators are always rated in terms of their outputs, from which it naturally follows that motors are rated in horsepower and generators in kilowatts.

The efficiency of a motor or generator is defined as being the ratio $\frac{\text{power output}}{\text{power input}}$ and is expressed as a per cent. The output and the input must, of course, be expressed in the same units in the ratio.

It is a fairly general rule to rate all kinds of apparatus in terms of output, but there are exceptions. Electric lamps and electric heaters are rated in terms of power input.

54. Examples.

1. A hoist raises a weight of 2,000 lb through a distance of 300 ft in a time of 1 min. Find the work done and the power expended.

If the efficiency of the hoist is 75 per cent and that of the motor is 90 per cent, find the horsepower of the motor and also the current taken by the motor if the voltage is 115.

$$\text{Work done} = 2{,}000 \times 300 = 600{,}000 \text{ ft-lb}$$
$$\text{Power expended} = 600{,}000 \text{ ft-lb per 60 sec} = 10{,}000 \text{ ft-lb per sec}$$
$$= \frac{10{,}000}{550} = 18.2 \text{ hp}$$
$$= \frac{18.2 \times 746}{1{,}000} = 13.6 \text{ kw}$$
$$\text{Power input to hoist} = \frac{13.6}{0.75} = 18.1 \text{ kw} = 24.3 \text{ hp}$$
$$\text{Power input to motor} = \frac{18.1}{0.9} = 20 \text{ kw}$$

Since watts = volts $\times$ amperes, $20 \times 1{,}000 = 115 \times$ amperes, and

$$\text{Current} = 174 \text{ amp}$$

2. An electric iron takes 5 amp at 115 volts. What does it cost to operate this iron for 2 hr if the cost of energy is 6 cents per kwhr?

$$\text{Rate at which energy is used} = 115 \times 5 = 575 \text{ watts} = 0.575 \text{ kw}$$
$$\text{Energy used in 2 hr} = 0.575 \times 2 = 1.15 \text{ kwhr}$$
$$\text{Cost of energy} = 1.15 \times 6 = 6.9 \text{ cents}$$

3. A 40-watt 115-volt tungsten lamp gives 472 lumens of light flux. What is the current taken by this lamp and what is the cost of energy for 15 lamps burning for an average time of 4 hr if the cost of energy is 5 cents per kwhr?

$$\text{Amperes} = \frac{\text{watts}}{\text{volts}} = \frac{40}{115} = 0.348 \text{ amp}$$
$$\text{Power} = 40 \times 15 = 600 \text{ watts} = 0.6 \text{ kw}$$
$$\text{Energy used} = 0.6 \times 4 = 2.4 \text{ kwhr}$$
$$\text{Cost of energy} = 2.4 \times 5 = 12 \text{ cents}$$

4. The efficiency of the heating element of an electric water heater is always 100 per cent, but some heat is always lost through the walls of the container. A

certain electric water heater has an over-all efficiency of 90 per cent. It takes 6 amp at 115 volts. How long will it take to raise 1 gal (8.33 lb) of water from 20°C to the boiling point, and what will it cost when the rate is 5 cents per kwhr?

$$\text{Energy stored in water} = 8.33(100 - 20) = 666.4 \text{ lb-cal}$$
$$= 666.4 \times 1,900 = 1,266,160 \text{ joules, or watt-sec}$$
$$\text{Energy input to heater} = 1,266,160 \times \frac{100}{90} = 1,406,840 \text{ watt-sec}$$
$$= 0.3908 \text{ kwhr}$$
$$\text{Cost of energy} = 0.3908 \times 5 = 1.954 \text{ cents}$$

Energy is supplied at the rate of $115 \times 6 = 690$ watts. Therefore the time required to absorb 1,406,840 watt-sec is

$$\frac{1,406,840}{690} = 2,039 \text{ sec} = 34 \text{ min}$$

5. If a ton (2,000 lb) of coal heats a house for a month, what would it cost to give exactly the same heating effect electrically if the cost of energy is 3 cents per kwhr?

With a good heating system 1 lb of coal burnt on the grate will deliver 8,000 Btu, or 4,450 lb-cal, to the house.

$$\text{Energy required per month} = 4,450 \times 2,000 = 8,900,000 \text{ lb-cal}$$
$$= 8,900,000 \times 1,900 \text{ watt-sec}$$
$$= \frac{8,900,000 \times 1,900}{3,600 \times 1,000} = 4,700 \text{ kwhr}$$
$$\text{Cost of energy} = 4,700 \times 3 = 14,100 \text{ cents} = \$141$$

The reason for the great difference in the cost of heating by the two methods is that the efficiency of a coal-burning heating system is about 60 per cent, while the efficiency of a coal-burning electric generating plant, together with its distribution system, is not greater than 20 per cent. Moreover, interest and depreciation must be paid on the equipment required to convert the heat into electrical energy and to distribute it throughout the city.

Problems

*6-1. *a.* A small room is lighted by a 100-watt 115-volt tungsten lamp. Find the current taken by the lamp.

b. What does it cost to light the room for 5 hr if the cost of energy is 10 cents per kwhr?

6-2. A 10-hp 230-volt motor has an efficiency of 85 per cent. Find:

a. The motor input at full load in kilowatts.

b. The current taken by the motor at full load.

c. The cost per year to run this motor on full load for 48 hr per week if the cost of energy is 3 cents per kwhr.

6-3. The load on a 115-volt generator consists of two hundred 40-watt tungsten lamps, 10 flatirons taking 500 watts each, and a 10-hp motor which has an efficiency of 85 per cent. Find:

a. The output of the generator in kilowatts.

b. The current taken by the load.

c. The horsepower of the driving engine if the efficiency of the generator is 88 per cent.

*6-4. Find the work done in ergs and the power expended in kilowatts in raising a weight of 5,000 lb through 200 ft in 1 min. If the efficiency of the hoisting mechanism is 75 per cent and that of the motor is 88 per cent, what is the average horsepower required from the line during the hoisting period? What is the average current taken from the line if the voltage is 110?

6-5. To keep a 40-ton car moving at 36 mph requires a tractive effort of 800 lb; find the horsepower developed by the motor, and the current drawn from the line if the line voltage is 550 and the motor efficiency is 90 per cent.

6-6. Find the power required to melt 10 lb of ice in 5 min. Find also the current taken from a 115-volt line and the cost of the operation if the cost of energy is 6 cents per kwhr. (The latent heat of ice is 80 cal per g.)

6-7. A conductor 20 cm long is moving through a uniform magnetic field of 8,000 lines per sq cm with a velocity of 30 m per sec, the direction of motion being perpendicular to both the field and the conductor. Find the emf between the ends of the conductor. If the ends of the conductor are joined through an external circuit of such resistance that a current of 50 amp flows through the conductor, find the retarding force. Find the power required to keep the conductor moving.

*6-8. Is there any such unit as a watt per second?

*6-9. Do you buy energy or power from the power company? Is your bill in kilowatts or in kilowatthours?

*6-10. A man claimed that his electric power cost him 10 cents per kw. What did he probably mean?

6-11. A house uses five lamps of 40 watts each for 4 hr a day. What would be the monthly bill at 10 cents per kwhr?

6-12. How many 40-watt lamps could be safely used on a 115-volt line with 6-amp fuses? If a 5-amp electric toaster were put on the same line, how many of the lamps could now be lit at once?

6-13. The load on a 230-volt d-c generator consists of 1,000 hp of motors with an average efficiency of 80 per cent. Find: (a) the current to supply the load; (b) the generator output in kilowatts; (c) the horsepower of the engine if the efficiency of the generator is 95 per cent.

*6-14. A conductor 20 cm long is moving through a uniform magnetic field of 1.2 webers per square meter at a velocity of 40 m per sec. Find the emf between the ends of the conductor. If the ends of the conductor are joined through an external resistance so that a current of 80 amp flows through the conductor, find the retarding force. Find the power required to keep the conductor moving.

6-15. Forty wires each 10 cm long are connected in series and made to cut across a field having a flux density of 12,000 lines per sq cm at the rate of 3,000 cm per sec.

  a. Find the emf generated in the circuit.

  b. If the resistance of the circuit is 10 ohms, what current will flow and what will be the power in watts to keep the wires moving?

  c. What is the force required to keep the wires moving?

  d. From your figures show that force × velocity (in watts) = volts × amperes.

6-16. An electric iron takes 550 watts from a 115-volt circuit. What is the resistance of the heating coil? If the voltage is reduced 10 per cent, what will be the approximate reduction in the temperature of the iron?

*6-17. If ten 40-watt tungsten lamps are placed in parallel with the flatiron, what will be the total current taken from the line? Will the current in the iron be changed by the addition of the lamps?

6-18. Three resistances, $R_a = 10$ ohms, $R_b = 15$ ohms, $R_c = 20$ ohms, are connected in series across 110 volts. Find the current flowing and the voltage drop across each resistance. The same resistances are connected in parallel across 110 volts. Find the current through each branch and the total current drawn from the line. Find the current through each resistance, the total current, and the voltage across each resistance, when R_a and R_c in parallel are connected in series with R_b across 110 volts.

6-19. How much electric power can be developed continuously at a water-power site on a river where the height of the fall is 200 ft and the regulated flow of the river is 5,000 cu ft per sec? Assume that the hydraulic efficiency is 90 per cent and that the efficiency of the generators is 96 per cent. The weight of 1 cu ft of water is 62.4 lb.

6-20. If coal of a calorific value of 13,000 Btu per lb is burned in a steam plant in which the over-all thermal efficiency of the boilers and steam turbines is 20 per cent and the efficiency of the generators is 95 per cent, find the coal consumption in pounds per kilowatthour of output.

6-21. What is the maximum amount of power that can be delivered over a two-conductor line of No. 14 B & S copper wire, if the input voltage is fixed at 110 volts, direct current, and the line is 1,000 ft long? What is the voltage at the receiving end, and what is the efficiency of transmission?

7

RESISTORS AND RHEOSTATS

55. Resistors. A resistor is a device used to introduce resistance into an electric circuit. Resistors are used for the following purposes: (1) As meter elements, for example, ammeter shunts and voltmeter multipliers. (2) To control current, for example, rheostats. (3) As heater elements to convert electrical energy into heat energy.

When used as meter elements, the most important requirement is that the resistance should be as constant and permanent as possible. In

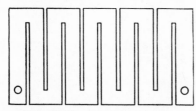

FIG. 30. Zigzag resistance unit.

particular, it should be practically independent of temperature over its range of operating temperatures.

When used to control current, the principal requirements are low cost, long life, and convenience. A fair constancy of the resistance is also desirable. In the case of heater elements there is the additional requirement that it should operate at a high temperature, and this usually conflicts with the requirement of long life.

The great majority of low-power resistors are made of various alloys of nickel, chromium, copper, iron, and manganese. These alloys have from about twenty-five to sixty-six times the specific resistance of pure copper, while their temperature coefficients of resistance are about one-twentieth that of copper. In general, the higher the specific resistance of the material, the shorter and stouter the resistance element and the simpler and stronger the construction.

Cast iron of various grades has about the same range of specific resistance as the alloys and is a very much cheaper material. It is very extensively used for the larger sizes of resistors in which the cost of the resistance material becomes one of the important cost items.

56. Construction of Resistors. The construction is determined chiefly by the current rating and the power. When the current and power are large, the resistors are generally constructed of cast-iron grids, as shown in Figs. 30 to 32. Figure 32 shows how the grid units are arranged in order to connect them all in series. The units A are mounted on iron rods B, which are insulated throughout their entire length by mica tubes C. The individual grids are separated from one another by washers, which are either of metal as at D and E or of insulating material as at F, depending on the direction in which it is desired to make the current flow. The four metal washers E act as terminals from which leads can be taken to switches or a faceplate controller.

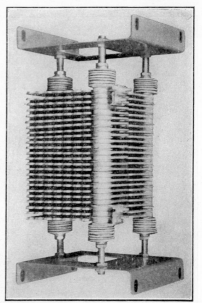

FIG. 31. Cast-iron grid resistor. (Westinghouse Electric Co.)

As the current rating is decreased, the saving resulting from the use of cast iron decreases to zero, and the cast grids become fragile. The type of construction then changes to that shown in Fig. 33. Here the resistor element is a rolled ribbon of stainless steel, or other resistance alloy, wound on edge to form a solenoid. The turns are spaced and supported by porcelain cleats mounted on the edges of steel plates.

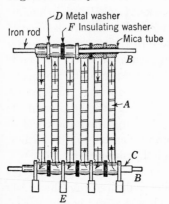

FIG. 32. Flow of current in a grid resistance.

For still smaller current ratings, the resistance alloys are made up in the form of wires or narrow ribbons and are wound flat in one layer on enameled steel or porcelain forms. Often they are covered over with a vitreous enamel after winding. This protects them from mechanical injury, chemical corrosion, and accidental electrical contact.

57. Rheostats. A rheostat is a variable resistance used to control current. It usually consists of a group of resistors and a switch panel. One very common arrangement is shown in Figs. 34 and 35. When the switch handle H, Fig. 34, is in the position shown, all nine resistors are in series with the circuit. As the handle is rotated counterclockwise from a to b, the resistors are cut out one by one.

58. Carbon-pile Rheostat. The carbon-pile rheostat, shown in Fig. 36, was developed to provide a smooth continuous variation of the cur-

FIG. 33. Group of four edgewise-wound resistor units.

rent, in contrast with the step-by-step variation of the standard type of rheostat shown in Fig. 34. It consists of one or more columns of thin

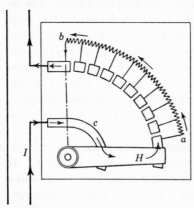

FIG. 34. Sliding-contact type of rheostat.

graphite disks A, enclosed in enameled steel tubes B. The resistance of such a column decreases as the mechanical pressure between the ends increases, because the contact between adjacent disks improves. In the rheostat shown in Fig. 36 the pressure is applied by turning the handwheel D and is communicated to the carbon pile through the plungers E. The two units shown may be connected in series or in parallel as desired, and the resistance of such a rheostat can be varied continuously through a total range of about 100 to 1.

59. Liquid Rheostats. Another method of obtaining a smooth continuous variation of resistance is by means of liquid rheostats. Figure 37

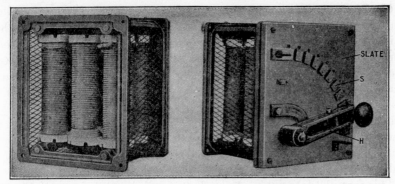

FIG. 35. Sliding-contact type of rheostat.

shows one type.   The liquid, which is usually water plus 1 or 2 per cent of sodium carbonate, is contained in a cylindrical tank of nonconducting material.   The electrodes are two per-forated metal disks supported by ver-tical metal rods.   The upper one is arranged to be raised or lowered by some suitable mechanical device, not shown in the figure.   Since the flow of the electric current in the liquid is confined to the space between the two electrodes, it follows that the resistance

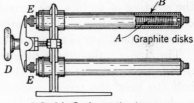

FIG. 36. Carbon-pile rheostat.

is directly proportional to the distance between them, and a wide range of smooth variation is readily obtained.

The liquid rheostat has a large temperature coefficient.   Its resist-ance at 80°C is only about one-quar-ter the resistance at 20°C.

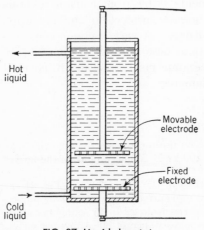

FIG. 37. Liquid rheostat.

It is generally necessary to pro-vide some means of cooling the liq-uid, unless the periods of operation are short and infrequent.   Copper coils, through which cold water is cir-culated, may be placed in the upper part of the tank, or the liquid may be circulated through an external cooler.

Liquid and carbon-pile rheostats provide the same type of electrical control, but the mechanical and cost differences result in the carbon pile being used only in small sizes and the liquid rheostat usually only in large sizes.

60. Rheostat Size. The size of a rheostat that is designed for continuous operation is determined principally by the amount of power that it is required to dissipate. According to the AIEE Standards, the temperature of a bare metallic resistor should not rise more than 375°C above the room temperature. In the case of resistors embedded in ceramic materials, the temperature rise of the surface should not exceed 300°C. At a temperature rise of 375°C each square inch of free radiating surface will dissipate about 7 watts, and at a rise of 300°C will dissipate about 6 watts. Consequently, a rheostat that is designed to dissipate W watts continuously must provide a radiating surface that is equivalent to a *free* radiating surface of $W/6$ or $W/7$ sq in.

This formula does not apply to the type of rheostat shown in Fig. 31, in which the inner sections have practically no free radiating surface. The cooling in this case is determined by the flow of air through the spaces and can be substantially increased by means of a fan.

Rheostats that are intended for brief intermittent operation, such as the starting of motors, are considerably smaller than those designed for continuous operation at the same power. Such rheostats are variously rated for operation 15 sec out of each 4 min, 30 sec out of each 4 min, etc.

The size of a rheostat is practically independent of the voltage as long as the power is constant. If the voltage is doubled, the current is cut in half (to keep the power constant). Therefore the resistance must be made four times as great. This is accomplished by cutting the cross section of the resistance wire in half and doubling its length. Thus the mass remains unchanged.

61. Heater Elements. These elements differ from control resistors chiefly in that they usually require greater protection and are often designed to operate at higher temperatures. A very common construction is to wind the resistance wire into a loose solenoid of about $\frac{1}{4}$ in. diameter, to embed this solenoid in ceramic insulation, and to cover it with a metal tube of slightly larger diameter.

Problems

7-1. How many ohms resistance would you use for loading the following 220-volt generators: 2 kw, 10 kw, 50 kw, and 500 kw? Which would be the largest and heaviest rheostat and why?

*7-2. It is found that cast-iron grid resistors of the type shown in Fig. 31 can dissipate about 1.0 watt per sq in. of actual iron surface, with natural air convection cooling. The resistance of cast iron varies from 22 to 45 μohms per cu in. Assuming that the cast iron available has a resistance of 30 μohms per cu in., design a cast-iron grid resistor to carry 130 amp with 110 volts across its terminals.

*7-3. The resistance of the above resistor is 0.846 ohm. Why not use 17 in. of No. 20 nichrome wire, which would have the same resistance?

7-4. How would a rheostat to absorb 500 watts at 10 volts differ from one for

500 watts at 100 volts? Explain in detail. Using the same size of resistance wire in each case, compare the weights of wire and arrangements in the two cases.

7-5. How many pounds of resistance wire are needed in a rheostat to absorb 10 kw for 5 sec, with a temperature rise of 100°C? The heat radiated during this interval will be negligible. The wire has a resistance of 500 ohms per cir mil-ft, it has a density of 0.31 lb per cu in., and its specific heat is 0.096. What should be the resistance of the rheostat and the cross section and length of the wire if the emf is 110 volts?

8

MAGNETIC CIRCUITS AND MAGNETIC
PROPERTIES OF IRON

62. Magnetic Field Due to a Ring Solenoid. A solenoid is a coil of wire wound in the form of a helix, as shown in Fig. 11. When an electric current is made to flow through such a coil, it acts as an electromagnet and the direction of the magnetic field may be found by the corkscrew rule, Art. 22.

The solenoid shown in Fig. 38 has been bent so as to form a ring. If the turns are close together, a magnetic survey will show that the field produced by such a solenoid is confined entirely to the space inside the solenoid and that the lines of force inside the solenoid are all circles, as shown in Fig. 38.

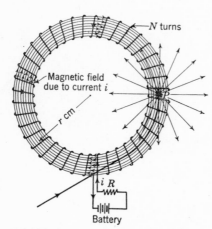

FIG. 38. Magnetic field produced by a ring solenoid.

In order to determine the strength of the magnetic field produced in the ring solenoid of N turns by a current of i abamp flowing through those turns, imagine a unit magnetic pole P inserted in the solenoid, as shown in Fig. 38, and pushed along the axis of the solenoid, against the force of the field, at a constant speed of 1 rps. In the figure the unit magnetic pole is pictured as being located at one end of an infinitely long fine flexible bar magnet. An air of mechanical feasibility may be given to this idealized apparatus by imagining frictionless guide bars of nonmagnetic nonconducting material to guide the unit pole along the axis of the solenoid.

As the unit pole moves along the axis of the solenoid, the lines of flux

58

from this unit pole cut the turns of the solenoid and generate emf in them. There are 4π lines of flux emanating from a unit pole (Art. 20) and each of these lines cuts every turn once while the unit pole makes one complete circuit. If therefore the unit pole makes one circuit per second, each turn of wire on the solenoid is cut by 4π lines per sec and has an emf of 4π abvolts generated in it. Therefore the total emf e generated in the solenoid is $4\pi N$ abvolts. The direction of this emf may be determined by the rules given in Art. 33 and it will be found that this emf is in the same direction as the emf of the battery. The effect of introducing this moving unit pole therefore is to increase the total emf acting in the circuit and consequently to increase the current. The current can be kept at its original value i either by reducing the emf of the battery or by increasing the resistance R.

As long as the unit pole is kept moving, it generates part of the emf required to maintain the current i. The unit pole moving along the axis of the solenoid constitutes an elementary generator converting mechanical energy into electrical energy, and, since there are no mechanical losses the efficiency of conversion is 100 per cent.

When the unit pole is traveling around the ring at the rate of 1 rps,

$$\text{Mechanical-power input} = Hl \qquad \text{ergs per sec}$$

where H = force with which the magnetic field opposes motion of unit pole, dynes

l = length of the solenoid, that is, of path traveled by unit pole, cm

Electric-power output of generator $= ei = 4\pi Ni$ ergs per sec

and these two powers are equal. Therefore

$$Hl = 4\pi Ni$$

and $$H = \frac{4\pi Ni}{l} \qquad \text{dynes on unit pole (oersteds)} \qquad (13)$$

But the strength of a magnetic field is measured in terms of the force that it exerts on unit pole. Therefore the strength of the magnetic field at the center of the solenoid is given by Eq. (13), where i is the current in abamperes.

If the current is measured in amperes and is denoted by I, then, since 1 abamp = 10 amp,

$$H = \frac{4\pi NI}{10l} \qquad \text{dynes per unit pole} \qquad (14)$$

In deriving Eq. (14), the unit pole was moved along the axis of the solenoid. If, however, it is made to hug the inner side of the solenoid, the distance traveled per revolution is appreciably less; yet every line from the pole cuts every turn just the same as before. Therefore the electric-power output is the same, and consequently the mechanical-power input must be the same. Therefore, since the distance is less, the force must be greater; consequently H is greater at the inner side of the ring than it is at the outer side. The value of H at the center is always slightly less than the average value of H over the cross section of the solenoid, but the difference is usually negligible, and the total number of lines of force in the solenoid may be taken as equal to the cross-sectional area of the solenoid multiplied by the value of H at the center.

63. Magnetic Materials—Permeability. Let us now fill the ring solenoid of Fig. 38 with a core of magnetic material, such as iron or steel or alloys of iron and nickel, and investigate the effect that this has upon the field.

In order to measure B, let us make a thin saw cut through the magnetic core at right angles to the field, so that a fine wire may be passed through to cut the field.

Keeping the solenoid current constant, so that the magnetizing force H will be constant, it will be found that the emf induced in the wire as it cuts across the field, when the solenoid is filled with magnetic material, is very much greater than when the solenoid contains no magnetic material. The magnetic induction B is evidently greatly increased by the presence of the magnetic material.

The permeability, μ, of a material is defined by the equation

$$\mu = \frac{B}{H} \tag{15}$$

where B is the value of the magnetic induction inside the solenoid when it is completely filled with the given material and H is the magnetizing force of the current in the solenoid. Let μ_0 equal the permeability of empty space. Then when B is in gauss and H is in oersteds, $\mu_0 = 1$.

In most magnetic materials the values of B obtained with decreasing values of H are considerably larger than those obtained with increasing values of H. Therefore if Eq. (15) is to be of any practical use the manner in which H is brought to the desired value must be specified. This is done in Art. 72.

Combining Eqs. (14) and (15), we obtain

$$B = \mu H = \frac{4\pi N I \mu}{10l} \qquad \text{gauss} \tag{16}$$

Then if A is the cross-sectional area of the solenoid in square centimeters, the total magnetic flux ϕ in the solenoid is

$$\phi = BA = \left(\frac{4\pi}{10}\right)(NI)\left(\frac{\mu A}{l}\right) \qquad \text{maxwells, or lines} \tag{17}$$

The product NI is called the *ampere-turns*.

For nonmagnetic materials $\mu = 1$.

64. Reluctance. From Eq. (17) it appears that the total flux produced in a ring solenoid is directly proportional to the cross-sectional area of the solenoid and to the permeability and is inversely proportional to the length of the solenoid, the ampere-turns NI being constant. Similarly, the electric current produced in a given conductor by a given emf is directly proportional to the cross-sectional area of the conductor and to the specific conductance (which is the reciprocal of the specific resistance) and is inversely proportional to the length of the conductor. Consequently, Ohm's law may be applied to the solution of magnetic circuits.

The factor $l/\mu A$ of Eq. (17) is called the **reluctance** of the magnetic path, just as $\rho l/A$ is called the **resistance** of the electrical path (Art. 40).

The magnetizing force of the current, which produces the magnetic field, is called the **magnetomotive force (mmf)** and is usually measured in **ampere-turns.** Then

$$\phi = \frac{4\pi}{10} \times \frac{\text{mmf, ampere-turns}}{\text{reluctance}} \tag{18}$$

which is similar to the Ohm's law equation

$$I = \frac{\text{emf}}{\text{resistance}}$$

except that Eq. (18) contains the constant $4\pi/10$. This constant can evidently be eliminated by changing the magnitude of the unit of mmf, and this has been done;

$$\phi = \frac{\text{mmf, gilberts}}{\text{reluctance}} \tag{19}$$

where 1 gilbert $= 10/4\pi$ amp-turns.

The ampere-turn is the more widely used unit of mmf, however, and the gilbert will not be referred to again in this book.

Unfortunately for the simplicity of what may be called the Ohm's law method of calculating magnetic circuits, the permeability of magnetic materials varies widely with flux density. Moreover, the relationship between permeability and flux density cannot be expressed by any simple mathematical equation (see Fig. 39). However, Eqs. (18) and (19) are readily applied if a permeability curve for the material in question is available. The procedure is to assume a value of flux density, which fixes the permeability, and then to solve for the mmf.

Example. How many ampere-turns would be required to produce a flux of 60,000 lines in a sheet-steel ring that has a mean diameter of 20 cm and a cross-sectional area of 5 sq cm?

$$\text{Required flux density} = \frac{60,000}{5} = 12,000 \text{ lines per sq cm}$$

From Fig. 39 we find that at this flux density sheet steel has a permeability of 2,200.

$$\text{Reluctance} = \frac{l}{\mu A} = \frac{20\,\pi}{2,200 \times 5}$$

Rearranging Eq. (18),

$$\text{mmf} = \phi \times \text{reluctance} \times \frac{10}{4\pi}$$

$$= 60,000 \times \frac{20\pi}{2,200 \times 5} \times \frac{10}{4\pi} = 273 \text{ amp-turns}$$

The most important field of application of "reluctance," "permeability," and the Ohm's law method of regarding magnetic circuits is in

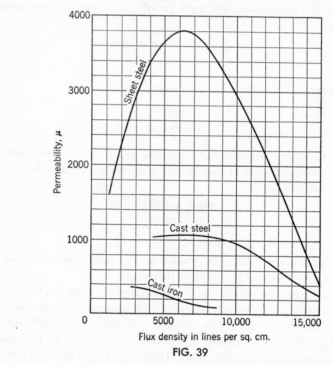

FIG. 39

theoretical treatments rather than in the obtaining of numerical solutions. When numerical solutions are required, a slightly different procedure, illustrated in Arts. 65 and 67, is more often used.

65. Magnetization Curves. The magnetic properties of iron and steel and their alloys are generally shown by means of magnetization curves such as those shown in Figs. 40 and 41. The data from which these

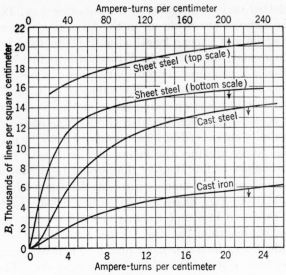

FIG. 40. Magnetization curves.

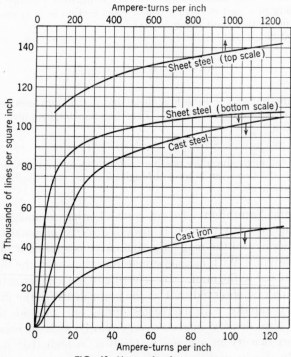

FIG. 41. Magnetization curves.

curves are plotted may be obtained in the following way: Test pieces of the magnetic material are made up in the form of a ring with a cross section of A sq cm and a mean length of magnetic path of l cm. These rings are then wound uniformly with N turns of insulated wire as in Fig. 38, and the flux ϕ is measured for different values of the exciting current I by means of special instruments. The values of ϕ/A, the flux density, are then plotted against corresponding values of NI/l as shown in Fig. 40, to give what is called the magnetization curve of the material.

The permeability curves of Fig. 39 are obtained from the magnetization curves of Fig. 40 by dividing the values of flux density shown on the curves by the values of flux density that would be produced in an air core by the same number of ampere-turns, as determined by Eq. (14).

For example, from Fig. 40 we see that a flux density of 13,000 lines per sq cm is produced in a uniform ring of sheet steel by an mmf of 6 amp-turns per cm length of the ring. From Eq. (14) we see that if the ring were made of air, the flux density produced in it by 6 amp-turns per cm would be $(4 \times \pi \times 6)/10 = 7.54$ lines per sq cm. Therefore the permeability is $13,000/7.54 = 1,724$, and this checks with the value shown in Fig. 39 for that particular flux density.

Example. How many ampere-turns would be required to produce 36,000 lines of magnetic flux in a cast-steel ring whose cross section is 3 sq cm, the mean length of the magnetic circuit being 50 cm?

The required flux density is

$$\frac{36,000}{3} = 12,000 \text{ lines per sq cm}$$

From the magnetization curves in Fig. 40 we find that 12,000 lines per sq cm are produced by 12.5 amp-turns per cm. Therefore the total number of ampere-turns required is

$$12.5 \times 50 = 625 \text{ amp-turns}$$

And this mmf can be produced by passing 1 amp through 625 turns, or by passing 5 amp through 125 turns, or 25 amp through 25 turns, etc., whichever happens to be most convenient.

66. Magnetic Saturation. In air, and all other nonmagnetic materials, the magnetic flux density is always directly proportional to the mmf producing it, and the magnetization curve is a straight line passing through the origin. With magnetic materials, however, the flux density is not proportional to the mmf. By referring to the magnetization curves in Fig. 40 it may be observed that at the lower densities the flux density increases very rapidly with increasing mmf, but that at the higher densities the flux density increases very slowly with increasing mmf. When the flux density in a given material is so high that it increases comparatively slowly with increasing mmf, the material is said to be nearly *saturated*. All magnetic materials exhibit this phenomenon of magnetic saturation, and the magnetization curves are often called saturation curves.

67. Solution of Composite Magnetic Circuits. Magnetic circuits of constant cross section that are composed entirely of air or other non-magnetic material are solved by means of Eq. (16) or (17), with $\mu = 1$. Magnetic circuits of constant cross section that are composed entirely of a single magnetic material are solved by means of magnetization curves,

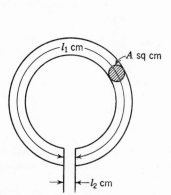

FIG. 42. Magnetic circuit with an air gap.

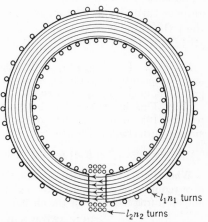

FIG. 43. Best possible arrangement of the exciting turns to give a uniform magnetic field. (Cross section through axis of ring.)

as illustrated in the example of Art. 65. In practice, however, magnetic circuits are generally composite, part of the magnetic path being through magnetic material and part through air. The magnetic circuit shown in Fig. 42 is typical of all such circuits and its solution is of fundamental importance in the design of electric machinery.

The magnetic circuit shown in Fig. 42 consists of l_1 cm of cast steel and l_2 cm of air, in series, the total length of the circuit being $l_1 + l_2$ cm. The cross-sectional area of the path is A sq cm throughout. It is required to determine the number of ampere-turns necessary to produce a given magnetic flux density in the air gap.

The method of solution is simple. The circuit is first solved as though it were composed entirely of cast steel, as in the example of Art. 65. This gives the ampere-turns In_1 per cm length of the solenoid for the cast-steel part of the circuit. Therefore Il_1n_1 amp-turns will be required on the cast-steel part of the circuit. The circuit is then solved as though it were composed entirely of air [Eq. (16)]. This gives the ampere-turns In_2 per cm length of the solenoid for the air part of the circuit. Therefore Il_2n_2 ampere-turns will be required for the air-gap part of the magnetic circuit. The total number of ampere-turns required is therefore equal to $Il_1n_1 + Il_2n_2$ amp-turns.

This method is equivalent to designing two complete solenoids, one for an all-steel core and the other for an all-air core, to give the same flux density. A slice of the desired thickness (l_2 cm) is then cut out of the solenoid designed for the all-steel core and is replaced by a similar slice cut from the solenoid designed for the all-air core. The result is a composite solenoid such as that shown in Fig. 43. The number of ampere-turns required for the air core is, of course, very much greater than the number required for the steel core, because the reluctance of air is very much greater than the reluctance of steel.

Example. If in Fig. 42 $l_1 = 49.5$ cm of cast steel and $l_2 = 0.5$ cm of air, how many ampere-turns would be required to produce a flux density of 12,000 lines per sq cm in the magnetic circuit?

From Fig. 40 we see that to produce 12,000 lines per sq cm in cast steel requires 12.5 amp-turns per cm length of the magnetic circuit. Therefore the ampere-turns required for the cast-steel part of the circuit is

$$Il_1n_1 = 49.5 \times 12.5 = 619 \text{ amp-turns}$$

When Eq. (16) is rewritten in the form $NI = 10Bl/4\pi\mu$, it appears that an air core requires $10B/4\pi$ amp-turns per cm and, since $l_2 = 0.5$ cm, the number of ampere-turns required for the air gap is

$$\frac{10 \times 12,000 \times 0.5}{4\pi} = 4,775 \text{ amp-turns}$$

Therefore   Total $= 619 + 4,775 = 5,394$ amp-turns

In order to produce a uniform field of 12,000 lines per sq cm throughout the circuit, the turns must be arranged as shown in Fig. 43, making $Il_1n_1 = 619$ and $Il_2n_2 = 4,775$.

Note that, although the length of the air gap is only 1 per cent of the total length of the magnetic circuit, it requires 88.5 per cent of the total ampere-turns.

68. Effect of Shifting the Exciting Turns from the Ideal Location. The solution of the foregoing example was based on the tacit assumption that the exciting turns for the air gap could be concentrated on the air gap in a single-layer coil of the same diameter as the steel. If this could be done, the flux would be uniform and the solution would be precise. However, in general it would be quite impossible to squeeze all the air-gap turns into a single layer. In practice it is generally not feasible to place any turns at all on the air gap. They must therefore be placed on the magnetic-material part of the circuit, as in Fig. 44.

The effect of shifting the air-gap turns in this way is to expand the boundaries of the air part of the magnetic circuit and thus create fringing or leakage magnetic flux. The flux that crosses from one pole to the other in the space outside the gap proper is called the *fringing* or *leakage* flux.

If the air-gap turns are placed as near to the gap as they are in Fig. 44, the flux density in the gap is almost exactly the same as with the ideal winding arrangement originally assumed.   The flux in the steel part of the magnetic circuit will be increased, however, by the amount of the fringing or leakage flux.   In general, the leakage flux is not utilized in any way, but it has to be carried by the iron part of the magnetic circuit, and the designer must be on his guard to see that it does not saturate the iron and thus introduce a large error into the calculation of the number of turns required for that part of the circuit.   Therefore if the air-gap ampere-turns are to be placed on the magnetic-material part of the circuit, as in Figs. 44 and 45, the designer should estimate the amount of the leakage flux and add it to the air-gap flux in order to determine the total flux in the magnetic material.   The magnetization curves then give him the required ampere-turns to produce this flux.

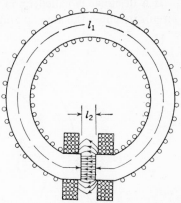

FIG. 44. Magnetic field produced when the air-gap exciting turns are placed on the steel core near the air gap.

Example.   If in Fig. 44 l_1 = 49.5 cm of cast steel and l_2 = 0.5 cm of air, and the air-gap ampere-turns are to be arranged as shown, how many ampere-turns will be required to produce a flux density of 12,000 lines per sq cm in the air gap?

$$\text{Ampere-turns for air gap} = \frac{10BL}{4\pi} = \frac{10 \times 12,000 \times 0.5}{4\pi}$$

$$= 4,775 \text{ amp-turns}$$

Leakage flux is estimated as 20 per cent of the gap flux.   Therefore

Flux density in steel = 12,000 × 1.20 = 14,400 lines per sq cm

From the magnetization curves, Fig. 40, 14,400 lines per sq cm in cast steel requires 26 amp-turns per cm.   Therefore the cast-steel part of the circuit requires 26 × 49.5 = 1,287 amp-turns.   And

Total mmf required = 4,775 + 1,287 = 6,062 amp-turns

When this result is compared with the solution of the example of Art. 67, it appears that neglecting the leakage flux altogether would have introduced an error of 11 per cent in the calculated total number of ampere-turns.

The magnitude of the error resulting from ignoring the leakage flux depends upon how near the magnetic material is to saturation.

It is usually quite difficult—if not impossible—to calculate the amount of leakage flux, and in practice the designer relies largely upon his experience to guide him in estimating it.   The leakage factors used in practice are chiefly of experimental origin.

If a designer is called upon to design some unusual type of magnetic circuit in which the air-gap ampere-turns must for some reason be located

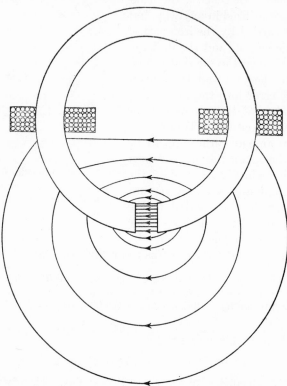

FIG. 45. Field produced when the air-gap exciting turns are remote from the air gap.

at a considerable distance from the air gap, as in Fig. 45, so that the leakage flux will be very large, then, unless he has had previous experience with some such type of unusual circuit, the only thing he can do is to build up a model and measure the leakage flux.   In such a circuit the leakage flux cannot be ignored even for rough calculations.   For example, the leakage flux in Fig. 45 will be about equal to the flux in the gap proper. Therefore if we are to have, say, 10,000 lines per sq cm in the air gap, the flux density in the cast steel in the upper half of the ring must be 20,000 lines per sq cm.   From Fig. 40 it is seen that this constitutes a very high degree of saturation in the steel.   Approximately 400 amp-turns per cm would be required to produce such a high density in the cast steel, whereas only 8 amp-turns per cm would be allowed if the leakage flux were ignored and the flux density in the steel taken as 10,000 lines per sq cm.

It is not economical to use such a high degree of saturation in the steel. Consequently, if the exciting turns are to be placed as in Fig. 45, the cross section of the steel should be increased so as to bring the flux density down to 12,000 lines per sq cm or less. The steel should be tapered off toward the pole faces so as to give the same gap dimensions as before, the gap dimensions being presumably determined by the conditions under which the magnet is to be used.

69. Residual Magnetism. If, after a piece of iron has been magnetized by means of an exciting coil, the exciting current is reduced to

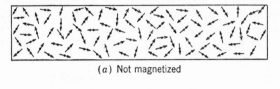

(a) Not magnetized

(b) Magnetized to complete saturation

FIG. 46. Arrangement of the molecules of an iron bar.

zero, it will be found that the magnetism has not become zero but that some of it, called the residual magnetism, remains. If the iron is soft and annealed and there is an air gap in the magnetic circuit, this residual magnetism will be quite feeble, and the last traces of it may be made to disappear if the iron is subjected to vibration. If hard steel is used, the residual magnetism will be strong, and it can be removed only with difficulty, so that permanent magnets are generally made of special hard steels such as cobalt steel.

70. Theory of Magnetism in Iron. In order to account for the peculiar magnetic behavior of iron, it is generally assumed that atoms of iron are equivalent to natural magnets, each with its own north and south pole. On this assumption the magnetic properties of iron may be illustrated by covering a large tray with small magnetic compasses packed closely together. If the trayful of compasses is not subjected to the influence of an external magnetic field, the compass needles will point in all directions, as Fig. 46a.

The direction of each individual compass needle is determined by the forces of repulsion and attraction between itself and all the surrounding needles. As a result of these forces the needles tend to arrange themselves in closed groups, the north and south poles joining hands so to speak. The tray as a whole exhibits no magnetic properties and represents an unmagnetized bar of iron. If we slip the tray into a long solenoid and pass a gradually increasing current through the solenoid, the current will produce a magnetic field that will tend to cause all the compass needles to point in the same direction, parallel to the axis of the solenoid. While the current is small, this force is small and only the most unstable groups are broken up by it, although all the groups are distorted to some extent. As the current is continuously increased, however, more and more groups break up and all the compass needles swing more nearly into line with the magnetic field of the solenoid, until eventually all the needles are pointing in the same direction as shown in Fig. 46b, which represents the condition of complete saturation of the iron. The magnetic fields of the small magnets add to the field produced by the solenoid, and the resultant field is very much stronger than that produced by the solenoid alone.

If the exciting current in the solenoid is reduced to zero, the molecular magnets tend to re-form into groups, but on account of molecular friction they do not return quite to their original positions but have a slight permanent displacement in the direction in which they have been lined up, and this accounts for the residual magnetism.

It is believed that the molecules of iron owe their magnetic fields to electric currents. Each atom contains spinning electrons, and a spinning electron may be considered equivalent to a minute solenoid of one turn. In nonmagnetic materials the magnetic fields produced by the various spinning electrons neutralize each other so that no external magnetic field is produced. In magnetic materials the fields do not neutralize each other. According to this theory, therefore, all magnetic fields are produced by electric currents, and a permanent bar magnet is merely an aggregation of minute short solenoids carrying permanent electric currents.

71. Hysteresis. If a bar of iron is placed in a solenoid and the current in the solenoid is reversed, the magnetism of the bar is reversed, the north pole becoming the south pole. The process of reversing the magnetism generates heat in the iron due to the friction which opposes the turning about of the atoms. The conversion of electrical energy into heat energy, as a result of molecular friction opposing changes in magnetism, is called the magnetic hysteresis loss.

72. Hysteresis Loop. Figure 47 shows how the magnetic induction B in a ring solenoid, filled with magnetic material, changes as the current is put through cyclic changes. Starting with completely demagnetized material, the graph of B traces the line oa as the magnetizing force H is increased from zero to the value op. It follows the line ab as H is reduced to zero. H is then reversed, increased to the value op', and reduced to zero, during which process the graph of B follows the line $bcde$. As H is again reversed and increased to op, the graph of B completes the loop to a.

It can be proved that the area of the loop is a measure of the energy converted into heat by hysteresis during one cycle of magnetization.

Figure 47 shows two values of B for each value of H, depending on whether the particular value of H is approached by an increasing H or a decreasing H. The magnetization curves of Figs. 40 and 41 show only one value of B for each value of H. One is led to inquire just what these magnetization curves really mean. The answer is that a magnetization curve is the locus of the peaks of the hysteresis loops produced by cyclic magnetizing forces of different maximum values. The magnetization curve for sheet steel in Fig. 40 states that a flux density of 15,000 lines per sq cm is produced by a magnetizing force of 14 amp-turns per cm, but this is true only if the steel has been put through at

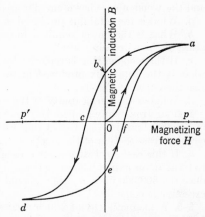

FIG. 47. Hysteresis loop. The residual magnetic flux density is represented by the distance ob. The coercive force required to reduce the residual magnetism to zero is represented by the distance oc.

least one complete cycle of magnetization with 14 amp-turns per cm as the maximum magnetizing force.

Note that in the case of a nonmagnetic material, such as air, the hysteresis loop becomes a single diagonal straight line passing through the origin.

Problems

8-1. A coil of 200 turns of No. 16 copper wire (see page 584) is wound in one layer on a wooden ring, as in Fig. 38. The ring has a mean diameter of 12 cm, and the wooden core has a circular cross section of 5 sq cm.

  a. What is the total flux produced in the core by an exciting current of 4 amp?

  b. What is the power required to maintain the exciting current, the temperature of the wire being 30°C?

  c. If the wooden ring is replaced by a cast-steel ring of the same dimensions, what is the total flux produced in the core by an exciting current of 4 amp? Use the curve of Fig. 40.

  d. What is the permeability of the cast steel at this flux density?

  e. If the number of turns is doubled, the voltage and the size of wire being unchanged, what will be the effect on the flux and on the power required?

8-2. *a.* How many ampere-turns are required to produce a total magnetic flux of 50,000 lines in a cast-steel ring which has a mean diameter of 12 cm, and a circular cross section of the steel core of 5 sq cm?

b. If this cast-steel ring is cut through radially by means of a milling machine to form an air gap of 0.2 cm, what will be the ampere-turns now required to produce the 50,000 lines, and how should the turns be distributed in order to avoid excessive leakage flux?

8-3. A coil of 400 turns of No. 16 copper wire (see page 584) is wound in one layer on a wooden ring, as in Fig. 38. The ring has a mean diameter of 10 in., and the wooden core has a circular cross section of 4 sq in.

a. What is the total flux produced in the core by an exciting current of 5 amp?

b. What is the power required to maintain the exciting current, the temperature of the wire being 30°C?

c. If the wooden ring is replaced by a cast-steel ring of the same dimensions, what is the total flux produced in the core by an exciting current of 5 amp? Use the curve of Fig. 41.

d. What is the permeability of the cast steel at this flux density?

8-4. *a.* How many ampere-turns are required to produce a total magnetic flux of 300,000 lines in a cast-steel ring which has a mean diameter of 10 in. and a circular cross section of the steel core of 4 sq in.?

b. If this cast-steel ring is cut through radially by means of a milling machine to form an air gap of 0.25 in., what will be the ampere-turns now required to produce the 300,000 lines, and how should the turns be distributed in order to avoid excessive leakage flux?

8-5. A magnetic circuit which carries a flux of 24,000 lines is made up of the following parts in series:

a. 20 cm of 2- by 2-cm cast iron.

b. 20 cm of 2- by 2-cm cast steel.

c. Two air gaps each 0.3 cm long and 2.1 by 2.1 cm cross section. Find the ampere-turns necessary to send the flux through each part of the circuit. Find total ampere-turns.

8-6. A cast-iron ring has a mean diameter of 50 cm and a cross section area of 40 sq cm. How many ampere-turns are required to set up a flux of 240,000 lines? What is the permeability of the ring? What is the value of the reluctance?

8-7. The magnetic circuit of a two-pole d-c generator, as shown in Fig. 8-7, is made up of the following parts:

a. Two cast-steel poles, each with a cross section of 110 sq cm and a magnetic length of 5 cm.

b. A cast-steel yoke with a cross section of 40 sq cm, in which half the flux goes each way, the average length of the magnetic path being approximately 40 cm (one-half the mean circumference).

c. Two air gaps, each with a magnetic length of 0.5 cm and an effective cross section of 100 sq cm. (The actual cross section of the air gap is 122 sq cm, but since nearly all the flux is carried by the teeth, and very little by the slots, the effective cross section of the air gap is about 18 per cent less than the apparent cross section.)

d. The sheet-steel teeth of the armature. The teeth are 1.75 cm long, and the cross section of all the teeth under one pole may be taken as 45 sq cm. (The teeth taper, but it has been found sufficiently accurate to take the section two-thirds of the way along the tooth toward the center of the armature.)

e. The sheet-steel armature core inside the teeth. Average cross section is

75 sq cm.   Average length is 8 cm (a little less than the armature diameter minus twice the tooth length.)

Half of the exciting ampere-turns are placed on each of the two poles.   How many ampere-turns per pole are required for each part of the magnetic circuit, to produce a flux of 850,000 lines through the armature?   Neglect leakage fluxes.

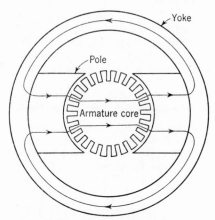

FIG. 8-7. Magnetic circuit of a two-pole d-c generator.

8-8. The magnetic circuit of a two-pole d-c generator, as shown in Fig. 8-7, is made up of the following parts:

a. Two cast-steel poles, each with a cross section of 22 sq in. and a magnetic length of 2.25 in.

b. A cast-steel yoke with a cross section of 8 sq in., in which half the flux goes each way, the average length of the magnetic path being approximately 19 in. (one-half the mean circumference).

c. Two air gaps, each with a magnetic length of 0.2 in. and an effective cross section of 20 sq in.   (The actual cross section of the air gap is 24.5 sq in., but since nearly all the flux is carried by the teeth, and very little by the slots, the effective cross section of the air gap is about 18 per cent less than the apparent cross section.)

d. The sheet-steel teeth of the armature.   The teeth are 0.8 in. long, and the cross section of all the teeth under one pole may be taken as 9.0 sq in.   (The teeth taper but it has been found sufficiently accurate to take the section two-thirds of the way along the tooth toward the center of the armature.)

e. The sheet-steel armature core inside the teeth.   Average cross section is 17 sq in.   Average length is 4.2 in. (a little less than the armature diameter minus twice the tooth length).

Half of the exciting ampere-turns are placed on each of the two poles.   How many ampere-turns per pole are required for each part of the magnetic circuit, to produce a flux of 1,200,000 lines through the armature?   Neglect leakage fluxes.

***8-9.** A circular solenoid is formed by winding wire on a wooden ring whose diameter of section is 2 cm.   The inside diameter of the ring is 10 cm.   There are 275 turns of wire wound on the ring, and a current of 1 amp is maintained in the coil.   Find the ampere-turns per centimeter, the flux density, and the total flux.

a. If a cast-steel core is substituted for the wooden core in the foregoing problem, what would be the flux density and the total flux?

b. If the voltage applied to the coil with the cast-steel core is doubled, what will be the total flux?

c. If the voltage and size of wire are unchanged but the number of turns is doubled, what will be the total flux?

d. If the area of cross section of the wire is doubled with the voltage and number of turns unchanged, what will be the total flux?

*8-10. How many amperes are required to produce a flux of 50,000 lines in the cast-steel core of Prob. 8-9? If a radial cut is made in the cast-steel ring of Prob. 8-10, how long an air gap must be made to double the reluctance of the magnetic circuit if the flux remains constant?

8-11. In the magnetic circuit of Fig. 8-11, the useful flux passes through the air gap between the two steel poles; a part of the flux is shunted through the cast-iron

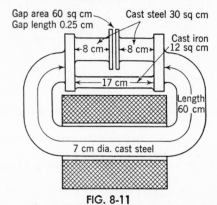

Gap area 60 sq cm
Gap length 0.25 cm
Cast steel 30 sq cm
Cast iron 12 sq cm
←8 cm→ ←8 cm→
←——17 cm——→
Length 60 cm
7 cm dia. cast steel

FIG. 8-11

part of the circuit. At low saturation a considerable part of the total flux is shunted through the cast-iron part, but as the flux density increases the cast iron becomes saturated, and a larger portion of the flux is deflected into the air gap. What percentages of the total flux in the yoke are shunted through the cast iron when the flux density in the air gap is 1,000 and 7,000 lines per sq cm, respectively? The foregoing arrangement illustrates the principle used in some practical cases when it is desired to modify the relation between the flux and the mmf by providing a highly saturated magnetic path in parallel with a feebly saturated one.

8-12. When the flux density in the gap, Fig. 8-11, is 7,000 lines per sq cm, find the flux density in the other parts of the circuit and the total ampere-turns required.

9

THE METER-KILOGRAM-SECOND (MKS) SYSTEM OF UNITS

73. Rationalized Units. It is a fundamental property of the geometry of space that the area of the surface of a sphere is equal to 4π times the radius. In electrical and magnetic calculations it is often convenient to surround a point source, such as a unit pole, with an imaginary sphere of such a radius that some particular point that we are interested in lies on the surface of the sphere. Thus the factor 4π frequently appears in calculations involving electricity and magnetism.

Now if the unit pole is redefined as being a symmetrical point source of one maxwell of flux, this new unit pole is $1/4\pi$ of the strength of the original unit pole, which was the source of 4π maxwells. Changing the strength of the unit pole in this way causes the factor 4π to disappear from all the formulas that originally contained it, but of course it reappears in certain other equations that did not previously contain it. The process of causing the 4π to disappear from the equations that originally contained it is called *rationalizing the units*. Its proponents claim that the rationalized system is simpler and more logical. They have been pushing their claims intermittently, and without much success, for over half a century. However, the adoption of the mks system may ultimately bring them victory, because a time of change is an opportune time in which to introduce changes.

74. The Meter-Kilogram-Second System of Units. The mks system of units was unanimously adopted by the International Electrotechnical Commission in 1935. This system retains unchanged in magnitude the joule, watt, coulomb, ampere, volt, ohm, farad, henry, and weber of the practical system based on the cgs system, but words the definitions in terms of the meter and kilogram instead of the centimeter and gram. Some new magnetic units are introduced, and also a new unit of force. Unfortunately the commission was so evenly divided on the question of rationalization of the mks units that this controversy still remains undecided. Whether or not the system is rationalized has no effect on any of the units named so far in this article, but the unit pole, and units of magnetomotive force, magnetizing force, permeability, and reluctance are altered by the factor 4π when the units are rationalized. The definitions of the mks units follow.

75. Definitions of the Meter-Kilogram-Second Units. The **meter** is defined as the distance between two parallel lines etched on a certain bar of platinum-iridium alloy kept in the archives of the International Bureau of Weights and Measures.

The **kilogram** is defined as the mass of a certain cylinder of platinum-iridium alloy kept in the archives of the International Bureau of Weights and Measures.

The **second** is defined as 1/86,400 of the average time taken by the earth to make one revolution relative to the sun.

The **newton** is defined as the force required to give a mass of one kilogram an acceleration of one meter per second per second. One newton = 10^5 dynes.

The **joule** is defined as the work done by a force of one newton when the point of application of the force moves through one meter in the direction of the force. One joule = 10^7 ergs.

The **watt** is defined as the power when one joule of work is being done per second. One watt = 10^7 ergs per second.

The **ampere** is defined as the constant current which, maintained in two parallel rectilineal conductors of infinite length and of negligible cross section separated by a distance of one meter, produces on each conductor a force equal to 2×10^{-7} newton per meter of conductor. One ampere = $\frac{1}{10}$ abampere.

The **volt** is defined as the difference in electric potential between two points in a conductor carrying a constant current of one ampere when the power dissipated between these two points is one watt. One volt = 10^8 abvolts.

The **ohm** is defined as the electric resistance between two points of a conductor when a constant difference of potential of one volt, applied between these points, produces in the conductor a current of one ampere, the conductor not being the source of an emf. One ohm = 10^9 abohms.

The **coulomb** is defined as the quantity of electricity transported in one second through any cross section of a conductor by a current of one ampere.

The **farad** is defined as the capacitance of a capacitor (electric condenser) in which a charge of one coulomb produces a difference of potential of one volt between the terminals of the capacitor.

The **henry** is defined as the self-inductance of a circuit in which an emf of one volt is produced by the changing of the electric current in the circuit when the current changes at the rate of one ampere per second. The henry is also used to measure mutual inductance, and is then defined as the mutual inductance between two circuits when a uniform change of one ampere per second in one of them produces an emf of one volt in the other. One henry $= 10^9$ abhenrys.

The **weber** may be defined as the amount of magnetic flux that must be cut per second by a conductor in order to generate one volt in the conductor.

The foregoing definitions are all independent of whether the system of units is rationalized or not. The following units have double definitions:

The **unit magnetic pole** is defined as a symmetrical point source of magnetic flux, which in the rationalized system emits one weber of flux, and in the unrationalized system 4π webers of flux.

Two unrationalized unit poles placed 1 m apart repel each other with a force of 10^7 newtons, or 1,120 tons.

The **ampere-turn** is the rationalized unit of *magnetomotive force* and may be defined as the magnetomotive force produced in a magnetic circuit by a current of one ampere circling around on the periphery of a cross section of the magnetic circuit. One ampere-turn is equal to 4π unrationalized units of magnetomotive force. The unrationalized unit has no name.

The rationalized unit of magnetizing force is the **ampere-turn per meter,** the meter being measured along the length of the magnetic circuit.

Probably all engineers use ampere-turns, and ampere-turns per meter, or per centimeter, or per inch, even if they use no other rationalized units. This is because the ampere-turn is such a natural and obvious unit.

The remaining mks units are outside the scope of this book and will therefore not be defined here.

76. Comparison between the Meter-Kilogram-Second System and the Practical System Based on the Centimeter-Gram-Second System. It is important to emphasize as strongly as possible that whenever a unit has a name, that name stands for one value, and one value only, regardless of the system of units used, except that the International units, which are experimental in nature, will differ from the other units by the amount of the experimental error, which is of the order of one-twentieth of 1 per cent.

An examination of the definitions in the preceding article tends to lead to the conclusion that the mks system of units is essentially the practical system based on the cgs units, except that a very much more powerful unit magnetic pole has been introduced, and the definition of the ampere has been rearranged so as to eliminate reference to a unit pole. As far as the scope of this book is concerned that conclusion is correct, and if the electrical industry in America had adopted the weber it would have been impossible to tell which of these two sets of units was being used in this book, except for those introductory articles on magnetism in which cgs units have been used. However, the electrical industry in America has not adopted the weber. In commercial practice the cgs unit of flux is used in making magnetic calculations, a procedure that introduces the factor 10^{-8}. The reason for this procedure is presumably that the weber is inconveniently large. Milliwebers might be used but this would introduce a factor 10^{-3}, and it is difficult to convince anyone that the factor 10^{-3} is superior to the factor 10^{-8}.

The mks system receives its strongest support from among those radio engineers and scientists who study electromagnetic waves. When the mks system is not used, the calculations may involve three different sets of units, namely, the cgs electromagnetic units, the cgs electrostatic units, and the practical units. Electrostatics and electrodynamics were originally developed independently, with the natural consequence that the two sets of units are quite different. The mks system is now complete enough to replace all three of these systems. Of course any one of these three older systems could be developed to replace the other two, but this has not been done. On the other hand many people are convinced that each of the two cgs systems is especially suited to its own particular field, and is definitely superior to any other system in that field, and that it would be a real loss if either of them were discarded.

77. Permeability in the Meter-Kilogram-Second System. When H is measured in ampere-turns per meter and B in webers per square meter, as is done in the mks system, the permeability of free space μ_0 is no longer unity but is equal to $4\pi10^{-7}$. This value is readily obtained from Eq. (16) by substituting webers per square meter for maxwells per square centimeter (gauss), which introduces the factors 10^{-8} and 10^4, and ampere-turns per meter for oersteds, which introduces the factors $4\pi/10$ and 10^{-2}. The product of these four factors is $4\pi10^{-7}$.

The relative permeability of any substance is the ratio of the permeability of that substance to the permeability of free space, and is therefore independent of the units used in measuring B and H. In practice, permeability curves always show the relative permeability. The permeability of any substance in any particular system of units is equal to the relative permeability multiplied by the permeability of free space in that system of units. Thus in the mks system, the permeability is equal to the relative permeability multiplied by $4\pi10^{-7}$, while in the cgs system the permeability is equal to the relative permeability multiplied by 1.

10

SOLENOIDS AND ELECTROMAGNETS

78. Pull of Solenoids. A solenoid is a conductor wound in the form of a helix. When an electric current is passed round a solenoid, a magnetic field is produced, the direction of which may be determined by the corkscrew law, Art. 22. This field may be represented by lines of force as shown in Fig. 48a.

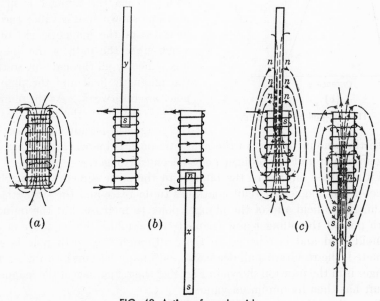

FIG. 48. Action of a solenoid.

If long bar magnets are placed in the solenoid field as shown in Fig. 48b, then the N pole of magnet x will tend to move in the direction of the lines of force and be pulled into the solenoid, while the S pole of magnet y will tend to move in a direction opposite to that of the lines of force so that it also tends to move into the solenoid.

79

If the current in the solenoid is reversed, the magnetic field of the solenoid will reverse and the magnets x and y will be repelled.

If, as in Fig. 48c, soft-iron plungers are used instead of bar magnets, then the plunger will be magnetized by the current in the solenoid; north poles will be formed where the lines of force leave the iron and south poles where they enter.   The polarity of the soft-iron plungers shown in Fig.

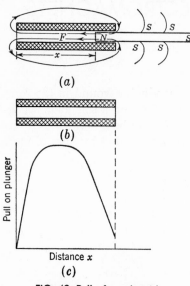

(a)

(b)

(c)

FIG. 49. Pull of a solenoid.

48c is the same as the polarity of the bar magnets in Fig. 48b, so that the plungers are pulled into the solenoid.

If the current in the solenoid is now reversed, the magnetic field of the solenoid will reverse but, since the polarity of the soft-iron plungers will also reverse, the direction of the pull on the plungers will be unchanged.

79. Variation of the Pull of a Solenoid. When the plunger is in the position shown in Fig. 49a, the reluctance of the magnetic circuit is large, since the path of the lines of flux is nearly all through air, so that the magnetic field and the plunger poles are both weak.   As the plunger moves toward F, the reluctance of the magnetic circuit decreases because the amount of iron in the magnetic path is increasing, so that the magnetic field and the plunger poles become stronger.

With further motion of the plunger in the same direction, the reluctance of the magnetic circuit continues to decrease and the strengths of the magnetic field and of the plunger poles to increase, but the induced south pole of the plunger now begins to come under the influence of the solenoid field and is repelled so that, although the north pole is still attracted, the resultant pull decreases and finally becomes zero when the plunger is in the position shown in Fig. 49b; the reluctance of the magnetic circuit has then its minimum value.

The pull on the plunger varies with its position, as shown in Fig. 49c; over a considerable range the pull is constant.

80. Ironclad Solenoids. In order to reduce the reluctance of the return part of the magnetic circuit and at the same time to protect the windings, the ironclad construction shown in Fig. 50 is used.   When the plunger is in the position shown in Fig. 50a, the reluctance of the magnetic circuit is nearly all in the air path ab.   As the plunger moves toward b, the flux increases and changes very rapidly toward the end of the stroke so that, while the average pull is not much higher than that of the same solenoid with an air return path, a large pull over a short distance is obtained at the end of the stroke as shown in curve B, Fig. 51.[1]

If a hole for the plunger be bored through the iron cover as shown in Fig. 50b, then there is no sudden jar at the end of the stroke but rather a cushion effect; the large increase of pull at the end of the stroke is lost, however, although this is seldom a disadvantage.

81. Circuit Breaker. The variation in the pull of a solenoid is taken advantage of in the type of circuit breaker shown diagrammatically in Fig. 52. Such a circuit breaker consists of the switch C closed against

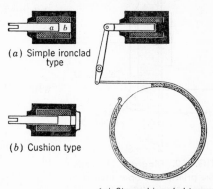

(a) Simple ironclad type

(b) Cushion type

(c) Stopped ironclad type

FIG. 50. Types of ironclad electromagnets.

the force of the spring S and held closed by the latch d. This latch is released by the plunger p, which is lifted when the line current passing round the solenoid M reaches a predetermined value. The spring S then forces the switch open. If the plunger p is moved farther into the solenoid by

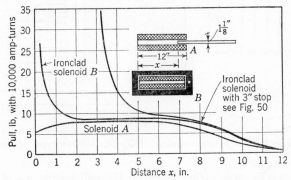

FIG. 51. Pull of electromagnets.

means of the adjusting screw a, then the current required to lift this plunger will be decreased. By this means the circuit breaker can be adjusted to open with different currents.

82. Lifting and Holding Magnets. These magnets are generally of the horseshoe or of the annular type shown diagrammatically in Figs. 53 and 54. As the iron to be lifted moves from a to b, Fig. 54, there is little change in the flux threading the coil M and therefore only a small pull;

[1] Taken from an article by C. R. Underhill, *Elec. World*, vol. 45, p. 934, 1905.

when the iron approaches close to the poles of the magnet, however, the flux increases rapidly and the pull, being proportional to the space rate of change of flux, becomes large. For such magnets the holding power may be determined very closely by Maxwell's formula[1]

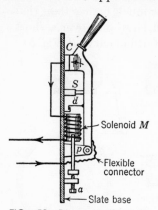

$$\text{Pull in dynes} = \frac{B^2 A}{8\pi} \qquad (20)$$

where B = flux density across contact surface, lines per sq cm

A = total pole face area, sq cm

FIG. 52. Diagram illustrating the principle of operation of an automatic circuit breaker. See Fig. 129 for a typical design.

Example. In the case of the magnet shown in Fig. 55, the scale on the iron to be lifted is assumed to be 0.05 cm thick. It is required to determine how the pull varies with the exciting current, the number of turns being 1,000.

To solve this problem, it is necessary to assume different values for the total

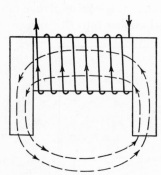

FIG. 53. Horseshoe type of electromagnet.

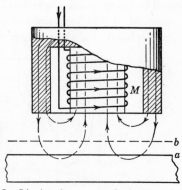

FIG. 54. Annular type of electromagnet.

flux in the magnetic circuit, then calculate the pull by the use of the above formula and the excitation by the use of the curves in Fig. 40.

l_1, length of cast-steel path = 20 cm
l_2, length of each air gap = 0.05 cm
l_3, length of cast-iron path = 12 cm
A_1, cross section of cast-steel path = $2 \times 4 = 8$ sq cm
A_2, cross section of each air path = 8 sq cm
A_3, cross section of cast-iron path = $4 \times 5 = 20$ sq cm

[1] Derivation of this formula is given by C. V. Christie, "Electrical Engineering," 6th ed., Chap. II, McGraw-Hill Book Company, Inc., New York, 1952.

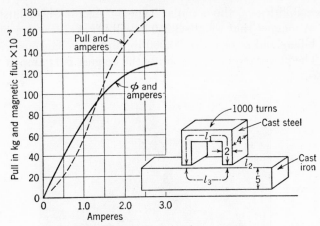

FIG. 55. Pull of a horseshoe magnet.

If ϕ, total flux = 80,000 lines, then

B_1, flux density in cast steel = 10,000 lines per sq cm
B_2, flux density in air gaps = 10,000 lines per sq cm
B_3, flux density in cast iron = 4,000 lines per sq cm

and　Ampere-turns per centimeter for cast steel = 8　　(see Fig. 40)

$$\text{Ampere-turns per centimeter for air gaps} = \frac{B_2 \times 10}{4\pi} \quad \text{(Arts. 62–63)}$$

$$= 8,000$$

Ampere-turns per centimeter for cast iron = 10　　(see Fig. 40)

and　Total ampere-turns = $8 \times 20 + 8,000 \times 2 \times 0.05 + 10 \times 12$
$$= 160 + 800 + 120 = 1,080$$

$$\text{Magnetic pull} = \frac{10,000^2 \times 2 \times 8}{8\pi} = 64,000,000 \text{ dynes}$$

$$= 65,000 \text{ g} = 65 \text{ kg}$$

Other values are worked out in the same way, the work generally being carried out in tabular form as below:

Total flux	Flux density			Ampere-turns per centimeter			Total ampere-turns				Am-peres	Pull, kg
	Steel	Air	Iron	Steel	Air	Iron	Steel	Air	Iron	Circuit		
64,000	8,000	8,000	3,200	6	6,400	7.5	120	640	90	850	0.850	42
80,000	10,000	10,000	4,000	8	8,000	10	160	800	120	1,080	1.080	65
96,000	12,000	12,000	4,800	12	9,600	15	240	960	180	1,380	1.380	94
112,000	14,000	14,000	5,600	23	11,200	20	460	1,120	240	1,820	1.820	126
128,000	16,000	16,000	6,400	48	12,800	29	960	1,280	348	2,588	2.588	164

These results are plotted in Fig. 55.

The possibilities of the annular type of magnet are illustrated in Fig. 56. A magnet that weighs 2,250 lb will lift skull-cracker balls up to 2,000 lb, billets and slabs up to 20,000 lb, and miscellaneous scrap up to 500 lb. The power required to operate the magnet is 11 amp at 200 volts or 2.42 kw.

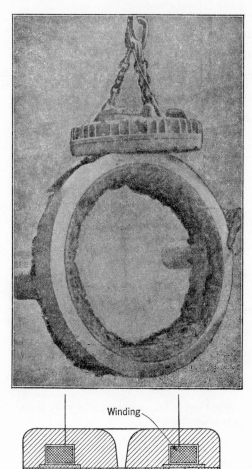

FIG. 56. Annular type of electromagnet.

83. Electromagnetic Brakes and Clutches. One type of brake used on crane motors is shown in Fig. 57. The annular steel frame A of the electromagnet is fastened to the housing of the motor and carries the exciting coil E. The sliding disk B is fastened to the frame A of the magnet by means of a sliding key F and is free to move axially but cannot rotate.

When the motor is disconnected, the magnet is not excited and the springs S push the disk B into the ring C, which is keyed to the motor shaft. The motor is thereby braked and brought rapidly to rest. When current is applied to start the motor, the coil E is excited at the same

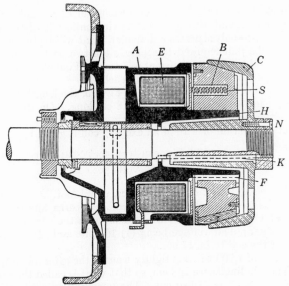

FIG. 57. Electromagnetic brake.

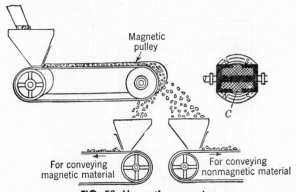

FIG. 58. Magnetic separator.

time and the disk B is attracted, releasing the ring C, so that the motor shaft is then free to rotate. Electromagnet clutches are built on the same principle.

84. Magnetic Separator. A useful application of the electromagnet is shown diagrammatically in Fig. 58. The magnetic pulley consists of an iron shell containing an exciting coil C that produces the magnetic field shown.   Any iron particles carried over this pulley by the conveyer belt are attracted and are therefore carried farther round than the non-magnetic materials with which they are mixed.

Problems

10-1. A cast-steel ring that has a mean diameter of 12 cm and a circular cross section of 5 sq cm is wound with 200 turns of wire, uniformly distributed.   If the steel ring is cut in two halves across a diameter, what will be the flux in the magnetic circuit and the pull required to separate the two parts if the air gaps are each 0.1 cm long and the exciting current is 3 amp?   Find also the total flux and the pull if the gaps are reduced to 0.001 cm each.

10-2. In the case of the magnet shown in Fig. 55, the length l_1 is made up of two pole pieces, each 4 cm long, and a yolk 8 cm long.   On this winding space of 8 cm the exciting coil is wound.

a. Show that the section of wire of an exciting coil is given by

$$\text{Circular mils} = \frac{10.6 \times \text{mean turn, feet} \times \text{ampere-turns}}{\text{volts per coil}}$$

where 10.6 is the resistance of copper per circular mil-foot.

b. Find the cross section of the wire, the number of turns, and the exciting current for a pull of 145 kg (take the current density in the wire to be 1 amp per 1,000 cir mils), the applied voltage being (1) 10 volts and (2) 120 volts.   Take the mean turn of the coil to be 17 cm.

c. When the coil of 1,700 turns is tightly wound, the external periphery measures 22 cm.   The winding space is 8 cm, so that what is called the radiating surface of the coil = 8 × 22 = 176 sq cm.   The temperature rise of the surface of such a coil being about 60°C for 0.1 watt per sq cm of radiating surface, what will be approximately the temperature rise of the above coil when the pull is 145 kg?

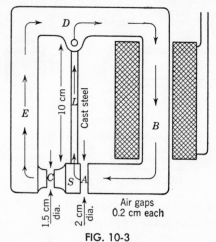

FIG. 10-3

10-3. Figure 10-3 shows a part of the mechanism of a magnetic relay.   For small values of exciting current, most of the flux crossing the air gap *A* will pass through *L* and back through the coil.   This will cause *S* to move to the right and

close gap A.   For large values of exciting current L will become saturated, and
then most of the flux crossing A will pass through gap C.   Since the magnetic
pull depends upon the *square* of the *density* of flux, the pull at C may become
greater than that at A, though ϕ_c is less than ϕ_a.   This will cause S to move to
the left and close gap C.   For some critical or operating value of current the pulls
in the two air gaps are equal.   It is desired to find the cross section of the lever L
such that the critical or operating current will occur when B, the flux density in
the main core, is 15,000 lines per sq cm.

Note that ALD and $ACED$ are parallel magnetic circuits.

Use the following figures as a continuation of Fig. 40:

Lines per square centimeter..	20,000	22,500	25,000	27,500
Ampere-turns per centimeter.	275	1,000	2,600	4,500

11

MUTUAL INDUCTION AND
SELF-INDUCTION

85. Mutual Induction. In generating emf by electromagnetic induction all that is required is that there should be relative motion between a conductor and a magnetic field, of such a nature that the conductor cuts the lines of magnetic flux. In electric generators this is accomplished either by keeping the magnets stationary and moving the conductors through the magnetic field or by keeping the conductors stationary and

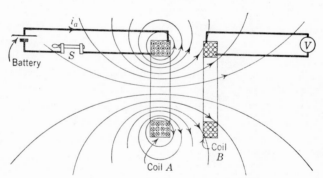

FIG. 59. Mutual induction. (Cross section through coils.)

moving the magnets, but it is possible to generate an emf without the movement of any mechanical parts. Consider Fig. 59, which is a cross section through the centers of two coaxial coils. Coil A, which consists of 12 turns of insulated wire, is connected to a battery through a switch S. Coil B is connected to a meter V that indicates flow of electric current.

As shown in the sketch, part of the magnetic field produced by the current flowing in coil A links with coil B. If switch S is opened, the magnetic field disappears and the pointer of the meter V deflects for a moment and then returns to zero. If switch S is closed, the meter again gives a momentary deflection, but in the opposite direction, showing that an emf is generated in coil B in one direction by a dying magnetic field, and in the opposite direction by a growing magnetic field.

In visualizing the process by which a dying magnetic field induces an emf in coil B, we should consider that a dying or disappearing magnetic field does not fade away as a rainbow fades; it collapses. Each line of force forms a closed loop, and when that line of force disappears we may visualize the loop as shrinking in area until it becomes a point and ceases to exist. A line of force disappearing in this way evidently cuts every conductor that it originally encircled and therefore generates emf in it. In a growing magnetic field the process is reversed. Each new line of force starts as a point—that is, a loop of zero area—and expands to its ultimate position. In expanding, it evidently cuts every conductor which it ultimately encircles.

The only justification for visualizing the growth and the dying of a magnetic field in this way is that it leads to conclusions in regard to the magnitude and direction of the induced emf which are strictly in accordance with experimental fact.

The generation of emf in a coil as the result of the changing of the current in an adjacent coil is called **mutual induction.** The coil producing the magnetic flux is called the **primary,** and the adjacent coil that experiences the induction is called the **secondary.**

86. Direction of the Electromotive Force Generated by Mutual Induction. The directions of the emfs induced in coil B by the collapsing and expanding fluxes from coil A may be determined by applying one of the rules given in Art. 33 for determining the direction of an induced emf. The directions obtained by applying these rules lead to the following general statement, which is known as **Lenz's law: Whether the flux is growing or dying, the emf induced by the changing flux tends to send a current in such a direction as to oppose the change of the flux.** That is, if the current in coil A is reduced to zero, by opening switch S, current will flow momentarily in coil B in the same direction as the current that was flowing in coil A and thus will tend to maintain the flux. If the resistance of the circuit through coil B were zero, this current would continue to flow forever, and the flux in coil B would be maintained forever. Such a coil would be equivalent to a permanent bar magnet. The flow of current in coil B is reduced to zero by the resistance of the wire, just as a body sliding on a rough plane is brought to rest by the frictional resistance of the plane.

Again, on closing switch S, current flows in both coils and the current in coil B is in the opposite direction to that in coil A, and so again opposes the change of flux.

87. Magnitude of the Electromotive Force of Mutual Induction. Let n be the number of turns in coil B, Fig. 59, and ϕ be the number of lines of flux linking with coil B, produced by the current i_a in coil A. Then since

1 volt is generated in a conductor when that conductor cuts magnetic flux at the rate of 10^8 lines per sec, it follows that the emf of mutual induction in coil B is given by the equation[1]

$$e_b = -n \frac{d\phi}{dt} 10^{-8} \quad \text{volts} \tag{21}$$

And since the flux ϕ is directly proportional to the current i_a that produces it, the equation for e_b may also be written[2]

$$e_b = -M \frac{di_a}{dt} \quad \text{volts} \tag{22}$$

where M is a constant made up of the three factors n, 10^{-8}, and the ratio of ϕ to i_a. The minus sign has been inserted in the equations to indicate the direction of e_b relative to i_a. Thus if i_a is clockwise and increasing, then e_b is counterclockwise. The constant M is called the *mutual inductance* of the two coils and is measured in *henrys*.

Definition of a henry: Two coils are said to have a mutual inductance of one henry if a rate of change of current of one ampere per second in one coil results in an emf of one volt being generated in the other coil.

88. Self-induction—Inductance. In Fig. 59 some of the magnetic flux produced by the current i_a links with coil B, and, when i_a stops or starts, this flux cuts coil B and induces emf in it; but *all* of the flux produced by i_a links with coil A itself and in growing or dying cuts its conductors and induces emf in them. The generation of emf in a coil as the result of the increasing or decreasing of the current in that coil is called *self-induction*. The emf of self-induction exists only while the current is changing.

Lenz's law applies equally to mutual induction and to self-induction. The emf of self-induction always opposes the change of current that produces it. As a result of the phenomenon of self-induction, a current of electricity possesses something analogous to momentum, and we may paraphrase Newton's laws of motion as follows: A current of electricity tends to continue flowing, and electricity at rest tends to remain at rest, unless acted upon by some external emf. The effect of self-induction may be negligible in certain circuits but is never absolutely zero in any actual circuit.

If in Fig. 60 the current i is changing, the flux ϕ is also changing and a voltage of self-induction is induced in the coil which, from Eq. (2), Art. 35, is given by

$$e_{si} = -n \frac{d\phi}{dt} 10^{-8} \quad \text{volts} \tag{23}$$

---

[1] $d\phi/dt$ is a symbol that represents the rate of increase of the flux ϕ in lines per second.

[2] di_a/dt is a symbol that represents the rate of increase of i_a in amperes per second.

where the minus sign is used because the direction of the emf is such that a current produced by it would oppose the change of the flux.

It is often desirable to express this voltage in terms of the changing current rather than of the changing flux produced by the current, so that we may write

$$e_{si} = -L\frac{di}{dt} \quad \text{volts} \tag{24}$$

where L is a constant called the inductance of the circuit or the coefficient of self-induction which, from Eqs. (23) and (24), has the value

$$L = n\frac{d\phi}{di}\, 10^{-8} \quad \text{henrys}^1 \tag{25}$$

The minus sign is required in Eq. (24) because when i is clockwise and increasing, so that di/dt is positive, e_{si} is counterclockwise.

The inductance of a circuit is as much a constant of the circuit as is its electric resistance.

A circuit is said to have an inductance of one henry if a rate of change of one ampere per second in the circuit induces an emf of one volt in that circuit.

Note that, if the inductance L is to be constant, then $d\phi/di$ must be constant; that is, ϕ must be proportional to i, which means that there must be no saturation of the magnetic circuit. In most practical cases the magnetic circuit is not saturated and L is either exactly constant or else approximately so. In all the circuits dealt with in this book, the inductance L is assumed to be constant, unless expressly stated otherwise.

If ϕ is proportional to i, then $d\phi/di$ is constant and is equal to ϕ/i, and Eq. (25) may be written

$$L = \frac{n\phi}{i}\, 10^{-8} \quad \text{henrys} \tag{26}$$

$$= \text{flux interlinkages per ampere} \times 10^{-8}$$

The inductance of a circuit in electrical calculations is analogous to the mass of a body in mechanical calculations. In mechanics the mechanical force F required to accelerate a body = its mass × the acceleration, or

$$F = M\frac{dv}{dt}$$

In electricity the emf e required to accelerate a current in a circuit = the inductance of the circuit × the current acceleration, or

$$e = L\frac{di}{dt} \quad \text{[see Eq. (24)]}$$

---

[1] $d\phi/di$ is a symbol representing the rate of increase in ϕ with respect to i in lines per ampere.

Note that in this equation e is the emf required to produce the acceleration, while e_{si} in Eq. (24) is the emf with which the coil opposes having its current accelerated. These two emfs must necessarily be opposite in sign, and equal in magnitude if there is no friction. The complete equation, which includes the emf required to overcome the friction, is given in Art. 90.

Thus **the mass of a body in pounds is equal to the force in poundals required to give it an acceleration of one foot per second per second,** while **the inductance of a circuit in henrys is equal to the emf in volts required to give the current an acceleration of one ampere per second.** (Not 1 amp per sec per sec because the ampere contains one "per second" itself, being equal to 1 coulomb per sec.)

The three terms *inductance, self-induction,* and *coefficient of self-induction,* all connected with the same phenomena, are apt to be confusing to a beginner; and it is important that there should be no confusion in such a fundamental thing.

The **inductance** of a circuit is that **property** of the circuit by virtue of which it opposes any change in the current. It is measured in henrys.

Self-induction is the **process** by which emf is induced in a circuit by the increasing or decreasing of the flux resulting from an increase or decrease in the current through that circuit.

A coil with an air core possesses a certain fixed amount of inductance whether it is connected in a circuit or not, but there is self-induction in the coil only when the rate of flow of the current through it is changing.

Coefficient of self-induction is simply the value of the inductance, either in henrys or in abhenrys.

89. Starting and Stopping a Current in a Coil. When switch S in Fig. 60 is closed, the current that flows in the coil does not instantaneously jump to its final value E/R, because, as the current increases, the flux threading the coil increases and in doing so induces an emf in the coil in such a direction as to oppose the increase of the current. The current therefore increases gradually as shown by the curve in Fig. 60. Starting a current in a coil is analogous to bringing a flywheel up to speed.

If, after the current in the coil has reached its final value, the driving emf (supplied by the battery) is suddenly reduced to zero, which can be accomplished in practice by closing switch K and then opening switch S, the current flowing in the coil does not stop instantaneously but continues to circulate, completing its circuit through the resistance R_1 and switch K. If the resistance of this circuit were zero, the current would continue to flow forever, just as a suddenly disconnected rotating flywheel would continue to rotate forever if there were no frictional resistance opposing its motion. The electric resistance of the circuit gradually reduces the current to zero, and the higher the resistance, the more rapid the rate of decrease of the current.

If switch S is opened suddenly, without first closing switch K, the current in the coil is reduced to zero almost instantaneously, and the lines of flux collapse very rapidly and generate a large emf in the coil. This emf is great enough to make the current continue flowing for an instant after the switch blade has actually broken contact. The current flowing across the gap between the blade and the jaws of the switch constitutes an electric arc and burns the switch contacts. Stopping a current by opening a switch is very much like stopping a flywheel by throwing a crowbar between the spokes; nevertheless this is the standard method of stopping a current. The method of stopping a current illustrated in Fig. 60 is used only in special cases, such as the magnetizing or "field" coils of large generators, where the self-induction is very large and would produce an arc that would burn the switch contacts quite seriously if the switch were opened suddenly in the ordinary manner.

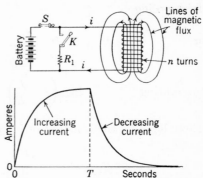

FIG. 60. Growth and decrease of current in a coil. Switch S is closed at zero time. Switch K is open during the time interval 0 to T. At the time T switch K is closed and S is opened, disconnecting the battery but leaving the current in the coil free to circulate through K and to be gradually reduced to zero by the resistance of the circuit.

90. Mathematical Treatment of Starting and Stopping a Current. In mechanics the fundamental equation of motion of a mass under the action of a force is

$$\text{Force} = \text{mass} \times \text{acceleration} + \text{friction}$$

or
$$F = M \frac{dv}{dt} + \text{friction} \qquad (27)$$

In the flow of electricity we have a similar equation

$$\text{Electromotive force} = \text{inductance} \times \text{acceleration} + \text{friction}$$

or
$$e = L \frac{di}{dt} + iR \qquad (28)$$

The electrical case is simpler because electrical friction is a linear function of the current, while mechanical friction is a more complicated function.

Note that in Eqs. (27) and (28) the word *friction* means the force required to overcome the friction.

Applying Eq. (28) to the starting of a current, as in Fig. 60 where the applied emf is constant at E volts, we have

$$E = L\frac{di}{dt} + iR$$

Transposing

$$i - \frac{E}{R} = -\frac{L}{R}\frac{di}{dt}$$

or

$$\frac{di}{i - \dfrac{E}{R}} = -\frac{R}{L}dt$$

Integrating

$$\log_\epsilon\left(i - \frac{E}{R}\right) = -\frac{Rt}{L} + \log_\epsilon C$$

where $\log_\epsilon C$ is the constant of integration.   This reduces to

$$i - \frac{E}{R} = C\epsilon^{-Rt/L}$$

or

$$i = \frac{E}{R} + C\epsilon^{-Rt/L} \tag{29}$$

When $t = 0$, $i = 0$, and therefore $C = -(E/R)$, and, substituting this value of C, the current is

$$i = \frac{E}{R}(1 - \epsilon^{-Rt/L}) \tag{30}$$

By means of Eq. (30) the curve of increasing current in Fig. 60 may be plotted accurately to scale for any given set of values of E, R, and L. The ratio L/R is often called the *time constant* of the circuit.   It is a kind of relative measure of the slowness of the response of the circuit to a change in the applied emf.

When in Fig. 60 switch K is closed, and simultaneously switch S is opened, the applied emf is removed and Eq. (28) becomes

$$0 = L\frac{di}{dt} + iR$$

where R now represents the sum of R_1 and the resistance of the coil. Transposing,

$$\frac{di}{i} = -\frac{R}{L}dt$$

Integrating

$$\log_\epsilon i = -\frac{Rt}{L} + \log_\epsilon C$$

whence

$$i = C\epsilon^{-Rt/L} \tag{31}$$

Let I_0 be the value of the current at the instant when K is closed and S is opened, and let the time t be measured from this instant. Then when $t = 0$, $i = I_0$, and therefore $C = I_0$. Substituting this value of C, the current is

$$i = I_0 \epsilon^{-Rt/L} \tag{32}$$

91. Gas-engine Ignition System. A good example of the practical application of mutual induction is to be found in the single-spark gas-engine ignition system now almost universally employed in automobile and airplane gasoline engines. Figure 61 illustrates this type of ignition

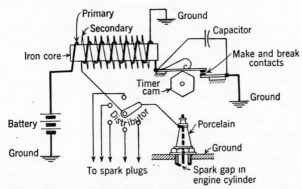

FIG. 61. Ignition system for a six-cylinder automobile engine.

system as applied to a six-cylinder automobile engine. The primary and secondary coils are wound on the same iron core, so that practically all the magnetic flux produced by the primary links with the secondary. The primary and secondary windings together with the iron core and the protective housing constitute what is generally called the *spark coil*.

Ground in this diagram actually means the cylinder walls and all metallic parts that are not insulated from the cylinder walls. Using the engine frame to complete the circuits reduces the wiring to a minimum and not only gives the engine a neater appearance but reduces the danger of engine failure due to the breaking of a wire.

The *timer cam* and the *distributor* are mounted on the same shaft and are geared to rotate at exactly half the speed of the engine shaft. Automobile engines are four-cycle and each cylinder can be fired only once for every two revolutions of the engine shaft.

As the timer cam rotates, it alternately closes and opens the primary circuit. During the time that the primary circuit is closed, the current in it grows after the manner indicated in Fig. 60 and so does the magnetic field produced by it. When the cam opens the primary circuit, the magnetic field collapses very rapidly and generates a large emf in the secondary winding, which has many more turns than the primary winding. During the instant that this large emf exists, the distributor has the circuit completed through the secondary winding to the proper spark plug, and the secondary circuit is therefore complete except for the spark gap at the spark plug. The emf is great enough to cause the current to jump this gap, and the resulting spark ignites the explosive mixture in the engine cylinder.

The function of the capacitor bridged across the make-and-break contacts is to assist in producing a quicker break and to reduce the sparking and burning at the make-and-break contacts.

Problems

11-1. The mutual inductance between the two windings of a spark coil is 10 henrys. A current of 2 amp in the primary is reduced to zero in 0.001 sec. What is the average emf induced in the secondary winding during this time?

11-2. Two coaxial coils (see Fig. 59) each have a mean diameter of 10 cm. Coil B has 500 turns. If a current of 4 amp in coil A produces an average flux density of 1,200 lines per sq cm through coil B, what is the mutual inductance of the two coils in henrys?

11-3. If in Fig. 60 switches S and K were both in the closed position, $I = 6$ amp, $R_1 = 100$ ohms, and switch S was suddenly opened, what would be the maximum emf across the resistance R_1?

11-4. *a.* Assuming that in Fig. 60 the inductance of the coil is 1 henry, the resistance of the circuit is 3 ohms, and the emf of the battery is 30 volts, plot the graph of the growth of the current for a period of 1 sec from the time that switch S is closed.

b. Assuming that switch K is closed 1 sec later than switch S, that switch S is opened at the instant that K is closed, and that the resistance of the circuit through the coil and switch K is 3 ohms, plot the graph of the current for another second.

c. If R_1 were 100 ohms, what would be the maximum voltage that would appear across R_1 during part (*b*) above?

12

ARMATURE WINDINGS FOR
DIRECT-CURRENT MACHINERY

92. Principle of Operation of the Electric Generator. The simplest type of electric generator is shown diagrammatically in Fig. 62. It consists of a permanent horseshoe magnet NS and a conductor ab. If the conductor ab is moved alternately up and down so as to cut the lines of force that pass from N to S, an emf will be generated or induced in the conductor that will cause an electric current to flow in the closed circuit $abcd$.

The direction of the emf in the conductor ab may be determined by the right-hand rule (Art. 33). The emf will reverse when the direction of motion of the conductor is reversed, so that current will flow first in one direction and then in the other; such a current is said to be alternating.

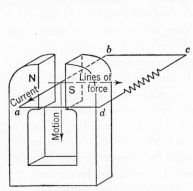

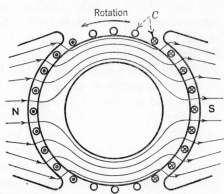

FIG. 62. Generation of emf.

FIG. 63. Magnetic flux and the emfs in a d-c generator.

93. Gramme Ring Winding. The following are the stages in the development of the generator of Fig. 62 into one which will give a direct current, that is, a current which flows continuously in one direction. The poles are bored out as shown in Fig. 63 and an iron core in the form of a ring is placed concentric with the pole faces so as to reduce the reluctance of the magnetic circuit.   The several conductors c mounted on this core rotate with it and cut the lines of force that pass from N to S, so that emfs are generated in these conductors, the directions of which, determined by the right-hand rule, are shown in Fig. 63 at a particular instant.

The conductors are now connected together as shown in Fig. 64 to form an endless helix.   Since the lines of flux pass through the iron core as shown in Fig. 63 rather than across the central air space inside the core, no lines are cut by the inner conductors so that only in the face conductors

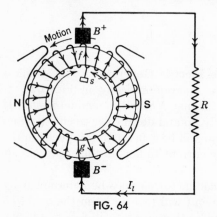

FIG. 64

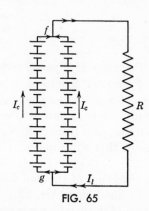

FIG. 65

c are emfs generated.   It will be noted that these emfs tend to send current up both sides of the winding from g to f, but that no current will circulate because the voltage tending to send current up the left-hand side of the winding is equal and opposed to that tending to send current up the right-hand side of the winding.   A difference of potential, however, will be found between f and g so that, if stationary brushes BB are placed at these two points so as to make continuous electric contact with the winding and are connected to an external circuit as in Fig. 64, current will flow through this circuit and through the two paths of the winding as shown, half of the current flowing up each side of the winding.   As long as the generator rotates at constant speed in the direction of the arrow, the voltage between f and g will be constant in magnitude and in direction.   If E_c is the average voltage generated in each conductor and Z is the total number of face conductors, then the voltage generated between the terminals is

$$E_g = \frac{Z}{2} E_c$$

and the line current is

$$I_l = \frac{E_g}{R + R_a} \qquad \text{amp}$$

where R = resistance of external circuit, ohms

R_a = resistance of armature winding and brush contacts, ohms

The current in each conductor is

$$I_c = \tfrac{1}{2}I_l$$

Power output of machine = $E_g I_l - I_l^2 Ra$ watts

The above voltage and current relations are often more readily appreciated from a diagram such as Fig. 65, where each of the face conductors in which voltage is being induced is represented by a battery.

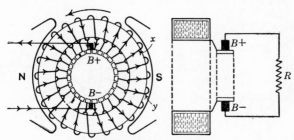

FIG. 66. Gramme ring winding.

FIG. 67. Armature with a Gramme ring winding.

94. Commutator and Brushes. Machines have been constructed in which stationary contacts $B-$ and $B+$, called brushes, were allowed to rub on the winding as shown in Fig. 64, but the windings were soon worn through by the brushes. The standard practice is to provide a special rubbing contact on each coil as shown at s, Fig. 64. The complete winding with its rubbing contacts is shown diagrammatically in Fig. 66 and is also shown in Fig. 67. The core and the winding together constitute what is called the *armature* of the machine, the complete set of rubbing contacts form what is called the *commutator*, and the individual contacts s (Fig. 64) are called the *commutator segments*.

95. Armature and Commutator Insulation. If the armature winding were to make contact with the iron core at two points such as x and y, Fig. 66, the voltage generated between these two points—in this particular case the voltage of three turns in series—would send a large current through the core from x to y. This current, although not available in the external circuit, would overheat the winding and would also represent a large waste of energy. The complete winding must therefore be insulated from the core, and the adjacent turns must be insulated from one another. This latter result is obtained by making the coils of cotton-covered wire. The commutator segments, being part of the winding, must also be insulated from one another and from the iron shell that supports them. The construction used is described in Chap. 13.

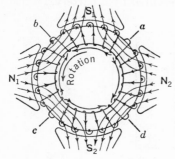

FIG. 68. Incomplete winding.

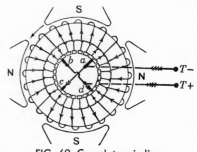

FIG. 69. Complete winding.

96. Multipolar Windings. It has been found economical in practice to build machines with more than two poles (Art. 101), the poles being arranged in pairs alternately N and S. In Fig. 69 the winding for a four-pole machine is shown diagrammatically. The direction of the lines of force and the emf in the conductors is shown in Fig. 68, from which diagram it may be seen that no current will circulate in the closed winding

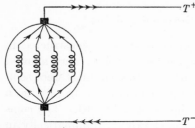

FIG. 70. Diagrammatic representation of a four-pole winding.

because the voltages in the conductors under the N poles are opposed by equal voltages in the conductors under the S poles. A difference of potential, however, will be found between a and b owing to the conductors cutting lines of force under pole S_1 and there is an equal difference of potential between a and d owing to the conductors cutting lines of force under pole N_2, so that b and d are at the same potential and may be connected together. For the same reason, the brushes at a and c may also be connected together as shown in Fig. 69. The external circuit to be supplied with current is connected between the terminals $T+$ and $T-$. This current will divide when it enters the machine and pass through the four paths in the winding as shown in Fig. 69 and also diagrammatically in Fig. 70.

97. Multiple, or Lap, Windings.   One obvious objection to the ring winding, as shown in Fig. 71, is that only the outer conductors 1, 3, 5, etc., cut lines of force, the remainder of the winding being inactive.   If the coils are wound on the core as in Fig. 72, there will be two active conductors per coil; and if the coil pitch is made approximately equal to the pole pitch, that is, if the distance between conductors 1 and 2 is made approximately equal to the distance between the centers of two adjacent poles, the voltages induced in the two active conductors of any one coil

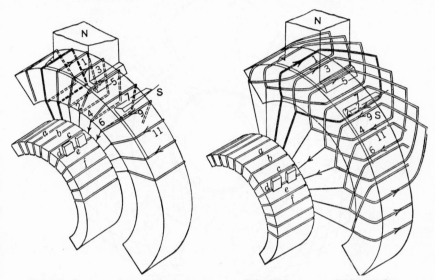

FIG. 71. Gramme ring winding.   FIG. 72. Lap, or multiple, winding.

will act in the same direction about that coil, so that the total voltage per coil is double that obtained with the Gramme ring winding of Fig. 71, and yet the total length of copper wire per coil is only slightly increased. Another important advantage of the drum winding of Fig. 72 is that it is much more easily wound and repaired.   The Gramme ring winding is now obsolete.

Since the end connections of this winding have to cross over one another as shown in Fig. 72, it is usual to arrange that the winding lie on the armature surface in two layers, the even-numbered conductors being placed below the odd-numbered conductors instead of alongside. The active or face conductors are placed in slots cut in the face of the iron core as shown in Fig. 76.

A perspective drawing such as that in Fig. 72 shows only a small part of the winding and it does not show the paths through the armature at all clearly.   A special type of drawing, shown in Fig. 73, is obtained by supposing the armature to be placed in a press and the commutator end of the machine forced back into the winding until the whole machine has been squeezed flat on to a plane, the rear end of the machine expanding and the commutator end contracting in the process. Figure 74 shows a third method of drawing an armature winding. The winding is supposed to be cut at one point and then unwrapped from the iron core and laid flat. This method shows the coils undistorted but breaks the continuity.

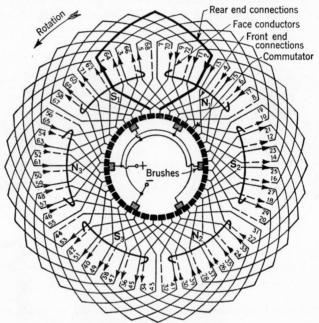

FIG. 73. Lap, or multiple, winding for a six-pole d-c machine. The arrowheads show the directions of the induced emfs. The dotted-line face conductors (even numbers) normally lie at the bottoms of the slots underneath the odd-numbered face conductors.

In Fig. 73 there are 72 active conductors lying in the slots, and the arrowheads on them show the directions of the induced emf when the armature is turning counterclockwise. There are three positive brushes spaced 120° apart and jumpered together; also three negative brushes are similarly arranged. This means that there must be three high-pressure points on the commutator and three low-pressure, or suction, points. That this is so may be checked by starting with any one conductor, for example, conductor 1, and traveling along the winding in the direction of the arrows. As we travel along conductors 1, 2, 3, 4, 5, and 6, in succession, each conductor contributes its increment of emf, but if we continue on, conductors 7 and 8 will contribute nothing, because they are not under a pole and are not cutting any flux, while conductor 9 will add a negative increment of emf since its arrow is opposing us. We have evidently passed the high-pressure point.   That part of the winding and commutator that lies between the commutator ends of conductors 6 and 9 is all at the same potential and is all a high-pressure area.   A positive brush should be placed at the center of this area, that is, bridging the two segments that connect to conductors 7 and 8.   The positions of the remaining five brushes may be checked in the same manner.

One-third of the total current enters the machine at each of the three negative brushes, and, since the winding branches two ways at each

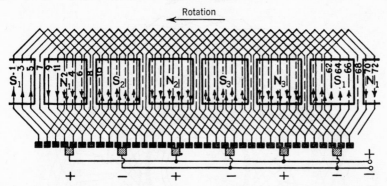

FIG. 74. Lap, or multiple, winding for a six-pole d-c machine.   The arrowheads show the directions of the induced emfs.

commutator segment, it follows that there are as many paths in parallel through the winding as there are poles.

Figure 73 shows six slots per pole, with two conductors per slot. In practice there are rarely less than nine slots per pole, unless the machine is quite small, and often four, six, eight, or more, conductors per slot.   The winding shown in Fig. 73 is full pitch.   That is, when conductor 1 is under the center of a south pole, conductor 2 is under the center of a north pole, as shown.   In practice the winding is often short pitch.   That is, conductor 2 is placed one slot nearer to conductor 1 than in a full-pitch winding.   This is done to facilitate commutation, as will be explained in Chap. 14.

98. Wave, or Series, Windings.   In winding the machine of Fig. 73 there is no reason why conductor 3 should not be placed under pole S_2 instead of under S_1.   If this is done and the winding completed, as shown in Fig. 75, the result will be a *wave*, or *series*, winding.

With this winding it will be found that there is only one high-pressure point and one low-pressure point, so that only two brushes are essential. That is, brushes a and b are sufficient without the four other brushes shown.   There are only two paths through the winding no matter how many poles there are, and half of the entire winding is traversed in going from brush a to brush b clockwise, and the other half in going counterclockwise.   The single high-pressure point, however, is common to the three commutator segments at b, d, and f, respectively, these segments being joined together at the instant shown by coils 17-18, 19-20, and 21-22, in which no emf is being generated.   Thus brushes b, d, and f all tap the winding at what is equivalent to a single point.   Similarly brushes a, c, and e tap the winding at the single low-pressure point.   Only two

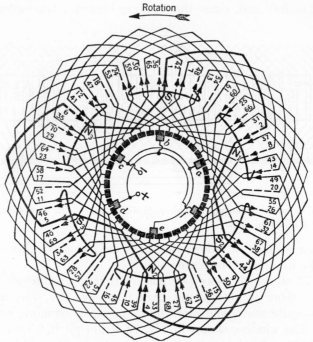

FIG. 75. Wave winding for a six-pole d-c machine.

brushes are needed, but a cheaper commutator is obtained if as many brushes are used as there are poles.   The length of the commutator segments is roughly proportional to the current per brush, and therefore using three brushes in parallel instead of one allows a substantial reduction in the weight of copper in the commutator.   In the case of the standard four-pole 600-volt wave-wound d-c street-railway motor, however, only two brushes are used, because the limited space available for the motor makes it practically impossible for the designer to render all four brushes accessible for adjustment and repair.

Wave windings, or two-circuit windings as they are often called, are extensively used for small and medium-sized four-pole machines of 220 volts or over, while the lap or multiple windings are used for low-voltage machines and for large machines of all voltages.

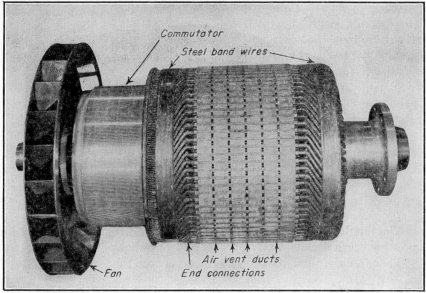

FIG. 76. Multiple-, or lap-, wound armature for a four-pole d-c machine.

FIG. 77. Two wave-wound eight-pole d-c armatures on a common shaft.

Wave windings are used wherever the use of a multiple winding would result in too small a conductor or too many conductors per slot.

99. The Electromotive-force Equation. Let ϕ be total lines of magnetic flux per pole. Z is total number of conductors in the slots. Then the flux cut by one conductor in one revolution $= \phi \times$ poles.

The flux cut per second by one conductor is

$$\phi \times \text{poles} \times \frac{\text{rpm}}{60}$$

The average emf generated in one conductor is

$$\phi \times \text{poles} \times \frac{\text{rpm}}{60} \times 10^{-8} \qquad \text{volts}$$

The number of conductors in series between a negative brush and a positive brush is equal to $Z/$(parallel paths through winding).

Therefore the total voltage generated between the terminals is

$$\text{Total voltage} = \frac{Z}{\text{paths}} \times \phi \times \text{poles} \times \frac{\text{rpm}}{60} \times 10^{-8} \qquad \text{volts} \quad (33)$$

By a suitable choice of the quantities in this equation the designer is able to wind armatures for different voltages. It may be noted, however, that, although all the coils shown in the diagrams have only one turn between adjacent commutator segments, it is often necessary to make the coils with several turns between segments in order that the voltages used in practice may be attained. The several turns are all placed in the same pair of slots.

100. Lamination of the Armature Core. The iron armature core on which the coils are mounted cuts magnetic flux as it rotates and has emf generated in it. In fact, the emf generated in the iron teeth that form the sides of the slots is equal to the emf generated in the copper conductors in those slots, since they both cut the same flux. The emf generated in the armature core cannot be utilized in any way, but it may cause a lot of energy to be wasted as heat if it is allowed to circulate current in the iron. Figure 78 shows a solid armature core (slots omitted for simplicity) and the whirl of eddy currents that result when the armature is rotated. It is possible to make a solid block of iron red hot by rotating it at high speed in a strong magnetic field. The power loss resulting from these eddy currents could be eliminated if the iron core could be made non-conducting in the direction in which the current tends to flow. This is approximately accomplished in practice by building the core up out of thin disks of varnished sheet steel, as indicated in Fig. 79. The slots are

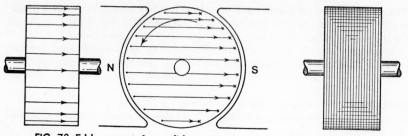

FIG. 78. Eddy currents in a solid armature core.   FIG. 79. Laminated armature core.

punched in each individual disk before varnishing.   The usual thickness
of the laminations is 0.014 to 0.025 in.

Problems

12-1. A wire passes 40 times a second across the pole face of a field magnet the
flux density of which is 15,000 lines per sq cm.   The pole face area is 30 by 30 cm.
What average emf is induced in the wire?

12-2. The armature of a d-c machine has 100 active conductors connected in
series between plus and minus brushes.   If these conductors cut 3,600 times per
min through a field of 2×10^6 lines, what average voltage is induced?

***12-3.** In Fig. 66, would the polarity of brushes $B+$ and $B-$ be changed if the
direction of rotation were reversed?

12-4. A six-pole d-c generator has 388 conductors on the armature.   The average emf induced per conductor is 2 volts and the allowable current per conductor
is 10 amp.

  a. Find the no-load terminal voltage and line current if the armature has a lap
or multiple-circuit winding.

  b. Find emf and line current if the winding is of the wave or two-circuit type.

12-5. A four-pole d-c generator driven at a certain speed and having a certain
field excitation has an average induced voltage per conductor of 2 volts.   The
current per conductor is limited by heating to 10 amp.   The generator delivers
to the line a current of 40 amp at an induced voltage of 120 volts.   Does the
armature have a multiple (lap) or series (wave) winding?   What is the total number of conductors on the armature?

***12-6.** The armature of a four-pole machine has 100 active conductors in series
between brushes.   The speed is 1,000 rpm.   Area of each pole face is 15 by 25 cm.
Flux density in air gap is 5,000 lines per sq cm.   Determine the emf induced
between brushes.

***12-7.** A six-pole d-c generator armature has 350 active conductors and a wave
or two-circuit winding.   The flux per pole is 6×10^6 lines of force.   What is the
generated voltage if the speed is 210 rpm?   If the output of the machine is 50 kw,
what is the current per conductor?

***12-8.** If this machine had a lap or multiple winding with 1,050 active conduc-
tors, what would then be the generated voltage at the same speed, the flux per pole
being unchanged?   If the output is still 50 kw, what is the current per conductor
and which machine requires the more copper?

12-9. An eight-pole d-c generator armature has 608 conductors. When running at 250 rpm, the induced voltage is 110. What is the flux density in the air gap if the pole area is 780 sq cm? Armature has a multiple winding.

12-10. A small bipolar drum armature has 40 slots, each containing 8 conductors per slot. The normal speed of the machine is 2,400 rpm and the flux per pole is 1,000,000 lines. What is the average emf induced in each conductor, and what is the total voltage generated?

*12-11. Draw the following winding diagrams:

a. Six-pole double-layer lap winding with 30 slots, 2 conductors per slot, and 1 turn per coil.

b. The same machine with six conductors per slot and three turns per coil; show only the first two coils.

c. Six-pole double-layer wave winding with 29 slots, 2 conductors per slot, and 1 turn per coil. If in cases *a* and *c* the average voltage per conductor is 10 and the safe current per conductor is 100, find the terminal voltage, line current, and kilowatt output for the two windings.

*12-12. Why is the magnetic circuit of an electric generator made of iron? Why is the armature core made of laminations, while the remainder of the magnetic circuit may be a casting? What would happen if a steel casting were used for the armature?

13

CONSTRUCTION AND EXCITATION OF DIRECT-CURRENT MACHINES

101. Multipolar Construction. Figure 80 shows a two-pole machine and also a six-pole machine built for the same output, the machines having the same armature diameter and the same total number of lines of flux crossing the air gaps. The armature core of the two-pole machine must be deep enough to carry half of the total flux, while in the six-pole machine

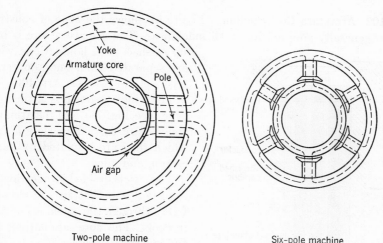

Two-pole machine   Six-pole machine
FIG. 80. Machines with the same output.

the total flux divides up among six paths so that the core need be only one-third of the depth of that of the two-pole machine. For the same reason the six-pole machine has the smaller cross section of yoke.

By the use of the multipolar construction, therefore, there is a considerable saving in material, but this is at the expense of an increase in the cost of labor because of the increased number of parts to be machined and handled.	The number of poles is chosen by the designer to give the cheapest machine that will operate satisfactorily.

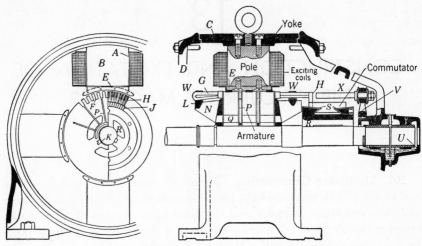

FIG. 81. Small d-c generator.

102. Armature Construction.	Figure 81 shows the type of construction generally adopted for small machines.	The armature core is built up of sheet-steel laminations, which are separated from one another by layers of varnish (see Art. 100).

The winding shown is of the drum type (see Fig. 76) and the armature coils G are carried in slots F from which they are insulated by paper, cotton, and mica.

The core is divided into sections by spacers P, so that air can circulate freely through the machine and keep it cool.	The core laminations and the spacers P are clamped between end heads N, which carry coil supports L attached by arms shaped like fans.	The coils are held against these supports by steel band wires W. Figure 82 shows a cross section of the slot and the two coil sides for a typical large 600-volt d-c generator.

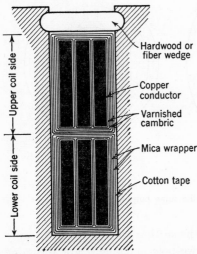

FIG. 82. Cross section of armature slot showing coils in place. (Six conductors per slot.)

Hardwood or fiber wedge

Copper conductor

Varnished cambric

Mica wrapper

Cotton tape

Upper coil side

Lower coil side

The conductors are rectangular in cross section so as not to waste any space, but small machines are wound with round wire because a rectangular section is not suited to very small conductors, especially when the number of conductors per slot is large.

103. Commutator. The commutator is built of segments J, Fig. 81, which are of hard-drawn copper. These segments are separated from one another by mica strips and are then clamped between two beveled-edge rings S, called cones, from which they are separated by mica, the segments being thereby insulated from one another and from the frame of the machine. The segments are connected to the winding through the leads, or risers, H, which have air spaces between one another as

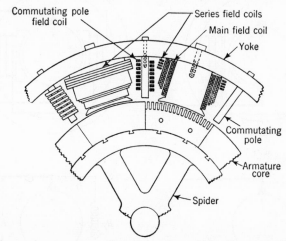

FIG. 83. Large d-c generator with commutating poles and compound excitation.

shown, so that air is drawn across the commutator and between the leads, thereby keeping the commutator cool.

104. Brushes. The brushes are held in position on the commutator by means of brush holders, which are attached to the studs X. These studs are insulated from the supporting arms V, and connection is made from these studs to the external circuit. The supporting arms V are usually mounted on a ring, which permits adjustment of the brush position by rotation of the entire brush rigging about the axis of the machine. This ring can be clamped in any position. An adjustable spring maintains a constant pressure between the brush and the commutator. Too low a pressure results in poor contact, sparking, and burning of the commutator. Too high a pressure results in excessive wear and in overheating of the commutator through friction. The usual values of brush pressure for carbon brushes are from 1.5 to 2 lb per sq in. of contact surface. Carbon brushes contain enough graphite to be self-lubricating.

105. Large Generators. Large generators are similar to small generators, except that they have more poles and the armature punchings are too large to be made in one piece. Figure 83 shows a section from a large d-c generator. The sheet-steel punchings that form the armature core are dovetailed to the spider, each successive layer being staggered with respect to the preceding layer so that the joints are all overlapped on both sides. Through bolts and end rings squeeze the laminations tightly together. It is necessary to insulate these bolts from the armature iron because they cut some of the magnetic flux and have alternating emfs induced in them.

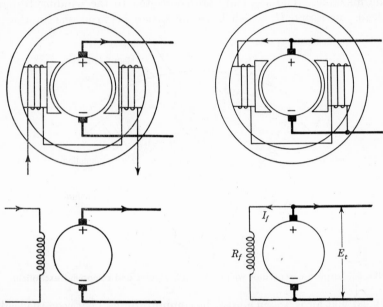

FIG. 84. Separately excited machine.   FIG. 85. Shunt-excited machine.

106. Commutating Poles. Most modern d-c machines of more than 1 hp are provided with *commutating poles* or *interpoles*. The function of these interpoles is to produce sparkless commutation, as will be explained in Chap. 14. The field coils of the commutating poles carry the full current of the machine and therefore consist of only a few turns of heavy conductor.

107. Poles and Yoke. The main poles are usually rectangular in cross section and are built up of sheet-steel laminations about 0.0625 in. thick. The reason for laminating the poles is that the movement of the armature teeth across the pole faces causes a fluttering of the flux. This induces eddy currents in the pole faces, which would involve an appreciable power loss if the pole faces were not laminated.

The yoke is not laminated and is usually made of mild cast steel.

108. Excitation. Permanent magnets are used as field poles for some very small generators called magnetos; all other machines are supplied with electromagnets the strength of which can readily be controlled by varying the exciting current through the field coil.

When the generator itself supplies this exciting current, it is said to be *self-excited;* when the exciting current is supplied from some external source, the machine is said to be *separately excited.* The different connections used are shown in Figs. 84, 85, 86, and 87. In each of these figures the lower diagram shows the convention used to represent any

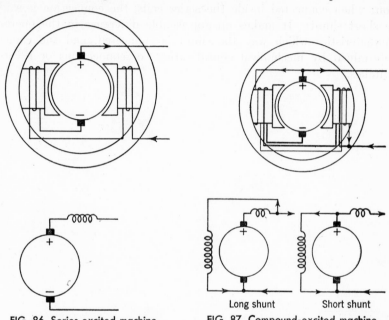

FIG. 86. Series-excited machine. FIG. 87. Compound-excited machine.

Long shunt Short shunt

machine employing the method of excitation specified in the title, while the upper part of the figure is a diagrammatic sketch of a two-pole machine employing the same method of excitation.

The different methods of excitation result in different operating characteristics, as will be explained in detail in Chap. 16.

Figure 84 shows a *separately excited* machine, the field current of which is supplied by another generator or a battery.

Figure 85 shows a *shunt-excited* machine in which the field coils are connected in shunt across the armature terminals. These coils have many turns of relatively small wire and carry a current $I_f = E_t/R_f$, the terminal voltage divided by the resistance of the field-coil circuit. This exciting current varies from about 0.5 per cent of the full-load current of the machine to about 5 per cent, depending chiefly on the size of the machine, the larger proportion of current being taken by the smaller machines.

Figure 86 shows a *series-excited* machine in which the field coils are in series with the armature and carry the total current of the machine. These coils must accordingly be formed of conductors of large cross section, and only a few turns are required.

Figures 87 and 83 show *compound-excited* machines in which there are both shunt and series-field coils. When the shunt coils are connected outside the series coils, the machine is said to have a long-shunt connection; when connected inside the series coils, the connection is said to be short shunt. It makes no appreciable difference in the operating characteristics which way the shunt is connected, and the choice is determined by mechanical considerations of connections or reversing switches.

14

THEORY OF COMMUTATION

109. Commutation. As each coil of a d-c generator passes a brush, the current in that coil is suddenly reversed. This is shown in Fig. 88. Figure 88a shows the brush in contact with a single commutator segment at the high-pressure point midway between the poles N and S. The arrowheads show the two equal currents I_c coming through the winding

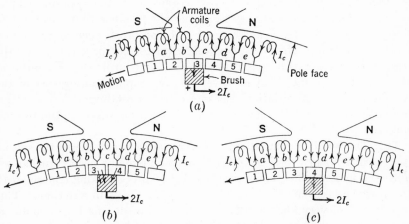

FIG. 88. Diagrams showing reversal of current in coil c.

from opposite directions and uniting to leave the winding at segment 3. The coils a, b, c, d, etc., are apparently those of a Gramme-ring winding, but they are intended to be a conventional representation of the coils of any or all types of windings of d-c generators.

Figure 88b shows the generator a fraction of a second later, with the coil c short-circuited by the brush. Coil c is now midway between the two poles and is not cutting the flux from either pole. The current flowing in coil c is now in the same condition as a disconnected rotating flywheel. It accordingly begins to die down.

An instant later, segment 3 has broken contact with the brush, as shown in Fig. 88c, and coil c is thus suddenly thrown in series with the row of coils under the south pole, and the current I_c coming through these coils must now flow through coil c.   That is, the current in coil c has been reversed.   The operation of reversing the current in an armature coil by means of the brush and commutator segments is called commutation.

Now the coil, owing to self-induction, resists the reversal of the current. The current flowing in each coil has created a local magnetic field encircling the conductors of that coil only.   As the current in coil c is being brought to zero, its local field is collapsing and is inducing an emf in the coil to maintain the current; and as the current is being brought up to its former value in the reverse direction, the local flux produced by that current is growing and cutting the coil and inducing an emf in it to oppose the growth of the current.   The magnitude of this emf of self-induction is directly proportional to the rapidity of the reversal.   Thus if at the instant when commutator segment 3 is just breaking contact with the brush the current in coil c is still flowing in the same direction as when that coil was to the right of the brush, then the current in coil c is called upon to reverse practically in zero time; the opposing emf of self-induction is therefore very large and the result is that current continues to flow directly from segment 3 to the brush even after contact has been broken.   This flow of current through the air gap between the segment and the brush constitutes a spark and burns the commutator. Continuous sparking, if at all severe, causes rapid deterioration of the commutator.   Commutation was one of the most important problems facing the designers of d-c machines and its solution was essential to their success.

110. Theory of Commutation.   We have already considered the special case (Art. 109) in which the current in coil c remains nearly unchanged until the instant when commutator segment 3 is breaking contact with the brush and is then called upon to reverse practically in zero time.   This case is that of very low resistance in the coil, brush, and brush contacts. In practice, carbon brushes are generally used and there is an appreciable resistance at the brush contacts.   The effect of this resistance is to aid commutation, because, as the contact area between segment 3 and the brush continuously decreases to zero, the resistance of this path continuously increases (the resistance of a path being inversely proportional to its cross-sectional area) and throttles off the current that is flowing along this path, thus gradually forcing the current to reverse in coil c.   This throttling, or pinching-off action, of high-resistance brushes aids commutation but is not sufficient to constitute a solution of the problem.

The time available for the reversal of the current is the time during which the coil is short-circuited by the brush.   What is really required, therefore, is to produce in some way in that coil, during the time that it is short-circuited, an emf of the proper magnitude and direction to cause complete reversal of the current in the time available.   This is accomplished in practice by placing a small pole, called an interpole, or a commutating pole, over the short-circuited coil, as shown in Fig. 89.   The

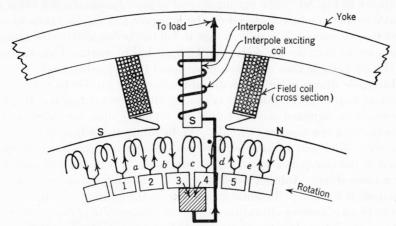

FIG. 89. Diagram showing an interpole and the method of exciting it.

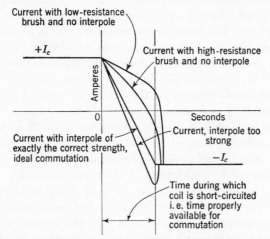

FIG. 90. Current in the short-circuited coil for various commutation conditions.

polarity of the interpole, in the case of a generator, will, of course, be opposite to that of the pole from which the coil has just come.   The graphs in Fig. 90 show the behavior of the current in coil *c* for various commutation conditions.   Note that in only one case is commutation completed within the time properly available.   In all the other cases the time has been extended, owing to the contact between the brush and segment 3 being prolonged by means of a spark.

The emf required to reverse the current in the coil is directly proportional to that current. Consequently, the strength of the interpole must be made directly proportional to the current output of the generator. This is accomplished by making the output current excite the interpole, as shown in Fig. 89. The output current is passed around a few turns of heavy copper conductor placed on the interpole and care is taken to see that there is enough iron in it so that it will not become saturated at any load current that the generator can be expected to carry. The strength of the interpole is then directly proportional to the load current.

Interpole design calculations are not sufficiently precise to enable the designer to provide an interpole of exactly the correct strength. It must therefore be adjusted on the test floor. This is done by varying the reluctance of the magnetic circuit. To facilitate this adjustment, brass and steel shims may be inserted between the interpole base and the yoke. Then, if the interpole is too strong, a steel shim is removed and replaced by a brass shim. Another possible way of adjusting the strength of the interpole is to change the number of turns on the exciting coil, but this is apt to be an expensive alteration on account of large size of the conductor.

Once the interpole is properly adjusted, it remains in adjustment.

111. Machines without Interpoles. Practically all modern generators and motors except those of small size are equipped with interpoles, but many old machines that have no interpoles are still in service. Commutation that is fairly free from sparking may be obtained on noninterpole generators by shifting the brushes forward in the direction of rotation.

In Fig. 89, coil c is cutting the flux from a south interpole of the proper strength, while short-circuited by the brush, and perfect commutation is accordingly obtained as explained above. If the interpole were removed and the brush were shifted about one segment's width to the left, then coil b would be short-circuited instead of coil c, and, since coil b is under the tip of the south pole, perfect commutation would be obtained in it if the flux being cut by coil b were of the proper density. Thus the tip of the south pole can be made to do the work of the missing south interpole, but, whereas the strength of the interpole was automatically adjusted by its exciting current to suit the load that the generator happened to be carrying, the main south pole does not increase in strength with increase of load current, and consequently perfect commutation for all loads can be obtained only by shifting the brushes to a different position for each load. At no load the brush should be in the central position as in Fig. 89, and with each increase of load the brush should be advanced a little farther in the direction of rotation of the armature.

In practice, therefore, the brushes are practically never in exactly the correct position for perfect commutation, and there are nearly always minute sparks at the toes of the brushes. On small noninterpole machines it is quite common practice to set the brushes to give perfect commutation at about two-thirds full load and leave them there. In that case, carbon brushes should be used, so that the relatively high-resistance brush contacts will aid in commutation.

In the foregoing theory the action at the positive brush has been described. The action at the negative brush is similar and need not be considered separately.

112. Brushes. Brushes are manufactured in a great variety of compositions and degrees of hardness. They may be classified roughly as carbon, carbon graphite, graphite, metal graphite, and copper. And the allowable current density at the brush contacts varies from 35 amp per sq in. in the case of carbon to 150 amp per sq in. in the case of copper.

Copper brushes are used only for machines designed for large currents at low voltages. Unless very carefully lubricated, they cut the commutator very quickly and, in any case, the wear is rapid. Graphite and carbon-graphite brushes are self-lubricating and are very widely used. Even with the softest brushes, however, there is a gradual wearing away of the commutator, and, if the mica between the commutator segments does not wear down so rapidly as the segments do, the high mica will cause the brushes to make poor contact with the segments, and sparking will result, with consequent damage to the commutator. To prevent this, the mica is frequently "undercut" to a level below the commutator surface by means of a narrow milling cutter.

Sooner or later, commutators generally wear out of true and must be turned down in a lathe, but interpole machines with soft brushes and undercut mica will run for a long time without any maintenance on the commutator. Noninterpole machines gradually burn their commutators to a rough surface unless the brushes are continually adjusted to the varying load, and they therefore require turning down much more frequently than interpole machines do.

No lubrication should be applied to the surface of a commutator with undercut mica, because the lubricant will collect carbon or graphite dust from the brushes and hold it in the grooves above the mica and thus provide leakage paths for the current from segment to segment, which may ultimately develop into a short circuit or "flashover" on the commutator. All modern brushes, except the copper ones, contain enough graphite to provide adequate lubrication.

113. Short-pitch Coils and Commutation. Referring to Fig. 73 it may be seen that the currents in conductors 56 and 67 are being reversed simultaneously. This is a full-pitch winding and these two conductors are in the same slot. They therefore both contribute to the same local field, which exists chiefly in the two adjacent teeth, going up one tooth and down the other. This field reverses when the currents producing it reverse, and thus induces the emf of self-induction that opposes commutation. In a short-pitch winding, conductors 56 and 67 are not in the same slot and therefore only half of the current in the slot reverses at any one time, and therefore only half of this local flux reverses at any one time. The emf of self-induction is not cut quite in half by changing from full pitch to short pitch because the end connections contribute something to the self-induction and they are not affected appreciably by the change. Changing from full pitch to short pitch reduces the emf of self-induction opposing commutation by approximately 40 per cent.

Problems

14-1. Why are modern machines provided with interpoles? If the interpole winding is disconnected, what will happen? If the direction of rotation of an interpole generator is reversed, the polarity of the main poles remaining the same, will it be necessary to reverse the interpole winding connections?

14-2. A four-pole d-c generator has 80 commutator segments, and the brush is wide enough to cover two segments completely. What is the length of time available for commutation when the speed is 1,500 rpm? If the self-inductance of each armature coil is 0.1 mh, what is the average emf of self-induction in a coil during commutation when the total load on the machine is 200 amp? The machine is multiple wound, short pitch.

*14-3. Why are the armature conductors insulated from the core, and why are the commutator segments insulated from the core and from one another? What insulating materials are generally used for this purpose?

*14-4. Find the time of commutation of some of the machines in the laboratory.

14-5. During commutation the flux of self-induction through the short-circuited coil of eight turns changes from 10^5 lines in one direction to the same value in the opposite direction in 0.001 sec. What is the average emf induced in the coil during this interval?

15

ARMATURE REACTION

114. The Cross-magnetizing Effect. Figure 91a shows the magnetic flux produced in a two-pole direct-current machine by the field current, when there is no current flowing in the armature winding. The armature teeth have been omitted so as to simplify the drawing. The flux density is practically uniform over the pole faces.

Figure 91b shows the magnetic flux produced by the armature current when there is no current flowing in the field coils. In order to obtain this condition, it is necessary to drive the current through the armature winding by means of some external source, such as a battery. The currents, flowing downward in all the armature conductors under the right-hand pole and up in all the conductors under the left-hand pole, magnetize the armature in a direction that may be determined by the corkscrew rule (Art. 22), and the lines return through the pole faces to complete the magnetic circuit.

Figure 91c shows the resultant distribution of magnetic flux when, as under load conditions, the armature is carrying current and the field coils are excited; Fig. 91c is obtained by combining the magnetic fields of Fig. 91a and b. Under pole tips a and c the magnetic field due to the current in the armature is opposite in direction to that due to the current in the field coils, while under tips b and d the two magnetic fields are in the same direction. Consequently, the armature current has the effect of weakening the magnetic field under pole tips a and c and of strengthening it under pole tips b and d. That is, the flux is crowded to pole tips b and d. A comparison between Fig. 91 and Fig. 12 (page 18) will show that Fig. 91 is simply a practical application of Fig. 12. The flux, reacting with the current-carrying armature conductors, creates a torque as explained in Art. 25. In the case of a generator this torque opposes the rotation, and the engine driving the generator must provide torque to overcome it. In the case of a motor, this torque produces the rotation.

One effect that results from the crowding of the magnetic flux to the pole tips is that the total flux is somewhat reduced. This is really a saturation effect.   The increase in the flux density under pole tips b and d is not so great as the decrease under pole tips a and c, owing to saturation effects at b and d.

Since the magnetic axis of the armature winding is perpendicular to the magnetic axis of the field coils, the magnetic effect produced by the armature current is called the cross-magnetizing effect of armature reaction.

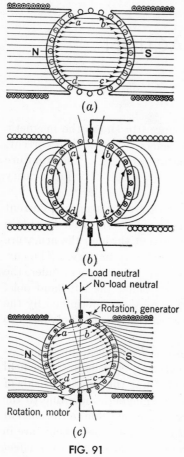

(a)

(b)

(c)

FIG. 91

115. No-load and Load Neutrals. The neutral of a d-c machine may be defined as that plane, through the axis of the armature, which also includes the dividing line, on the armature surface, that separates the area in which flux is entering the armature from the area in which flux is leaving the armature.   The no-load neutral bisects the angle formed by the axes of adjacent poles (180° in the case of a two-pole machine), but under load the neutral is shifted as shown in Fig. 91.   In the case of a generator the shift is in the direction of rotation.   In the case of a motor it is in the opposite direction to rotation.

116. Demagnetizing Effect. If a d-c generator is provided with commutating poles, the brushes are placed on the no-load neutral and remain there, and the only effect of armature reaction is the cross-magnetizing effect discussed in Art. 114.   If, however, the generator has no commutating poles, the brushes are shifted from the no-load neutral, in the direction of rotation, so as to improve commutation (Art. 111).   For perfect commutation they must be shifted beyond the load neutral as shown in Fig. 92a.

Now the magnetic field produced by the current in the armature winding moves with the brushes, and it is therefore no longer perpendicular to the magnetic axis NS of the field coils but acts in the direction oz.   It may, however, be considered as the resultant of two magnetic fields, one in the direction oy, called the cross-magnetizing component, and the other in the direction ox, called the demagnetizing component, because it is directly opposed to the field produced by the field coils.   Figure 92b and c

shows the armature winding separated into two parts so as to produce these two components. The conductors in Fig. 92b, when carrying current, produce a cross-magnetizing effect that is evidently the same as that discussed in Art. 114. The conductors in Fig. 92c produce the demagnetizing effect. The number of conductors that contribute to the

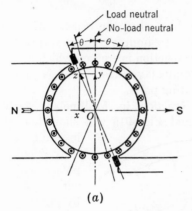

(a)

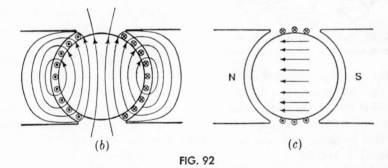

(b)　　　　　　　　　　　　　　　　　　(c)

FIG. 92

demagnetizing effect is directly proportional to the angle by which the brushes are advanced from the no-load neutral.

Let θ = this angle, degrees (see Fig. 92a)

　　Z = total number of armature conductors

　　I_c = current per conductor

Then the number of demagnetizing armature ampere-turns is

$$\frac{2\theta}{180} \times \frac{ZI_c}{2}$$

(ZI_c is divided by 2 because it requires two conductors to make a single turn.)

If series-field turns are placed on poles N and S of Fig. 92c to neutralize the demagnetizing ampere-turns, then half of these series turns will be placed on each of the two poles, and it is therefore usual to express the demagnetizing effect in ampere-turns per pole. The number of demagnetizing ampere-turns per pole is

$$\frac{2\theta}{180} \times \frac{ZI_c}{4} \tag{34}$$

Thus it appears that, when the brushes of a generator are advanced under load, in order to improve commutation, a demagnetizing component of armature reaction is created which reduces the flux and therefore lowers the terminal voltage. This is another point in favor of providing commutating poles.

117. Armature Reaction in Multipolar Machines. A comparison between Fig. 93 and Fig. 91b will show that the armature reaction in multipolar machines is practically identical with that in two-pole machines. In both cases the whirl of flux produced at each pole by the current in the armature conductors under that pole strengthens one pole tip and weakens the other and crowds the flux toward the far pole tip.

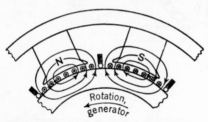

FIG. 93. Flux produced by the armature current alone in a multipolar machine.

Equation (34) applies to multipolar machines as well as two-pole machines, because the angle 180° in the denominator and the factor Z in the numerator must both be divided by the number of pairs of poles, and these two operations cancel out. Note that the angle θ must be expressed in mechanical degrees in this formula, and not in electrical degrees. (Electrical degrees are defined in Art. 245.)

118. Effect of Armature Reaction on Commutation. Figure 91b shows that the flux produced by the current in the armature conductors is in direct opposition to the fields of the commutating poles. This does not, however, interfere with the proper functioning of these poles, because their strengths are adjusted on the test floor to give good commutation, and, since the armature reaction is present when the adjustment is made, it is automatically taken care of. Therefore, when the commutating poles are correctly adjusted, they are strong enough to provide the required reversing field, in spite of armature reaction. Since the commutating-pole flux and the flux of armature reaction are both produced by the load current, they strengthen and weaken together as the load increases and decreases, and the ratio of their strengths is always correct, except that at heavy overloads saturation in the commutating pole limits its strength.

In the cases of generators that have no commutating poles, the brushes are shifted in the direction of rotation, and the next pole tip is made to function as a commutating pole. But it may be seen from Fig. 91b and c that the effect of armature reaction is to weaken these pole tips as the load increases, whereas they ought to be strengthened in order to provide good commutation.

This effect may be reduced by making the air-gap clearances larger so that there is a large reluctance in the path of the cross field. Increasing the air gap also increases the reluctance of the main magnetic path, and, in order to produce the required main flux, it is then necessary to increase the number of exciting ampere-turns on the poles. The machine is then said to have a stiff magnetic field because it is not greatly affected by armature reaction. Machines equipped with interpoles do not require so stiff a field as those not so equipped and are consequently made with smaller air gaps and do not require so many exciting ampere-turns.

Problems

15-1. The brushes of a 230-volt 50-kw four-pole multiple-wound d-c generator are advanced 6 mechanical degrees from the no-load neutral. There are 232 armature conductors. Calculate demagnetizing armature ampere-turns per pole at full load.

*15-2. The armature of a separately excited generator can be spun around by hand when the armature circuit is open, but, when a resistance is connected across its terminals, it becomes much more difficult to turn it. What is the cause of the increased retarding torque?

16

CHARACTERISTICS OF DIRECT-CURRENT GENERATORS

119. No-load Saturation Curves. The voltage generated in the armature winding of a direct-current machine, being proportional to the rate of cutting the lines of magnetic flux, is proportional to the speed and to the flux per pole. Therefore

$$E_0 = Kn\phi$$

where E_0 = voltage generated at no load
  K = a constant
  ϕ = lines of flux per pole
  n = rpm
A comparison with Eq. (33), Art. 99, shows that

$$K = \frac{Z}{\text{paths}} \times \text{poles} \times \frac{10^{-8}}{60}$$

but at the moment we are not concerned with the magnitude of K.

A curve that shows how E_0 varies with the exciting current I_f, when the speed is constant, is called a no-load saturation curve. Such a curve is shown in Fig. 94. It is readily obtained by separately exciting the generator, driving it at the desired constant speed, varying I_f by means of the rheostat r, and measuring I_f and E_0. The curvature, or saturation effect, is much less pronounced in the magnetic circuit of a machine than in a continuous iron ring. This is due to the fact that in a machine the air gap is a large proportion of the total reluctance, and air displays no saturation effect.

The voltage e_r, generated when $I_f = 0$, is due to residual magnetism. If the residual magnetism is reversed, this voltage will be $-e_r$, and if a complete hysteresis loop is obtained for the machine, as explained in Art. 72, it will pass through the two points e_r and $-e_r$. The extreme

126

thinness of this hysteresis loop is due to the fact that the air gap displays
no hysteresis effect.

120. Self-excitation.   Most d-c generators are self-excited.   Consider
a generator connected as shown in Fig. 95.   The straight line *or* is the

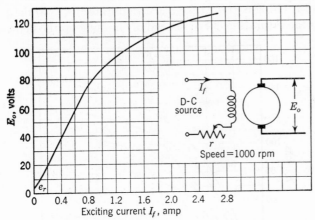

FIG. 94. Saturation curve of a d-c generator.

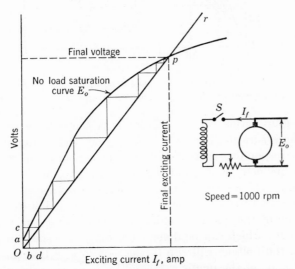

FIG. 95. Self-excitation, illustrating the building-up process.   Residual magnetism somewhat exaggerated.

graph of the voltage required to drive the current I_f through the resistance R_f of the field circuit.   Its equation therefore is $E = I_f R_f$, which is
the equation of a straight line of slope R_f.

Suppose that switch *s* is open and that the generator is running at the speed at which the saturation curve was taken. Owing to residual magnetism a voltage *oa* will be generated (somewhat exaggerated in the figure). If switch *s* is now closed, this voltage will produce a field current equal to *ob*, which in turn will raise the generated voltage to *oc*, which will raise the field current to *od*, etc. Actually, of course, the changes in voltage and exciting current take place simultaneously, so that the voltage follows the saturation curve instead of climbing up the flight of stairs.

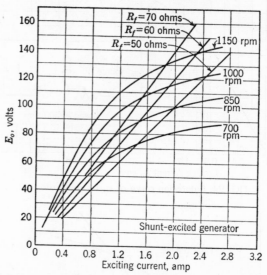

FIG. 96. Method of determining the no-load generated voltage E_0, and the exciting current I_f, of a shunt-excited generator, for any combination of speed and field-circuit resistance.

The building-up action continues as long as the voltage generated (as given by the saturation curve) is greater than the voltage required to drive the corresponding current I_f through the field circuit (as given by the straight line *or*). It stops at the point *p* where the saturation curve crosses the line *or*, because beyond this point the voltage generated is less than that required to maintain the corresponding field current.

If the slope of the line *or* is reduced by decreasing the resistance of the field circuit, which can be done if there is a rheostat already in the field circuit, the voltage will rise to the new intersection point. However, if the slope of the line is increased by increasing the resistance of the field circuit, the voltage will fall to the new intersection point. Notice that the slope of *or* can easily be made large enough so that the voltage will be little more than the residual voltage *oa*. This is usually expressed by saying that the voltage will not build up if the resistance of the field circuit is too high. Too low a speed will also prevent the voltage building up because the ordinates of the saturation curve are proportional to the speed, and reducing the slope of the saturation curve has the same effect as increasing the slope of the line *or*.

Figure 96 shows the method of determining the no-load terminal voltage and the field current of a shunt-excited generator for any combination of speed and field-circuit resistance. The only experimental datum required is a single saturation curve at any known speed. The saturation curves for all other speeds are calculated by proportion. Straight lines are drawn through the origin with slopes equal to the field-circuit resistances that may be used, and the intersections of the two sets of lines give the terminal voltages and field currents. For example, when the

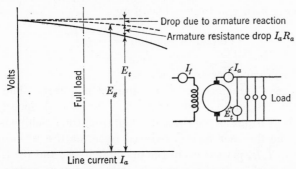

FIG. 97. Voltage-characteristic curve of a separately excited generator.

field-circuit resistance is 70 ohms and the speed is 1,150 rpm, the voltage will be 130 volts and the field current 1.86 amp.

It frequently happens that, when a generator is started up for the first time, the emf generated in the armature due to residual magnetism sends a current through the field coils in such a direction as to oppose the residual flux, and the voltage, instead of building up, is reduced. In such a case it is necessary to reverse the connections of the field coils so as to pass current through them in the opposite direction.

121. Voltage Characteristic of a Separately Excited Generator or of a Magneto. The voltage characteristic of a separately excited generator shows the variation of terminal voltage with the line current when the speed and the exciting current are kept constant. Such a curve is shown in Fig. 97. The terminal voltage E_t drops as the current taken from the generator is increased because:

1. The flux per pole is reduced by armature reaction, as explained in Chap. 15, so that E_g, the emf generated by cutting this flux, is also reduced.

2. The terminal voltage E_t is less than the generated voltage E_g by the armature-resistance drop $I_a R_a$, that part of the generated voltage required to force the armature current through the resistance of the armature winding and of the brush contacts.

To obtain such a curve experimentally, the generator is loaded on a bank of lamps, or some other suitable load that can readily be adjusted, as shown in Fig. 97. The speed and the exciting.current I_f are kept constant, while the current taken from the machine is gradually increased by connecting an increasing number of lamps in parallel across the terminals, that is, by providing more paths through which current can pass. Simultaneous readings of the voltage E_t and of the current I_a are taken and the results plotted as in Fig. 97.

The **voltage regulation** of a generator is defined as the percentage change in the terminal voltage when full load is thrown off the machine, the speed being kept constant. Therefore

$$\text{Voltage regulation} = \frac{E_0 - E_t}{E_t}$$

where $E_0 =$ voltage generated at no load.

122. Voltage Characteristic of a Shunt Generator. This curve is shown in Fig. 98 for a constant-speed shunt-excited generator. The terminal voltage drops as the current taken from the machine is increased because (1) the flux per pole is reduced by armature reaction, (2) the armature drop $I_a R_a$ is used up in the machine itself, and (3) the exciting current I_f is equal to E_t/R_f, where R_f is the constant resistance of the shunt-field circuit, so that, as the terminal voltage drops, the exciting current decreases and causes the voltage to drop still further. Because of this third effect the terminal voltage of a generator with a given load will be lower when the machine is shunt excited than when separately excited, if adjusted for the same no-load voltage in both cases.

To obtain such a curve experimentally, the machine is connected up as shown. The speed and the resistance of the shunt-field circuit are kept constant, while the current taken from the machine is gradually increased, and simultaneous readings are taken of the voltage E_t and the current I_t. These results are plotted as in Fig. 98.

As the resistance of the external circuit is decreased, the current supplied by the machine increases and the terminal voltage drops, until point d is reached. A further reduction in the external resistance allows an increased current to flow for an instant, but this increase of current reacts by armature reaction and causes such a large drop in voltage and in exciting current that the armature current drops below its previous value. In the extreme case when the generator is short-circuited, that is, when the terminals of the machine are connected through a circuit of negligible resistance, then the terminal voltage must be zero and there can be no field excitation, so that the only current that can flow in the short circuit is that produced by the voltage due to the residual magnetism. This point is shown at C, Fig. 98.

If a shunt generator is suddenly short-circuited, it will carry a very large current for a moment because, although the terminal voltage is zero, or nearly zero, the inductance of the field coils tends to maintain the field current.   Within a second or two, however, the field current will drop practically to zero, and the armature current will then be merely that produced by the residual magnetism.   This self-protective characteristic of the shunt generator is a valuable one.   Certain other special

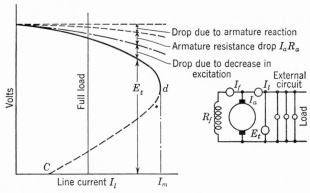

FIG. 98. Voltage-characteristic curve of a shunt generator.

machines, such as arc-welding generators (Art. 202), are also designed to have this self-protective feature.

123. Self-excited Compound Generators.   The various types of apparatus which ultimately consume the electrical energy are mostly designed to operate at constant voltage.   Consequently, the drooping voltage characteristics of the shunt and separately excited generators are undesirable for all except special types of service.   The voltage may be maintained constant on both shunt and separately excited generators by inserting an adjustable resistance, called a field rheostat, in series with the field coils, and then, as the load on the generator increases and the voltage drops, some of the resistance may be cut out either automatically or by hand so as to increase the excitation and thus raise the voltage.

A better way to accomplish the same purpose is to place a few series turns on the poles, as shown in Figs. 83 and 87.   The line current passes through these series coils and thus continuously increases the total magnetizing ampere-turns as the load increases.   By putting on the proper number of series turns, the generator may be made to give the same terminal voltage at full load as at no load.   The generator is then said to be flat compounded.   If still more series turns are added, the voltage will be higher at full load than at no load, and the generator is then said to be overcompounded.

Generators for lighting or power service are generally self-excited and are slightly overcompounded to take care of the voltage drop in the distribution circuits so that the voltage at the customers' premises may be approximately constant.

The amount of compounding can be adjusted by connecting a suitable resistance in parallel with the series field, as shown in Fig. 99, so as to by-pass some of the current.

If the series field is connected in reverse, so that it opposes the shunt field, the generator is said to be differentially compounded. In a differential compound generator the voltage drops very rapidly with increase

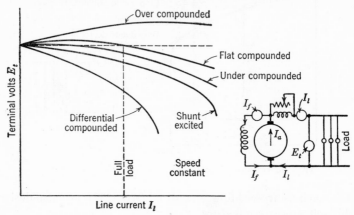

FIG. 99. Voltage characteristics of compound generators.

of load, and short circuits cannot injure it. Such a machine, with the main field separately excited, may be used for such special purposes as arc welding, where the generator is practically short-circuited every time the electrode touches the work. Modern arc-welding generators, however, are usually of special design (see Art. 202).

124. Fields of Application of Separate and Self-excitation. Separate excitation requires a separate source of direct current and is therefore usually more expensive than self-excitation. On this account it is generally used only where self-excitation would be relatively unsatisfactory. For example, when the application of the generator requires that its voltage be varied over a wide range, as in the Ward Leonard system of speed control, Art. 169, separate excitation is used because self-excitation would be unstable at the lower voltages.

Separate excitation gives a quicker and more precise response to changes in the resistance of the field circuit and is accordingly used where quick and definite response to control is important.

The d-c generator that provides the field current for another generator is called an exciter.

Separate excitation may be used in order to facilitate the application of some delicate type of automatic control, which can then control the very small field current of the exciter, rather than the relatively large field current of the main generator.

Separately excited generators may be compounded the same as when self-excited.

125. The Voltage Characteristic of a Series Generator. In a series generator the series-field coil is the only field coil. Consequently, the load current is the only field current, and, when the load is not connected, the terminal voltage is only that due to residual magnetism. Curve A, Fig. 100, shows what the relation between terminal voltage and current

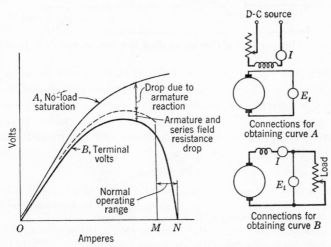

FIG. 100. Voltage characteristic of a series generator.

in a series generator would be if armature resistance and armature reaction were negligible; the voltage would increase with the load current since this is also the exciting current. Curve A is really the no-load saturation curve of the machine and is determined by separately exciting the field coils, as shown in the diagram, so that no current flows in the armature. Curve B shows the actual relation between terminal voltage and load current; the drop of voltage between curves A and B consists of the portion due to the reduction in the flux per pole caused by armature reaction, and the IR drop of voltage in the armature winding, brush contacts, and series-field coils.

Series generators were once used quite extensively as constant-current generators for the operation of arc lamps in series. Over the operating range, which for this type of service lies between the vertical lines M and N, Fig. 100, the current changes only slightly for relatively large changes in the load resistance, the effect of the change in load resistance being largely neutralized by a corresponding change in the terminal voltage.

The terminal voltage, and consequently the current, can be varied by means of a variable resistance shunted across the field coils. Series generators are still used in a few special applications, namely, as series boosters (Art. 126); and as generators in the Thury system of electric transmission, a system that is not used in America.

126. Series Booster. A series booster is a series generator that is connected in series with a line, as in Fig. 101, generally for the purpose of

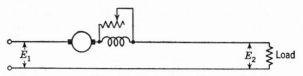

FIG. 101. Series booster neutralizing the IR drop in a line, so that $E_2 = E_1$ at all loads.

neutralizing the IR drop in the line, so that E_2 will be equal to E_1. Since its function is to neutralize an IR drop, its emf should be proportional to the current. Therefore it must operate on the rising part of the voltage characteristic. That is, it must be so selected that the line current under normal operating conditions will not exceed about one-half of ON, Fig. 100.

Problems

*16-1. *a.* A d-c shunt generator was tested with the brushes shifted forward in the direction of motion. The voltage drop between no load and full load was 6 volts. What are the causes of this drop in voltage?

b. If the brushes had been placed on the neutral position, why would the voltage drop have been different and what would you expect its value to be? Why are the brushes not placed on the neutral position in noninterpole machines?

c. Series-field coils were added to the machine and the voltage dropped 20 volts from no load to full load. What was the cause of this excessive drop?

d. After the series-field coil circuit had been fixed, the voltage was found to increase by 6 volts from no load to full load while flat compounding was desired. What changes would you suggest should now be made?

*16-2. Plot the magnetization curve from the following data obtained by test on a separately excited 25-kw 120-volt generator connected as shown in Fig. 94, and run at a constant speed of 900 rpm. (Keep this curve for later problems.)

Voltage at no load	4	40	60	80	100	120	140 volts
Exciting current	0.0	0.67	1.03	1.50	2.07	2.94	4.35 amp

Explain why the curve bends over and why there is a small voltage with no exciting current.

Is the polarity of this machine changed by (*a*) reversing the direction of rotation and (*b*) reversing the connections of the exciting coils?

16-3. *a.* If the exciting voltage of the generator of Prob. 16-2 is constant at 120, what must the resistance of the field-coil circuit be so that the generated voltages may be 40 volts, 100 volts, 120 volts, the speed being 900 rpm?

b. If the field coils have a resistance of 33 ohms, specify the rheostat to give a range of voltage from 40 to 120.

c. If the resistance of the field-coil circuit is kept constant at 41 ohms, what is the exciting current if the exciting voltage is 120, and what is the generated voltage when the speed is 700 rpm, 900 rpm, 1,100 rpm?

16-4. A d-c generator is shunt connected as in Fig. 95.

a. If the direction of rotation is reversed, will the machine build up?

b. If in addition the residual magnetism is reversed, will the machine then build up?

c. If the connections of the exciting coils of the original machine are reversed, will the machine then build up?

d. If the direction of rotation is reversed and also the connections of the exciting coils, will the machine build up and will the polarity of the brushes be changed?

16-5. *a.* When the generator of Prob. 16-2 is shunt connected, find the resistance of the field-coil circuit so that the generated voltages may be 40 volts, 100 volts, 120 volts, the speed being 900 rpm. Why do the figures differ from those in Prob. 16-3?

b. If the resistance of the field-coil circuit is kept constant at 41 ohms, what is the generated voltage when the speed is 700 rpm, 900 rpm, 1,100 rpm? Explain why the figures differ from those in Prob. 16-3.

16-6. Plot the following data for the saturation curve of a d-c generator; rpm = 1,000 (normal and constant).

Terminal volts	5	22	42	60	75	93	103	110	120
Shunt-field current	0	0.1	0.2	0.3	0.4	0.6	0.8	1.0	1.5

16-7. With the foregoing generator running at a constant and normal speed of 1,000 rpm, insert resistance in the field-coil circuit; plot the no-load terminal voltage against resistance of the field circuit for the following cases: (*a*) machine separately excited from 110-volt mains; (*b*) self-excited, shunt connected; (*c*) self-excited, compound connected, short shunt. The resistance of the shunt-field winding is 80 ohms.

16-8. Specify the graded field rheostat (total resistance, maximum current, and minimum current-carrying capacity) to change the voltage from 120 to 40 volts for the three types of connections in Prob. 16-7.

16-9. With no field rheostat find the terminal voltage with speeds of 250, 500, 1,000, and 1,500 rpm when the generator of Prob. 16-6 is (*a*) separately excited from 110 volts and (*b*) shunt excited. Which machine is most sensitive to change of speed? Why?

*16-10. Will the no-load emf of the generator of Prob. 16-6 (field rheostat short-circuited) be increased or decreased after a load run that has raised the temperature of the generator field 60°C above room temperature of 20°C? What will be the value of E_0 after the load run? Can it be brought to 120 volts again, and, if so, how?

*16-11. Tabulate the three causes of voltage drop in d-c shunt generators under load.

16-12. A 250-volt 100-kw d-c generator has 940 shunt-field turns on each pole. When running at rated speed, a shunt-field current of 7.0 amp produces a terminal voltage of 250 volts at no load, but 9.4 amp are required to produce the same terminal voltage at full load.   Calculate the number of series-field turns per pole required to make the machine flat compound.

16-13. A separately excited generator, the saturation curve of which is shown in Fig. 94, requires a field current of 1.7 amp to produce a no-load generator voltage of 110 volts at 1,000 rpm.   At full-load, armature reaction reduces the flux 4 per cent, and the speed of the prime mover drops 2 per cent.   What field current will be required to produce 110 volts at the terminals at full load?   Full-load current is 91 amp, and the resistance of the armature winding and brush contacts is 0.04 ohm.

16-14. A d-c compound generator is rated 250 volts, 200 kw, 900 rpm.   The terminal voltage is 250 volts at full load, 245 volts at half load, and 235 volts at no load.   The speed drops 2 per cent from no load to full load.   The resistance of the series field is 0.002 ohm, the shunt field 32 ohms, the shunt-field rheostat 6 ohms.   Neglecting the variation of the resistances with temperature, and assuming that the resistance of the armature winding and brushes is constant at 0.008 ohm, calculate:

  a. The generated voltage at each load.

  b. The ratio of the flux at each load to the flux at no load.

  c. The power lost as heat in each winding at full load, and express it as a per cent of the power output of the generator.

17

THEORY OF OPERATION OF
DIRECT-CURRENT MOTORS

Direct-current motors are fundamentally identical with the d-c generators that have the same type of excitation.   The difference lies in the use to which they are put.   When a machine is being used to convert electrical energy into mechanical energy it is called a motor; and when the same machine is being used to convert mechanical energy into electrical energy it is called a generator.   Moreover, in various practical applications d-c machines operate alternately as motors and as generators.

127. Electromagnetic Torque in a Direct-current Machine.   If a current is flowing through the armature conductors of a d-c machine, as in Fig. 102b, where the crosses and dots indicate the directions of the currents, then, since these conductors are carrying current and are in a magnetic field, they are acted upon by forces, all of which tend to turn the armature in a counterclockwise direction.   Regardless of whether the machine is rotating or is stationary, or whether it is acting as a motor or as a generator, the force on each conductor is given by the equation

$$F = Bli \quad \text{dynes} \tag{10}$$

This equation was derived in Art. 49.   The working length of the conductor, l cm, and the current, i abamp, are the same for all the conductors of this machine; but the flux density varies considerably, especially near the pole tips.   If we let B represent the *average* radial flux density at the average radius r cm at which the conductors are placed and if Z is the total number of armature conductors, then the electromagnetic torque, T, is given by

$$T = ZFr$$
$$= ZBlir \quad \text{dyne-cm}$$

It is more convenient to have the electromagnetic torque expressed in terms of the total armature current, I_a, in amperes, rather than in terms of the current per conductor in abamperes, and in terms of the total flux per pole, ϕ, rather than in terms of the average flux density, B. Now

$$i = \frac{I_a}{10 \times \text{paths}} \quad \text{and} \quad B = \frac{\phi}{A}$$

where A is the sectional area of the flux path at radius r. Also

$$A = \frac{2\pi r l}{\text{poles}}$$

therefore

$$T = \frac{Z\phi l I_a r}{20\pi r l} \times \frac{\text{poles}}{\text{paths}}$$

$$= \frac{Z\phi I_a}{20\pi} \times \frac{\text{poles}}{\text{paths}} \quad \text{dyne-cm}$$

hence

$$T = K_t \phi I_a \tag{35}$$

where K_t is a constant for any one machine.

128. Driving and Retarding Torques in Generators and Motors. Figure 102 shows two identical machines, turning in the same direction, but

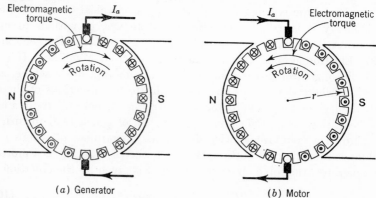

(a) Generator   (b) Motor

FIG. 102. (a) Retarding electromagnetic torque in a generator and (b) driving electromagnetic torque in a motor.

one is operating as a generator and the other as a motor. The generator, Fig. 102a, is driven by an engine in the counterclockwise direction. It generates an emf, and if an external circuit is connected to its terminals, it supplies electric power to that circuit and current flows through its armature conductors in the directions indicated by the crosses and dots. Since these armature conductors are carrying current and are in a magnetic field, they are acted upon by forces, all of which tend to turn the generator in the clockwise direction. These forces therefore produce a retarding torque which opposes the rotation of the generator. The magnitude of this retarding torque is given by Eq. (35). To keep the generator running, the driving torque of the engine must be great enough to overcome this retarding torque and to overcome also the friction at the bearings and brushes, the windage forces, and the magnetic drag caused by hysteresis and eddy currents in the iron of the armature, all of which oppose the rotation of the generator to some extent.

The same machine operating as a motor is shown in Fig. 102b. A voltage from some external source, such as a battery or a generator, is applied at the motor terminals and forces current through the armature conductors in the directions shown. Since these conductors are carrying current and are in a magnetic field, they are acted upon by forces which cause the armature to rotate in the counterclockwise direction. The magnitude of the driving torque produced by these forces is given by Eq. (35). Now if the armature rotates, the conductors cut lines of flux, and an emf is generated in the armature winding in exactly the same way as if the machine were being driven by an engine. This emf acts in the same direction as in Fig. 102a, since the two machines have the same poles and rotate in the same direction. This generated emf is therefore opposed to the current in the conductors in Fig. 102b, and is therefore opposed to the applied emf. For this reason the emf generated by the motor is called the *back emf*, or *counter emf*, of the motor.

In the case of both generator and motor there are forces acting on the armature conductors, owing to the fact that they are carrying current and are in a magnetic field. These forces produce the driving torque in the case of a motor and the retarding torque in the case of a generator. There is also an emf generated in the armature of each machine inasmuch as it is rotating in a magnetic field. This emf acts in the direction of the current flow in the case of a generator but opposes the current flow in the case of a motor.

Let E_g = back emf generated by motor
E_t = applied or line voltage
I_a = armature current
R_a = resistance of armature winding and brushes
Then by Kirchhoff's second law, since the voltage generated in the motor opposes the flow of the current,

$$E_t - E_g = I_a R_a \tag{36}$$

Rearranging $$I_a = \frac{E_t - E_g}{R_a} \quad \text{(current equation)} \tag{37}$$

Equation (36) may also be written as

$$E_t = E_g + I_a R_a \tag{36a}$$

In this equation it is important to note that $I_a R_a$, which is the component of applied voltage required to force the current through the resistance of the armature circuit, is usually only about 5 per cent of E_t.   The remaining part of E_t is required to overcome E_g.

If we multiply both sides of Eq. (36a) by I_a, we obtain

$$E_tI_a = E_gI_a + I_a^2R_a$$

where E_tI_a = power input to armature of motor, watts
$\quad I_a^2R_a$ = power lost as heat in armature circuit
$\quad E_gI_a$ = power converted into mechanical power by motor
This mechanical power is that due to the conductors pushing against the sides of the teeth.   The power available at the shaft as mechanical power

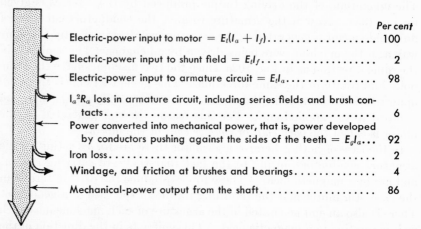

	Per cent
Electric-power input to motor = $E_t(I_a + I_f)$	100
Electric-power input to shunt field = E_tI_f	2
Electric-power input to armature circuit = E_tI_a	98
$I_a^2R_a$ loss in armature circuit, including series fields and brush contacts	6
Power converted into mechanical power, that is, power developed by conductors pushing against the sides of the teeth = E_gI_a	92
Iron loss	2
Windage, and friction at brushes and bearings	4
Mechanical-power output from the shaft	86

FIG. 103. Power-flow diagram for a shunt or compound motor, showing typical values for a 10-hp 220-volt motor (not to scale).

output is less than the converted power by the amount of the power losses caused by friction at the bearings and brushes, by air resistance, and by the magnetic drag caused by hysteresis and eddy currents in the iron.   The power-flow diagram is shown in Fig. 103.   The power losses will be dealt with more thoroughly in Chap. 19.

129. The Back Electromotive Force.   The existence of the back emf, discussed in the preceding article, may readily be shown by experiment. If for example a voltmeter is connected across the terminals of a motor as in Fig. 103A, then as long as switch S is closed the voltmeter will read the applied voltage E_t, but the instant after switch S is opened, disconnecting E_t and reducing I_a to zero, the voltmeter reading will suddenly drop from E_t to E_g, and will then gradually decrease to zero as the motor slows down and stops.

130. Theory of Motor Operation.   The power taken by a motor from the mains changes automatically to suit the mechanical load.   Consider the case of a motor connected as shown in Fig. 103A, the applied voltage, the exciting current I_f, and the magnetic flux per pole being constant. If the motor is at standstill and the switch S is closed, a large current $I_a = E_t/R_a$ will flow through the armature, the back voltage E_g being zero, since the armature conductors are not cutting lines of force. The armature conductors, since they are carrying current and are in a magnetic field, are acted upon by forces that cause the motor to rotate. As

the motor increases in speed, the back emf E_g also increases, since it is proportional to the rate at which the armature conductors cut lines of flux, and therefore I_a decreases, since $I_a = (E_t - E_g)/R_a$. The motor will stop accelerating when this current has dropped to such a value that the electromagnetic driving torque is just equal to the sum of the mechanical load or brake torque and the torque wasted by friction, windage, and iron loss.

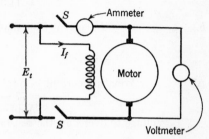

FIG. 103A. Experimental determination of the back emf of a shunt motor.

If now the mechanical load on the motor is increased, the driving torque due to the armature current is not sufficient to overcome the increased brake torque and the motor must slow down. As the speed decreases, however, the back emf E_g also decreases and allows a larger current to flow through the armature, and a larger current means an increased driving torque, since $T = K_t \phi I_a$. Thus the driving torque increases as the motor slows down, and the motor will stop slowing down as soon as the driving torque again becomes equal to the total retarding torque of the brake, friction, etc.

If the load on the motor is decreased, the driving torque due to the armature current is more than sufficient to overcome the decreased brake torque, and the motor must accelerate. As it increases in speed, however, the back emf E_g also increases and causes the armature current I_a to decrease. The motor will stop accelerating and the speed and armature current become constant when the driving torque due to the current has dropped to such a value that it is just sufficient to overcome the decreased retarding torque. The electric power taken by the motor from the mains therefore changes automatically to suit the mechanical load on the motor. The back emf of the motor regulates the flow of current as effectively as the governor regulates the flow of steam in a steam engine.

Example. A 110-volt d-c motor, connected to the mains, as shown in Fig. 103A, delivers 10 hp. If the efficiency is 88 per cent, the exciting current I_f is 2 amp, and the armature resistance is 0.08 ohm, find (a) the motor input, (b) the current taken from the mains, (c) the armature current, and (d) the back emf.

a.   Motor output $= 10$ hp

$$\text{Motor input} = \frac{\text{output}}{\text{efficiency}}$$

$$= \frac{10}{0.88} = 11.36 \text{ hp}$$

$$= 11.36 \times 746 = 8{,}477 \text{ watts}$$

b. I_t, current from mains $= \dfrac{\text{watts input}}{\text{applied voltage}}$

$$= \frac{8{,}477}{110} = 77 \text{ amp}$$

c.   Armature current $=$ total current $-$ exciting current
$$= 77 - 2 = 75 \text{ amp}$$

d.   Applied voltage $= 110$
Voltage to overcome the resistance drop $= I_a R_a$
$$= 75 \times 0.08 = 6 \text{ volts}$$
Back emf $E_g = E_t - I_a R_a$
$$= 110 - 6 = 104 \text{ volts}$$

131. Speed Equation. When a motor is running, the back emf is always less than the applied emf by $I_a R_a$, the armature resistance drop, so that

$$E_g = E_t - I_a R_a$$

Now E_g is generated in the motor armature because the conductors are cutting lines of force so that, in a given machine, E_g is proportional to the flux per pole and to the speed, or

$$E_g = k\phi \times \text{rpm}$$

where k is a constant.   Therefore

$$\text{rpm} = \frac{E_g}{k\phi}$$

but $E_g = E_t \quad I_a R_a$

Therefore $\text{rpm} = \dfrac{E_t - I_a R_a}{k\phi}$ (38)

where rpm $=$ motor speed
$E_t =$ voltage applied at motor terminals
$I_a R_a =$ armature-resistance drop
$\phi =$ flux per pole of motor

Now in the speed equation [Eq. (38)] E_t is constant, and the term $I_a R_a$ is a minor one, being usually only a few per cent of E_t; therefore the speed equation states that if the flux ϕ is reduced the motor must speed up. That this is correct may be checked by noting that, since the armature resistance R_a is quite small, the motor must generate a voltage E_g nearly equal to the line voltage E_t in order to restrict I_a to its proper value; and therefore, if ϕ is reduced, the motor must turn faster in order to generate the required E_g. If it did not do so, the current I_a would be very large and create a large torque to make it do so.

132. Theory of Commutation Applied to Motors. The theory of commutation outlined in Chap. 14 was for illustration purposes applied only to generators, but it applies also to motors, with minor modifications as follows:

In the case of a motor the current is flowing in the opposite direction to the generated emf E_g, whereas in the generator the current is in the

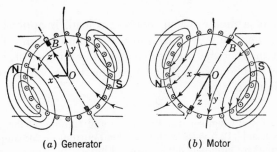

(a) Generator   (b) Motor

FIG. 104. Armature magnetic field in a generator and in a motor.

same direction as the generated emf. Therefore in a motor the current to be reversed in the coil, while that coil is short-circuited by a brush, is flowing in the opposite direction to that of the current in a generator, and consequently the emf required to force the reversal of the current should be in the opposite direction to that required for a generator. This means that the interpoles on a motor should have polarities opposite to those of the interpoles on a generator, or, if the motor has no interpoles, the brushes should be retarded to secure good commutation, whereas they should be advanced in the case of a generator.

It may be noted that, if a generator with interpoles is used as a motor, the polarities of the interpoles automatically reverse to the proper polarities, because their exciting coils are connected in series with the armature and their polarities therefore reverse when the armature current is reversed.

133. Armature Reaction in Generators and Motors. In Fig. 104, which shows a generator and a motor, respectively, with the brushes shifted so as to improve commutation, the distribution of magnetic flux due to the armature acting alone is as shown by the lines. The armature field acts in the direction oz and may be considered as the resultant of a cross-magnetizing component in the direction oy and of a demagnetizing component in the direction ox (see Art. 116), and, in the case of both the generator and the motor, the most important effects of the reaction of the armature field on that due to the exciting current in the field coils are that the demagnetizing effect reduces the flux per pole, while the cross-magnetizing effect causes the flux density to decrease under the pole tips toward which the brushes have been shifted, a condition which tends to cause poor commutation.

In order to provide the correct commutating field at all loads, without shifting the brushes, it is necessary to provide commutating poles. This is particularly necessary for adjustable-speed motors operating at high speeds, for under this condition the field is relatively weak and the armature magnetizing influence relatively more effective in producing flux distortion.

The speed of a motor, when carrying a load, is appreciably affected when the brushes are moved to improve commutation. This is due to the fact that moving the brushes changes the number of demagnetizing ampere-turns and consequently changes the flux ϕ, which appears in the speed equation [Eq. (38)].

Problems

17-1. A generator when separately excited and running at 900 rpm gives 120 volts at no load and 112.5 volts with a full-load current of 208 amp. The resistance of the armature circuit is 0.024 ohm. Find:

a. The voltage drop in the armature circuit.

b. The actual voltage generated at full load.

c. The cause of the loss of the 2.5 volts (120 − 117.5), which is no longer generated at full load.

d. If this machine, run as a motor with the same field current as before, is loaded so as to take an armature current of 208 amp from a 120-volt circuit, what is the back emf of the motor and at what speed does the machine run?

e. If this motor on no load takes such a small current that armature reaction can be neglected, what is the back emf at no load, the increase in magnetic flux over the full-load value, the no-load speed?

17-2. *a.* If a separately excited motor, which takes an armature current of 100 amp on full load from a 120-volt line, runs at 1,200 rpm both at no load and at full load, what is the back emf of the motor if the armature resistance is 0.05 ohm, and what is the reduction of flux at full load due to armature reaction?

b. If the same machine, run as a separately excited generator, has to deliver 100 amp at 120 volts, what will then be the voltage drop in the armature circuit, the actual voltage generated, the speed of the generator, and the voltage at no load?

*17-3. From a study of the formula for an induced emf in a motor

$$E_g = E_t - I_a R_a = k\phi \times \text{rpm}$$

Answer the following questions:

a. What effect will a change in ϕ or exciting current have upon the speed, brake torque remaining the same? Why? Could the speed of a motor be regulated by adjusting the field rheostat? Why?

b. In a noninterpole motor whose brushes are set for sparkless commutation, what will be the effect of armature reaction upon the speed? Why? (See Art. 133.)

*17-4. A d-c generator when separately excited and running at 1,000 rpm gives 250 volts at no load and 235 volts with a full-load current of 100 amp. The resistance of the armature circuit is 0.1 ohm.   Find:

   a. The voltage drop in the armature circuit at full load.

   b. The actual voltage generated at full load.

   c. The cause of the additional voltage drop.

   d. If this machine, run as a motor with the same field current, is loaded so as to take 100 amp from a 250-volt circuit, what is the back emf of the motor and at what speed does the machine run?

   e. If this motor on no load takes such a small current that armature reaction can be neglected, what are the back emf at no load, the increase in magnetic flux over the full-load value, the no-load speed?

17-5. If a separately excited motor, which takes an armature current of 100 amp on full load from a 250-volt line, runs at 1,200 rpm both at no load and at full load, what is the back emf of the motor if the armature resistance is 0.1 ohm, and what is the reduction of flux at full load due to armature reaction?   If this same machine, run as a separately excited generator, has to deliver 100 amp at 250 volts, what will then be the voltage drop in the armature circuit, the actual voltage generated, the speed of the generator, and the voltage at no load?

18

CHARACTERISTICS OF DIRECT-CURRENT MOTORS

Shunt-wound Motors

The shunt motor is so called because its field circuit is connected i shunt or parallel with the armature across the power mains, as show diagrammatically in Fig. 105. It is the same machine as the shur generator.

134. Starting Fractional-horsepower Shunt Motors. Very small shur motors may be started simply by closing switch S, Fig. 105. The fiel

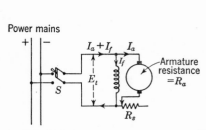

Power mains

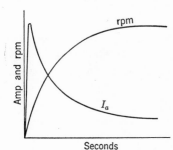

FIG. 105. Shunt-motor connections.

FIG. 106. Starting current when no startii resistance is used. (Fractional-horsepow shunt motor.)

current I_f very quickly rises to its full value, E_t/R_f (where R_f is th resistance of the field coils), and the magnetic flux ϕ grows with it. Th armature current I_a also rises very rapidly to the value given by th equation $I_a = (E_t - E_g)/R_a$, Art. 128, and, since $E_g = 0$ when the arma ture is stationary, the value of I_a at start is several times the normal ful load value. The torque developed, which is given by the equatio $T = K_t\phi I_a$, is therefore very large and the motor accelerates ver rapidly. As soon as the armature starts to rotate, it begins to genera an emf E_g which is proportional to the speed and which opposes the cu

146

rent I_a. Thus I_a drops rapidly as the motor speeds up, as shown in Fig.
106, and becomes constant when the speed becomes constant.

If the armature were prevented from rotating, the very large initial
starting current would continue to flow and would burn out the winding
in a few seconds. In practice, motors are generally protected by fuses
that will melt and open the circuit before the armature winding becomes
hot enough to burn the insulation.

135. General Method of Starting Shunt Motors. If large or medium-
sized shunt motors were started by simply switching them on to the line
as described in Art. 134, the initial rush of current would be so great owing
to the very low resistance of the
armature winding, and so prolonged
owing to the high moment of inertia of the rotating parts, that the
machine would be damaged by burning before it got up to speed. Moreover, the very large momentary current taken from the distribution
mains would be objectionable in
that it would pull down the voltage
of the system in the vicinity of the
starting motor and thus interfere
with the operation of other motors,
lamps, etc., connected to the system.

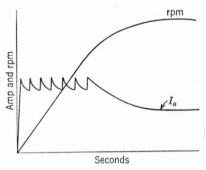

FIG. 107. Starting current when a starting
resistance is used.   Starting resistance R_s
cut out in six steps.

Therefore the excessive rush of current on starting must be prevented by
inserting an additional resistance R_s temporarily in the armature circuit
(Fig. 105). This resistance is cut out step by step as the motor comes
up to speed, with the result that the starting current is as shown in Fig.
107. The uniformity of the current peaks in Fig. 107 corresponds to an
ideal manipulation of the starting resistance and would rarely if ever be
obtained with manual control.

Shunt motors are generally provided with a field rheostat which is connected in series with the field circuit as in Fig. 109 and which is used to
weaken the flux for purposes of speed control. This rheostat should
always be set at zero when starting the motor, so as to obtain the maximum amount of starting torque per ampere of armature current. If the
shunt motor is connected to a mechanical load that is not easy to start,
and if an attempt is made to start the motor with the field rheostat set at
its maximum resistance, which is usually sufficient to reduce the flux to
one-quarter its maximum value, the armature current required to start
may be from four to six times full-load current, which would burn the
sliding contact of R_s and would probably burn out the resistance as well.
The commutator might also suffer some surface burning.

Example. A 10-hp 110-volt d-c shunt motor has an efficiency of 88 per cent, an exciting current of 2 amp, and an armature resistance of 0.08 ohm. Find (a) the starting resistance R_s required for full-load torque at start; (b) the starting current if no starting resistance were used.

a.

$$\text{Motor input} = \frac{\text{output}}{\text{efficiency}}$$

$$= \frac{10}{0.88} = 11.36 \text{ hp}$$

$$= 11.36 \times 746 = 8{,}477 \text{ watts}$$

$$\text{Current from mains} = \frac{\text{watts input}}{\text{applied voltage}}$$

$$= \frac{8{,}477}{110} = 77 \text{ amp}$$

$$\text{Armature current} = \text{total current} - \text{exciting current}$$
$$= 77 - 2 = 75 \text{ amp}$$

$$\text{Total resistance required at starting} = \frac{\text{applied voltage}}{\text{full-load armature current}}$$

$$= {}^{110}\!\!/_{75} = 1.47 \text{ ohms}$$

$$\text{Starting resistance } R_s = \text{total resistance} - R_a$$
$$= 1.47 - 0.08 = 1.39 \text{ ohms}$$

b. Starting current if no starting resistance is used $= \dfrac{\text{applied voltage}}{\text{armature resistance}}$

$$= \frac{110}{0.08} = 1{,}375 \text{ amp}$$

$$= 18.4 \text{ times full-load current}$$

136. Operating Characteristics. The characteristic curves of a motor show how the torque and the speed vary with the armature current, the applied voltage being constant. These curves may readily be determined from the formulas:

$$\text{Torque developed} = K_t \phi I_a,$$

$$\text{rpm} = \frac{(E_t - I_a R_a)}{k\phi} \qquad \text{(Art. 131)}$$

where E_t = applied voltage

$\quad I_a$ = armature current, amp

$\quad R_a$ = armature resistance, ohms

$\quad I_a R_a$ = armature-resistance drop, seldom exceeding 5 per cent of E_t when motor is carrying full load

$\quad \phi$ = flux per pole

$\quad k, K_t$ = constants

In the case of the shunt motor (see Fig. 108), the applied voltage E_t and the exciting current I_f are constant and so also is the flux per pole, the effect of armature reaction being neglected; then

$$\text{Torque developed} = K_t \phi I_a$$
$$= \text{a constant} \times I_a$$

which is the equation of a straight line through the origin.

$$\text{rpm} = \frac{E_t - I_a R_a}{k\phi}$$
$$= \text{a constant} \times (E_t - I_a R_a)$$

The curves corresponding to these equations are shown in Fig. 108.   The torque delivered to the mechanical load by the pulley is less than the

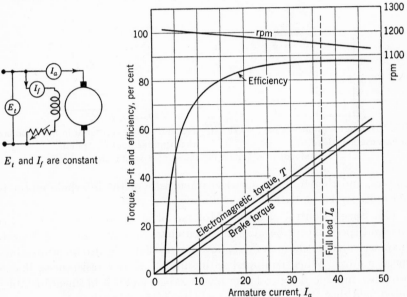

E_t and I_f are constant

FIG. 108. Characteristic curves of a shunt motor, 10 hp, 230 volts.

electromagnetic torque by the amount of the retarding torque caused by bearing friction, brush friction, iron loss, and the windage resistance. The drop in speed as the load increases is due to the fact that E_g must decrease in order to allow the additional current to flow.   The characteristic curves shown in Fig. 108 may be obtained experimentally by applying various measured brake torques and measuring the corresponding speed and armature current.

137. Effect of Armature Reaction on the Speed.   In the preceding article the effect of armature reaction was neglected and the flux ϕ was assumed constant.   With noninterpole motors, however, the brushes are shifted backward from the neutral so as to improve commutation, and this introduces a demagnetizing component of armature reaction which causes the flux per pole to decrease as the load increases (see Art. 133), so that the speed, being equal to $(E_t - I_a R_a)/k\phi$, drops only slightly from no load to full load, since the increase in the value of $I_a R_a$ is largely compensated for by the decrease in the value of ϕ.

With motors equipped with interpoles the brushes are on the neutral and there is no demagnetizing component of armature reaction. The cross-magnetizing component does tend to reduce the flux slightly, as explained in Art. 114, but, on the other hand, the series interpole winding opposes the cross-magnetizing component. The net result is that the total flux in the main poles is more nearly constant than in noninterpole

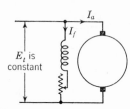

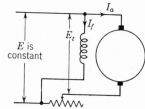

FIG. 109. Insert resistance in the field circuit to increase the speed.   FIG. 110. Insert resistance in the armature circuit to decrease the speed.

Methods of adjusting the speed of a shunt motor.

motors, and therefore the speed characteristic of the interpole motor is not quite so flat as that of the noninterpole motor.

138. Speed Control of Shunt Motors. The shunt motor is called a constant-speed motor because its speed changes only slightly with load. Its most valuable characteristic, however, is that it is also an adjustable-speed motor. When equipped with suitable control resistances, it can provide a fine speed control over a wide range, and it is in the adjustable-speed field that the shunt motor finds its chief application.

Adjustable-speed operation can best be investigated by means of the speed equation, rpm $= (E_t - I_a R_a)/k\phi$ (Art. 131). When the motor is connected to a constant-voltage line, as in Fig. 109, with E_t equal to the rated voltage of the motor and with the field rheostat set at zero resistance, it will run at a certain speed that is called the full-field or base speed. To obtain speeds higher than the full-field speed, ϕ, the flux per pole, may be reduced by inserting resistance in series with the field coils, as in Fig. 109. To obtain speeds lower than the full-field speed, the voltage E_t applied to the motor terminals must be decreased, which can most easily be done by inserting resistance in series with the armature, as shown in Fig. 110.

The two methods of speed control, when both are made available for the same motor, can provide a continuous speed range from zero up to the maximum speed for which the motor is designed. In the case of iotors without commutating poles, however, the maximum speed is mited to about 1.7 times full-field speed by the commutation becoming ad. This is due to the fact that decreasing ϕ weakens the flux at the ole tips, which are serving in the place of commutating poles.

139. Speed Variation of Shunt Motors by Field Control. Inserting esistance in the field circuit of a shunt motor, as in Fig. 109, decreases ie field current I_f and therefore also the flux ϕ; consequently, according o the speed equation, rpm $= (E_t - I_a R_a)/k\phi$, the motor must run aster.

While the formula shows that the speed increases when the flux ϕ s decreased, it is advisable to study more fully how this takes place. If he flux per pole is suddenly decreased, the back emf of the motor drops nd allows more current to flow in the armature. The increase in the rmature current is very much greater than the decrease in the flux, so hat the torque developed is greater than necessary for the load and the iotor accelerates. The following example illustrates this.

Example. A 10-hp 110-volt d-c shunt motor, undergoing a brake test, is run-ing at 900 rpm and is delivering 10 hp to the brake, while drawing an armature urrent of 75 amp from a 110-volt line. The resistance of its armature circuit is .08 ohm. Find:

a. The brake torque at full load.
b. The back emf at full load.
c. The electromagnetic driving torque at full load.

If the flux per pole is suddenly reduced 20 per cent by inserting resistance in he field circuit, find:

d. The back emf at the instant after the flux is changed.
e. The armature current at the same instant.
f. The electromagnetic driving torque at the same instant.
g. The final steady-state value of the armature current, assuming that the >rake torque is kept constant.

Answers:

a. The brake torque at full load is

$$\frac{\text{Horsepower} \times 33,000}{2\pi \times \text{rpm}} = \frac{10 \times 33,000}{2\pi \times 900} = 58.5 \text{ lb at 1 ft radius}$$

b. The back emf at full load is

$$E_g = E_t - I_a R_a$$
$$= 110 - (75 \times 0.08) = 104 \text{ volts}$$

c. The electric power converted into mechanical power is

$$E_g I_a = 104 \times 75 = 7,800 \text{ watts}$$
$$= \frac{7,800}{746} = 10.45 \text{ hp}$$

The driving torque is

$$\frac{10.45 \times 33,000}{2\pi \times 900} = 61.0 \text{ lb at 1 ft radius}$$

The difference between the driving torque and the brake torque is $61.0 - 58.5$ = 2.5 lb-ft, and this is equal to the retarding torque caused by friction, windage, and iron loss in the motor.

d. If the flux per pole is suddenly reduced 20 per cent the back voltage E_g is also reduced 20 per cent, because the speed has not had time to change appreciably. In general, electrical changes are much more rapid than mechanical changes. Therefore the new back voltage is

$$E_g = {}^{80}\!/_{100} \times 104 = 83.2 \text{ volts}$$

e. Then

$$I_a = \frac{E_t - E_g}{R_a} = \frac{110 - 83.2}{0.08}$$
$$= 335 \text{ amp}$$

or 4.46 times full-load current.

f. Then the driving torque (since it is proportional to the flux and to the armature current) is

$$61.0 \times {}^{80}\!/_{100} \times {}^{335}\!/_{75} = 218 \text{ lb-ft}$$

or 3.6 times full-load driving torque.

g. The electromagnetic driving troque momentarily available for acceleration is

$$218 - 61 = 157 \text{ lb-ft}$$

The motor therefore accelerates rapidly. As it does so, E_g increases, and therefore I_a and the driving torque decrease, thus decreasing the rate of acceleration. The acceleration decreases to zero as the decreasing driving torque approaches equality with the total retarding torque due to the brake, friction, windage, and iron loss.

Figure 111 shows these changes graphically. The armature current I_a does not jump instantaneously to its maximum value when the flux is

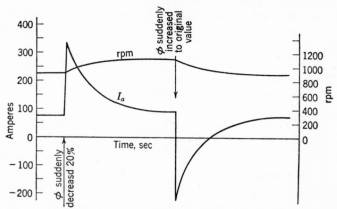

FIG. 111. Effect of field control on armature current and speed of a shunt motor, mechanical brake torque assumed constant.

suddenly changed, but does rise very rapidly compared with the relatively slow mechanical change of speed.

If the mechanical brake torque is kept constant, independent of the speed, then the final steady-state values of T, I_a, and rpm, after the change, may be determined as follows:

1. Since the brake torque is by hypothesis unchanged, the driving torque must have the same value as before the change, namely, 61.0 lb-ft.

2. Since $T = K_t \phi I_a$ and ϕ is reduced 20 per cent, the new steady-state I_a must be correspondingly larger so as to keep the product ϕI_a constant. Therefore

$$I_a = \frac{75}{0.8} = 93.7 \text{ amp}$$

3. The new steady-state $E_g = E_t - I_a R_a = 110 - (93.7 \times 0.08) = 102.5$ volts. The original steady-state E_g was 104 volts. Then since $E_g = k \times \text{rpm} \times \phi$, $\text{rpm} = E_g / k\phi$. Therefore the new steady-state speed is

$$900 \times \frac{102.5}{104} \times \frac{100}{80} = 1{,}110 \text{ rpm}$$

Figure 111 also shows what happens when the flux is suddenly increased again to its original value. E_g is suddenly increased to 128.2 volts.

$$I_a = \frac{110 - 128.2}{0.08} = -227 \text{ amp}$$

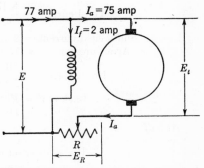

FIG. 112. Resistance inserted in the armature circuit causes the speed to decrease.

That is, since the back voltage is greater than the line voltage, the armature current is reversed, and the motor is momentarily operating as a generator feeding energy into the line. The driving torque is also reversed, and the machine slows down very quickly. As it does so its generated voltage E_g decreases and soon becomes less than E_t. Meanwhile I_a is decreasing to zero, reversing, and building up in the normal direction for a motor.

140. Speed Variation of Shunt Motors by Armature-resistance Control. The speed of a motor may be lowered by decreasing the voltage applied to its armature terminals. This may be done by connecting a resistance in the armature circuit as shown in Fig. 112.

The speed is given by the formula, $\text{rpm} = (E_t - I_a R_a)/k\phi$, where $I_a R_a$ seldom exceeds 5 per cent of E_t, so that, to obtain half speed, the applied voltage E_t must be reduced to about 50 per cent of normal, the other 50 per cent of the line voltage being absorbed by the resistance inserted in the circuit; under these conditions, the loss in the resistance, which is equal to $E_R I_a$, is about equal to the armature input $E_t I_a$, and the efficiency of the system is less than 50 per cent. The actual efficiency may b figured out as in the following example:

Example. A 10-hp 110-volt 900-rpm shunt motor has a full-load efficiency 88 per cent, an armature resistance of 0.08 ohm, and a shunt-field current 2 amp. If the speed of this motor is reduced to 450 rpm by inserting a resistanc in the armature circuit, the torque of the load being constant, find the motor ou put, the armature current, the external resistance, and the over-all efficiency.

At normal speed:

$$\text{Motor output} = 10 \text{ hp}$$

$$\text{Motor input} = \frac{10}{0.88} = 11.36 \text{ hp} = 8,477 \text{ watts}$$

$$\text{Total current} = \frac{8,477}{110} = 77 \text{ amp}$$

$$\text{Shunt-field current} = 2 \text{ amp}$$

$$\text{Armature current} = 75 \text{ amp}$$

$$\text{Brake torque} = \frac{10 \times 33,000}{2 \times \pi \times 900} = 58.5 \text{ lb at 1 ft radius}$$

$$\text{Back emf} = E_t - I_a R_a$$
$$= 110 - (75 \times 0.08) = 104 \text{ volts}$$

At half speed:

$$\text{Horsepower output} = \frac{\text{torque} \times 2\pi \text{ rpm}}{33,000}$$

Since the torque is assumed constant, the output is proportional to the speed an is equal to 5 hp.

The torque is equal to $K_t \phi I_a$, and, since the torque is constant and so also the excitation, therefore I_a, the armature current, is the same as at full speed an is equal to 75 amp.

The back emf E_g is generated in the armature owing to the cutting of lines c flux and is equal to a constant $\times \phi \times$ rpm and, since the flux is constant, there fore E_g is proportional to the speed and is equal to $0.5 \times 104 = 52$ volts.

$$\text{Voltage applied to armature} = E_g + I_a R_a$$
$$= 52 + (75 \times 0.08) = 58 \text{ volts}$$

$$\text{Voltage drop across external resistance} = 110 - 58 = 52 \text{ volts}$$

$$\text{Current in this resistance} = 75 \text{ amp}$$

$$\text{Resistance} = {}^{52}\!/_{75} = 0.7 \text{ ohm}$$

$$\text{Loss in resistance} = 52 \times 75 = 3,900 \text{ watts}$$

$$\text{Total input} = 110 \times (75 + 2) = 8,470 \text{ watts}$$

$$\text{Motor output} = 5 \text{ hp} = 5 \times \frac{746}{1,000} = 3.73 \text{ kw}$$

$$\text{Over-all efficiency} = \frac{3.73}{8.47} = 44 \text{ per cent}$$

Since the armature current and therefore the armature copper los have the same value at half speed as at full speed, the torque being con stant, the temperature rise will be the greater at the slow speed because of the poorer ventilation.

From the foregoing problem it may be seen that, when the speed of a motor is reduced by armature resistance, the output is decreased and is directly proportional to the speed, while the temperature rise, even with this reduced output, is greater than normal because of the poorer ventilation. The over-all efficiency also is exceedingly low, the percentage loss in the resistance being approximately equal to the percentage reduction in speed, that is, being 50 per cent of the total input at half speed and 75 per cent of the total input at quarter speed.

141. Speed Regulation of a Shunt Motor.   When the speed of a motor varies considerably with change of load, the speed regulation is said to be poor. When the speed is practically constant at all loads, the speed regulation is said to be good.

The speed regulation of a d-c motor is the change in speed when the load is reduced gradually from rated full load to zero, the line voltage and field rheostat setting being kept constant.

Suppose that the speed of a shunt motor has been adjusted by means of a resistance in the armature circuit, as shown in Fig. 112, so as to give a definite speed at a definite load, then, when the load is increased, the armature current I_a and the voltage E_R will increase and therefore the voltage E_t will decrease and the speed of the motor will drop; the speed regulation is therefore poor when armature-resistance control is used.

For example, in the problem of Art. 140, where the motor is running at half speed under armature-resistance control and is carrying full-load current, if the brake torque is doubled, the motor will stop, because at double the current the IR drop in the control resistance will equal the line voltage and E_g will have to drop to zero in order to allow this current to flow.

Again, if the brake load is removed entirely, the motor will speed up to generate a larger back voltage to reduce the armature current. An armature current of about 5 amp will provide sufficient torque to overcome friction and windage, and, when $I_a = 5$ amp, the IR drop in the control resistance will be only $5 \times 0.7 = 3.5$ volts, instead of the 52 volts that existed before the brake torque was removed. Thus the voltage applied to the armature will rise $52 - 3.5 = 48.5$ volts, and the speed will therefore nearly double.

When the speed of a shunt motor is adjusted by means of a resistance in the field-coil circuit, as in Fig. 109, the speed regulation is good. The speed is given by the formula rpm $= (E_t - I_a R_a)/k\phi$ so that, since E_t is constant, as also is the flux ϕ once the field-circuit resistance is adjusted, the drop in speed between no load and full load will seldom exceed 5 per cent, since $I_a R_a$ at full load seldom exceeds 5 per cent of E_t.

142. Armature-resistance Control versus Field Control. Field control of shunt motors gives definite speeds that are nearly independent of load, and all speed changes are made without any impairment of the efficiency of operation. On the other hand, it is limited to speeds above the base speed that is obtained with full field. Within its speed range it gives a control that is practically ideal.

Armature-resistance control is inferior to field control in that it reduces the efficiency of operation at the same rate that it reduces the speed. This severely limits its field of application and in general results in its being used only for short-time reductions in speed, except in the case of small motors where the amount of energy involved is not important.

Another point of inferiority of armature-resistance control is that no one setting of the rheostat corresponds to any definite speed, the speed being determined as much by the load as by the control resistance. This may or may not be an objection in a particular application. On the other hand armature-resistance control gives a speed range that field control cannot touch, namely, the range between zero speed and full-field speed, and therefore it is an important and valuable method of speed control.

The limitations of the armature-resistance method of speed control have resulted in the application of other methods of reducing E_t. These will be discussed in Chap. 20.

Series-wound Motors

143. Torque. The series motor is connected to the power mains as shown diagrammatically in Fig. 113. The applied voltage E_t is constant, while the field excitation increases with the load, since the load current I_a is also the field current.

The torque developed, being equal to $K_t \phi I_a$, increases directly with ϕ the flux pe pole and with I_a the armature current. Now ϕ increases with I_a, since that current is also the exciting current, and, if the magnetic circuit of the machine is not saturated, ϕ is directly proportional to I_a, and the torque is therefore proportional to $I_a{}^2$. In an actual motor, the flux per pole does not increase so rapidly as the exciting current, owing to saturation of the magnetic circuit, but varies with I_a as shown in Fig. 113. Using this flux curve and the torque equation, $T = K_t \phi I_a$, the electromagnetic torque has been determined and plotted in Fig. 113.

Full-load current in the machine produces the same flux per pole and therefore the same torque at starting as when the motor is running at full load and normal speed, or full-load torque is developed with full-load current. Since the flux increases with the current, twice full-load torque is developed with considerably less than twice full-load current. In Fig. 113 twice full-load torque is developed with 1.67 times full-load current. In the case of the shunt motor, the flux per pole is constant and the torque is directly proportional to I_a, so that twice full-load torque requires twice full-load current.   For heavy starting duty, therefore, the series motor is better than the shunt motor in that it requires less starting current from the line.

144. The Starting Resistance. As in the case of the shunt motor (see Art. 135), a starting resistance must be inserted in series with the armature, unless the motor is small, so as to limit the starting current.   This resistance is gradually decreased as the motor comes up to speed.

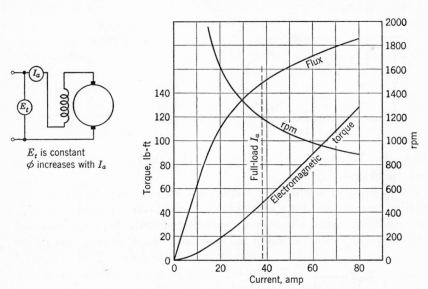

E_t is constant
ϕ increases with I_a

FIG. 113. Characteristic curves of a series motor, 10 hp, 230 volts.

145. Operating Characteristics. The characteristic curves of a series motor may readily be determined from the fundamental formulas:

$$\text{Torque} = K_t \phi I_a$$
$$\text{rpm} = \frac{E_t - I_a R_a}{k \phi}$$

where E_t = applied voltage

I_a = armature current, amp

R_a = combined resistance of armature and series-field coils

$I_a R_a$ = armature and series-field drop, seldom exceeding 7 per cent of E_t when motor is carrying full load

ϕ = flux per pole

K_t, k = constants

In the case of the series motor, the applied voltage E_t is constant, while the flux per pole varies with I_a, as shown in Fig. 113.   The curves of torque and speed on an armature current base are plotted in Fig. 113 in accordance with the foregoing torque and speed equations.

It is important to note that, as the load and therefore the armature current decrease, the flux per pole decreases and the machine must speed up to give the required back emf. At light loads the speed becomes dangerously high and for this reason a series motor should always be geared or direct-connected to the load. If a series motor were belted to

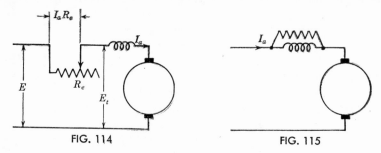

FIG. 114   FIG. 115

the load and the belt broke or slipped off, then the motor would run away and would probably burst.

Series motors are suited for crane work because they develop a large starting torque, slow down when a heavy weight is being lifted, and speed up with light loads. Crane motors are geared to the hoisting drum and are always under the control of the operator. Street-railway motors are generally series motors. Their powerful starting torque renders them peculiarly suitable for this service.

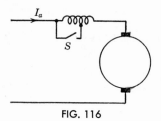

FIG. 116

146. Speed Adjustment. The speed of a series motor is proportional to $(E_t - I_a R_a)/\phi$, so that, for a given current I_a, the speed may be changed by altering E_t, the applied voltage, or ϕ, the flux per pole.

If a resistance R_e is inserted in series with the armature, as shown in Fig. 114, then the voltage applied at the motor terminals is reduced by $I_a R_e$ and the lower back emf required is obtained at a lower speed.

With constant applied voltage and a given armature current, the speed may be increased by decreasing the flux per pole. This may be done as shown in Fig. 115 by shunting the series field winding with a resistance, so that, of the total current I_a, only part is allowed to pass through the field winding. The flux per pole may also be reduced by short-circuiting part of the field winding as shown in Fig. 116; if the switch S is closed, the exciting ampere turns are reduced, and this causes a decrease in flux and consequently an increase in speed.

Compound Motors

147. Compound Motor. This motor is a compromise between the shunt and the series motor and is connected to the power mains as shown diagrammatically in Fig. 117. The applied voltage E_t is constant and so also is the shunt current I_f, but the current in the series-field coils increases with the load, so that the flux per pole increases with the load but not so rapidly as in the series motor.

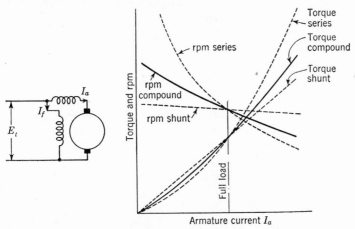

FIG. 117. Characteristic curves of a compound motor.

If a shunt and a compound motor have duplicate armatures and the same excitation at full load, then at this load they will develop the same torque and run at the same speed, since

$$\text{Torque} = K_t \phi I_a$$

$$\text{rpm} = \frac{E_t - I_a R_a}{k \phi}$$

For loads greater than full load, the flux per pole of the shunt motor is unchanged, while that of the compound motor is increased owing to the series-field coils. Therefore the compound motor has the greater torque but the lower speed. For loads less than full load, on the other hand, the flux per pole of the compound motor is less than that of the shunt motor owing to the decrease of the current in the series-field coils, so that the torque is less and the speed is greater than in the shunt machine.

The speed and torque characteristics of a compound motor, a series motor, and a shunt motor, all three designed to give the same full-load torque and speed, for purposes of comparison, are shown in Fig. 117. Unlike the series motor, the compound motor has a safe maximum speed at no load and so cannot run away on light loads. The speed of a compound motor may be decreased below normal by means of a resistance inserted in the armature circuit, and increased above normal by means of a resistance in the field-coil circuit.

Compound motors are suitable for driving such machines as rock crushers, which may have to be started up full of rock, because they develop the large starting torque with a smaller current than the shunt motor, while they drop in speed as the load comes on and thereby allow a flywheel connected to the shaft to take the peak of the load. They are also used for elevators and to some extent for streetcars, and wherever it is desired to combine the characteristics of a series motor with a safe maximum speed. Fractional-horsepower motors that are started by switching them directly onto the line are usually given a little compounding to ensure a quick start.

Large shunt motors operating at high speeds are subject to large fluctuations in armature current as the line voltage fluctuates, especially if the loads that they are driving have high moments of inertia. A sudden drop in line voltage may easily cause the armature current to drop to zero or even to become negative momentarily. Equally violent surges of armature current are caused by sudden increases in line voltage. These fluctuations can be greatly reduced by adding a small amount of series field. A shunt motor that has been slightly compounded in order to stabilize the power demand is generally referred to as a *stabilized shunt motor*.

148. Differential Compound Motors. If the connections to the series-field coils of a compound motor are interchanged so as to reverse the direction of flow of the current through the coils, then the series coils will oppose the flux, and the flux will decrease instead of increasing with increasing load. This will cause the motor to speed up instead of slowing down with increasing load. That is, the slope of the speed curve is reversed. Such a motor is unstable near full load. An increase of load causes the motor to begin slowing down, which reduces E_g and allows extra armature current to flow. This extra current develops additional torque but it also reduces the flux and E_g and allows still more current to flow, which still further reduces the flux. The process is cumulative and very rapid. Within a few seconds the motor is turning at a very high speed and drawing an enormous current, and if there were no protective devices in the line it would either burn up or fly to pieces. In connecting up compound motors, care should be taken to avoid the differential connection.

There have been a few applications of differential compound motors with weak compounding, designed to give the same speed at full load as at no load.

Problems

18-1. *a.* The armature of a d-c shunt motor when delivering full load takes 50 amp from a 125-volt supply line. When the armature is held stationary, only 6 volts are required to send full-load current through the armature. Explain.

b. How much current would the armature take if full-line voltage were impressed across the brushes at starting?

c. How much resistance must be inserted in series with the armature in order to limit the starting current to 1.5 times the full-load current?

d. What is the value of starting torque with normal field and 1.5 times normal full-load current?

e. What is the value of counter emf developed when this motor is operating at full load?

18-2. A d-c shunt motor connected to a 220-volt line runs at 1,500 rpm at no load and at 1,475 rpm at full load of 90 amp. The resistance of the armature is 0.08 ohm.

a. What is the counter emf of motor at full load?

b. What is the percentage reduction in flux at full load due to armature reaction?

c. What will be the speed and the voltage actually generated in the armature when this machine, running as a separately excited generator, with the same field current is delivering full-load current of 90 amp at a terminal emf of 220 volts?

d. What will be the terminal emf at no load, the speed being as found in *c*?

18-3. A 30-hp 120-volt 900-rpm shunt motor has an efficiency of 88 per cent at full load. The voltage drop in the armature circuit is 4 per cent and the exciting current is 1.4 per cent of the full-load current.

a. Find the full-load current in the line, the armature current, and the resistance of the armature circuit.

b. Find the torque developed at the driving pulley at full load.

c. Specify the starting resistance to keep the starting current down to 1.25 times full-load current. What will be the starting torque under these conditions?

d. Would this same starting resistance be suitable for all 120-volt 30-hp shunt motors, no matter of what speed? Give reasons.

e. Specify the starting resistance for a 10 hp 120-volt shunt motor to give 1.25 times full-load torque.

f. What would happen if the 30-hp starter were used for the 10-hp motor and the 10-hp starter for the 30-hp motor?

18-4. A 30-hp 120-volt 900-rpm series motor has an efficiency of 88 per cent at full load. The voltage drop in the armature is 4 per cent and in the exciting coils is 1.5 per cent.

a. Find the full-load current in the line, the armature current, the resistance of the armature and that of the field coils.

b. Find the torque developed at the pulley at full load.

c. Specify the starting resistance to keep the starting current down to 1.25 times full-load current. What will be approximately the starting torque under these conditions?

*18-5. If the shunt motor of Prob. 18-3 is connected as shown in Fig. 133 and is protected by suitable fuses, what will happen:

a. If the starting arm is moved over too rapidly?

b. If the field-coil circuit is open and an attempt is made to start the motor?

c. If the field-coil circuit breaks while the motor is running on no load?

d. If the starter has a no-field release as in Fig. 134 and the field-coil circuit then breaks while the motor is running on no load?

e. If there is an instantaneous overload of 100 per cent?

f. If there is an overload of 50 per cent for some time?

g. If the torque of the load is increased 50 per cent, what is approximately the current taken from the line, also the speed of the motor and the output?

*18-6. If the series motor of Prob. 18-4 is connected up with a suitable starting resistance, is protected by fuses, and belted to the load, what will happen:

a. If the field-coil circuit is open and an attempt is made to start the motor?

b. If the field coils are short-circuited and an attempt is made to start the motor?

c. If the field-coil circuit breaks while the motor is running?

d. If the belt breaks?

e. If the torque of the load is increased 50 per cent, what is approximately the current taken from the line, also the speed of the motor and the output?

f. If the hp load on the motor is increased 50 per cent, what is approximately the current taken from the line, the torque developed, and the speed in terms of the values at full load?

18-7. A 30-hp 120-volt 900-rpm shunt motor is operating at rated load, speed, and voltage. $I_a = 209$ amp; $R_a = 0.023$ ohm. A resistance of 0.05 ohm is inserted suddenly in the armature circuit. Assuming that the torque of the load remains constant, find:

a. The back emf at normal load and speed.

b. The armature current immediately after the resistance has been inserted.

c. The torque developed at the same instant.

d. Explain why the speed drops. What happens while conditions are becoming steady?

e. What is the final speed of the motor?

*18-8. Draw a diagram of connections for a shunt motor which runs at 1,000 rpm under a certain prony-brake load. What will be the effect upon the operation of the motor (speed, commutation, etc.) under the following conditions:

a. If field terminals are reversed?

b. If line wires are reversed?

c. If brushes are shifted against direction of rotation?

d. If they are shifted forward?

e. If a resistance is inserted in field circuit? In the armature circuit? In the line?

f. If the armature is removed and the field bored out so that the air gap is lengthened and the armature is then inserted?

g. If the air gap is decreased by "shimming" up the poles?

h. If the armature is rewound with a fewer number of turns of larger wire?

i. If it is rewound with a larger number of turns of smaller wire?

j. If some of the field turns are short-circuited?

k. If field is rewound with the same number of turns of wire of twice the cross section?

l. If there should be no residual magnetism in the field poles?

*18-9. A 30-hp 240-volt 900 rpm shunt motor has an efficiency of 88 per cent at full load. The voltage drop in the armature circuit is 4 per cent, and the exciting current is 1.4 per cent of the full-load current.

a. Find the full-load current in the line, the armature current, the resistance of the armature circuit.

b. Find the torque developed at the driving pulley at full load.

c. Specify the starting resistance to keep the starting current down to 1.25 times full-load current; what will be the starting torque under these conditions?

d. Would this same starting resistance be suitable for a 120-volt 30-hp shunt motor?

e. Specify the starting resistance for a 10-hp 240-volt shunt motor to give 1.25 times full-load torque.

f. What would happen if the 30-hp starter were used for the 10-hp motor and the 10-hp starter for the 30-hp motor? The motors are protected by fuses and it is necessary to develop the full-load torque of the motor at starting.

*18-10. A 30-hp 240-volt 900-rpm series motor has an efficiency of 88 per cent at full load. The voltage drop in the armature is 4 per cent, and in the exciting coils is 1.5 per cent.

a. Find the full-load current in the line, the armature current, the resistance of the armature and that of the field coils.

b. Find the torque developed at the pulley at full load.

c. Specify the starting resistance to keep the starting current down to 1.25 times full-load current. What will be approximately the starting torque under these conditions?

*18-11. If the shunt motor of Prob. 18-9 is carrying full load and a resistance of 0.5 ohm is inserted suddenly in the armature circuit, the torque of the load remaining constant, find:

a. The back emf at normal load and speed.

b. The armature current immediately after the resistance has been inserted.

c. The torque developed at the same instant in percentage of full-load torque.

d. Explain why the speed drops, also what happens while conditions are becoming steady.

e. What is the final speed of the motor?

*18-12. If, on the other hand, the exciting current is reduced suddenly so as to reduce the flux suddenly to 80 per cent of normal value, find:

a. The armature current immediately after the flux has been changed.

b. The torque at the same instant.

c. Explain in detail what happens while conditions are becoming steady, also what is the final speed, the horsepower being kept constant.

d. Why should the field rheostat be moved slowly when increasing the speed? Is it as important to move it slowly when the field is being strengthened?

18-13. A shunt motor is to be rewound as a series motor to give the same full-load speed and torque. The data on the shunt machine are as follows: 40 hp, four poles, 120 volts, full-load armature current 275 amp, shunt-field current, 5 amp, shunt field has 900 turns per pole.

a. Find the number of turns for the series field.

b. Give, briefly, the technical reasons for the differences in the characteristic curves caused by the change in method of excitation.

18-14. The saturation-curve data for a 220-volt 10-hp shunt motor, running at 1,000 rpm, are as follows:

Volts	6	80	120	160	200	240	280
Field amp	0	0.17	0.26	0.375	0.52	0.735	1.09

R_a = 0.2 ohm, including brushes. No-load I_a = 3 amp.

a. The motor is running at rated speed and voltage and is carrying no load. The resistance of the field circuit is suddenly increased 20 per cent. Trace out step by step the sequence of events until everything becomes constant again. Sketch curves showing the changes in current, driving torque, and speed, on a time base to scale as far as possible. (The time cannot be to scale since the moment of inertia of the armature is not given.)

b. The motor is running at rated speed and voltage and is carrying no load. The resistance of the field circuit is suddenly decreased 20 per cent. Trace out step by step the sequence of events and illustrate by sketching curves as in part (*a*).

18-15. The shunt motor of Prob. 18-14 is running at rated speed and voltage and is carrying no load. Calculate the change in speed for a 20 per cent drop in line voltage.

18-16. A d-c series motor is drawing 40 amp from a 220-volt line and is running at 1,000 rpm. Assuming that the brake torque is kept constant, calculate the change in speed for a 20 per cent drop in line voltage. $R_a = 0.25$ ohm, including brushes and series field.

19

LOSSES, EFFICIENCY, AND HEATING

149. Mechanical Losses in Electric Machinery. In order to keep the armature of an electric machine rotating, power is required to overcome the windage or air friction, the bearing friction, and the friction of the brushes on the commutator. This power is not available for useful work and is called the mechanical power loss in the machine.

In a given machine this loss increases with the speed, but at a given speed it is practically independent of the load.

150. Copper Losses. If R_a is the resistance of the armature circuit, including the armature winding and the series-field and commutating-pole coils, then, to force a current I_a through this circuit, a voltage equal to $I_a R_a$ is required. This armature circuit drop at full load seldom exceeds 5 per cent of E_t, the terminal voltage.

The power expended in overcoming this voltage drop is equal to $I_a{}^2 R_a$ watts and, since this power is not usefully employed, it is called the copper loss in the armature circuit.

In addition to the $I_a{}^2 R_a$ loss in the copper part of the armature circuit, there is a loss due to the resistance of the brush contacts. This resistance is often included as part of R_a, but better accuracy is obtained by keeping it separate because it varies widely. It is approximately inversely proportional to I_a, so that the voltage drop at the brush contact is almost independent of the current. It is usually about 1 volt at each brush, or 2 volts for the circuit. The brush-contact loss is equal to $2E_d I_a$ watts, where E_d is the voltage drop at one brush contact.

If, again, R_f is the resistance of the shunt-field coil circuit, Fig. 118, and I_f is the shunt current, then the power expended in exciting the machine is equal to $I_f{}^2 R_f$ watts, where I_f, which is equal to E_t/R_f, seldom exceeds 3 per cent of the current in the armature of the machine.

151. Hysteresis Loss. Figure 119 shows an armature that is rotating in a two-pole magnetic field. If we consider a small block of iron ab, then, when it is under the N pole as shown, lines of force pass through it from a to b; half a revolution later the same piece of iron is under the

S pole and the lines of force then pass through it from *b* to *a* so that the magnetism in the iron is reversed.   To reverse continuously the molecular magnets of the armature iron, an amount of power is required which is called the hysteresis loss in the machine (see Art. 71).   It would be expected that the hysteresis loss would be directly proportional to the number of reversals per second, that is, to the speed, and it has been found experimentally that the variation of hysteresis loss with changes

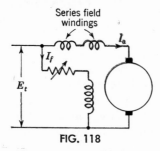

Series field
windings

FIG. 118

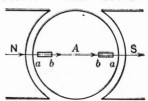

FIG. 119. Reversal of flux in the armature core as the armature rotates.

in speed and flux density may be expressed with sufficient accuracy by the equation

$$\text{Hysteresis loss} = K_h \times \text{rpm} \times B^{1.6} \tag{39}$$

where B is the maximum flux density in the cycle and K_h is a constant.

152. Eddy-current Loss.   As the armature A, Fig. 119, rotates, emfs are induced in the iron, and, if the armature were made of a solid block of iron, large eddy currents would circulate in it (see Art. 100).   The power required to maintain these currents is called the eddy-current loss in the armature and is kept down to a very small percentage of the rated power of the machine by building the armature iron up out of thin laminations of varnished sheet steel.   The eddy-current loss is directly proportional to the square of the speed and to the square of the flux density. This would be expected from theoretical considerations, because doubling either the speed or the flux density doubles the voltage generated in the iron and consequently doubles the eddy currents, and the eddy-current loss is quadrupled because it is a summation of I^2R losses in the iron. Therefore we may write

$$\text{Eddy-current loss} = K_e \times (\text{rpm})^2 \times B^2 \tag{40}$$

The iron losses are independent of the load except in so far as the load may affect the maximum flux density B.   Armature reaction crowds the flux toward the pole tips, thus increasing the maximum flux density, although the average flux density is somewhat decreased.   It is common practice, however, to ignore the increase in iron loss caused by armature reaction.

153. Total Loss.   The total power loss in a d-c machine consists of:

Mechanical losses $\begin{cases} \text{Windage} \\ \text{Bearing friction} \\ \text{Brush friction} \end{cases}$

Iron losses . . . . . . $\begin{cases} \text{Hysteresis loss} \\ \text{Eddy-current loss} \end{cases}$

Copper losses. . . . $\begin{cases} I_a{}^2 R_a \text{ (armature, commutating field, and series-field} \\ \quad \text{loss and brush-contact loss)} \\ I_f{}^2 R_f \text{ (shunt-field loss)} \end{cases}$

In the special case of generators and motors that are operating at constant voltage and constant speed, the only power loss that varies with the load is the $I_a{}^2 R_a$ loss.   All the other losses are considered to be constant, independent of load variations.

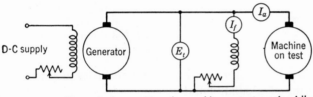

FIG. 120. Measurement of losses in d-c machine, the machine on test running idle as a motor.

The mechanical and iron losses at any given speed and terminal voltage can readily be measured by running the machine idle as a motor at that speed and voltage.   Figure 120 shows the connections for such a test.   A generator or other source of controlled direct-current voltage is required.   The field of the generator is adjusted to give the desired value of E_t.   The field of the machine on test is then adjusted to give the machine the desired speed.   The machine is then running as a motor but, since it is not belted or otherwise coupled to any mechanical load, its output is zero.   Therefore the electric-power input, which is equal to $E_t I_f + E_t I_a$ watts, is all loss. $E_t I_f$ is the shunt-field copper loss; therefore $E_t I_a$ includes all the other losses, and therefore the mechanical and iron losses together are equal to $E_t I_a - I_a{}^2 R_a$ watts. R_a can readily be measured with the armature stationary by the voltmeter-ammeter method (Art. 48).   If R_a is measured with the machine cold, it should be corrected to the normal operating temperature.

Since the machine is running idle, I_a is quite small and the $I_a{}^2 R_a$ term may be neglected without appreciable error, as may be seen from part (b) of the following example:

Example. A 50-kw 120-volt 900-rpm shunt generator has an armature resistance of 0.008 ohm, not including the brush contacts. At full load the contact voltage drop at each brush is one volt.

a. Calculate the voltage E_t at which it must be run idle as a motor, in order that the flux density may be the same as when it is running as a generator delivering 50 kw at 120 volts, the speed being 900 rpm in both cases.

$$\text{Full-load current} = \frac{50,000}{120} = 417 \text{ amp}$$

In the generator at full load

$$E_g = E_t + I_a R_a + 2 \text{ volts}$$
$$= 120 + (417 \times 0.008) + 2 = 125.3 \text{ volts}$$

When running idle as a motor the armature current is so small that the difference between E_g and E_t may be ignored. Therefore if we make E_t equal to 125.3 volts, when driving the machine idle as a motor at 900 rpm, the flux will be approximately correct, and so will the iron loss.

b. On test it is found that when $E_t = 125.3$ volts, and the speed has been adjusted to 900 rpm by means of the field rheostat, the machine running as a motor with no brake load, then $I_a = 20$ amp. Find the mechanical and iron losses.

$$\text{Armature input at no load} = 125.3 \times 20 = 2,506 \text{ watts}$$
$$\text{Mechanical and iron losses} = 2,506 - I_a{}^2 R_a$$
$$= 2,506 - (20^2 \times 0.008)$$
$$= 2,506 - 3.2 = 2,503 \text{ watts}$$

Another method of measuring the power losses in a machine is to drive it by means of a small shunt motor. The machines are connected as shown in Fig. 121. To measure the mechanical losses alone, the machine

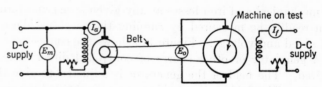

FIG. 121. Measurement of losses in a d-c machine, the machine on test being driven by a small motor of known efficiency.

on test is left unexcited. The field current of the motor is adjusted until the machine on test is being driven at the desired speed. Let E_2 and I_2 be the input voltage and current to the armature of the motor for this condition, as read by the voltmeter E_m and the ammeter I_a. The belt is then removed. Let E_1 and I_1 be the input voltage and current for this condition, the speed being the same as before. Then $E_2 I_2 - E_1 I_1$ is the increase in power input to the motor as the result of the belt being put on, and all this increase in power goes out on the belt except for a small increase in the armature copper loss in the motor, which may be corrected for as follows: Let R_m be the resistance of the armature circuit of the motor, including brushes.   Then

$$\text{Power input to belt} = E_2I_2 - E_1I_1 - (I_2{}^2 - I_1{}^2)R_m \qquad (41)$$

and this is equal to the mechanical losses of the machine on test, ignoring the power loss in the belt. E_2 and E_1 should be approximately equal, so that the iron loss in the motor will not change appreciably.

If the foregoing test is repeated, but with the machine on test excited to give the desired value of E_g, Eq. (41) will give the combined mechanical and iron losses for that value of E_g, and since the mechanical losses are already known, the iron losses are obtained by subtraction.

154. Efficiency of a Machine

$$\textbf{True efficiency} \text{ of a machine } = \frac{\text{power output}}{\text{power input}}$$

In the case of small motors it is easy to measure the power output by means of a prony brake, and the power input by means of electric instruments, and thus the true efficiency is readily obtained.   In the case of large motors it is usually practically impossible to measure the power output, and in the case of generators it is usually practically impossible to measure the power input.   Therefore **conventional efficiencies** are much more widely used than true efficiencies.

$$\text{Conventional efficiency of a generator} = \frac{\text{power output}}{\text{power output} + \text{losses}}$$

$$\text{Conventional efficiency of a motor} = \frac{\text{power input} - \text{losses}}{\text{power input}}$$

The conventional efficiency is always a little higher than the true efficiency because the conditions under which the losses are measured are slightly more favorable to the machine than are the normal operating conditions.   In particular the conventional efficiency ignores the fact that the iron loss actually increases slightly with increase of load, due to the distortion of the flux by armature reaction.   Also there are eddy-current losses in the copper that are not included in the computed conventional efficiency.   These additional losses are called the stray load losses and are difficult to determine.   It has been agreed that in computing conventional efficiencies for d-c machines the stray load losses at any kilowatt load shall be taken as being 1 per cent of that load.   This statement does not apply to machines small enough for the convenient measuring of true efficiencies.[1]

[1] See Standards of the American Institute of Electrical Engineers.

Example. Draw the conventional efficiency curve for a d-c flat-compounded generator, rated 1,000 kw, 600 volts, given the following data:

R_a = resistance of armature and series field windings
= 0.006 ohm at normal operating temperatures

$$\text{Output current at full load} = \frac{1,000,000}{600} = 1,666 \text{ amp}$$

E_g at full load = $600 + (1,666 \times 0.006) + 2 = 612$ volts
Mechanical and iron losses at rated speed = 24 kw, with E_g at 612 volts.
I_f = shunt-field current to make E_g equal to 600 volts at no load and rated speed
= 12 amp

Computations

At full load:

$$I_a = \text{output current plus } I_f = 1,678 \text{ amp}$$

$$\text{Mechanical and iron losses} = 24.0 \text{ kw}$$
$$\text{Shunt-field loss} = E_t I_f = 600 \times 12 = 7.2 \text{ kw}$$
$$I_a{}^2 R_a \text{ loss} = 1,678^2 \times 0.006 = 16.9 \text{ kw}$$
$$\text{Brush-contact loss} = 2 \times 1,678 = 3.36 \text{ kw}$$
$$\text{Stray load losses} = 1\% \text{ of } 1,000 = 10.0 \text{ kw}$$
$$\text{Total power losses} = 61.5 \text{ kw}$$
$$\text{Generator output} = 1,000 \text{ kw}$$
$$\text{Generator input} = 1,061.5 \text{ kw}$$
$$\text{Full-load efficiency} = 94.2 \text{ per cent}$$

At half load:

$$I_a = \frac{1,666}{2} + I_f = 833 + 12 = 845 \text{ amp}$$

$$\text{Mechanical and iron losses} = 24.0 \text{ kw}$$
$$\text{Shunt-field loss} = E_t I_f = 600 \times 12 = 7.2 \text{ kw}$$
$$I_a{}^2 R_a \text{ loss} = 845^2 \times 0.006 = 4.28 \text{ kw}$$
$$\text{Brush-contact loss} = 2 \times 845 = 1.69 \text{ kw}$$
$$\text{Stray load losses} = 1\% \text{ of } 500 = 5.0 \text{ kw}$$
$$\text{Total power losses} = 42.17 \text{ kw}$$
$$\text{Generator output} = 500 \text{ kw}$$
$$\text{Generator input} = 542.2 \text{ kw}$$
$$\text{Half-load efficiency} = 92.2 \text{ per cent}$$

Other values are worked out in a similar way and the results plotted as in Fig. 122.

Approximate values for the full-load efficiency of standard generators and motors are:

Full load, kilowatts	Full-load efficiency, per cent
1	80
5	83
25	88
100	91
500	94
1,000	95

The reader may find it interesting to prove for himself that in the case of a generator or motor operating at constant voltage and constant speed the efficiency is a maximum at that particular load at which the variable losses are equal to the fixed losses. In order to prove this, it is necessary to include the brush-contact resistance in R_a, and then to assume that R_a is constant.

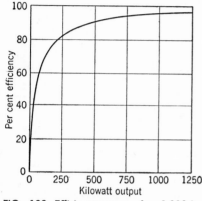

FIG. 122. Efficiency curve of a 1,000-kw 600-volt d-c generator.

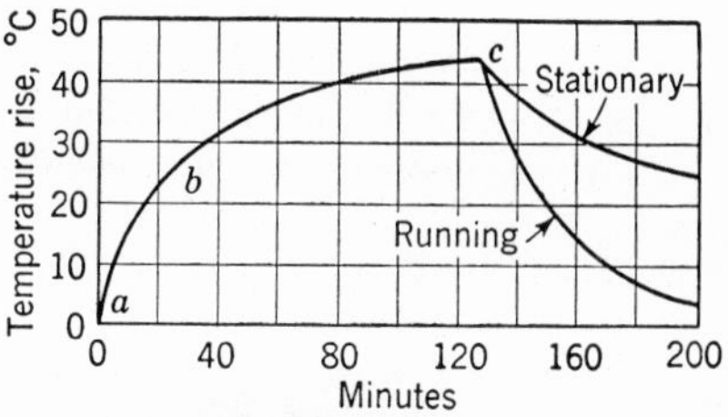

FIG. 123. Heating curves of armature windings of electric machines.

155. Heating of Electric Machinery. The losses in an electric machine are transformed into heat, which causes the temperature of the machine to rise above that of the surrounding air. The temperature becomes stationary when the rate at which heat is generated is equal to the rate at which it is dissipated. The rate at which heat is generated depends upon the magnitude of the losses.

The rate at which heat is dissipated depends on the difference between the temperature of the machine and that of the surrounding air. At first after starting under load this temperature difference is small, very little heat is dissipated, and the temperature rises rapidly, as shown in Fig. 123. As the temperature increases, more of the heat is dissipated and the temperature rises more slowly as from b to c. The ultimate temperature rise evidently depends upon the magnitude of the losses. In the case of the armature the principal loss is the $I_a{}^2 R_a$ loss and therefore the ultimate temperature rise depends upon the magnitude of the load. In fact, in practice the magnitude of the load that the machine can carry continuously is limited only by the permissible temperature rise. If the load is now taken off the machine, the $I_a{}^2 R_a$ loss is removed and the temperature will drop rapidly at first and then more slowly, as shown in Fig. 123, the temperature drop being more rapid when the machine is rotating than when stationary because of the better ventilation and the better convection of heat.

156. Permissible Temperatures. Insulating materials lose their mechanical and dielectric strengths at high temperatures; for example, cotton becomes brittle at temperatures greater than 95°C and begins to char at slightly higher temperatures, so that, when cotton is used to insulate machines, 90°C is set as the highest allowable temperature.

The following table gives the highest temperatures at which various types of insulation may be operated without being damaged.

Classification of Insulating Materials

Class	Description	Limiting safe hottest-spot temperature, °C
0.........	Cotton, silk, paper, and similar materials when neither impregnated nor immersed in oil	90
A.........	Impregnated cotton, silk, paper, etc., and enamel coatings on conductors	105
B.........	Mica, glass, asbestos, and other inorganic materials, in built-up form combined with an organic binder	125
C.........	Mica, glass, asbestos, with silicone binder	175

157. Limits of Output of Electric Machines. As stated above, the magnitude of the constant load which an electric machine can carry continuously is limited only by the temperature at which the machine can operate without damage to its insulation. But since it takes a considerable time for a machine to attain its final temperature (see Fig. 123), it follows that, as far as temperature is concerned, electric machines can carry momentary loads greatly in excess of the allowable continuous loads.

In the case of noninterpole machines the magnitude of the possible momentary load is limited by sparking at the commutator. With interpole machines the magnitude of the possible momentary load is greater than with noninterpole machines, but the commutating poles usually begin to saturate as the overload rises much above 50 per cent, and at 100 per cent overload there will generally be sparking at the commutator, unless the commutating poles have been specially designed for such overloads.

Permissible speed variation, in the case of motors, and permissible voltage variation, in the case of generators, may also be limiting factors.

158. Rating of Electric Machines. *a. Continuous Rating.* The constant load that an electric machine can carry continuously without its temperature exceeding the safe limit depends upon the temperature of the surrounding air.   For example, a motor insulated with impregnated cotton that could carry 10 hp continuously when placed in a room temperature of 40°C, without its hottest-spot temperature exceeding 105°C, could carry approximately 12.7 hp continuously with the same hottest-spot temperature if placed in a room temperature of 0°C.   However, for the sake of convenience it is desirable to assign a definite horsepower rating to a given motor, or a kilowatt rating to a generator.   It has accordingly been decided[1] that the rating of a machine shall be based upon the load that it could safely carry if placed in a room temperature of 40°C, and the allowable temperature rise for rating purposes for any machine is therefore computed by subtracting 40°C from the limiting safe hottest-spot temperature corresponding to the type of insulation involved.

The tests to determine temperature rises on given machines are actually carried out at any room temperature that happens to be convenient, the assumption being made that the temperature rise is independent of the room temperature.

b. Short-time Rating.   A continuous rating is not very satisfactory when applied to a motor that operates for only a few minutes at a time. For example, the continuous rating of a totally enclosed motor is only about 60 per cent of its rating when not enclosed; yet the load which it could carry for a 5-min period without overheating would be about the same whether the motor were enclosed or not, because it would be determined chiefly by the heat storage capacity of the motor.   Consequently, various short-time ratings have been standardized and are applied to motors that are to be operated intermittently.

The short-time rating of an electric machine is the maximum constant load that the machine can carry, starting cold, for the specified time interval without its temperature rise exceeding the standard limit.   As the specified time interval is reduced, the rating increases.   For example, the 1 hr rating of an electric locomotive is usually about 30 per cent greater than the continuous rating for the same locomotive, the temperature rise being the same for both ratings.

159. Measurement of Temperature Rise.   The three most usual methods of measuring temperature rise are (1) by thermometer, (2) by measuring the increase of resistance of the conductors, and (3) by means of embedded temperature detectors.

1. Thermometers are applied to the hottest accessible parts of the machine, the bulbs being covered by small felt pads.   The temperatures of rotating armatures and commutators can be measured only when the machine is stopped.   The highest temperature read on any thermometer is called the observed temperature, and the hottest-spot temperature is taken as being equal to the observed temperature plus 15°C.

[1] See Standards of the American Institute of Electrical Engineers.

2. The measurement of the increase of temperature by measuring the increase of resistance of the conductors is generally applied only to field windings. The resistance is first measured at the known room temperature before starting the machine and is again measured after operation. The rise of temperature is calculated by means of Eq. (8), Art. 42. This gives the *average* rise of temperature of the conductor, but the inner layers of the field winding are at a higher temperature than the outer layers, since the heat must flow outward, and thus the hottest-spot temperature rise is taken as being equal to the average temperature rise plus 10°C.

3. Embedded temperature detectors are used very extensively for the measurement of temperatures in large a-c generators with stationary armatures. Thermocouples, or resistance temperature detectors, are located in the slots as nearly as possible at the estimated hottest spots and are connected directly to indicating and recording instruments. They are used not only in the acceptance test of the machine but also throughout the life of the machine to guide the operator so that he will not damage the machine by overheating it. It is customary to add 5°C to the temperatures indicated by embedded detectors to allow for the probability that none of the detectors are located at what is actually the hottest spot.

The foregoing additions of 15°, 10°, and 5°C are not treated as corrections in practice; that is, they are not applied on the test floor. Instead the engineer applies them in writing his specifications. For example, if he is writing the specification for a machine to be insulated with class A insulation, and intends to use thermometers for measuring the temperature rise, he subtracts the standard room temperature of 40°C from the limiting temperature of 105°C, and then subtracts the allowance of 15°C, and specifies that the temperature rise as measured by thermometer shall not exceed 50°C.

Problems

19-1. The following data were obtained by means of a brake test on a 10-hp 120-volt 900-rpm shunt motor:

Applied voltage	Exciting current	Armature current	Speed, rpm	Torque, lb at 1 ft
120	2	3.5	920	0.0
120	2	19.0	915	14.2
120	2	35.0	910	28.7
120	2	52.0	905	43.0
120	2	69.0	900	58.0 (full load)
120	2	87.0	895	73.0

Plot torque and speed on an armature-current base. Plot efficiency on a horsepower-output base.

19-2. The same machine was supplied with series-field coils instead of shunt-field coils and the test data obtained were as follows:

Applied voltage	Armature current	Speed, rpm	Torque, lb at 1 ft
120	37	1,550	17.6
120	54	1,150	34.8
120	71	900	58.0 (full load)
120	89	780	83.0

Plot torque and speed on an armature-current base. Plot efficiency on a horsepower-output base.

19-3. From the test data in Prob. 19-1 find the mechanical and iron losses at 920 rpm and the resistance of the field-coil circuit.

19-4. The resistance of the armature circuit is 0.094 ohm. Calculate the efficiency of this shunt motor from the losses up to 25 per cent overload and compare the figures with those of the test curve.

19-5. The 10-hp 120-volt 900-rpm shunt motor in Prob. 19-1 has an efficiency of 87 per cent, and the resistance of the armature circuit is 0.094 ohm.

a. If the speed is reduced to 450 rpm by means of a resistance in the armature circuit, the torque being constant at full-load value, what are the value of the resistance, the loss in the resistance, the output of the motor, and the over-all efficiency?

b. Why does the motor run hotter than on normal load?

c. If the torque is reduced to half-full-load value, the external resistance being unchanged, what is the approximate speed of the motor?

19-6. If the armature of the 10-hp motor in Prob. 19-5 is rewound with twice the original number of turns, the wire being of half the original cross section, what will be the speed on full load, the permissible armature current, and the permissible output? Explain why this motor with 5 hp load will be hotter than the original machine with 10-hp load.

*19-7. A shunt motor was bought to drive a fan at 1,200 rpm. Owing to a mistake in the pulley sizes the fan speed was 1,350 rpm. Why did the motor spark and run hot?

19-8. A shunt-wound pump motor takes 30 amp at 240 volts. When tested at the factory the no-load current was 2 amp in the armature and 1 amp in the field-coil circuit, while the armature resistance was 0.4 ohm. What is the power supplied to the pump?

19-9. When a 100-kw generator is running at 450 rpm and generating 125 volts, the eddy-current loss is 400 watts and the hysteresis loss 600 watts. What will these losses be at (*a*) 80 volts, 450 rpm; (*b*) 125 volts, 600 rpm?

19-10. A series motor runs at 600 rpm at full load and has an eddy-current iron loss of 200 watts and a hysteresis loss of 300 watts. If the brake torque is reduced until the speed is doubled, what will then be the magnitude of these losses?

20

DIRECT-CURRENT-MOTOR APPLICATIONS

160. Field of Application of Direct-current Motors. In order to understand the nature and extent of the field of application of d-c motors, it is necessary to realize that the major extensive electric-power systems of the world are at present all alternating current.[1] The reasons for this will be developed later on in the book.

Since the electrical energy is delivered to the customer's locality in the a-c form, it follows that, if d-c motors are to be used, apparatus must be installed to convert the alternating current into direct current, and consequently it is cheaper to use a-c motors wherever the load is such that satisfactory service can be given by them. It follows therefore that d-c motors are in the main used only where the service which they give is sufficiently superior to that obtained from any a-c motor at present developed to justify the additional expense of installing the apparatus to convert from alternating to direct current. Even so, it is estimated that about one-third of all the motors used in the industries of the United States are direct current.

One should not, however, jump to the conclusion that d-c motors are inherently superior to a-c motors. There are many types of constant-speed service for which a-c motors are superior to d-c motors. It is in adjustable- and variable-speed operation that the d-c motors show their superiority, and for the more exacting types of service this superiority is sufficiently great to warrant the installation of aparatus for conversion of alternating into direct current.

161. Open, Semi-enclosed, and Totally Enclosed Motors. The power output that a motor can carry continuously is limited by the safe temperature rise. Any improvement in the cooling system increases the power rating of the motor. The cooling of a motor depends largely on

---

[1] An alternating current is one that flows back and forth in the conductor in a manner similar to the motion of the piston of a reciprocating steam engine or gasoline motor.

he circulation of air through the core and windings, so that the frame should be as open as possible.

If chips and flying particles are liable to get into the windings, the openings in the frame should be covered with perforated sheet metal; the motor is then said to be semi-enclosed. This screen throttles the air supply on which the cooling of the machine largely depends, so that, in order to keep down the temperature rise, the output of a motor has to be lower when semi-enclosed than when of the open type.

When a motor has to be totally enclosed, as for open-air service, the output of the machine has to be considerably reduced so as to keep the temperature down to a safe value.

A 10-hp 230-volt 600-rpm motor with 40°C rise on full load as an open machine can be used to deliver 9 hp when semi-enclosed and about 3 hp when totally enclosed at the same voltage and speed and with the same rise in temperature.

162. Effect of Speed on the Cost of a Motor. For a given horsepower output, a high-speed motor is always cheaper than a slow-speed motor; thus, for example, the following table gives the weights and costs corresponding to various rated speeds, for a 10-hp 230-volt shunt motor.

Rated speed, rpm	Weight, lb	Cost
1,800	500	$ 430
1,200	600	$ 520
600	1,000	$ 820
300	1,500	$1,140

The reason for this is as follows: If a given motor frame is supplied with two armatures, one of which, A, has half as many conductors as B but the conductors have twice the cross section and can therefore carry twice the current, then, when run at the same voltage, armature A with half the conductors must run at twice the speed of B to give the same back emf, but, since armature A can carry twice the current of B, it can therefore deliver twice the output. Thus the armature of a 10-hp 600-rpm motor could be rewound to deliver 20 hp at 1,200 rpm, 15 hp at 900 rpm, or 5 hp at 300 rpm and these armatures would all have approximately the same weight and cost.

It follows that standard motors are all high speed. Low-speed motors are used where it is desired to drive low-speed machines by direct-connected motors without the use of reduction gears or belts and pulleys. Low-speed or medium-speed motors are also used sometimes in preference to high-speed motors for services where noiseless operation is particularly desirable.

163. Classification of Adjustable-speed Shunt-motor Applications. The field of application of adjustable-speed shunt motors may be classified as follows: (1) constant horsepower, (2) constant torque, (3) torque decreasing with speed.

164. Constant-horsepower Adjustable-speed Shunt-motor Applications. In this field the power required from the motor is independent of the speed, and therefore the torque required is inversely proportional to the speed. Lathes and boring mills, for example, require constant horsepower at all speeds of the machine spindle if the cutting speed is to be the same for all diameters of the work. With this type of load the motor must be large enough to develop the full horsepower at the lowest speed.

Let us assume that the specified speed range is 300 to 1,200 rpm, and that 10 hp is required at all speeds. This speed range can be obtained by field control from a direct-coupled adjustable-speed shunt motor, rated 10 hp 300 rpm, and the motor will be fully loaded at all speeds. Note that a shunt motor, operating with field control only, cannot carry any more power at high speeds than at low speed because, in order to double the speed, the flux must be reduced by one-half and this reduces the torque per ampere of armature current by one-half; double the speed at half the torque gives the same power as before.

In the foregoing application a saving of $710 can be made in the cost of the motor if it is feasible to use gears, or coned pulleys, to effect the major portion of the speed control, this being the difference in cost between an 1,800- and a 300-rpm motor. From this saving must, of course, be subtracted the cost of the gears or belts and pulleys. In the case of lathes and boring mills it is always feasible to use gears or coned pulleys, but in many other applications the relatively slow and clumsy speed control that they provide would be unsatisfactory compared with the smooth, continuous, and almost instantaneous response obtained with field control.

165. Constant-torque Adjustable-speed Shunt-motor Applications. In this field the torque required is the same at all speeds, and therefore the horsepower is proportional to the speed.

Armature-voltage control, in which the applied armature voltage E_t is varied while the field current is kept constant, results in the maximum allowable power being proportional to the speed and is therefore ideally suited to this type of load. Unfortunately there is no inexpensive way of varying E_t except by inserting resistance in the armature circuit, and this results in low efficiency at low speeds and also in poor speed regulation. However, if the reduced-speed operations are infrequent, or of short duration, armature-resistance control may be quite satisfactory. Otherwise field control must be used, although this will require a more expensive motor.

To illustrate, let us assume that the specified speed range is 300 to 1,200 rpm and that 10 hp is required at the high speed. The power required at 300 rpm is then only 2.5 hp, but, if field control is to be used, a 10-hp 300-rpm motor will be required. If, on the other hand, armature-voltage control is used, the motor will be 10 hp 1,200 rpm, which will mean a saving of $620 as compared with the cost of the 300-rpm motor.

166. Torque Decreasing with Speed, Shunt-motor Applications. Fans and centrifugal pumps are good examples of this type of load. The only practical difference between this type of application and the constant-torque type discussed in the preceding article is that, if armature-resistance control is used, the control rheostat must have a higher total resistance in order to obtain the low speeds with the smaller armature currents. Manufacturers have a special line of armature-resistance control rheostats for this particular field.

167. Combined Armature-resistance and Field Control of Shunt Motors. When the range of speed control normally required is, say, from 1,200 to 1,800 rpm, but it is also necessary to be able to reduce the speed to lower values for short periods of time, for example, while making adjustments on the driven machinery, the motor is provided with both armature resistance and field control. This makes it possible to install a 1,200-rpm motor, whereas if field control alone were used it would be necessary to install an expensive low-speed motor.

168. Multiple-voltage Systems. When a large number of adjustable-speed motors are in operation in a machine shop, the three-wire system

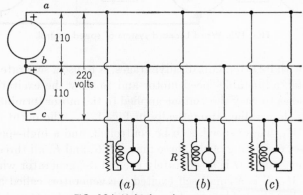

FIG. 124. Multiple-voltage system.

shown diagrammatically in Fig. 124 has been used to some extent. Two generators in the powerhouse are connected in series and three leads a, b, and c are taken to each adjustable-speed motor, the voltage between a and c being 220 and between a and b and also between b and c being 110 volts. To obtain the lowest speed from a motor operating on this

system, the field coils are connected across the 220-volt mains so as to
give the maximum flux while the armature is connected across either of
the 110-volt circuits as shown at a, Fig. 124.   The speed may then be
gradually increased by inserting resistance R in the field-coil circuit as
shown at b.   When the speed has been doubled in this way, the armature
is then connected across the 220-volt mains with all the resistance R cut
out of the field-coil circuit, and the speed may again be gradually increased
by once more reducing the field excitation by means of the resistance R
as shown at c.   By this means, a total speed range of 4 to 1 may be
obtained without the magnetic flux being reduced at any time to less than
half its normal value, and the efficiency is high over the whole range of
speed because no resistance is inserted in the armature circuit at any
time.

169. Ward Leonard System of Speed Control.   One very effective
method of obtaining a wide speed range, without the use of armature

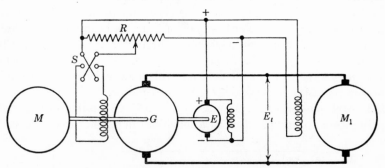

FIG. 125. Ward Leonard system of speed control.

resistance with its attendant disadvantages, is to use a separate generator
to drive each adjustable-speed motor and to vary the excitation of the
generator so as to vary the voltage applied to the motor terminals.   Such
a system is shown diagrammatically in Fig. 125.   The outfit consists of
the motor M_1, whose speed is to be controlled, and a high-speed motor-
generator set consisting of the three units M, G, and E, all three mounted
on the same shaft. G is a separately excited d-c generator which drives
the motor M_1, E is a small self-excited d-c generator, called an exciter
which supplies the field current for both the generator G and the motor
M_1, and M is the motor which drives the generators G and E.   In practice M is usually a constant-speed a-c motor, although sometimes it is a
diesel engine, or a d-c motor if the power supply happens to be direct
current, in which case the exciter E may be omitted and the field currents obtained from the line.

The motor-generator set runs at approximately constant speed, being driven by a constant-speed motor, and therefore the voltage generated by the exciter E, the field currents, the voltage E_t, and the speed of the motor M_1 are all constants as long as no change is made in the adjustment of the rheostat R. The speed of the motor M_1 can, however, be adjusted to any value from zero to a maximum in either direction by means of the potentiometer rheostat R and the double-throw reversing switch S. Each position of the slider on the rheostat gives a definite speed on the motor M_1 and the speed changes almost as rapidly as the contact is moved. That is, the response is almost instantaneous. For example, in one application of this type of speed control, a 100-hp motor, driving a shear for cutting sheet steel, accelerates to its full speed of 450 rpm, makes the cut, and stops, all in less than 1 sec. Even the 2,000- to 7,000-hp motors used to drive reversing steel rolling mills are reversed from full speed in one direction to full speed in the opposite direction in from 3 to 7 sec by this method.

When the sliding contact of the rheostat R is at the extreme right, the motor M_1 is running at full speed. All that it is necessary to do in order to reverse the motor is to slide the moving contact of R to the extreme left, throw over the reversing switch S, and then move the sliding contact back to the right again.

The reason for the very rapid response of the motor speed to any change in the rheostat setting is best understood by considering the armature-current equation, $I_a = (E_t - E_g)/R_a$. Now R_a is small, and in normal operation E_t and E_g are nearly equal, consequently if E_t is suddenly doubled by sliding the rheostat contact to the right, I_a becomes very large, and the driving torque $(K\phi I_a)$ also becomes very large and the motor accelerates very rapidly. Similarly if E_t is suddenly cut in half by sliding the rheostat contact to the left, I_a reverses and a very large negative driving torque results. Consequently, the motor slows down very rapidly until E_g is again smaller than E_t. During this momentary period of reversed I_a, the motor M_1 is actually functioning as a generator and is converting its rotational kinetic energy into electrical energy. The generator G becomes a motor and drives the motor M, causing it to become a generator, and so the rotational kinetic energy of the motor M_1 is fed back into the power supply.

170. Applications of the Ward Leonard System of Speed Control. This type of speed control has a high capital cost, because three machines are required to do the work of one. Motor M converts the electrical energy received from the line (not shown) into mechanical energy, which is transmitted by the shaft to the generator G. This generator converts the mechanical energy back into electrical energy and the motor M_1 converts it back into mechanical energy again. Moreover, each machine wastes from 5 to 8 per cent of the energy in the process. However, there are many applications of motor drives in which the quality of the service is of supreme importance and the cost is a relatively unimportant factor.

The Ward Leonard system of speed control, with various minor modifications, is very extensively used. The chief applications are to be found in steel mills for reversing rolling mills, seamless tube mills, and shears, for high- and medium-speed elevators in tall buildings, for mine hoists, and for paper machine drives. The electric locomotives of the Great Northern Railway operate on the Ward Leonard system, and so do electric shovels and car dumpers. The delicate speed adjustment necessary for operating gun turrets is sometimes obtained by means of the Ward Leonard system, and there are numerous other applications.

171. Regenerative Action of the Ward Leonard System. One important feature of the Ward Leonard system is its regenerative operation. For example, when a locomotive equipped with the Ward Leonard system is descending the side of a mountain, it tends to speed up under the force of gravity, and thus increases the speed of the motor M_1 until its generated emf E_g is greater than E_t. The current I_a circulating through G and M_1 is accordingly reversed. M_1 therefore runs as a generator and drives G as a motor, which in turn speeds up the motor M, causing it to become a generator and to feed electrical energy back into the trolley wire. Not only is a considerable amount of energy salvaged in this way but the braking action is greatly superior, in smoothness, power, and safety, to that obtained with any type of friction brake.

An elevator descending with a heavy load or ascending with a very light load (less than the counterbalancing weight) also feeds electrical energy back into the power system. Similarly the kinetic energy stored in the rotating and moving parts of a reversing mill is partially salvaged when the system is brought to rest, as pointed out in Art. 169.

In the case of diesel-electric trains, the motor M in Fig. 125 is a diesel engine, and it is therefore impossible to obtain regenerative braking. Also the motors M_1 are series motors. Smooth and powerful electric braking is obtained, however, by operating the motors M_1 as separately excited generators and connecting load resistors across their terminals.

172. Use of Flywheel with Ward Leonard System. If the violent fluctuations of power demand that result from many of the applications of the Ward Leonard system are likely to be objectionable, that is, if they are likely to cause large fluctuations in the voltage of the power system and so interfere with the operation of other equipment connected to the same system, a flywheel is mounted on the shaft of the motor-generator set, and the motor M must then be of a type that has a drooping speed characteristic in order to allow the flywheel to store and release energy. Whether a flywheel is necessary or not depends upon the relative sizes of the power system and the motor-generator set. Of course, only load peaks of very short duration can be smoothed out with a flywheel.

173. Recent Modifications of the Ward Leonard System. The control rheostat R in Fig. 125 is shown as a sliding-contact type of rheostat, which is suitable for low-powered sets, but which has not been applied to high-powered sets because of burning at the contacts. In order to avoid this burning it has been common practice to use contactor switches of the type shown in Fig. 131 to vary the resistance. About 20 contactor switches are required for a high-powered set. These contactor switches are expensive and noisy, and require a lot of maintenance. They can be eliminated if two exciters are provided instead of one. One of these exciters is then a self-excited constant-voltage exciter, and it provides the field current for the main motor M_1 and for the second exciter. The second exciter provides the excitation for the main generator G. The control rheostat controls the field current of the second exciter instead of the field current of the main generator. In this way the power to be handled by the rheostat is greatly reduced, so that contactor switches are not required. The substitution of the second exciter for the contactor switches is a recent development, and this second exciter is of special

design. The exciter built by the General Electric Company for this type of service is called an amplidyne and is described in Arts. 198 and 199. The application of the amplidyne to Ward Leonard speed control is shown in Fig. 163.

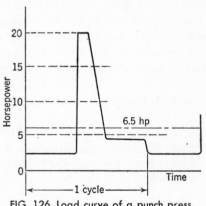

FIG. 126. Load curve of a punch press.

174. Shears and Punch Presses. The load curve of a punch press is shown in Fig. 126. In order that the peak load may be carried by the motor without sparking, a motor of about 15 hp would be required, which is much greater than the average load of 6.5 hp. To take the peak load off the motor, a flywheel is generally supplied with the press, and, in order that the flywheel may be effective, the speed of the motor must drop as the load comes on.

A shunt motor is not suitable for such service as it does not drop sufficiently in speed and so does not allow the flywheel to take the load.

A series motor cannot be used because it would run away when the clutch of the press was released and would probably cause the flywheel to burst.

The motor generally used on large presses, if direct current is available, is compound excited. This motor drops in speed as the load comes on and thereby allows the flywheel to give up energy, while the maximum speed at no load cannot exceed a safe value.

A drooping speed characteristic may be obtained from a shunt motor by connecting a resistance permanently in series with the armature as shown in Fig. 127, the resistance having such a value that the voltage drop e_r at full load is about 5 per cent of E. When the load on the motor increases, the voltage drop across the resistance increases, that applied to

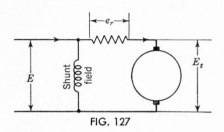

FIG. 127

the motor terminals decreases, and the speed of the motor drops. When the load on the motor decreases, the voltage across the motor increases, the speed rises, and energy is again stored in the flywheel. The resistance in the power mains supplying the motor may sometimes be sufficient to produce this effect. The only objection to the method is that an amount of power equal to $e_r I_a$ watts is lost in the control resistance.

175. Gear Motors. Many machines, such as conveyers, elevators, mixers, ball mills, rotary screens, stokers, crushers, punch presses, etc., operate at low shaft speeds. Since low-speed motors are expensive, it is standard practice to insert reducing gears, or belts and pulleys, between the motor and the load when low shaft speeds are required. Manufacturers of electric motors now build an extensive line of gear motors, in which the motor and the reducing gears are assembled as a single unit. Speeds as low as 4.4 rpm are available in standard designs.

Problems

*20-1. What limits the output of a d-c motor?

*20-2. Specify the type of motor to be used for the following installations, giving reasons for your choice:

(a) Lathe   (e) Railway car
(b) Mine hoist   (f) Punch press
(c) Concrete mixer   (g) Express elevator
(d) Steel rolling mill   (h) Reciprocating pump

*20-3. Does the speed of a shunt motor vary appreciably when the line voltage is increased or decreased?

20-4. If the voltage of a plant is changed permanently from 120 to 240 volts, what change is necessary on both the shunt and the series motors so that their characteristics may not be changed?

20-5. The data for the magnetization curve of a 30-hp 120-volt 900-rpm motor are given in Prob. 16-2; plot the curve.

  a. Specify the additional field resistance required to obtain an increase in speed of 50 per cent at no load.

b. If the voltage applied to this motor is only 100 volts due to excessive line resistance, what will be the magnetic flux as a fraction of its normal value?

c. What will then be the speed of the motor and the current required for a load of 30 hp? Why is the temperature rise greater than normal?

d. Show that, if the voltage applied to a shunt motor is reduced, the starting torque for a given current is reduced, but that in the case of a series motor it is unchanged.

e. When started cold, the foregoing motor runs at 900 rpm. At the end of 3 hr the average temperature rise of the field coils is 40°C. How much is the exciting current reduced and what is now the speed of the motor?

*20-6. Why is it that, when the speed of a noninterpole 50-hp motor is doubled by field weakening, sparking occurs at less than 50-hp, whereas in the case of an interpole motor the speed may be increased to three times the normal value without sparking, the load being 50 hp?

21

DIRECT-CURRENT-MOTOR STARTERS AND CONTROLLERS

176. Switches. If a switch is opened in a circuit carrying current, an arc is formed across the gap between the opening contacts. If the current is small and the voltage and self-induction in the circuit are low, this arc is a mere spark that is extinguished before the contacts are more

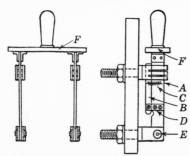

FIG. 128. Quick-break type of knife switch.

than a small fraction of an inch apart. A knife switch, such as that shown in Fig. 128, is suitable for opening such a circuit. The life of the switch will be lengthened if it is provided with a quick-break attachment.

The quick-break switch shown in Fig. 128 has a main contact blade A and an auxiliary contact blade B held together by the spring C. When this switch is opened, the blade B is retained by friction until A has been withdrawn, the spring C then pulls out the blade B so quickly that no appreciable arc is formed. This quick-break principle in different forms is largely used when circuits carrying current have to be opened.

177. Auxiliary Carbon Contacts. In the switch shown in Fig. 129, the main contact blocks a and b are bridged by an arch c of leaf copper, and an auxiliary carbon contact d is in parallel with the contact a. When this switch is opened, the contact a is the first to be broken, but the circuit is not interrupted, since current can still pass through the contact d. This latter contact is broken when the switch opens farther, and an arc is formed which burns the carbon tips. Since these tips volatilize without melting, they remain in fairly good shape and, when badly burned, can readily be replaced; the carbon contacts have the additional advantage that by their means a comparatively high resistance is inserted in the circuit and the current is reduced before the circuit is broken.   The tripping mechanism of a circuit breaker was explained in Art. 81.

Circuit breakers of this type are in general use for currents up to 16,000 amp and voltages up to 1,500 volts.

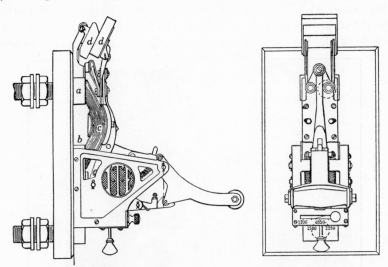

FIG. 129. Circuit breaker with auxiliary carbon contacts.

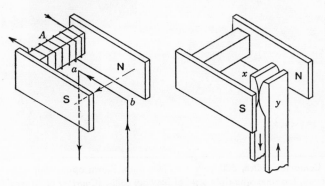

FIG. 130. Principle of the blowout coil.

178. Blowout Coils.   If the conductor ab, Fig. 130, is carrying current and is in the magnetic field NS, it is acted on by a force that tends to move it upward.   If ab is an arc formed between two contacts x and y as they are separated, this arc will be forced upward and will lengthen and break. The coil A, which produces the magnetic field, is called the magnetic blowout coil.

The application of this principle to a contactor switch is shown in Fig. 131.   The contactor switch is closed against the opposition of the steel spring by the magnetic pull exerted on the armature by the iron-cored operating coil. This coil is energized by a separate control circuit that goes back to a push button or master switch. The contactor remains closed so long as the current in the operating coil is maintained, but springs open when this current is interrupted. As the switch contacts separate an arc forms between them, which is blown rapidly upward by the field of the blowout coil, transfers to the arcing horns, and continues

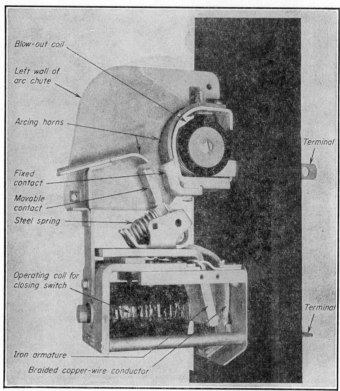

FIG. 131. Contactor switch, 600 volts d-c, 300 amp, shown open, with right wall of arc chute removed, together with right pole of blowout coil. (*Courtesy of General Electric Co.*)

to rise until it breaks, the arc life being of the order of 0.01 sec. The blowout coil is in series with the switch contacts, so that it is the current that is to be interrupted that produces the magnetic field to blow out the arc. This switch does not open automatically on overloads unless provided with a separate overload relay to open the control circuit to the operating coil.

179. Thermal Overload Relay. A thermal overload relay consists of two parts: (1) a small switch that is normally held either open or closed against the force of a spring by means of a catch and (2) a thermal device for tripping the catch. This thermal device is usually a bimetallic strip which is heated by current passing directly through the strip or by a heater coil surrounding the strip. The bimetallic strip consists of two thin layers of different metals welded together. The metals are chosen to have quite different temperature coefficients of expansion, and, since the strip is firmly fixed at one end, the other end deflects as the temperature rises. The heater coil is in series with the circuit that is to be protected and is therefore designed to have a low resistance. It is provided with a shunt if the current is large.

Such a device will not operate on momentary overloads, such as occur during the starting of a motor, but will operate if the overload persists long enough to heat up the bimetallic strip to the tripping point.

The magnetically operated contactor switch of Fig. 131 can be made to give automatic overload protection if one inserts the contacts of a thermal overload relay in the circuit of the operating coil and connects its heater coil in series with the main circuit.

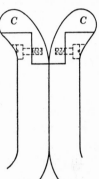

FIG. 132. Removable horn tips for contactor switches.

180. Horn Gaps. The intense heat of an arc causes convection currents of air to flow upward so that, if the switch jaws are shaped as shown in Fig. 132, the arc stream will be blown upward and will finally break between the arcing tips C, which may be removable.

This effect may be exaggerated by enclosing the contact in an arc chute of such shape that the gases, expanding suddenly, can pass out only through the switch contacts. Such arc chutes, as, for example, that in Fig. 131, when combined with magnetic blowout coils, are very effective.

181. Fuses. A fuse is a piece of metal inserted in a circuit that is intended to melt and open the circuit before excessive currents have had time to damage the remainder of the circuit by overheating.

The melting or blowing of a fuse is accompanied by an arc and by spattering of the fused metal, so that it is generally advisable to mount the fuse in the center of a fiber tube. Sometimes the tube is then filled with oil or a fireproof powder to quench the arc. A fuse has heat storage capacity and, as far as protection from excessive current is concerned, combines the functions of the thermal overload relay and the magnetic contactor switch. Fuses are available for currents up to 600 amp at voltages up to 600 volts and for currents up to 300 amp at voltages up to 34,500 volts and also for smaller currents at voltages up to 132,000. The higher voltages are alternating current only.

182. Protection from Overloads and Short Circuits. Electric circuits and machines must be protected from overloads and short circuits, and this is accomplished by automatically disconnecting the circuit or machine from the line when such conditions occur.

An overload in general can injure a cable or machine only by overheating it to a temperature that will damage the insulation, and, since all materials have heat storage capacity, it follows that moderate momentary overloads do no damage.   Therefore the protective equipment should not operate on such overloads.   On the other hand, short circuits or other faults begin doing damage immediately and very rapidly. Therefore they should be disconnected as quickly as possible.

The circuit breaker with instantaneous overload trip provides the most rapid and dependable protection against short circuits and is used in many important installations.   Fuses are much cheaper and are used extensively for the protection of the smaller and less important installations.

The best protection against overloads is given by thermal overload relays controlling automatic switches, such as circuit breakers or magnetic contactor switches.   If magnetic switches are required in any case for the normal operation of the motor, this method of protection is not expensive.

In the case of small low-voltage motors fuses are often the only protection provided.   They respond too quickly to momentary overloads, and this often means that they must have current ratings too high to provide adequate protection against moderate continuous overloads.

Circuit breakers are often provided with an inverse-time-limit attachment.   This is simply an adjustable dashpot that delays the movement of the tripping mechanism.   The length of the delay is approximately inversely proportional to the current through the trip coil, so that the breaker responds slowly to moderate overloads but opens quickly on heavy short circuits.   The delay feature makes it possible to obtain selectivity in the operation of circuit breakers that are in series on the same system.   By adjusting the time delays, the breaker that is nearest to the fault is made to open first.   This removes the fault, and therefore the other breakers do not open at all.   In this way the interruption is localized.

183. Motor Starters for Shunt and Compound Motors.   The function of a motor starter is primarily to limit the armature current when starting, so as neither to damage the motor nor unnecessarily disturb the power system.   The total resistance of the starter usually limits the starting current to from 1.0 to 1.5 times full-load current, and this resistance is cut out step by step as the motor comes up to speed.   The armature current resulting from an ideal manipulation of the starter is shown in Fig. 107.

A starter that may be used to perform the operations described above is shown diagrammatically in Fig. 133.   When the arm A, which is made of metal, is moved clockwise onto the first stud, by means of an insulated handle, not shown, the field coils are fully excited, while the armature and the whole starting resistance are put in series across the line. As the arm is gradually moved over to the final stud, the starting resistance is gradually cut out of the armature circuit, but the current I_f in the field coils remains practically unchanged, since the starting resistance R_s is small compared with R_f, the resistance of the field coils.

The starting arm must not be moved over too rapidly or the starting resistance will be cut out before the speed and therefore the back emf will have time to increase and limit the current. The arm, however, must not be left on one of the intermediate studs because, in order to keep down the cost of the starting resistance, it is made small and will not carry full-load current, without injurious heating, for more than about 15 sec.

184. No-voltage Release. Suppose that a motor is running at normal speed and that the power supply is interrupted owing to some trouble in the powerhouse or in the line; the motor will stop. If the power supply is now reestablished, with the starting arm still in the running position, there will be no starting resistance in series with the armature to limit the current.

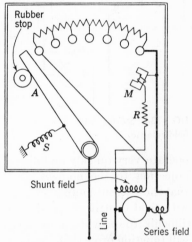

FIG. 133. Starter with no-voltage release, for a shunt or compound motor.

To take care of such a contingency, the starter is usually provided with a no-voltage release, as shown at M, Fig. 133. The starting arm is moved from the starting to the running position against the tension of the spring S and is held in the running position by the electromagnet M. If the power supply is now interrupted, the motor will slow down and stop. The exciting current does not drop to zero as soon as the power supply is interrupted, because the voltage E_g generated by the motor is across the field circuit. That is, the motor has automatically become a self-excited generator with no prime mover to drive it. As it slows down, its voltage decreases and consequently its field current also decreases, which causes a further decrease in voltage. At about half speed the magnet M becomes too weak to hold the arm against the pull of the spring, and the arm is pulled back to the starting position. The resistance R may be omitted if the line voltage is low enough to make it feasible to design the coil of M for full-line voltage.

Another method of exciting the magnet M is to connect it in series with the field coils of the motor, as shown in Fig. 134.   When connected in this way, it not only acts as a no-voltage release but also protects the motor against the hazard of a break in the field circuit.

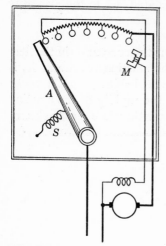

FIG. 134. Starter with a no-field release.

If the field circuit is accidentally broken, the field current is interrupted, and the flux and back voltage drop approximately to zero, thus allowing a very large current to flow through the armature winding.   The magnet M, however, releases the starting arm, which flies back to the starting position and interrupts this current before any damage is done.

The no-voltage release of Fig. 133 is the standard protection.   It does not protect against a break in the field circuit, but all motors are protected by either circuit breakers or fuses, and the very large armature current resulting from a break in the field circuit causes the breaker or fuses to operate very quickly and disconnect the motor from the line.   The chief objection to the no-field release is that most shunt motors are operated with field control of speed, and it is difficult to provide a magnet that will function properly over the whole range of field current.   The no-field release is used chiefly in special applications where the chances of the field circuit being broken are unusually high, as for example in experimental laboratories.

185. Speed-regulating Motor Starters for Shunt and Compound Motors.   Motor starters are available in which the speed-controlling equipment is incorporated with the starting equipment to form a single control unit.   These speed-regulating starters may be divided into three classes according to the type of speed control they provide: (1) field-resistance speed control only; (2) armature-resistance speed control only; (3) combined field and armature-resistance speed control.

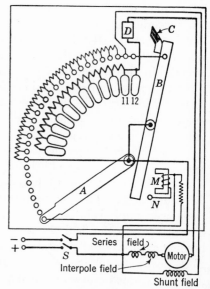

FIG. 135. Speed-regulating d-c motor, starter for shunt and compound motors, providing field-resistance speed control only.

A typical motor starter with field-resistance speed control is shown in Figs. 135 and 136.   The main arm A and the auxiliary arm B are shown in the stopped position.   Closing switch S connects the shunt field directly across the line through arm B and thus provides maximum field for starting. The main arm A is then moved upward by hand against the torque of a coiled spring. Arm A makes contact with two rows of studs.   The outer row will be used for field control after the motor has been brought up to speed but is at present short-circuited by arm B.   The inner row controls the resistance in series with the armature, and this resistance is cut out step by step as arm A is turned clockwise.

FIG. 136. Motor starter. (*General Electric Company.*) See Fig. 135 for wiring diagram.

As arm A is moved from 11 to 12, a projection (not shown) swings arm B counterclockwise, so that its copper-leaf contact C makes contact with stud D, thus shorting out the armature-starting resistance, so that arm A can now be moved back without cutting any resistance into the armature circuit.   Arm B is held closed by the no-voltage-release electromagnet M, which is energized when arm B makes contact with stud N.

The coiled spring of arm A was caught by arm B as the latter swung closed, so now arm A will stay in any position in which it is placed.   Arm B, in closing, removed the short circuit from the field-control resistance, and therefore resistance can be cut into the field circuit by turning arm A counterclockwise.

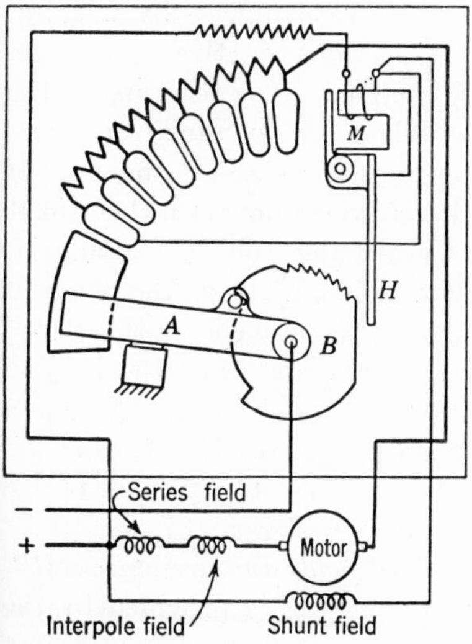

If the voltage fails or if switch S is opened, the no-voltage release M is deenergized, and arm B is thrown open by the action of the spring against which it was closed.   In doing so it releases the spring of arm A, so that arm A also is thrown to the stop position.

FIG. 137. Speed-regulating d-c motor starter for shunt and compound motors, providing armature-resistance speed control only.

If at any time when the motor is running, arm A is moved to the stop position, as in Fig. 135, it short-circuits coil M and thus operates the no-voltage release.

A motor starter designed to provide armature-resistance speed control is shown in Figs. 137 and 138.   It differs from the simple starter of Fig. 133 on the two following points:

1. Its resistance element must be able to carry the full-load current of the motor continuously and must therefore be considerably larger.

FIG. 138. Motor starter.   (*General Electric Company*.)   See Fig. 137 for wiring diagram.

2. The no-voltage release must be modified so as to allow the arm to remain in intermediate positions between "off" and full-speed.

This latter modification is accomplished by means of the ratchet wheel

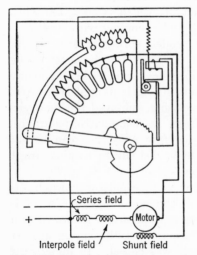

FIG. 139. Speed-regulating d-c motor starter for shunt and compound motors, providing combined field- and armature-resistance speed control.

B, which is pushed clockwise by arm A and counterclockwise by a spiral spring. As long as the no-voltage-release magnet M is energized, the ratchet wheel is prevented from turning counterclockwise by the arm H and therefore cannot push the arm A back toward the "off" position. If, however, voltage fails on the line or if the arm A is moved to the "off" position (as in Fig. 137), the holding coil M becomes deenergized, and a spring pulls the arm H out, allowing the ratchet wheel to fly back to the position shown in Fig. 137.

Combined field- and armature-resistance speed control is provided by the starter shown in Figs. 139 and 140. Its no-voltage release is identical with that of Fig. 137, but in this case it has been connected in such a way that it is not deenergized when the arm is moved to the "off" position. In any case it is not good practice to stop a motor by moving the arm to the "off" position, because then the starter arm must interrupt the armature current and this causes burning at the first contact stud.   The line switch should be used to stop the motor, and the starter will then automatically reset itself to the "off" position.

In Fig. 139 the jumper from the first armature stud to the last field stud normally carries no current.   Its purpose is to guard against the possibility of the field circuit being opened by a poor contact between the arm and the field studs.

The sliding-contact type of starter described in this article is liable to give trouble, owing to arcing at the contacts, if used for motors larger than 30 hp at 115 volts, or 50 hp at 230 to 550 volts.   For larger motors, switches must be used, as in Fig. 144.   In many cases the switches are of the contactor type, and the control is made automatic, as in Fig. 148.

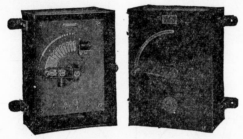

FIG. 140. Motor starter.   (*General Electric Company.*)   See Fig. 139 for wiring diagram.

186. Controllers for Series Motors.   Series motors are largely used for crane service and the controller used with them must be arranged to reverse the direction of rotation by reversing the armature connections and must also give speed regulation by means of resistance in the armature circuit.

A simple type of controller for this purpose is shown in Fig. 141. The path of the current through the controller is shown in Fig. 141a when the motor is running in one direction and in Fig. 141b when the direction is reversed.

The controller shown in Fig. 141 is supplied with a blowout coil A which produces a magnetic field that passes from the front arms B to the back arms C.   These arms are of iron.   This magnetic field passes vertically through the panel and thus is at right angles to the arc formed when a sliding contact leaves a segment; it therefore acts to blow out the arc.

187. Drum-type Controllers.   These controllers are particularly suited for adjustable-speed motors, which have to be started and stopped frequently, because the various operations are performed readily by the movement of a single handle and take place in their proper order.   The controller is entirely enclosed and can readily be made weatherproof, while contact with the live parts is prevented.

A simple type of drum controller is shown in Fig. 143.   It consists of a cast-iron cylinder A, insulated from a central shaft to which the operating handle B is keyed.   To this drum, the copper contact segments a, b,

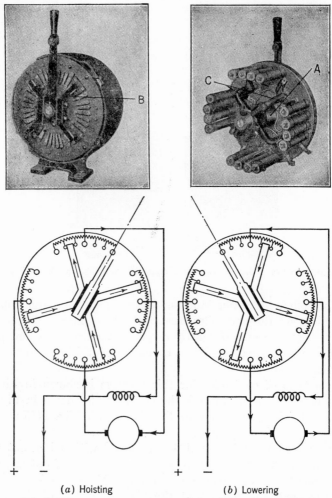

(a) Hoisting   (b) Lowering
FIG. 141. Faceplate controller for a small reversing-series motor.

c, d, and e are attached; these are in electrical contact with the drum and therefore with one another.   The drum carries also a brush contact m which slides over stationary field-resistance contacts that are mounted on the slate C; the contact m is not visible, being hidden by the drum.   The armature resistance is connected to the stationary fingers f, g, h, j, and k

which are insulated from one another and from the stationary base on which they are mounted.

The action of such a controller may readily be understood from Fig. 142, which shows the controller drum developed on to a plane; the vertical

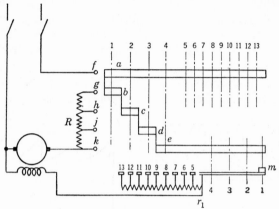

FIG. 142. Developed diagram of machine-tool controller.

dotted lines indicate the successive positions of the contact drum with respect to the row of stationary fingers.

In position 1, the fingers f and g make contact with segments a and b of the drum, and the armature current passes through the whole armature resistance, while the field coils are fully excited, the exciting current passing through the contact m. In position 4, the armature resistance is all cut out but the field coils are still fully excited. In position 5, the brush m makes contact with field segment 5 and the resistance r_1 is inserted in the field-coil circuit. With further motion of the drum from position 5 to position 13, the resistance in the field-coil circuit is gradually increased, the magnetic field is weakened, and the speed of the motor is thereby increased above normal.

Drum-type controllers generally contain no protective devices, and therefore it is

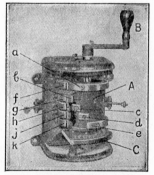

FIG. 143. Drum-type controller.

usual to provide separate protection in the form of a single-pole contactor switch and a thermal overload relay. These may be mounted at any convenient distance from the motor. The operating coil, Fig. 131, of the contactor switch is connected across the line, and therefore acts as a no-voltage relay. It is important that this switch should not reclose when voltage comes back on the line, unless the drum controller is in the "off" or "start" position. This may be accomplished by providing a pair of auxiliary contacts on the contactor switch and using them to open the circuit of the operating coil when the contactor opens. The drum controller is then provided with a special pair of contacts that are closed only when the controller is in the "off" position. These contacts are connected in parallel with the auxiliary contacts on the contactor switch. Thus the circuit through the operating coil is closed when either the contactor switch is closed or the drum controller is in the "off" position.

188. Automatic Starters. The tendency in the operation of electrical machinery is to make the starters and controllers self-governing. This

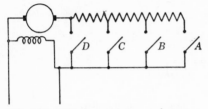

FIG. 144. Multiple-switch type of starter.

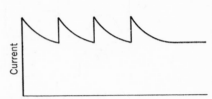

FIG. 145. Current cycle in the armature circuit during starting.

not only protects the machinery from injury by careless or unskilled operators but also provides a more uniform and a speedier control.

The number of variations and modifications of the various types of automatic and semiautomatic control is very large and is growing rapidly. It may be assumed that no series of operations is too complicated to be performed by an automatic electric controller, provided that the cost is not prohibitive. Many modern electric substations are entirely automatic. A master drum controller with associated relays starts the machinery up when it is needed, regulates it, and closes it down again, without the supervision of any human being, and if anything goes wrong it shuts the plant down and sends a telegram back to headquarters for help.

There is practically no limit to the number of switching operations that can be performed by one revolution of a single drum controller, since the length and diameter of the drum may be increased to make room for as many contacts as are desired.

We shall here, however, consider only two types of automatic d-c motor starters, which are widely used, namely, the d-c magnetic controller with definite timing, and the controller with timing determined by the magnitude of the armature current. Both of these types of controllers cut out the starting resistance in steps by closing switches as indicated in Fig. 144. Switch A is closed first, followed by B, C, and then D, with a suitable time interval between successive closings. The corresponding armature current is shown in Fig. 145.

189. Magnetic Controller with Definite Timing. A typical master controller switch to give definite timing is shown in Fig. 146. When the solenoid S is excited by the closing of the push-button switch P, it exerts a pull upon the rocker arm M, which carries the four contactor switches A, B, C, and D. The rocker arm moves forward at a slow definite rate which is fixed by the clockwork escapement mechanism Q to which the rocker-arm shaft N is geared. The gaps between the contacts of switches A, B, C, and D are progressively greater from A to D. As the rocker arm moves forward, switch A closes first but does not stop the forward motion

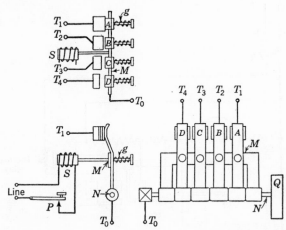

FIG. 146. Direct-current magnetic master controller switch with definite timing, showing side elevation, front elevation, and plan.

of the rocker arm because the switches are only held against the rocker arm by the spiral springs g, which begin to compress as soon as the switches make contact.

Thus this master controller is simply a mechanism that closes four switches in succession with a definite fixed time interval between successive closings. The time interval can be adjusted over fairly wide limits by changing the period of the pendulum in the escapement mechanism Q.

To open the switches, the solenoid circuit is opened and the rocker arm is then thrown back by the action of a spring (not shown) which was compressed when the rocker arm was pulled forward.

One obvious method of applying this master controller switch is simply to connect the four switches in as the switches A, B, C, and D of Fig. 144, and that is the way in which it is applied to small low-voltage motors. Fig. 147 shows the connections.

To start the motor, switch K, Fig. 147, is closed and the "start" button is depressed. This completes the circuit through the operating solenoid S which closes the controller contacts A, B, C, D, one after the other, thus cutting out the starting resistance step by step. As the rocker arm M moves in, it operates the auxiliary switch Y, which short-circuits the start button, so that the release of this push button will not interrupt the holding current through solenoid S, and at the same time inserts a resistance in series with the solenoid so as to reduce the holding current to the minimum required and so save power. The current required to hold the master switch closed is considerably less than that required to close it.

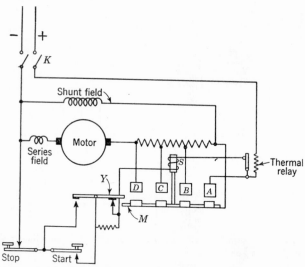

FIG. 147. Direct-current magnetic controller with definite timing for starting small motors.

The thermal relay provides overload protection by interrupting the holding current of solenoid S if it becomes too hot. To stop the motor, the "stop" button is depressed. This interrupts the holding current of solenoid S and the master controller switch then flies open.

The connections shown in Fig. 147 are used for 110-volt motors up to 10 hp and for 220-volt motors up to 20 hp. The heavier currents of larger motors cannot be handled by the contacts of the master controller switch. Separate contactor switches are therefore provided and the master controller switch opens and closes their operating circuits as shown in Fig. 148. To start the motor, switch K is closed and the start button is depressed. This completes the circuits through the solenoids of both the line contactor L and the master controller switch S. The line contactor L closes immediately, thus starting the motor with the full starting resistance in series. After a suitable time interval, contact a of the master controller closes, completing the circuit through the operating solenoid of contactor A, which closes and short-circuits a section of the starting resistance.   Contactors B and C are closed in the same way after suitable time intervals, thus cutting out all the starting resistance.

To stop the motor, the stop button is depressed, thus interrupting the holding currents of the line contactor L and of the master controller switch S.   These switches, which were closed against springs, accordingly fly open, followed by the contactors C, B, and A, as their holding currents are interrupted.

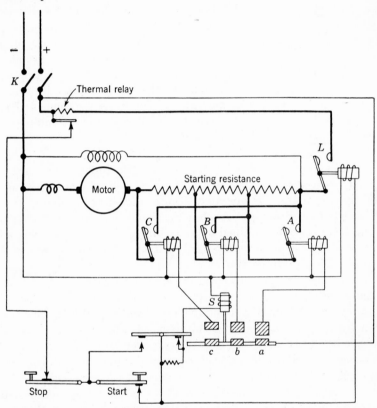

FIG. 148. Direct-current magnetic controller with definite timing for starting large motors.

There is no limit to the size of motor that can be started by this type of controller.

190. Automatic Starter with Current-controlled Timing.   The automatic controller with definite timing is not suited to the operation of motors which may occasionally have to start under unusually severe conditions, or where the starting conditions are variable and it is desirable to have maximum acceleration.   For example, in street-railway operation, cars are occasionally required to start on an upgrade, fulled loaded, and with snow on the track.   If a definite timing starter were used and its timing set long enough to meet this condition, then the acceleration under normal starting conditions would be so slow as to be entirely unsatisfactory. What is required for this type of service is a starter that will automatically adjust its timing to suit the starting conditions and so give the maximum possible acceleration at all times. That is, the closing of each successive contactor should occur when the armature current has dropped to a certain predetermined value. This is accomplished in two different ways. One type of controller employs special relays that will operate only when the current falls below a certain value. Another type of controller makes use of the fact that the emf generated by the motor is proportional to its speed. At start, the voltage across the armature is quite small, most of the line voltage being consumed as IR drop in the starting box. As the motor speeds up, the voltage across its armature rises, while that across the starter drops. The relays are connected across the armature terminals, and are set to operate at different voltages; thus they close in sequence at certain definite speeds, and each one in closing short-circuits a portion of the starting resistance.

The no-voltage- and overload-release attachments are generally supplied on a separate panel. The main switch, being then of the magnetic-switch type, is operated from a push-button circuit.

191. Dynamic Braking. A smooth, powerful, and well-controlled braking action can be obtained on a machine driven by an electric motor by converting the motor temporarily into a generator driven by that machine. The retarding torque of the generator then acts as a brake upon the machine and can be controlled by varying the current output of the generator. If the current output from the generator is fed back into the supply line, the braking is said to be *regenerative;* but if the generator is loaded by simply connecting a suitable resistance across its armature terminals, the braking is said to be *dynamic,* or *rheostatic.*

In dynamic braking the motor is converted into a generator by simply disconnecting it from the line and connecting a resistance across its armature, although in the case of the series motor it is sometimes advisable to excite the series field separately in order to obtain better control of the braking.

A peculiarity of dynamic braking is that the braking action disappears as the machine comes to rest, and consequently, in the case of such loads as crane hoists, friction brakes must be applied if it is desired to hold the load stationary. Dynamic braking is widely used for cranes, hoists, elevators (when not equipped with Ward Leonard control), and all types of machinery where the free-stopping period is too long for the particular service involved. In most cases the application of the dynamic braking is automatic.

In regenerative braking the motors are converted into generators by making the generated emf greater than the line emf. This is very readily done if the Ward Leonard system is used (see Arts. 169 to 171) but is not so simple with ordinary systems where the motors are driven directly from the line. Large d-c electric locomotives operating in mountain divisions generally use regenerative braking when descending long grades but use air brakes for stopping at stations. It is impossible to brake a train to rest with regenerative braking unless Ward Leonard control is used and only a few locomotives are using that system at present. Dynamic-braking control equipment is cheaper, lighter, and less complex than regenerative control equipment, and it can be used for stopping at stations. Consequently, it is used in preference to regenerative braking except in cases where the amount of energy regenerated would justify the more complex system.

Problems

21-1. Determine the resistance steps required in the starting box for a 110-volt 10-hp shunt motor, in order that the armature current can be kept within the limits of 1.0 and 1.5 times full-load current. The resistance of the armature circuit is 0.08 ohm, and the full-load armature current is 80 amp.

21-2. The resistance of the armature circuit of a 220-volt 10-hp shunt motor is 0.32 ohm. Its full-load speed with full-field current is 1,200 rpm. What value of resistance must be inserted in series with the armature to give a speed of 600 rpm when the motor is carrying its full-load armature current of 40 amp? If the brake torque is then reduced by one-half, at what speed will the motor run? Neglect the small change in flux due to armature reaction.

21-3. The saturation curve of a 110-volt 10-hp shunt motor is given in Fig. 94. The resistance of its field winding is 42 ohms. Specify the field rheostat to give a speed range of 900 to 1,800 rpm.

*21-4. What will happen if the field circuit of a shunt motor is broken while the motor is running under load? What in the case of a series motor?

22

PARALLEL OPERATION OF DIRECT-
CURRENT GENERATORS

In order to secure a high degree of continuity of service, important electrical loads are generally supplied by two or more generators operating in parallel, a common requirement being that if any one of the generators should fail the remaining generators should be able to carry the entire load. In any case the normal growth of the load will often require the addition of other generators from time to time.

192. Parallel Operation of Shunt Generators. Figure 149 shows two shunt generators arranged to be operated in parallel. The two main con-

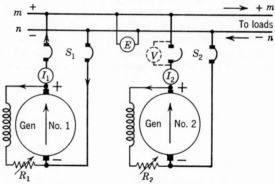

FIG. 149. Parallel operation of shunt generators.

ductors, m and n, to which all the generators and loads are connected, are generally referred to as the *bus*. The operating condition shown is that one side of circuit breaker S_2 is open, and generator 1 is carrying the entire load.

When it is desired to put generator 2 into service, its prime mover is started and brought up to speed. Its terminal voltage E_2 is then adjusted by means of its field rheostat R_2 until E_2 is equal to the bus voltage E. In order to do this, it is necessary to have two voltmeters, one connected permanently across the bus to measure E, and the other connected temporarily across the terminals of the incoming machine by means of a selector switch, not shown, which enables the operator to connect the voltmeter across any generator in the powerhouse.   When E_2 is equal to E, the positive terminal of generator 2 is at the same potential as bus bar m, and if a voltmeter V were connected across the open switch, as shown dotted, it would indicate zero voltage.   Therefore no current will flow when the switch is closed.   Figure 150 shows graphically the condition that now exists.   Assuming, for example, that generator 1 is carrying full load, then the full-load terminal voltage of generator 1 is equal to the no-load terminal voltage of generator 2.   The two generators can be made to

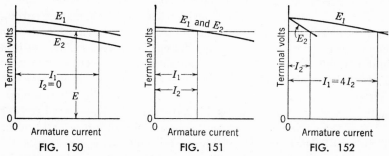

FIG. 150   FIG. 151   FIG. 152

FIGS. 150, 151, 152. Division of load between shunt generators in parallel.

share the load, in any proportion desired, by either reducing R_2 or increasing R_1, thus changing the field current, and either raising E_2 or dropping E_1.   In practice, part of the adjustment would be made on each machine, so as to keep the bus voltage E unchanged.   It should be realized of course that $I_1 + I_2 = $ a constant, no matter how the load is shared.

Figure 151 shows the case of two identical generators with their field currents adjusted to make them share the load equally.   The E_1 curve of Fig. 150 has been lowered, and the E_2 curve raised, until they have met and coincided on a curve halfway between their original positions, thus keeping E unchanged.

As I_1 decreases and I_2 increases, due to the manipulation of the field rheostats, the retarding electromagnetic torques change similarly, with the result that generator 1 begins to speed up while generator 2 begins to slow down, thus causing the governors of the prime movers to adjust the power inputs to the required amounts.   In general a drop in speed of 2 per cent is enough to cause a governor to increase the power input from no load to full load.

If the voltage characteristics on a current base coincide throughout their entire lengths, as in Fig. 151, then the two generators will automatically share the load equally at all loads, and this is highly desirable if the two machines have the same power ratings. The general case, including machines of different power ratings, may be expressed as follows: Two generators will automatically divide the load between them according to their respective capacities if they have the same drop in voltage from no load to full load. Figure 152 shows this condition met with the power rating of generator 1 equal to four times that of generator 2.

To disconnect generator 2, its excitation should be reduced, while that of generator 1 is increased, until all the load has been transferred to generator 1, and I_2 is zero. Switch S_2 may then be opened.

The operation of two shunt generators in parallel is very stable. When, owing to a momentary increase in the speed of its prime mover, generator 1 generates a slightly larger voltage and therefore takes more than its proper share of the load, the increasing of the armature current in generator 1 has the effect of reducing its terminal voltage, while the simultaneous decreasing of the armature current in generator 2 causes its terminal voltage to rise. Thus the equality of the terminal voltages is maintained by only a small shift in the load. Furthermore, if the engine driving generator 2 fails for an instant, that machine slows down, its generated voltage drops, and load is automatically transferred to generator 1. If the engine failure persists for more than a few seconds, its speed will drop sufficiently so that the generated voltage of generator 2 will be less than the bus voltage E. The armature current in generator 2 will then reverse and it will operate as a motor, turning in the same direction as before but at a somewhat reduced speed. Thus a generator that is operating in parallel with other generators will not allow its prime mover to stop, even though that prime mover has ceased to supply energy.

193. Loading Back Tests. Load tests on large electric machines to determine whether the temperature rise is within the specified limit and whether the commutation is sparkless must be made by some method whereby the power developed by the machine is not dissipated but is made available for the tests; otherwise the power supply may not be large enough to allow the machine to be tested, while the cost of such a test would be excessive.

If the machine to be tested is a generator, it is driven at normal speed by a motor of the same voltage but of larger capacity, and both machines are connected to the power-supply mains as in Fig. 153, which shows the running condition. Note that the voltage E of the power supply must be equal to the voltage rating of the generator, as otherwise the test will be of no practical value.

At the start of the test, switches S_1 and S_2 are open so that the generator is not connected to the line. The motor M is started in the usual way by means of a starting box (not shown), and its speed is adjusted by means of its field rheostat until it is driving the generator at rated speed. The excitation of the generator is then adjusted until its terminal voltage is equal to E. The simplest way to determine the equality of the voltages is to close switch S_1 and connect a voltmeter V across the open switch S_2. When V reads zero, the voltages are equal, and S_2 may then be closed without causing any current to flow. It may be found that V is approximately double the line voltage. In that case the polarity is wrong and must be corrected by interchanging the leads at the switch terminals.

If switch S_2 is closed when V is equal to zero, there will be no current through the generator. If the excitation of G is now increased so as to increase its generated voltage, then current will circulate through the two machines in the directions shown by the arrows, and G will deliver power

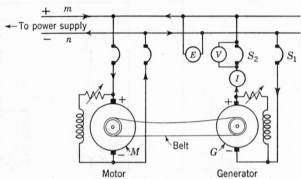

FIG. 153. Loading back test on a generator.

to the mains m, n, while the motor M, which drives G, will take from these same mains an amount of power equal to the output of G plus the losses in the two machines. The power required to supply the losses is all that is taken from the power supply.

Assuming, for example, that the generator is rated 1,000 kw and that the efficiency of each machine is 95 per cent, then the electric-power output of the generator to the mains m, n, is 1,000 kw. The mechanical power transmitted by the belt is $1,000/0.95 = 1,053$ kw, while the electric-power input to the motor is $1,053/0.95 = 1,108$ kw. The power required from the power supply is $1,108 - 1000 = 108$ kw.

194. Compound Generators in Parallel. A and B, Fig. 154, are two compound generators which are operating in parallel. If, owing to a momentary increase in speed, generator A takes more than its proper share of the total load, the series excitation of A increases, its voltage rises, and it takes still more of the load, so that the operation is unstable. In an instant, machine A is not only taking all the load but is driving machine B as a differential compound motor. The overload on A opens its circuit breaker and disconnects it from the line.

To prevent this instability, the points e and f, Fig. 155, are joined by a connection of large cross section and of negligible resistance, called an equalizer connection. The series coils P and Q are thus connected in parallel with one another between the equalizer and the negative main n, and the total current from the negative main n always passes through these coils in one direction and divides up between them inversely as their resistance, independently of the distribution of the load between the machines. If now, owing to a momentary increase in speed, machine A takes more than its proper share of the total load, as indicated in Fig. 155, and therefore less is left for machine B, the series excitation of the two machines is unchanged, since the total load is unchanged, so that the

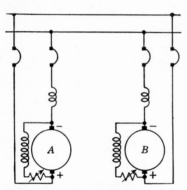

FIG. 154. Compound generators in parallel, without the equalizer connection.

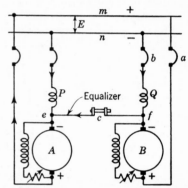

FIG. 155. Compound generators in parallel, with an equalizer connection and with generator A taking more than its share of the load.

machines act as shunt generators with a superimposed excitation that is constant as long as the total load is constant. The shifting of the load from B to A decreases the voltage of A and increases the voltage of B, so that the terminal voltages of A and B are maintained equal by a small shift in load. The operation of the machines has therefore been made stable by the addition of the equalizer connection. If switch c is opened, one of the generators will open its circuit breakers within a few seconds.

To connect machine B in parallel with machine A, which is already running, bring the machine up to speed with the switches a, b, and c open, close switches b and c in order to excite the series coils, then adjust the shunt excitation until E_B is equal to E, and finally close switch a. The machine may then be made to take its share of the load by increasing its shunt excitation. To disconnect the machine, its shunt excitation should be reduced until all the load has been transferred to A; the switches should then be opened in the reverse order.

195. Division of Load among Compound Generators. When a single compound generator has too much compounding, a shunt in parallel with the series-field coils will reduce the current in these coils and thus reduce the compounding.

When one of a number of compound generators in parallel is found to take more than its share of the load, then its compounding must be reduced. This, however, can no longer be accomplished by placing a shunt in parallel with the series coils of that machine. For example, the shunt S in Fig. 156a will not only reduce the current in the series coils Q but will at the same time reduce the current in the series coils P, since the

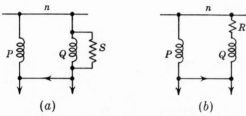

(a) (b)

FIG. 156. Showing the method of changing the compounding of compound generators that are operating in parallel.

two sets of series coils and the shunt S are then all connected in parallel between the negative main and the equalizer, and the total line current will divide among them inversely as their resistance. The compounding of both machines will therefore be reduced.

To reduce the current in the series coils Q without at the same time reducing that in the coils P, a resistance must be placed in series with Q, as shown in Fig. 156b. Since the total current must still pass through P and Q in parallel, it follows that inserting a resistance in series with Q increases the compounding of generator A while decreasing that of generator B. The function of the resistor R is simply to equalize the compoundings so that the generators will share the load properly.

23

SPECIAL DIRECT-CURRENT MACHINES

196. Compensating Windings. The armature current of a d-c machine distorts the magnetic field and shifts or crowds it toward one side of the poles, as explained in Art. 114. Any very sudden and violent change in the magnitude of the armature current causes an equally rapid shifting of the flux. The flux in shifting generates a voltage in the coils, which may, if of sufficient magnitude, cause the commutator to flashover.

This shift of the flux across the pole faces may be practically eliminated by means of a compensating winding placed in slots cut in the pole faces

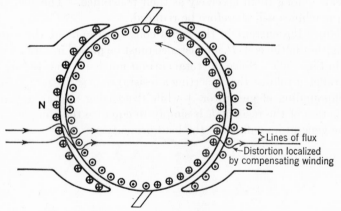

FIG. 157. Compensating winding, two-pole generator.

as shown in Fig. 157. This winding is connected in series with the armature winding, and, if it is designed to have the same number of turns, its cross-magnetizing effect will always be equal and opposite to that of the armature winding and there will be no shifting of the flux to the pole tips. The flux is still distorted, of course, as otherwise there would be no torque, but the distortion is very much localized and is confined to the immediate vicinity of the conductors.

A compensating winding adds considerably to the cost of a machine and doubles the armature copper loss, but it makes the machine able to withstand the most violent fluctuations of load that can be applied to it. Compensating windings are used quite extensively on the generators and motors of Ward Leonard sets, particularly in steel mills.   They are also used for other types of severe service.

FIG. 158. 600-volt 2,500-hp 14-pole d-c motor with compensating winding in the pole faces.   Note the large amount of copper strap required for the end connections of this winding.   (*Courtesy General Electric Co.*)

197. The Direct-current Generator as a Direct-current Power Amplifier.   The basic principle of most control devices, whether manual or automatic, is that a small amount of power controls the application of a relatively large amount of power.   The controlled device and its controller, taken together, are fundamentally a power amplifier, regardless of the special features that may be added to obtain special results.

If a d-c generator is driven at constant speed, and if the magnetic circuit is far from saturation, the power output of the generator will be proportional to the power input to the field, and any power variations made in the field circuit will be faithfully reproduced in the generator output, the ratio of the two powers being approximately a constant.   A d-c generator can be conveniently designed with a field copper loss equal to 1 per cent of the full-load power output.   Such a generator will give a power amplification of 100 when used as an amplifier.

If an amplification greater than 100 is required, the output of this generator can be fed into the field of a second generator, as shown in

Fig. 159. The over-all power amplification will then be 10,000. The final power output all comes from the motor, not shown, that drives generator G_2. The original power input is all wasted as I^2R loss in the field coils.

Note that if a conductor material of one-half the specific resistance of copper were available the I^2R power input to the fields could be cut in half and the amplification would be 200 per stage instead of 100. However, in many applications this would not be an improvement because the rapidity of response is directly proportional to the ratio of R to L in the field circuit (Art. 90) and the principal objection to this type of amplifier is the slowness of its response. The delay between the sudden application of an emf to the field and the approximate completion of the resulting

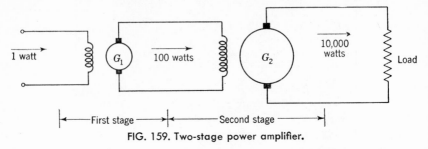

FIG. 159. Two-stage power amplifier.

change in the output is of the order of 1 sec for a two-stage amplifier, and for many applications this is too great a delay. High amplification and quickness of response are mutually conflicting aims, and for each application the designer must determine as best he can the most suitable balance between them.

198. The Amplidyne. The term *amplidyne* is the trade name given by the General Electric Company to its version of the *metadyne* as developed for power amplification and control. The name is both descriptive and pleasing and there seems to be quite a tendency to adopt it as a standard technical term. The term *metadyne* has not been precisely defined. As a practical working definition it would be reasonably accurate to say that the term metadyne includes all armature-reaction excited machines used in control work. Thus all amplidynes are metadynes but not all metadynes are amplidynes.

The amplidyne is a d-c generator of special design that combines in one machine a greater amplification than the two-stage amplifier of Fig. 159, together with from ten to twenty times the speed of response.

Figure 160 will serve to represent an ordinary two-pole, separately excited d-c generator, rated 100 volts, 100 amp, 10 kw. The only unusual feature of Fig. 160 is that the spaces between the two poles N_c and S_c are shown filled in with iron, N_a and S_a, so as to reduce the reluctance of the path of the flux produced by armature reaction. Thus the generator shown in Fig. 160 differs from the usual d-c generator only in that the flux of armature reaction is considerably larger than usual.

When this generator is driving a current of 100 amp through the 1-ohm load resistance R, its terminal voltage is 100 volts, and the power input required for its field might reasonably be 100 watts, or 1 per cent of the rated output.

The flux ϕ_c produced in the poles N_cS_c by the field current I_c in the field coils FF is indicated by the two dotted lines. The flux of armature reaction ϕ_a is shown by the full lines. These two fluxes are at right angles

to each other in the armature and are approximately equal if the generator is delivering 100 amp at 100 volts.

Suppose now that the resistance R is gradually reduced to zero, while the field current is reduced so as to keep I_a constant at 100 amp. It will be found that when R is zero the field current required to circulate 100 amp through the short-circuited armature winding is only about 5 per cent of the field current required when the termi-nal emf is 100 volts. Since the power input to the field coils varies as the

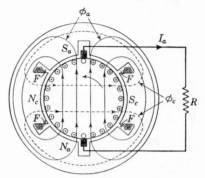

FIG. 160. A two-pole d-c generator designed to produce a large armature-reaction flux.

square of the field current, this power input is now equal to 5 per cent of 5 per cent of 100 watts, or 0.25 watt. Thus a field input of only 0.25 watt results in the production of a field ϕ_a as powerful as the field produced directly by a field input of 100 watts. Therefore, if this flux can be used to generate a voltage to be applied to some external load, the over-all power amplification will be 400 times the power amplification of an ordinary d-c generator, and this means a power amplification of 40,000.

There is no difficulty in utilizing the flux ϕ_a. Two load brushes B_3B_4 are placed midway between the short-circuited brushes B_1B_2, as shown in Fig. 161. An emf E_L of 100 volts is produced across these brushes by the conductors cutting the vertical flux ϕ_a. The cutting of ϕ_c does not contribute anything to this emf. Incidentally ϕ_c is now only 5 per cent of ϕ_a. The load brushes B_3B_4 are connected to the external load. A generator excited in this way is called an armature-reaction excited machine.

It is necessary to provide a compensating winding placed in slots in the stator iron, as shown in Fig. 161, and connected in series with the load, to neutralize the armature reaction of the load current, because this armature reaction is in direct opposition to ϕ_c. If the compensating winding were not provided, I_c would have to be large enough to neutralize this armature reaction and to provide the required ϕ_c as well. The power input to the field would then be at least 100 watts and the amplidyne would be in no way superior to an ordinary d-c generator.

In Fig. 161 the innermost circle of crosses and dots shows the directions of the load current I_L in the armature conductors. The crosses and dots placed inside the armature conductors show the directions of the short-circuit current I_a in the armature conductors. The net current in the armature conductors between B_1 and B_4, and also between B_2 and B_3, is equal to one-half the sum of I_a and I_L. In the rest of the armature the net current is equal to one-half the difference between I_a and I_L.

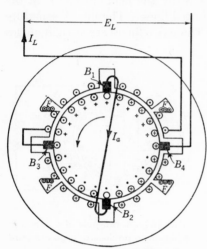

FIG. 161. The amplidyne.

The compensating winding must be so designed and connected that its cross-magnetizing mmf will be equal and opposite to the cross-magnetizing mmf of the load-current component of the armature current. Both of these magnetomotive forces are horizontal in Fig. 161.

The basic equation of the amplidyne, ignoring saturation, is

$$E_L = K_1\phi_a = K_2I_a = K_3\phi_c = K_4I_c$$

The current I_c is generally called the control current, and the winding FF in which it flows is generally called the control winding. This winding occupies so little space that it is easy to find room for several control windings. Each of these control windings can then be assigned to a separate supervisory device that watches over some one feature of the complete operation. In this way the amplidyne can be made to show an almost superhuman wisdom.

The high speed of response of the amplidyne is made possible by the fact that its control field requires only about 1 or 2 per cent of the number of ampere-turns used on the field of an ordinary direct-current generator. Consequently, the inductance of its field winding is much smaller and the rate of change of the field current much more rapid. Laminating the poles and yoke also increases the speed of response.

199. Current-limiting Connection, Amplidyne Control. Figure 162 shows an amplidyne-excited d-c generator equipped with a simple type of

current-limiting device.   When the operator desires to increase the power
output of the generator, he increases the field current I_1 in the control
winding f_1.   This increases the voltage of the amplidyne and so increases
I_f and I, but as I passes through the value that makes IR equal to E_b, the
current I_2 reverses, so that its mmf in f_2 now opposes the mmf of I_1 in f_1,
and thus limits the current I.   This current-limiting connection is what
is called a feedback circuit, and as IR passes through equality with E_b the
feedback changes from positive to negative.   In practice, the circuit is
usually rather more complicated, and a third control field f_3 is often supplied by an antihunting circuit, which
still further stabilizes the operation.
Protective relays or limit switches are
often arranged to pass the right amount
of current through one of the control
field windings to reduce the amplidyne
voltage to zero.

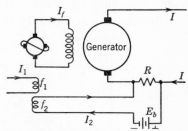

FIG. 162. Current-limiting connection, amplidyne control.

200. Applications of the Amplidyne.
The applications are so numerous that
they cannot be treated adequately in a
general textbook of this kind.   All that
can be done is to give a few typical examples by way of illustration.
The reader is referred to the technical press.[1]

When the amount of power to be controlled is small, the amplidyne
may be used as the main generator.   For example, in Fig. 125 the generator G might be an amplidyne, and no other modification of this wiring
diagram is required.   However, since the amplidyne is generally provided with several control fields, some of these fields would probably
be used to set current and speed limits, or to make the operation partly
or wholly automatic.

When the amount of power to be controlled is greater than 25 kw the
present practice is to use the amplidyne as a variable-voltage exciter for
the main generator, as in Fig. 163.   In that case a second exciter E,
operating at constant voltage, is required to provide constant field for the
motor M_1, to drive the amplidyne by means of the shunt motor S, and to
provide the control field for the amplidyne.   The reversing switch of
Fig. 125 can be eliminated by taking one side of the field to a center tap
on the rheostat R.   Current-limiting control is not shown but is usually
provided.

There are two main points of superiority of the arrangement of Fig.

[1] The Amplidyne Generator, *Gen. Elec. Rev.*, March, 1940; Design Characteristics of
Amplidyne Generators, *Gen. Elec. Rev.*, March, 1940; Industrial Applications of
Amplidyne Generators, *Gen. Elec. Rev.*, March, 1940; What Is the Amplidyne, *Gen.
Elec. Rev.*, August, 1943; The Amplidyne, *Elec. Eng.*, May, 1946.

163 over that of Fig. 125. (1) Since the amplidyne has several control fields that require very little power, it is easy to superimpose various automatic features on the basic manual control. (2) Since the amount of power to be handled by the controller R of Fig. 163 is only about one-quarter of 1 per cent of the power to be handled by the controller of Fig. 125, the controller is much smaller and less expensive. When the power is large, the arrangement of Fig. 125 requires electrically operated contactor switches to vary R, and as many as 20 contactor switches may be required. They are fairly expensive and the maintenance is relatively high. Also they are noisy. When an amplidyne is used, no contactor switches are required to vary R.

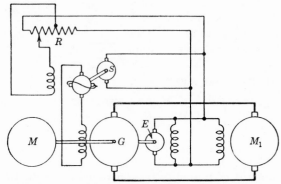

FIG. 163. The amplidyne applied to Ward Leonard speed control.

201. Third-brush Direct-current Generator. This generator utilizes armature reaction to control or limit its output current. To illustrate its principle of operation, let us consider its application to the charging of an automobile battery during normal operation of the car. The generator is belted to the engine shaft, and the chief peculiarity of this application of d-c generators is that the battery must be charged from a generator whose speed varies over a wide range. In order to avoid an excessive rate of charging at high speeds and at the same time maintain a fair charging rate at moderate speeds, it is necessary either to provide some sort of automatic regulating device or to design the generator to have a voltage characteristic curve that drops off very steeply after the current exceeds a certain chosen value.

Figure 164 shows a generator that is arranged to have such a voltage characteristic. It differs from an ordinary shunt-excited generator only in that a third brush is provided and the field coils are connected across the brushes A and C instead of across the brushes A and B.

The voltage across AC can be varied from zero to a maximum by shifting the brush C from the position occupied by brush A to the position occupied by brush B. Suppose that brush C is placed at the center of the north pole, then at no load the magnetic field is uniform and the voltage across AC is half the voltage across AB, since only the conductors under the upper half of the north pole are contributing to the voltage across AC. Now when current is taken by the battery, armature reaction crowds the flux toward the lower half of the north pole (see Art. 114). Thus the flux cut by the conductors between A and C is reduced, the voltage across AC is reduced, the field current is reduced, and the voltage across AB is reduced. In this way, armature reaction is utilized to regulate the charging current. The charging rate can be varied by altering the position of the third brush C.

A relay is required to disconnect the generator from the battery whenever the speed drops below the minimum value at which the generator

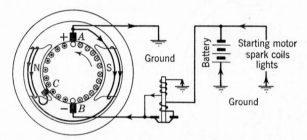

FIG. 164. Third-brush generator method of charging an automobile battery.

can generate a voltage equal to that of the battery. The relay is opened by the reversal of the current that occurs as the generated voltage drops below that of the battery. Note that, if the battery were to become disconnected from the circuit when the car was going 50 mph, the voltage of the generator would rise to several times its normal value. It is the current taken by the battery that holds the voltage down when the car is going at full speed.

The third-brush generator has been used very extensively in the past for charging automobile batteries, but today most automobiles use a straight shunt-excited generator and rely on automatic voltage and current regulators to control the charging rate. This method is described in Art. 227.

202. Arc-welding Generator. Arc welding is now used very extensively in metal construction of all kinds. The special feature of this application of a d-c generator is that the load is inherently unstable. The resistance of an arc decreases so rapidly with increase of current that less voltage is required to maintain a large current than to maintain a small one. Consequently, if an arc is started across a d-c source, it will either extinguish itself almost immediately, or else develop into what is practically a short circuit.

In order to stabilize the arc, it is necessary that the voltage of the generator should rise very quickly when the current decreases, and also drop very quickly when the current increases. It is not sufficient that the steady-state voltage characteristic should be steep. That is, it is not sufficient that the voltage change should be large, but it must also take place quickly.

It is also desirable that the generator should be self-excited, so as to avoid the expense and space requirements of a separate exciter. These two requirements appear to be contradictory however, because an ordinary self-excited generator is inherently slow in its response.

One satisfactory solution of the problem of designing a direct-current arc-welding generator is shown diagrammatically in Fig. 165. The machine has four poles, but the poles are not alternately north and south, and fundamentally the machine is a two-pole third-brush generator. The two poles N_1N_2 may be considered to be a single north pole split in two, so that different excitations may be applied to the two halves for the purpose of accentuating and controlling the shifting of the flux caused by armature reaction. The armature winding is an ordinary two-pole winding.

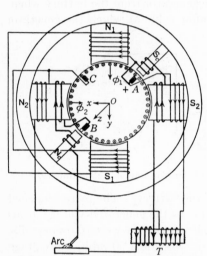

FIG. 165. Direct-current arc-welding generator. (*General Electric Company.*)

The main field coils are connected across the brushes A and C, and the voltage impressed on them is that generated by the flux ϕ_1 from pole N_1. Poles N_1 and S_1 are designed to be highly saturated, so that they will not be affected appreciably by armature reaction. Consequently, ϕ_1 is constant, and the voltage impressed on the main field coils is constant. Thus the excitation is equivalent to separate excitation.

Poles N_2S_2 are not saturated and are provided with differential compound windings. Now the mmf of the current in the armature winding is in the direction oz. It may be resolved into the two components ox and oy. The component oy has very little effect because it is acting on a saturated magnetic circuit, but the component ox and the differential series field together reduce ϕ_2 and in fact often reverse it. When ϕ_2 is reversed, the output voltage $E_{AB} = E_{AC} - E_{CB}$, and this becomes zero at a moderate value of armature current. The magnitude of this current is readily adjusted by changing taps on the series field. The two commutating poles N_c and S_c function in the usual manner.

The function of the transformer T is to speed up the response of the generator. If the load current I begins to decrease, the flux in the transformer T also decreases, and this decreasing flux induces an emf in series with the main field coils of N_2 and S_2. This induced emf is in a direction to increase the field current and thus raise the terminal voltage of the machine, so as to oppose the decrease in I. Increases in I are similarly opposed. Note that a similar transformer action takes place between the same two circuits on poles N_2 and S_2, but unfortunately the polarity is in the wrong direction, so that this transformer action tends to slow down the response. Transformer T neutralizes the undesirable transformer action between the series and main field coils on poles N_2 and S_2.

It should be noted that the self-inductance of the entire main circuit through the machine and load is a very important factor in helping to stabilize the arc because it acts instantaneously to oppose any change in the current.

24

PRIMARY AND STORAGE BATTERIES

A battery cell is a device for transforming potential chemical energy into electrical energy. It consists essentially of two electrodes of different materials immersed in an electrolyte that reacts much more vigorously with one electrode than with the other. A typical primary battery cell is shown on page 6.

The fundamental difference between a **primary battery** and a **storage battery** is that when the active elements of a primary battery have been consumed they are replaced by new material, but when the active elements of a storage battery have been consumed the battery is connected to a d-c generator, or rectifier, and current is driven through the battery in the reverse direction, with the result that the chemical action is reversed and the active elements are reformed. This process is called charging the battery.

203. Dry Cells. These are by far the most widely used type of primary battery. They are used for local-battery telephone sets, gasoline-engine ignition for small engines, flashlights, radio sets where electric power is not available, bell ringing, etc. There are many types but nearly all consist of carbon, zinc, and ammonium chloride with other ingredients.

A typical form of dry cell is shown in Fig. 166. The active electrode takes the form of a cylindrical zinc can, which also serves as the container. The inactive electrode is a carbon rod. The electrolyte is a solution of ammonium chloride (NH_4Cl) in water. In order to avoid the danger of spilling out the electrolyte, it is thickened into a paste by the addition of a suitable filler. A dry battery is not really dry and in fact ceases to function if the moisture leaks out.

The chemical action is briefly as follows: The ammonium chloride, being dissolved in water, becomes dissociated into NH_4^+ and Cl^- ions. Zinc ions (Zn^{++}) pass into solution from the zinc wall to unite with the Cl^- ions to form zinc chloride, a chemical action that may be expressed by the equation

$$Zn^{++} + 2Cl^- \rightarrow ZnCl_2 \tag{42}$$

Each zinc ion in passing into solution leaves 2 excess electrons behind in the zinc electrode. These excess electrons, repelling each other, expand over through the external load circuit into the carbon electrode. There they are picked up by the excess NH_4^+ ions in a chemical action that may be written

$$2MnO_2 + 2NH_4^+ + 4H_2O + 2 \text{ electrons} \rightarrow$$
$$2NH_4OH + 2Mn(OH)_3 \quad (43)$$

The carbon rod is not affected by the chemical reactions and is merely a means of completing the circuit.

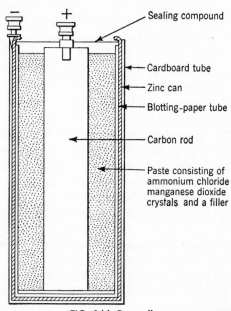

FIG. 166. Dry cell.

The terminal emf of a single dry cell on open circuit is about 1.5 volts. The life of a dry cell comes to an end when the zinc has been consumed to such an extent that holes begin to appear in the zinc can. The moisture then seeps out and the cell ceases to function.

204. Battery Connections. If E_o is the open-circuit voltage of a battery, R_b is the internal resistance, and R is the resistance of the external circuit, then the current $I = E_o/(R_b + R)$ and has a maximum value on short circuit equal to E_o/R_b.

If n batteries are connected in series, then the current is

$$I = \frac{nE_o}{nR_b + R} \quad (44)$$

If R is large compared with nR_b, as is usually the case, then the current is approximately proportional to the number of cells connected in series.

If n batteries are connected in parallel, then the current is

$$I = \frac{E_o}{(R_b/n) + R}$$

and an increase in the number of batteries does not produce any considerable increase in the current as long as R is large compared with R_b/n. The usual reason for connecting cells in parallel is to divide the load and so make the battery last longer.

205. The Weston Standard Cell. Standardizing laboratories, whose function is to calibrate instruments and to make accurate measurements of all kinds, require accurately known standards whose values will remain constant over long periods of time. The Weston standard cell is the best and the most widely used standard of emf at the present time. When made up in its saturated form out of pure ingredients, it can be relied upon to produce an open-circuit emf of 1.0183 volts at 20°C. In its unsaturated form it gives an emf of about 1.0188 volts. The saturated form is the more accurate but its voltage varies considerably with temperature and consequently the unsaturated form is used wherever the temperature is not under close control. The unsaturated form has a very small temperature coefficient but it should not be subjected to temperatures lower than 4°C or higher than 40°C.

The Weston cell uses cadmium and mercury for its electrodes, cadmium sulfate for its electrolyte, and mercurous sulfate for the depolarizer. The accuracy of the Weston cell can be relied upon only if the current drain upon it is limited to momentary currents of a few microamperes. When properly used, it has a long life but old cells should be checked against new cells from time to time to determine whether they have begun to weaken.

206. Action of the Lead Storage Battery. If a plate of lead peroxide (PbO_2) and one of lead (Pb) are placed in a solution of sulfuric acid (H_2SO_4), a battery is formed with the peroxide plate at the higher potential. The theory of operation is as follows:

The sulfuric acid is dissociated into H^+ ions and $SO_4^=$ ions.

The action at the positive (PbO_2) plate is

$$PbO_2 + SO_4^= + 4H^+ + 2 \text{ electrons} \underset{\text{charge}}{\overset{\text{discharge}}{\rightleftharpoons}} PbSO_4 + 2H_2O \quad (45)$$

The 2 electrons absorbed on discharge in Eq. (45) are abstracted from the positive plate, which accordingly becomes positively charged; that is, it acquires a deficiency or partial vacuum of electrons. If now the negative plate (Pb) is connected to the positive plate through some external circuit, electrons will pass over through this circuit from the negative plate to the positive plate. The negative plate is thus left with a slight positive charge that attracts the excess SO_4 ions, and the following action takes place at the negative plate:

$$SO_4^= + Pb \overset{\text{discharge}}{\underset{\text{charge}}{\rightleftharpoons}} PbSO_4 + 2 \text{ electrons} \qquad (46)$$

The 2 excess electrons in the foregoing equation are freed on the negative plate. Thus during the discharge electrons are continually being set free on the negative plate and are continually being abstracted from the positive plate. The result is a flow of electrons from the negative plate to the positive plate through the external circuit. The flow of electrons is necessary to the chemical action, which stops if the external circuit is opened. Note that during discharge both plates are converted into lead sulfate, that acid is consumed, and that water is produced. The lead sulfate is insoluble and remains on the plates. The terminal voltage of a single lead cell during discharge is about 2 volts.

If current is driven through the cell in the reverse direction, the chemical actions at the two plates will also be reversed, with the result that the lead sulfate on the positive plate will be converted into lead peroxide, while the lead sulfate on the negative plate will be reduced to spongy lead. Also water will be consumed and acid produced.

207. Construction of the Plates. When fully charged, the positive plates are chocolate in color and the peroxide is hard, while the negative plates are gray in color and the spongy lead is so soft that it can be scraped off with the fingernail.

There are two ways of forming the active material. By the Planté process the material is formed electrochemically out of the lead plate itself, the plates being grooved or made in the form of a grill so as to have a large exposed surface.

Pasted plates are made by spreading a paste of the active material on to a supporting grid of lead hardened with a small quantity of antimony.

Planté plates are used largely for stationary batteries; they are heavier and more costly than pasted plates, but are also more durable and less liable to lose active material by rapid charging and discharging. For automobile and motor-truck service, pasted plates are generally used because they are lighter than Planté plates.

208. Construction of a Lead Battery. To obtain large capacity from a battery, a large surface must be exposed to the electrolyte, and, since the size of a single plate is limited, increased capacity must be obtained by connecting a number of plates in parallel to form a group as shown in Figs. 168 and 169, there being one more plate in the negative than in the positive group. Two sets of plates are then sandwiched together, adjoin-

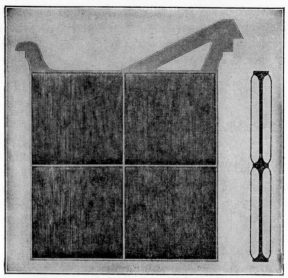

FIG. 167. Planté plate, side view and cross section.

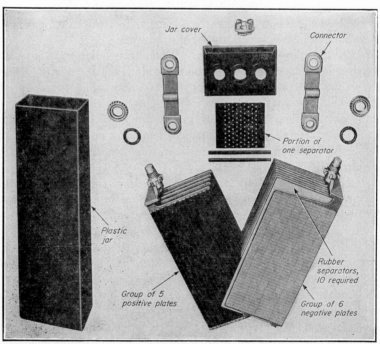

FIG. 168. Exploded view of a lead storage battery. (*Courtesy of Exide Batteries of Canada.*)

ing plates being separated from one another by perforated plastic, hard rubber, or wooden separators.   The plate groups are placed in an acid-proof tank, made of glass, plastic, hard rubber, or wood lined with lead. Covers must always be provided in order to prevent the escape of electrolyte due to spraying when the cells are gassing freely toward the end of the charge.

In the flat-plate type of lead battery, shown in Figs. 168 and 169, the positive plates have a shorter life than the negative plates because of

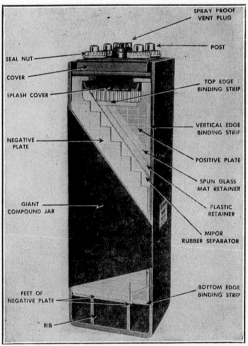

FIG. 169. Cut-away view of completely assembled lead storage battery.   The purpose of the retainers is to minimize the dropping off of active material.   (*Courtesy of Exide Batteries of Canada.*)

greater dropping off of the active material.   In the Exide Iron-clad battery the dropping off of the active material from the positive plates is practically eliminated by enclosing the active material in slotted plastic tubes arranged in rows, as shown in Fig. 170.   Each tube has a thin lead rod down its center, and these rods are joined together at the top to form the positive terminal.   The negative plates are flat as in other lead batteries.

209. Voltage of a Lead Storage Battery.   The internal generated voltage E_i, produced by the chemical action, depends on the strength of the electrolyte and increases slightly as the acid becomes stronger.   It therefore increases during charge and decreases during discharge.   Moreover, since acid is formed in the pores of the active material during charge and water is formed during discharge and since it takes time for the acid or water to diffuse out, it follows that the strength of the acid that is in actual contact with the active material is considerably greater during charge than the average strength of the acid, while during discharge it is considerably less than the average.   Therefore E_i is greater during charge than during discharge, even for the same degree of charge.

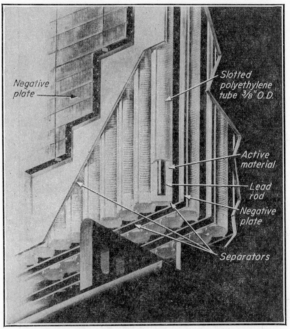

FIG. 170. Cut-away view of Exide Iron-clad lead storage battery. (*Courtesy of Exide Batteries of Canada.*)

The terminal voltage of a battery is equal to $E_i + IR_b$ while charging and to $E_i - IR_b$ while discharging, where R_b is the internal resistance of the battery and I is the current.

Figure 172 shows a series of consecutive alternate discharge and charge curves for the same lead cell at different discharge rates.   The curves were taken in alphabetical order.   In each case the charge was continued until the terminal voltage and the specific gravity of the acid became constant, showing that the active materials were completely formed; the discharge was stopped when the terminal voltage dropped to about 1.8 volts, the minimum safe value at the normal discharge rate.   If the discharge is carried much further than this, it becomes difficult to clear the plates of sulfate on recharging.

The ratio $\dfrac{\text{average voltage on discharge}}{\text{average voltage on charge}}$ is called the volt efficiency.
The higher the rates of charge and discharge, the lower the volt efficiency.
At the normal 8-hr rate of charge and discharge this efficiency is seldom less than 80 per cent.

The *rated capacity of a battery* is given in ampere-hours at a definite discharge rate, generally the 8-hr rate. The actual usable capacity is less at high-discharge rates than at low-discharge rates, because at high rates the action does not penetrate so deeply into the active material, owing to the slowness of the diffusion of the acid.

When a battery is exhausted at a high rate of discharge, as in the prolonged cranking of gasoline engines, the dying away of the voltage is simply due to the fact that all the acid in actual contact with the active material has been consumed. If the battery is allowed to rest for a few minutes, until fresh acid diffuses into

FIG. 171. Central-station type of lead cell.

the plates, the discharge can be repeated. Several discharges can be obtained in this way before the battery finally fails to recuperate, but

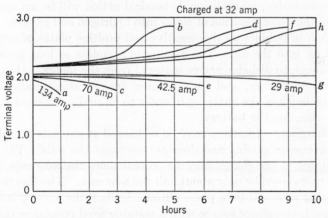

FIG. 172. Charge and discharge curves of the same lead cell at different discharge rates.

each successive discharge will be of shorter duration than the preceding one.

210. Ampere-hour Efficiency. The ratio

$$\frac{\text{ampere-hours output on discharge}}{\text{ampere-hours input to recharge}}$$

is called the ampere-hour efficiency. It would be 100 per cent if it were not for the gassing on charge, which represents a nonreversible chemical reaction (Art. 212). If the charging is discontinued each time, as soon as the gassing becomes appreciable, the ampere-hour efficiency will be nearly 100 per cent. But the ampere-hour capacity obtained from the battery will be less with this method of operation, and it will be advisable to give the battery a full charge from time to time in order to avoid deterioration of the otherwise unused lead sulfate.

The ampere-hour efficiencies, for the four cycles of alternate discharge and charge shown in Fig. 172, work out at 82, 85, 89, and 91 per cent, respectively.

211. Watthour Efficiency. This quantity is

$$\frac{\text{watthr output}}{\text{watthr input to recharge}} = \frac{\text{amp-hr output} \times \text{av discharge voltage}}{\text{amp-hr input} \times \text{av charging voltage}}$$
$$= \text{amp-hr efficiency} \times \text{volt efficiency}$$

Operating at low rates of charge and discharge and at reduced ampere-hour capacity both tend to raise the watthour or energy efficiency. Actual watthour efficiencies obtained in practice range from about 75 to 85 per cent, depending on the type of service.

212. Gassing during Charge. If the charging current is maintained after all the lead sulfate has been converted, or if at any time the charging current is excessive, an additional chemical action will be set up, which consists of the decomposition of water into hydrogen and oxygen. These gases collect in bubbles on the negative and positive plates, respectively, and pass off into the air. The gassing is harmless as long as it is not violent enough to dislodge active material from the plates. However, it means wasted energy, and the charging current is generally reduced toward the finish of the charging in order to minimize the gassing and to avoid overheating the battery.

213. Charging. A battery may be recharged at any rate that does not produce excessive gassing and does not overheat the cells. The rate at the beginning of the charge may be several times the 8-hr rate, but the finishing rate should be only about half the 8-hr rate. The tapering off of the charging rate will take place automatically if the battery is charged from a constant-voltage source with a suitable fixed resistance connected in series, provided that the voltage of the source is only slightly larger than the maximum voltage of the battery. The terminal voltage of the battery rises as the charge progresses and gradually reduces the current.

Figure 173 is a graphical record of a typical charge by this method.   The completion of the charge is indicated by the leveling off of the curves of volts and specific gravity of electrolyte.   There is no lower limit to the rate at which a lead storage battery may be charged.

A battery should be recharged as soon as possible after it has been discharged.   While it will not seriously injure the plates to permit the battery to stand idle for some little time in a discharged state, a persistent repetition of such practice will cause the plates to deteriorate.   The deterioration is caused by the gradual hardening of the lead sulfate into

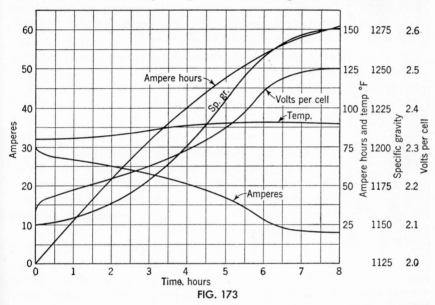

FIG. 173

a form that will not take part in the charging reaction.   This hardening is called *sulfation*.   If a lead storage battery has to stand idle for a long period, it should be left fully charged, and may need an occasional recharge.   The allowable time interval between recharges of an idle battery varies widely with the temperature.   It may be as much as 6 months if the temperature is below 0°C.

Batteries should be overcharged occasionally to minimize sulfation and also to even up the cells and to make sure that they are all charged up to their full capacity.

Evaporation of the electrolyte should be made good by the addition of pure water, the acid does not evaporate, and, unless there is excessive spraying due to the gases given off, the quantity of acid in the cell will not change.

214. Specific Gravity of the Electrolyte.   Increasing the percentage of acid in the electrolyte shortens the life of the battery, but reduces its weight, size, and cost.   Also the voltage characteristics at high discharge rates are substantially improved.   Consequently, automobile batteries use strong electrolytes, the specific gravity ranging from a maximum of 1.300 when fully charged to a minimum of 1.100 when fully discharged. Stationary batteries use a much larger volume of electrolyte, with the result that the specific gravity may vary as little as from 1.210 when fully charged to 1.180 when fully discharged.   The proper range of specific gravities may be obtained from the manufacturers.

The amount of charge in a battery is most accurately determined by measuring the specific gravity of the electrolyte, provided that the maximum and minimum values for that battery are known.   The specific gravity may readily be measured by a hydrometer of the type shown in Fig. 174.

The voltage of a battery is not an accurate index of its condition because the voltage depends largely on the rate of discharge.   Voltage readings on open circuit are of little value because this voltage is almost independent of the amount of charge still in the battery.

215. Applications of Lead Storage Batteries.   Unless the amount of electrical energy required is very small, it can be obtained more cheaply from a storage battery than from a primary battery, provided that charging facilities are readily available.   Lead storage batteries are used for automobile lighting and starting, lighting plants for country residences, lighting on steam-railway trains, submarines, telephone common-battery systems

FIG. 174. Hydrometer for testing the specific gravity of the electrolyte.

in towns and cities, telephone repeater stations and carrier systems, railway signaling, emergency lighting, operating control equipment in powerhouses and substations, and as a reserve on d-c distribution systems to maintain the service in the event of a failure of the normal power supply.   This last application requires batteries of very large size.

216. The Edison Storage Battery.   When fully charged, the active materials are nickel dioxide (NiO_2) at the positive plate and iron (Fe) at the negative plate.   The electrolyte is a solution of potassium hydroxide (KOH) in water.   It has been found that adding lithium hydroxide to the electrolyte results in a more complete utilization of the NiO_2, thus increasing both the capacity and the life.

On discharge the NiO_2 is converted to NiO, and the iron to FeO, while the electrolyte remains unchanged.   The net result therefore is simply a transfer of oxygen from the positive plate to the negative plate, but during this transfer electrons are extracted from the positive plate and are deposited on the negative plate, and the accumulating positive and negative charges will soon stop the chemical action unless the negative charge is allowed to flow over to the positive plate through an external circuit.

Remembering that the KOH dissociates into K^+ and OH^- ions when dissolved in water, the chemical action at the negative plate may be written

$$\text{Fe} + 2OH^- \underset{\text{charge}}{\overset{\text{discharge}}{\rightleftharpoons}} \text{FeO} + H_2O + 2 \text{ electrons}$$

The 2 electrons are deposited on the negative plate. The FeO is not soluble in the electrolyte and remains on the plate.

The chemical action at the positive plate may be written

$$\text{NiO}_2 + 2K^+ + H_2O + 2 \text{ electrons} \underset{\text{charge}}{\overset{\text{discharge}}{\rightleftharpoons}} 2KOH + \text{NiO}$$

Neither the NiO_2 nor the NiO is soluble in the electrolyte and therefore the nickel never leaves the positive plate. Note that the two reactions together consume two molecules of KOH in the dissociated form while the reaction at the positive plate produces two molecules of KOH, so that the strength of the electrolyte does not change.

Both of the discharge reactions desire to take place and both contribute to the potential difference between the two plates. The positive plate is about 0.6 volt above the electrolyte, and the negative plate is about 0.8 volt below the electrolyte, so that the total potential difference is $0.6 + 0.8 = 1.4$ volts.

The foregoing chemical reactions, although sufficient to account for the difference of potential obtained, are not the only reactions that take place in the Edison storage battery. The fully charged positive plate contains NI_2O_3 as well as NiO_2, and on discharge $Ni(OH)_2$ is formed as well as NiO. Also at the negative plate on discharge $Fe(OH)_2$ and Fe_3O_4 are formed as well as FeO, but the general principle of these reactions is the same; namely, that oxygen is transferred from the positive plate to the negative plate on discharge, and in the reverse direction on charge.

Toward the finish of the charging action, hydrogen and oxygen appear at the plates as gases, which bubble up through the electrolyte just as in the lead cell.

217. Construction of the Plates. The positive or nickel plate shown in Fig. 175b consists of a nickel-plated steel grid carrying perforated steel tubes, one of which is shown in Fig. 175a. These tubes are heavily nickel plated and are filled with alternate layers of nickel hydroxide and flaked metallic nickel. The hydroxide is acted on electrochemically and becomes nickel oxide. This oxide is such a poor conductor of electricity that the flaked nickel is added to bring the inner portions of the oxide into metallic contact with the surface of the tubes and thereby reduce the internal resistance of the cell.

The negative or iron plate shown in Fig. 175c consists of a nickel-plated steel grid holding a number of rectangular pockets filled with

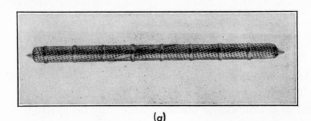

(a)

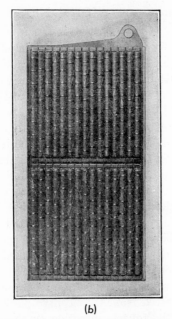

(b)

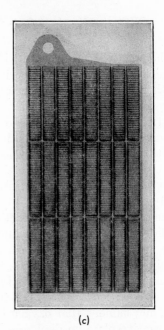

(c)

FIG. 175. Plates of an Edison storage battery. (a) One tube from a positive plate. (b) Thirty tubes assembled to form one positive plate. (c) Negative plate. (*Courtesy of Thomas A. Edison Inc.*)

powdered iron oxide. Each pocket is made of two pieces of perforated steel ribbon flanged at the side to form a little flat box which may be filled from the end.

218. Construction of an Edison Battery. A number of like plates are connected in parallel to form a group, there being one more plate in the negative than in the positive group. Two sets of plates are then sand-

wiched together as shown in Fig. 177, adjoining plates being separated
from one another by strips of hard rubber.

The tank is made of cold-rolled steel welded at the joints, and is heavily
nickel plated as a protection against rust. The top carries two terminals,
as well as a combined gas vent and filling aperture.

The electrolyte used consists of a 21 per cent solution of potash in distilled water to which a small amount of lithia is added. No corrosive

FIG. 176   FIG. 177

FIG. 176. An Edison storage battery consisting of 30 cells in series, and rated 450 amp-hr.
(Courtesy of Thomas A. Edison Inc.)

FIG. 177. Cut-away view of an Edison cell consisting of 8 positive plates and 9 negative
plates. (Courtesy of Thomas A. Edison Inc.)

fumes are given off from this electrolyte, so that no special care need be
taken in mounting the cells.

219. The Voltage of an Edison Battery. Figure 178 shows how the
voltage of an Edison battery changes when the battery is charged and
then discharged. The voltage characteristics are similar to those of a
lead battery.

There is no lower limit to the voltage of an Edison battery because
in it there is nothing equivalent to sulfation, but discharge is not continued below a useful lower limit.

220. Characteristics of an Edison Battery. These batteries are rated
at a 7-hr charging rate and a 5-hr discharge rate with the same current
in each case, the ampere-hour efficiency being about 82 per cent at this

rate and the internal heating not more than permissible. A higher rate of discharge may be used as long as the internal temperature does not exceed about 45°C; continual operation at higher temperatures shortens the life of the cell. A longer charge rate than 7 hr should not be used because, with low currents, the iron element is not completely reduced; this, however, does not permanently injure the cell but makes it necessary to overcharge the cell at normal rate and then discharge it completely to bring it back to normal condition.

Because of the comparatively high internal resistance of the Edison battery, the volt efficiency is lower than in the lead cell, as may readily be seen from Fig. 178, and, since the ampere-hour efficiency is not any higher, the watthour efficiency of the Edison cell is also lower.

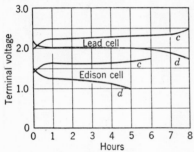

FIG. 178. Charge and discharge curves of a lead cell and an Edison cell. c = charge; d = discharge.

The great advantages of the Edison cell are that it is lighter than the lead cell and is more robust, it can remain charged or discharged for any length of time without injury, and so little sediment is formed that the makers seal it up. Since no acid fumes are given off, the cell may be placed in the same room as other machinery without risk of corrosion of that machinery. It also has a long life, although the electrolyte must be changed from time to time, whenever its specific gravity falls below 1.16. When it is desired to change the electrolyte, the battery should first be completely discharged down to zero voltage and left short-circuited for 2 hr or more. Refill with the new electrolyte immediately after dumping out the old. Never allow the cells to stand empty, and never let the level of the electrolyte drop below the tops of the plates. Distilled water must be added from time to time to make up for the loss of water by gassing. When it is desired to take the battery out of service for a long period, simply discharge down to zero voltage and store the battery with the terminals short-circuited. The Edison cell is not damaged by freezing.

Note this striking contrast between the lead battery and the Edison battery, that the lead battery *must be fully charged* before storing, while the Edison *should be completely discharged* before storing, although it suffers little or no permanent injury from being stored in a charged condition.

The chief disadvantages of the Edison cell are its high cost, low efficiency, and high internal resistance. Since the lead cell is both cheaper and more efficient than the Edison cell, it is very much more extensively used. In fact, the Edison cell may be regarded as a special-service cell to be used only where lightness, freedom from acid fumes, or ability to withstand neglect are particularly important, and where momentary high discharge currents are not required, since its high internal resistance will not allow it to deliver such currents.

Problems

24-1. *a.* Twelve primary cells, each having an emf on no load of 1.5 volts and an internal resistance of 0.25 ohm, are connected in parallel to an external circuit that has a resistance of 0.5 ohm.   What is the current in the external circuit; also that in each cell?

b. If the twelve cells are connected in two parallel groups of six in series, what is then the current in the external circuit and that in each cell?

c. If one of the cells in this latter case is taken out of circuit, what is then the current in the external circuit and that in each cell?   What also will be the circulating current if the external circuit is disconnected?

24-2. *a.* Taking the curves of charge and discharge given in Fig. 178, page 234, what is the volt efficiency for a lead cell and also for an Edison cell?

b. If the rating of the lead cell is 100 amp-hr, at the 8-hr rate, what current can be drawn from this cell for 8 hr and what will be the voltage of the cell at the end of this time?   If the cell takes 14.5 amp for 8 hr to recharge, what is the ampere-hour and the watthour efficiency?

c. What current may be drawn from this cell at the 4-hr rate?

24-3. A small storage battery with three cells in series and a capacity of 100 amp-hr at the 8-hr rate is charged from 110-volt mains at the 8-hr rate.   What is the battery voltage at the beginning of the charge and at the end (see Fig. 178)? Specify the charging resistance.   What does it cost to charge the battery if the cost of charging is 8 cents per kwhr?   What would it cost to charge four such batteries in series?

*24-4. What is meant by the capacity of a storage battery?   Why is the rating made in ampere-hours?   What effect has the discharge rate on the capacity?

*24-5. Discuss the precautions that must be taken in the operation of lead cells.

*24-6. What is meant by volt efficiency of a battery?   Ampere-hour efficiency? Watthour efficiency?

25

OPERATION OF STORAGE BATTERIES

221. Voltage Control. The chief difficulty in the operation of storage batteries is that the terminal emf varies over a wide range between full charge and complete discharge. The voltage of a lead cell reaches about 2.6 volts during the finish of the charge, begins the discharge at about 2.1 volts, and drops to 1.85 volts at the end of the discharge. Thus a 55-cell battery, which would nominally be called a 110-volt battery, actually varies from 143 to 102 volts. This is much too large a variation for most practical applications, and various methods have been developed to overcome it. These may be classified as (1) end-cell control, (2) counter-emf cell control, (3) resistance control, (4) booster control, and (5) carbon-pile voltage regulator.

Note that, if the battery can be taken out of service during charging, most of the need for voltage control disappears, but it is not usually feasible to do so. In some small isolated residence-lighting systems, however, the load is disconnected while charging the battery, and no voltage control of any kind is used.

222. End-cell Control. This method is illustrated in Fig. 179. Whenever it is desired to shut down the generator, switch S is opened, and the battery then carries the load. While the battery is being charged, switch S is closed to the right, and the charging current is regulated by means of the generator field rheostat. The end-cell switch C_2 enables the proper voltage to be applied to the load at all times, while the other end-cell switch C_1 is required so as to avoid overcharging the end cells. If it is desired to take the battery off the line for repairs or servicing, the generator is started up and switch S is thrown to the left. The battery circuit breaker may then be opened.

In order that the end-cell switch may not open the circuit when passing from one contact to that adjoining, or short-circuit any one cell, this switch is generally constructed as shown diagrammatically in the detail diagram, Fig. 179, with a main contact a and an auxiliary contact b electrically connected through a resistance r but otherwise insulated from one

236

another. As the switch is moved over the contacts, it bridges one cell for a moment, but the resistance r keeps the current that flows through this cell from being dangerously large.

Since the end cells are gradually put in circuit as discharge proceeds, they are never so completely discharged as the rest of the battery, so that, when the battery is being recharged with all the cells in series, the end cells should be cut out one by one as they become fully charged and begin to gas freely.

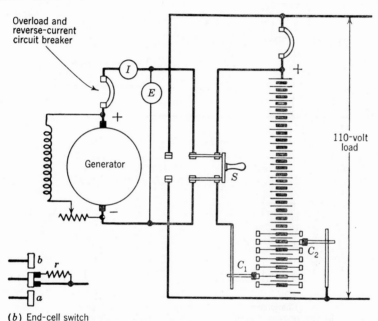

(*b*) End-cell switch

FIG. 179. End-cell system of battery control—charging.

223. Counter-electromotive-force Control. Electrolytic cells are connected in the line on the load side of the battery, as shown in Fig. 180. These cells consist of nickel plates immersed in an alkaline solution. They are not batteries and no current flows through them if they are short-circuited, but, if a current is driven through them, water is split up into hydrogen and oxygen at the plates and a counter emf of about 2 volts is set up in each cell. Enough of these cells must be provided to hold the line voltage E_l down to a satisfactory value during the finishing charge. They are short-circuited out one by one during discharge as required.

A variable resistance could be used in place of the counter-emf cells but the great superiority of the cells is that their counter emf varies only lightly with the current, whereas the IR drop in a resistance is directly proportional to the current.   Consequently, if during the finishing charge a large part of the load were switched off, the IR drop would practically disappear, and the voltage impressed on the remaining load would be practically that across the battery.   This would be high enough to burn out electric lamps in a short time.   Consequently, it is not safe simply to substitute resistance for the counter-emf cells of Fig. 180 without further modification.

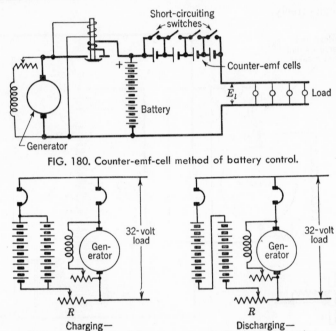

FIG. 180. Counter-emf-cell method of battery control.

FIG. 181. Resistance system of battery control.

224. Resistance Control.   The danger, mentioned in the preceding article, of excessive voltage appearing across the load during charging when resistance control is used may be eliminated by dividing the battery into two sections and connecting these two sections in parallel while charging and in series while discharging.   Figure 181 shows the connections for this method of operation.   The voltage of the generator is kept constant at 32 volts, while the resistance R regulates the rates of charge and discharge.   An ammeter and voltmeter are, of course, required to guide the operator.

This method of operation is wasteful of energy and is therefore only suited to small installations.   Approximately 36 per cent of the energy is wasted in the resistance R during charging and another 8 per cent while discharging.

225. Booster Control. The fundamental idea of this type of control is illustrated in Fig. 182, where a small low-voltage d-c generator, called a booster, is shown connected in series with the battery. The magnitude of the emf generated by the booster can be controlled by means of the booster-field rheostat, while its direction can be reversed by reversing the field terminals. When it is desired to charge the battery, the booster field is given the proper polarity to make the emf of the booster oppose the emf of the battery, whereas, when it is desired to have the battery carry part or all of the load, the emf of the booster is reversed, so that it assists the battery. With this arrangement the emf of the main generator may be kept constant, while the booster compensates for the voltage variations inherent in battery operation and also controls the rates of charge and discharge.

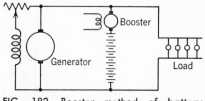

FIG. 182. Booster method of battery control.

The operation of the booster is usually made partly automatic by means of various combinations of shunt and series fields. Sometimes the booster is used only for charging and is shorted out during discharge.

226. Carbon-pile Voltage Regulator. The most widely used systems of car lighting on steam passenger trains employ storage batteries, shunt-excited generators, and carbon-pile regulators. Figure 183 is a simplified schematic diagram of the regulator on the lamp side of the battery. Sometimes only one carbon pile is used, but two, connected in cascade as in Fig. 183, provide a much closer control of the voltage.

If the battery is being charged, then the voltage E_b increases and the lamp voltage E_l also increases slightly. This increases the pull on the plunger a, which increases the pressure on the carbon pile r and decreases its resistance. More current therefore flows in the coil b, which is connected in series with r across the lamp circuit, so that the plunger b is raised and the pressure on the carbon pile R is decreased and its resistance increased. The greater part of the increased battery voltage is therefore absorbed by the resistance R and the lamp voltage remains approximately constant.

The shunt-excited charging generator is driven from an axle of the car, and the rate of charging is controlled by another carbon-pile regulator.

227. Automobile-battery Charging. The problem is to obtain completely automatic charging from a generator that is belted to the engine shaft, and which consequently operates at widely varying speeds. The generator is usually an ordinary shunt-excited machine, designed to generate the battery voltage at a car speed of about 10 mph. The charging current is limited to a safe maximum by a vibrating-type current regulator, shown at A, Fig. 184.

At start the field resistor R_1 is shorted out by the contacts of regulators A and V, both of which are in the closed position. As soon as the charging current reaches the limit for which the spring is set, the contacts open at A, thus inserting R_2 in parallel with R_1, in place of the short. The field current immediately begins to decrease, and so does the generator voltage and the charging current, whereupon the contacts at A close, causing the field current, generator voltage, and charging current to rise again. This

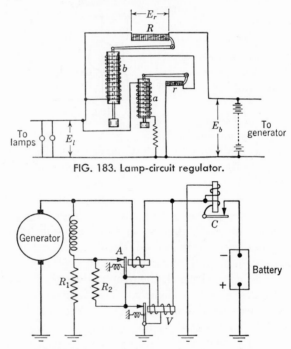

FIG. 183. Lamp-circuit regulator.

FIG. 184. Automobile-battery-charging regulators.

cycle is repeated many times per second, with the result that the charging current pulsates slightly but does not exceed the limit set. The proportion of the cycle during which the contacts of A are open is roughly proportional to the car speed.

The purpose of the vibrating-type voltage regulator V is to reduce the charging rate to a mere trickle as the battery becomes fully charged. As the charge nears completion, the voltage of the battery rises, as shown in Fig. 172, and V opens its contacts, thus removing the parallel path entirely. The field current and the charging current immediately begin to decrease, whereupon V recloses its contacts, the reclosing being greatly accelerated by the fact that when it opened its contacts it interrupted the current through its series winding. If this series winding were omitted, V would vibrate too slowly for satisfactory operation, because of the voltage changes being so small relative to the changes in charging current.

The cutout C disconnects the battery from the generator whenever the voltage of the generator drops below that of the battery.

The basic system illustrated in Fig. 184 is used extensively, and various modifications of it are also employed.

Problems

25-1. A 115-volt lighting load on a country estate is to be carried by a lead storage battery, and the battery must be charged without taking it out of service. A voltage variation from 113 to 120 volts at the battery is considered permissible. How many cells will be required?

a. If end-cell control is used, how many cells must be controlled by the end-cell switch?

b. If counter-emf cell control is used, how many counter-emf cells will be required?

c. If resistance control is used, as in Fig. 181, and the total charging current is to be 10 amp, what is the maximum value of resistance required?

d. If a booster is used to control during both charge and discharge, how many cells will be required, and what should be the voltage rating of the booster?

25-2. A small isolated power plant has a day load of 50 hp, at 110 volts, and a night load of twenty-five 40-watt 110-volt tungsten lamps. The lamp load has to be carried for 12 hr by a storage battery. Assume charging as in Fig. 181, and a total charging current of 30 amp. Specify the battery, the charging resistance, the size of the generator, and the horsepower of the engine. State the assumptions made.

26

DIRECT-CURRENT TRANSMISSION AND DISTRIBUTION

228. Size of Conductor. The size of the conductor to be used to carry a given current may be determined by any one of the following three factors: (1) permissible temperature rise of the conductor; (2) permissible voltage drop in the conductor; (3) an economic balance between the value of the I^2R loss in the conductor and the capital charges against the conductor.

1. Permissible temperature rise is always the determining factor in deciding what size of conductor should be used in the windings of electric machines or in the wiring of small buildings. It is also usually the determining factor in the case of insulated power cables where the insulation would be damaged to the point of failure if the temperature exceeded certain rather low limits.

In order to minimize the danger of fire being caused by overheated electric conductors, the maximum currents to be carried by the various sizes of copper conductors, when used for interior wiring, have been limited by the National Electric Code (see Table 12 in the Appendix).

2. Permissible voltage drop in the conductor is often the determining factor in deciding upon the sizes of conductors to be used in distributing electrical energy in d-c lighting systems. The amount of light emitted by tungsten lamps varies widely with the voltage, and the lighting is generally considered unsatisfactory if the voltage varies from the rated voltage by more than 5 to 8 per cent, depending upon the quality of service to which the public has become accustomed.

3. The power loss in a conductor is equal to I^2R watts, where R is the resistance of the conductor. This loss is therefore inversely proportional to the cross-sectional area of the conductor. The capital cost of the conductor is approximately directly proportional to the size of the conductor. Consequently, as the size of the conductor is increased, the value of the

power loss decreases, while the interest charges increase, and therefore there must be a size of conductor which will make the sum of these two costs a minimum. The application of this principle is best illustrated by means of a simple example.

Example. Determine the most economical size of conductor to carry a direct current of 5,000 amp in an electrolytic refining plant, given that the electric power is bought at a flat rate of $40 per year per kw, that copper bus bar in place costs 60 cts a pound, and that interest and depreciation together are to be taken at 10 per cent per annum.

A copper conductor 1 sq in. in cross section has a resistance of 0.0091 ohm per 1,000 ft at 50°C and weighs 3,850 lb per 1,000 ft.

$$\text{Capital cost} = 3,850 \times 0.60 = \$2,310.00 \text{ per } 1,000 \text{ ft}$$
$$\text{Annual interest charge} = 10 \text{ per cent} = \$231.00 \text{ per } 1,000 \text{ ft}$$
$$\text{Power loss} = I^2R = 5,000^2 \times 0.0091 = 227.5 \text{ kw per } 1,000 \text{ ft}$$
$$\text{Annual value of power loss} = 40 \times 227.5 = \$9,100.00 \text{ per } 1,000 \text{ ft}$$
$$\text{Interest} + \text{value of power loss} = 231 + 9,100 = \$9,331 \text{ per } 1,000 \text{ ft}$$

If the cross section is increased to 2 sq in., the capital cost and the interest will be doubled, and the power loss and its value will be cut in half. Thus the costs for any other size of conductor can be determined by simple proportion and listed in a table as shown below.

(1)	(2)	(3)	(4)	(5)	(6)
Conductor cross section, sq in.	Capital cost of copper	Annual interest on copper	Power loss, kw	Annual value of power loss	(3) + (5)
1	$ 2,310	$ 231	227.50	$9,100	$9,331
2	4,620	462	113.75	4,550	5,012
3	6,930	693	75.83	3,033	3,726
4	9,240	924	56.87	2,275	3,199
5	11,550	1,155	45.50	1,820	2,975
6	13,860	1,386	37.91	1,517	2,903
7	16,170	1,617	32.50	1,300	2,917
8	18,480	1,848	28.44	1,137	2,985
9	20,790	2,079	25.09	1,011	3,090
10	23,100	2,310	22.75	910	3,220

The foregoing calculation ignores the fact that the temperature of the copper would be different at different current densities and that therefore the specific resistance would not actually be constant. Taking this into account would modify the power-loss figures to some extent, but, since the curve of total cost is quite flat at its minimum, the exact location of that minimum is not important.

From this table it appears that the most economical size of copper bus bar to carry the 5,000 amp is one with a cross section of 6.3 sq in.   Or, in other words, the most economical current density for the particular cost data given is

$$\frac{5,000}{6.3} = 800 \text{ amp per sq in.}$$

In this particular problem the variation in the cost of the supporting structures was negligible, but, when the conductors are wires or cables strung on poles or steel towers, the cost of the poles or towers increases with the size of the conductor, and therefore the calculation involves three variable costs instead of two.

In many cases the current to be carried by the conductors will increase from year to year as new loads are connected to the system.   In such cases the calculation of the most economical size of conductor becomes much more laborious, and the accuracy of the result depends largely upon the engineer's prophetic abilities.

229. Choice of Voltage.   Power = volts × amperes; 10 kw can be delivered by 1 amp at 10,000 volts, 10 amp at 1,000 volts, 100 amp at 100 volts, 10,000 amp at 1 volt, or by any other combination of volts and amperes whose product equals 10,000, but the cost will not be the same for all voltages.   If the power is to be constant, then every time the voltage is doubled the current is cut in half, and therefore, if the most economical size of conductor is used, the size of the conductor is cut in half, and the I^2R loss is cut in half.   On the other hand, the higher the voltage, the greater the cost of insulating the conductors.   If the conductors are provided with an insulating coating, its cost is practically constant up to 600 volts and then increases gradually with the voltage.   If the conductors are bare and are supported by porcelain insulators, the cost of the insulators is negligible up to several thousand volts.   The table on page 245 gives a fair idea of the way in which the cost of the insulators increases with the voltage.

Considering the transmission line alone, the most economical voltage to use, in transmitting a given amount of power, may be determined by calculating the capital cost of the line and the value of the I^2R loss in the line, for a number of different voltages.   The sum of the annual interest and depreciation charges and the annual value of the I^2R loss may then be plotted on a voltage base.   The voltage at which this sum is a minimum is the most economical voltage to use.   Inasmuch as the capital cost of the copper and the value of the I^2R loss are both inversely proportional to the voltage, while the capital cost of the insulators is very small up to several thousand volts, it follows that as far as the transmission line itself is concerned the most economical voltage to use will in general be

	Cost of one
Volts	*insulator*
4,000	$ 0.21
6,900	0.41
13,800	1.00
23,000	2.60
34,000	3.30
46,000	5.00
69,000	8.40
115,000	25.00
230,000	50.00

quite high.   And, in fact, the major transmission lines operate at voltages of from 110,000 to 380,000 volts.   These lines, however, are all alternating current.

In spite of the fact that economical transmission requires high voltages, the voltages actually used on d-c systems are all rather low: 115 to 230 volts for lighting and small motors, 600 volts for street railways, and 1,200 to 3,000 volts for mainline electric railways.   The reason why such low voltages are used is that it is impracticable to build the motors, lamps, heaters, etc., which consume the electrical energy, to operate at high voltages, and in any case safety considerations frequently limit the voltage on the consuming apparatus to a low value, where such apparatus is to be operated by or is accessible to the general public.

What is really required therefore is a safe, reliable, and inexpensive device, which can be inserted between the transmission line and the consuming apparatus, to convert the high voltage and low current of the economical transmission line into the low voltage and high current required by the consuming apparatus, that is, a piece of apparatus to perform the same function in electrical transmission that a pair of reduction gears does in mechanical transmission, in which a high torque and low speed are readily and efficiently converted into a low torque and high speed or vice versa.   A suitable device of this type has not as yet been developed for d-c systems, but in a-c systems we have a very satisfactory piece of apparatus to perform this operation, called the transformer, and that is the main reason why a-c systems are used so extensively.   In a-c systems the transformer enables the transmission lines to be operated at the high voltages required for economical transmission and the consuming devices to be operated at the low voltages required for such apparatus. The power loss in the transformer is usually less than 2 per cent, and it is a stationary piece of apparatus that requires practically no attention.

230. Series and Multiple Systems of Distribution.   There are two methods of distributing electrical energy, the series system and the multiple system.   In the series system the energy-consuming devices are connected in series as in Fig. 185.   In the multiple system they are all con-

nected in parallel as in Fig. 186.   The series system is confined almost
entirely to street lighting and electrolytic refining and smelting plants.
In the series street-lighting system the lamps are all designed to carry the
same current, and all the lamps on any one circuit are connected in series.
If one of these lamps burns out, it is short-circuited by an automatic cutout.   This decreases the resistance of the circuit by the amount of the
resistance of one lamp and the current accordingly rises.   The increase of

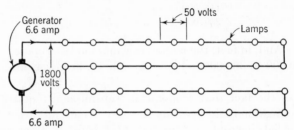

FIG. 185. Series system of distribution, as used for street lighting.   Thirty-six lamps at
50 volts each equal 1,800 volts.

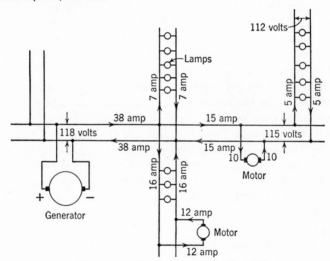

FIG. 186. Multiple system of distribution.

current operates an automatic regulating device at the supply station,
which reduces the voltage and brings the current back to its normal value.
The advantage of the series system is that it is a high-voltage low-current
system, which makes for economical transmission, as explained in Art.
229.   It is, however, suitable only for the operation of loads which are
practically identical and which go on and off together.

The multiple system shown in Fig. 186 is the standard system for
distributing electrical energy.   Each load unit can be operated quite

independently of any other loads on the system, except in so far as the voltage drop in the line is affected. In the system shown, the voltage varies from 118 volts at the generator to 112 volts at the point farthest from the generator, the average voltage being 115. The lamps are rated at 115 volts and therefore no lamp is operated at more than 3 volts above or below its rated voltage. The variation in voltage is, of course, due to the IR drop in the line.

231. Edison Three-wire System. The three-wire system was devised in order to enable the distribution to be carried out at double the voltage at which the loads operate, thus effecting a substantial saving in the

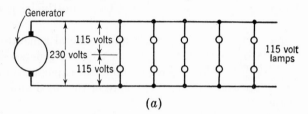

(a)

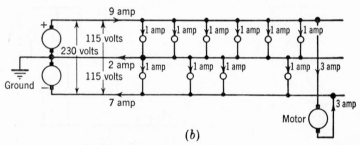

(b)

FIG. 187. Three-wire system of distribution.

amount of copper required and in the I^2R losses (see Art. 229). The first step in the development of the three-wire system was to operate the lamps in pairs, the two 115-volt lamps being connected in series across a 230-volt line as shown in Fig. 187a. The next step was to devise some means whereby each lamp of the pair could be switched on and off independently of the other lamp. This was accomplished by stringing a third wire as shown in Fig. 187b and feeding the system from two 115-volt generators connected in series. Thus if there are six lamps connected to the positive side and four to the negative side, then four of the six lamps on the positive side may be considered as connected in series with the four on the negative side, the four pairs being fed at 230 volts, while the remaining two lamps on the positive side are fed at 115 volts. The third wire is generally called the neutral wire because it is grounded and is therefore at zero potential, while the positive wire is at a potential 115 volts above ground and the negative wire 115 volts below ground.

Fractional-horsepower motors are generally 115 volts and are connected to the line in the same way that the lamps are, but all larger motors are 230 volts and are connected across the outer wires, as shown. Since the neutral wire carries only the unbalanced current, it may be considerably smaller than the outers.

Wherever the d-c multiple system of distribution is used, it is always three-wire. In Europe the idea was carried further by going to five-wire systems, the major part of the distribution being then carried out at four times the lamp voltage. These systems have mostly been discarded, however.

In large three-wire systems, which require several generators to feed them, the majority of the generators may be 230-volt generators and connected only across the outers, as long as sufficient capacity is provided in the pairs of 115-volt generators to take care of the maximum unbalance that might arise.

232. Three-wire Balancer Sets. The three-wire system may be fed entirely from 230-volt generators if three-wire balancer sets are provided

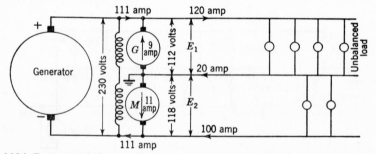

FIG. 188A. Three-wire balancer set, showing possible values of voltages and currents when carrying an unbalanced load.

to transfer energy from the lightly loaded side to the heavily loaded side, as required. The three-wire balancer set consists of two identical 115-volt d-c machines mounted on the same shaft and connected in series as shown in Fig. 188A. When the loads are balanced, these two machines run as motors and draw only enough power to supply their losses, and, since the machines are identical and the applied voltage and the field current are the same, they tend to run at exactly the same speed, and there is no torque in the connecting shaft.

Suppose for a moment that the balancer set is not there, that 120 lamps are connected across the positive side and 100 across the negative side, and that the resistance of each lamp is 115 ohms. Then the resistance of the load from the positive outer to the neutral is equal to the resistance of one lamp divided by the number of lamps in parallel, that is, it is equal to $^{115}\!\!/_{120} = 0.958$ ohm. The resistance from the neutral to the negative outer is $^{115}\!\!/_{100} = 1.15$ ohms. The total resistance of the two in series is $0.958 + 1.15 = 2.108$ ohms.

$$\text{Current} = \frac{230}{2.108} = 109.1 \text{ amp}$$

therefore $E_1 = 109.1 \times 0.958 = 104.6$ volts
and $E_2 = 109.1 \times 1.15 \;\;= 125.4$ volts
$$E_1 + E_2 = \overline{230.0} \text{ volts}$$

Each lamp on the positive side carries $\dfrac{109.1}{120} = 0.91$ amp

Each lamp on the negative side carries $\dfrac{109.1}{100} = 1.091$ amp

From the foregoing calculation it appears that increasing the load on the positive side decreases E_1 and increases E_2. When the balancer set

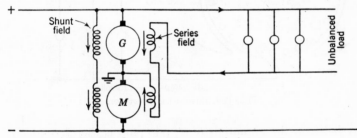

FIG. 188B. Compound three-wire balancer set.

is running, the back voltages of the two machines are the same and are nearly equal to 115 volts. Consequently, a decrease in E_1 causes machine G to act as a generator and to supply current to the heavily loaded side, while an increase in E_2 causes machine M to speed up and drive the generator G. In this way, energy is transferred from the lightly loaded side to the heavily loaded side.

The balancer set can be made more effective in equalizing the voltages E_1 and E_2 by adding series-field coils connected as shown in Fig. 188B. The unbalanced current flows through the series coils, increasing the flux in the generator G and so raising its generated voltage, and decreasing the flux in the motor M and so causing it to speed up slightly and still further raise the generated voltage of G.

233. Three-wire Generator. A third way of taking care of the unbalanced current is to use a three-wire generator. Figure 189 shows how the neutral wire is connected to the generator. A reactance coil C is connected across two diametrically opposite points on the armature winding, through slip rings (not shown), and the neutral wire is connected to the center of the coil.   When a is at the plus brush, b is at the minus brush and 230 volts are impressed across the coil.   When a and b are at the centers of the poles, there is no emf across the coil, and, when a is at the minus brush and b at the plus brush, 230 volts are again impressed on the coil, but in the reverse direction.   Thus the emf impressed upon the coil by the generator is an alternating emf, and, since the inductance of the coil C is very high, very little current is caused to flow through it by this alternating emf.[1]   The potential at the center tap of the coil C is always

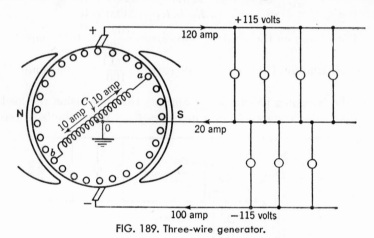

FIG. 189. Three-wire generator.

midway between the potentials of a and b and is therefore always zero. The neutral current, being direct current, flows very easily through the reactance coil.

This is the cheapest method of obtaining a three-wire system and is the one generally used in privately owned localized plants, such as are frequently found in large office buildings, department stores, hotels, hospitals, and universities.

233A. Direct-current Watthour Meter.   This meter is a small slow-speed d-c motor complete with armature winding, commutator and field coils, as shown in Fig. 190 but containing no iron in its magnetic circuit. The rotating armature drives a chain of reducing gears and dials that record the kilowatthours consumed by the load.

The torque developed in the armature is given by the equation $T = K\phi I_a$, where ϕ is the field flux produced by the line current I and I_a is the armature current.

$$I_a = \frac{E - E_g}{R_a}$$

---

[1] The theory of the three-wire generator will be understood much more readily after reading Chap. 29.

where E_g is the back voltage generated in the armature, R_a is the resistance of the armature winding plus the resistance R, and E is the line voltage.

Now E_g is very small, since the speed is low and the field is weak; consequently I_a is practically proportional to E and is constant if E is constant. In a 110-volt meter, R_a is of the order of 2,500 ohms so that I_a is about 0.044 amp.

Since there is no iron in the magnetic circuit, ϕ is proportional to I, and therefore, since I_a is proportional to E as explained above, it follows

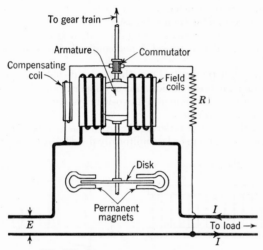

FIG. 190. Direct-current watthour meter.

that the torque is proportional to EI; that is, the torque is proportional to the power in the load circuit.

If the dials are to record kilowatthours correctly at all loads, the speed of the meter must be directly proportional to the power; and since the driving torque is directly proportional to the power, it follows that a brake torque must be provided directly proportional to the speed. This is accomplished by mounting a flat aluminum disk on the armature shaft and placing permanent magnets so that their fluxes are cut by the rotating disk, as shown in Fig. 190. The eddy currents produced in the disk are directly proportional to the speed and develop a brake torque directly proportional to the speed.

The compensating coil increases the driving torque by a small amount which is constant if I_a is constant, that is, if E is constant. The position of the compensating coil is adjusted on test to make the torque resulting from its field equal to the friction brake torque at the brushes and bearings and in the gear train. In this way the effect of friction is practically eliminated, but compensation is correct at one voltage only, and the friction may increase with years of service.

Problems

26-1. Determine the most economical current density to use in copper bus bars when (*a*) power is bought at $30 per year per kw of maximum demand and (*b*) power[1] is bought at 1 cent per kwhr, and the plant operates at full load for 8 hr a day, 310 days a year. Assume that interest and depreciation may be taken as 9 per cent, and that copper bus costs 50 cents a pound in place.

26-2. A 230-volt 10-hp d-c motor is located 600 ft from the power supply and is to be fed by code-type rubber-insulated copper conductors in iron-pipe conduit. Assuming that the efficiency of the motor is 83 per cent:

a. What size of conductor should be used?

b. If, on account of some auxiliary equipment, it is specified that the voltage drop in the feeder shall not exceed 5 per cent, what size of conductor will be required?

26-3. Assuming that the neutral of a three-wire distribution system is one-half the size of the outers, express the amount of copper in the three-wire system as a percentage of the amount of copper in a two-wire system to supply the same loads, with the same voltage variation.

26-4. To show the effect of tapering the main conductors of a distribution system on which the load is more or less uniformly distributed, consider the following

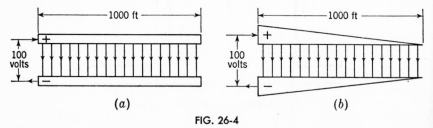

(*a*)   (*b*)

FIG. 26-4

idealized case. In Fig. 26-4*a* the main conductors, marked + and −, each have a uniform cross section of 6 sq in. The load of 4,000 amp is uniformly distributed, as indicated, so that 4 amp leave each foot of positive conductor. In Fig. 26-4*b* the same load is fed by conductors that have been tapered so that the current density in them is everywhere the same. Assuming that both types of mains are made of copper with a resistance of 11.5 ohms per cir mil-ft and that the amount of copper in the tapered mains is the same as in the uniform mains, calculate the power loss in the mains for both cases. Also calculate the voltage between conductors at the far end and at the mid-point for both mains.

26-5. A d-c watthour meter is fundamentally a shunt motor; yet its speed is directly proportional to its field current, while the speed of an ordinary shunt motor is approximately inversely proportional to its field current. Explain this paradox.

---

[1] Strictly speaking this word should be "energy" and not "power," but "power" is the word in general commercial use.

27

ALTERNATING VOLTAGES AND CURRENTS

234. Simple Alternating-current Generators. If the single-turn coil *abcd*, shown in perspective in diagram *E*, Fig. 191, is mounted on a cylindrical armature core of laminated iron, as shown in cross section in diagrams *A*, *B*, *C*, and *D*, and is rotated between the poles *N* and *S* so

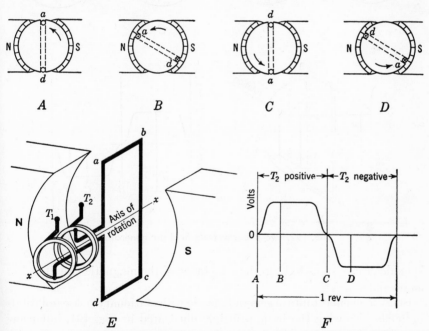

FIG. 191. Simple two-pole alternator (a-c generator) with stationary poles.

that conductors *ab* and *cd* cut lines of flux, an alternating emf will be generated in these conductors and will appear across the terminals T_1T_2. The conductors *bc* and *da*, which complete the internal circuit, and which are called the *end connections*, cut only leakage flux and the earth's field, and no appreciable emf is induced in them. The directions of the emfs in conductors ab and cd are shown in diagrams A, B, C, and D, for different positions of the conductors relative to the poles.   In diagrams A and C the conductors are not cutting flux, and the emf is zero.   In diagram B the emfs are in the directions d to c and b to a, thus adding, and making terminal T_2 positive.   In diagram D the emfs are in the direction a to b and c to d, thus adding, and making T_1 positive.   The graph of the emf on a time base is shown in diagram F.   If an external circuit is connected to terminals T_1 and T_2, an alternating current will flow, that is, electricity will oscillate back and forth in the circuit.   The cylindrical armature core

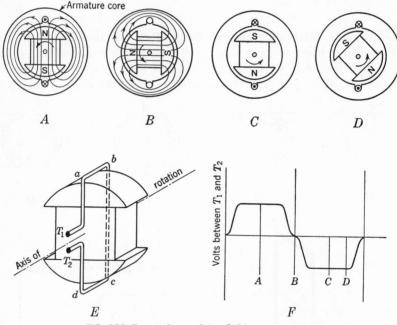

FIG. 192. Two-pole revolving-field a-c generator.

is made of iron so as to keep the reluctance of the magnetic circuit as low as possible.

Small a-c generators are generally made with stationary poles and rotating coils, following the basic principle illustrated in Fig. 191, but using several coils connected in series.   Large a-c generators are made with stationary coils and rotating poles, as shown diagrammatically in Fig. 192. Diagram A shows the generator in cross section, while diagram E shows the rotor and coil in perspective, with the armature core omitted for the sake of clarity.   As indicated in diagram A the flux from the rotating magnet divides, half returning each way through the armature core.   The directions of the emfs in conductors ab and cd are shown in diagrams A, B,

C, and D, for different positions of the rotor relative to the coil. The graph of the emf on a time base is shown in diagram F.

235. The Wave Form. If the air gap between the poles and the armature core is of uniform length, as in Figs. 191 and 192, then the strength of the magnetic field is uniform across the pole faces, and the generated emf, being proportional to the rate of cutting of the lines of flux, varies as in diagram F of Figs. 191 and 192. If, however, the pole face is shaped as in Fig. 193, the flux density in the air gap, and therefore the rate of cutting of flux, may be so regulated that the generated emf in each conductor will

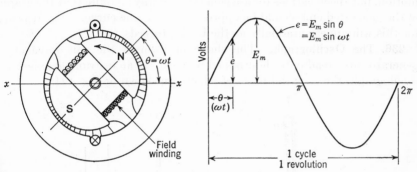

FIG. 193. Generating a sine wave of emf. (The field winding is fed through slip rings, not shown.)

vary according to a sine wave equation. The emf is then said to be *simple harmonic*, and may be represented by the equation

$$e = E_m \sin \theta \qquad (47)$$

where e is the emf generated at any instant, E_m is the maximum value of e, and θ is the angle that the magnetic axis NS of the rotor makes with the horizontal line xx. Now θ is directly proportional to the time, and it will be convenient, and sometimes necessary, to express θ as a function of the time.

Let f = the frequency of the emf wave, in cycles per second. At the end of one cycle,

$$\theta = 2\pi \text{ radians}$$

At the end of f cycles, that is, at the end of 1 sec,

$$\theta = 2\pi f \text{ radians}$$

At the end of t sec,

$$\theta = 2\pi f t \text{ radians}$$
$$= \omega t \text{ radians}$$

where $\omega = 2\pi f$ = number of radians per second.

Therefore Eq. (47) may be written

$$e = E_m \sin \omega t \tag{48}$$

Simple harmonic motion is the smoothest form of reciprocating motion. A mass suspended by a spiral spring oscillates vertically with simple harmonic motion, and so does the pendulum of a clock. In fact, mechanical oscillations are generally simple harmonic motion. It would be unwise at this early stage of the discussion to attempt to explain why it is so desirable that alternating currents should flow with simple harmonic motion, but specifications for a-c generators always require that the graph of the generated emf should be approximately a sine curve. The reasons for this will appear gradually as the book proceeds.

236. The Oscillograph. The shape or form of the emf wave of a generator may readily be determined by means of an instrument called an oscillograph, the essential parts of which are shown in Fig. 194.

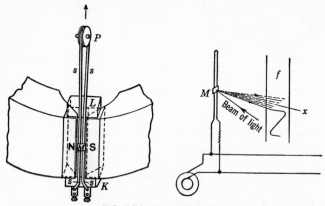

FIG. 194. The oscillograph.

In the narrow gap between the poles NS of a magnet are stretched two parallel conductors ss formed by bending a strip of phosphor bronze back on itself over an ivory pulley P. A spiral spring attached to this pulley serves to keep a uniform tension on the strips, and a guide piece L limits the length of the vibrating portion to the part actually in the magnetic field. A small mirror M bridges across the strips as shown.

If current is passed through the strips ss, then one strip will advance and the other will recede and the mirror will thereby be tilted about a vertical axis. If the current is alternating, then the mirror will tilt backward and forward with a frequency equal to that of the current, and the deflection will be proportional to the current. (The natural frequency of vibration of the mirror must be considerably higher than the frequency of the current or else the deflection will not follow the current variations accurately.)

If now a beam of light is directed on the mirror, the reflected beam will move to and fro in the horizontal plane, its displacement from the zero position x being proportional to the current flowing, so that, if a photographic film f is moved downward at a constant speed, a curve will be traced on it by the beam of light. This curve will be the wave of the emf applied at the oscillograph terminals.

Another widely used type of oscillograph is described in Chap. 41.

237. Frequency. In the two-pole machine shown in Fig. 193, the emf between the terminals passes through a complete cycle while the rotor makes one revolution. In the six-pole machine shown in Fig. 195,

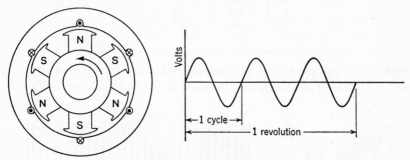

FIG. 195. Six-pole a-c generator.

the emf in each conductor passes through three cycles, one cycle per pair of poles, while the rotor makes one revolution.

If p is the number of poles, then

$$\text{Cycles per revolution} = \frac{p}{2}$$

and

$$\text{Cycles per second} = \frac{p}{2} \times \frac{\text{rpm}}{60} = \frac{p \times \text{rpm}}{120} = f$$

By far the most widely used frequency in America is 60 cycles per sec, although 50 and 25 cycles per sec are used to some extent.

Example. If a 60-cycle generator has 24 poles, at what rpm must it be run?

$$f = \frac{p \times \text{rpm}}{120}$$

therefore

$$60 = \frac{24 \times \text{rpm}}{120}$$

and

$$\text{rpm} = 300$$

Table 2 gives the relation between poles, speed, and frequency.

It is important to note that an a-c generator has a definite speed for a given frequency and cannot be run above or below that speed without changing the frequency. In a d-c generator the voltage may be varied by varying the speed, but in the case of an a-c generator this cannot be done without at the same time changing the frequency.

TABLE 2

Poles	Revolutions per minute		
	25 cycles	50 cycles	60 cycles
2	1,500	3,000	3,600
4	750	1,500	1,800
6	500	1,000	1,200
8	375	750	900
p	$\dfrac{3,000}{p}$	$\dfrac{6,000}{p}$	$\dfrac{7,200}{p}$

238. Vibrating-reed Type of Frequency Meter.   In this type of instrument a number of steel strips are fastened at one end as shown in Fig. 196,

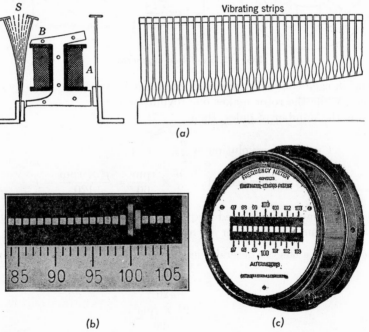

FIG. 196. Vibrating-reed type of frequency meter: (a) interior construction; (b) scale when frequency is 100 cycles; (c) external appearance.

while the current whose frequency is to be determined is passed through the coil A.   The reeds are attracted twice in a cycle by the electromagnet B and that reed which has a natural frequency equal to twice the frequency of the current will be set in violent vibration. The reeds have their ends whitened and appear as white bands when vibrating. The external appearance of such an instrument is shown in Fig. 196c.

239. Average Value of Current and Voltage. The average value of an alternating current or voltage is zero because similar sets of positive and negative values occur. The term average is generally applied to the average value during the positive part of a cycle as indicated in Fig. 197.

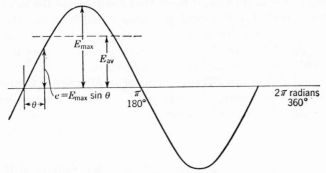

FIG. 197. Average value of an alternating emf.

If the graph of emf is a sine curve so that $e = E_m \sin \theta$, then E_{av}, the average emf, is equal to the area under the positive half of the sine curve divided by the length of the base, or

$$E_{av} = \frac{1}{\pi} \int_0^\pi e\, d\theta = \frac{1}{\pi} \int_0^\pi E_m \sin \theta\, d\theta$$

$$= \frac{1}{\pi} \left[-E_m \cos \theta \right]_0^\pi = \frac{2}{\pi} E_m$$

Similarly, if $i = I_m \sin \theta$, then

$$I_{av} = \frac{2}{\pi} I_m \tag{49}$$

Students who are not familiar with calculus can obtain the same result from the trigonometric tables by adding up the sines of 1°, 3°, 5°, 7°, etc., up to 89°, and dividing the sum by the number of sines taken, that is, by 45. The result will be 0.6366, showing that the average value of a sine curve is 0.6366 when the maximum value is 1; consequently, if the maximum value of a sine curve is E_m, the average value will be $0.6366E_m$. The average value of a sine curve is actually exactly equal to $2/\pi$, and $2/\pi = 0.63662$, approximately.

Average values of alternating voltages and currents have very little practical application. Electricity is used as a means of getting work done, whether that work is the turning of a shaft, the transmission of a message, or the heating of the filament of an electric lamp, and an alternating current whose average value is 1 amp does not heat a given resistance at the same average rate as an unvarying direct current of 1 amp. It is much more convenient to measure an alternating current in terms of the equivalent unvarying direct current that would do work at the same average rate, under the same conditions.

240. The Effective Value of an Alternating Current. An alternating current is said to have an *effective value* of I amp if, when passed through a given resistance of R ohms, it heats that resistance at the same average rate as a constant direct current of I amp would heat it. Or, in other words, the effective value of an alternating current is the number of amperes of direct current that would heat a given resistance at the same average rate as that alternating current heats it.

241. Calculation of the Effective Value of an Alternating Current When Its Graph Is a Sine Curve. Let i be the value of the alternating current at any instant. Then, by hypothesis,

$$i = I_m \sin \theta$$

Let I be the direct current that would heat a resistance of R ohms at the same average rate as the alternating current i. Then I^2R watts is the rate at which electrical energy is being converted into heat by the direct current, and i^2R watts is the rate at which electrical energy is being converted into heat at any instant by the alternating current. Then, since the average rate of heating is to be the same for both,

$$
\begin{aligned}
I^2R &= \text{average value of } i^2R \\
&= \text{average value of } (I_m \sin \theta)^2 R \\
&= I_m^2R \times \text{average value of } \sin^2 \theta* \\
&= I_m^2R \times \tfrac{1}{2}
\end{aligned}
$$

Therefore $$I = \frac{I_m}{\sqrt{2}}$$

That is, the effective value of an alternating current is equal to the maximum value divided by $\sqrt{2}$ if the graph is a sine curve (see Fig. 198 for a graphical representation).

When an alternating current or voltage is specified, it is always the effective value that is meant unless there is a definite statement to the contrary. Thus an alternating current of 10 amp is one that has the same heating effect as 10 amp direct current. It has a maximum value of $10\sqrt{2}$, or 14.1 amp, and an average value of $2/\pi \times 14.1$, or 9 amp, if its graph is a sine curve.

---

* Average value of $\sin^2 \theta = \dfrac{1}{\pi} \displaystyle\int_0^\pi \sin^2 \theta \, d\theta = -\dfrac{1}{\pi} \displaystyle\int_0^\pi \dfrac{1}{2}(\cos 2\theta - 1)\, d\theta$

$$= -\frac{1}{2\pi}\left[\frac{1}{2}\sin 2\theta - \theta\right]_0^\pi = \frac{1}{2}$$

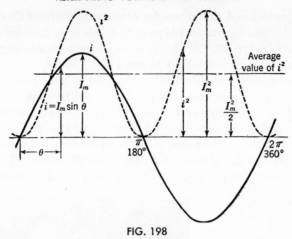

FIG. 198

242. Calculation of the Effective Value of an Alternating Current, for Any Shape of Curve. Let i be the value of the alternating current at any instant. I is the effective value of this alternating current. Then, by definition of the effective value,

$$I^2R = \text{average value of } i^2R$$

or $$I = \sqrt{\text{average value of } i^2}$$

If the curve is symmetrical about the x axis, the value of I can be determined by plotting a curve of i^2 for a half cycle and measuring the area under the curve. This area, divided by the base, is equal to the average value of i^2. Then I is equal to the square root of this average value. If the curve is unsymmetrical it will be necessary to average i^2 over a full cycle.

The equation $I = \sqrt{\text{average value of } i^2}$ is frequently used as the definition of the effective value of an alternating current. In words it becomes: **the effective value of an alternating current is the square root of the average of the squares of the instantaneous values of the current.** Similarly, the effective value of an alternating voltage is the square root of the average of the squares of the instantaneous values of the voltage. Effective values are sometimes called **root-mean-square** values (rms values).

243. Symbols. Hereafter in the text the following symbols will be used for alternating voltages and currents:

$$e, i \quad \text{instantaneous values}$$
$$E_m, I_m \quad \text{maximum values}$$
$$E_{av}, I_{av} \quad \text{average values}$$
$$E, I \quad \text{effective values}$$

244. Voltmeters and Ammeters for Alternating-current Circuits. The moving-coil permanent-magnet type of instrument as used for d-c circuits was described in Art. 28. If this type of meter were connected into an a-c circuit, the moving coil would be acted on by forces, tending to turn it first in one direction and then in the other, but, owing to its inertia, the coil itself would not move and the reading would be zero.

In order that a moving-coil instrument may be used for the measurement of alternating currents, it must be arranged that the magnetic field is reversed at the same time that the current in the moving coil reverses, so that the torque will always be in the same direction. This result is obtained by replacing the permanent magnet of the d-c instrument by a

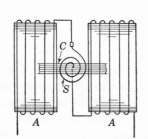

FIG. 199. Electrodynamometer type of instrument.

pair of stationary coils, as shown in Fig. 199. The current to be measured is passed through the stationary coils AA and the moving coil C in series, the current being taken in and out of the moving coil through two spiral springs S, of which only the upper one is shown in Fig. 199. The two sides of the moving coil are then acted upon by pulses of force which are always in the same direction and which turn the coil against the opposition of the spiral springs S, attempting to line its magnetic axis up with that of the fixed coils. Owing to the inertia of the moving coil and pointer, the coil will take up a position where the constant restraining torque of the spiral springs is equal to the average value of the deflecting torque produced by the current.

The deflecting torque is proportional to the current i in the moving coil C, and to the flux ϕ produced by the current i in the fixed coils AA. The deflecting torque is therefore proportional to i^2; and the *average* deflecting torque on coil C, in any given position of that coil, is proportional to the *average* value of i^2 and is therefore proportional to the square of the effective value of the current.   Thus the deflection of the coil is determined by the effective or equivalent d-c value of the current, and, if the meter is calibrated by passing known direct currents through it, it may then be used to measure alternating current and will indicate the effective value.

When this instrument is to be a voltmeter, a suitable high resistance is connected in series with the coils, and the current required to produce full-scale deflection is of the order of 40 ma.   When it is to be an ammeter, a shunt is connected across the moving coil, while the stationary coils are designed to carry the entire current.   The shunt is such that the current through the moving coil is only about 40 ma at full scale.

There are other types of a-c meters which are less expensive than the electrodynamometer type and which are widely used where maximum accuracy is not required.

Problems

27-1. A 24-pole generator is driven at 300 rpm.   What is the frequency of the generated emf?   How many poles would a 25-cycle generator have for the same speed?   How many poles has a turbogenerator that gives 60 cycles at 3,600 rpm?

*27-2. An eight-pole generator is attached to the same shaft with an adjustable-speed d-c motor, for use in a testing laboratory.   If the speed of the motor can be varied from 225 to 2,000 rpm, determine the possible range of frequencies of emf generated by the generator.

*27-3. Draw a curve of $\sin^2 \theta$.   Show that the average value of $\sin^2 \theta$ is equal to 0.5 times the maximum value, and that therefore the average heating effect of an alternating current with a maximum value of 1 amp is the same as that of a direct current of $1/\sqrt{2}$ amp.

a. Which produces the greater heating effect, 25-amp direct current or an alternating current which has a value of 25 amp as measured by an instrument?

b. Will an alternating voltage of 2,200 as measured by an instrument or a direct voltage of 2,200 break down insulating material the more readily?

*27-4. Draw a sine wave of current with an effective value of 6 amp.   If this be the curve obtained by an oscillograph at *a* in the adjoining circuit, plot the curves that you would expect to obtain by oscillographs placed at *b* and *c*, respectively.

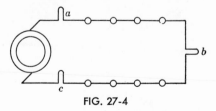

FIG. 27-4

*27-5. The foregoing diagram represents a 6-amp series lighting circuit.   When the current at *a* has the maximum value of 8.5 amp in one direction, what will be the value and direction of the currents at *b* and *c* at the same instant?

*27-6. Find the average value of one-half cycle of the foregoing curve, taking at least 10 ordinates, and compare this with the value given in Art. 239 of text. Will the average value for a quarter cycle be the same? Of a whole cycle? Of an eighth of a cycle?

*27-7. The effective value of an alternating voltage is defined as equal to $\sqrt{\text{average value of } e^2}$. Show by squaring the foregoing chosen ordinates that this is equal to $E_{\max}$ divided by $\sqrt{2}$. Why is $\sqrt{\text{average value of } e^2}$ not the same as average value of e?

*27-8. Explain clearly, as to a nontechnical man, the difference between alternating and direct currents.

a. What actually happens in the wire?

b. What is the frequency of supply in this city?

c. Why do we not see the lamps flicker?

d. What is the frequency of flicker?

e. What is meant by amplitude of a sine wave?

27-9. Find the number of poles for each of the following a-c generators:

a. 14,000 kw 25 cycle, driven by steam turbine at 1,500 rpm.

b. 14,000 kw 60 cycle, driven by steam turbine at 1,800 rpm.

c. 14,000 kw 25 cycle, driven by low-head water wheel at 58 rpm.

d. 14,000 kw 60 cycle, driven by low-head water wheel at 55 rpm.

27-10. An engine builder whose engine runs normally at 650 rpm wishes a direct-connected 60-cycle generator. How many poles should the generator have? What would you suggest to the builder?

27-11. The graphs of four alternating currents are, respectively, (a) a sine curve, (b) an isosceles triangle, (c) a semicircle, and (d) a rectangle (flat top, vertical sides). They all have a maximum value of 10 amp. Calculate their effective values.

28

REPRESENTATION OF ALTERNATING
CURRENTS AND VOLTAGES

245. Electrical Degrees. If the vector *op* (Fig. 200) rotates in the counterclockwise direction, and the angle θ is measured from the x axis, then *om*, the projection of *op* on the y axis, is equal to *op* sin θ, and its value, plotted in Fig. 200*b*, passes through one cycle while θ increases through 360°, or 2π radians. Thus a rotating vector may be used to

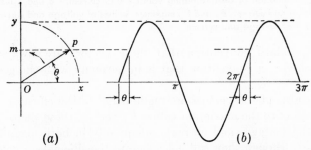

FIG. 200. Representation of an alternating voltage.

generate graphically a sine curve. If now *op* is drawn to scale equal to E_m (Fig. 193), then each time *op* rotates through 360° it will generate graphically the cycle of emf shown in Fig. 193. In the case of a two-pole generator, as in Fig. 193, the rotor also rotates through one revolution in generating 1 cycle of emf, but the six-pole generator shown in Fig. 195 generates 3 cycles per revolution. Therefore if the vector *op* is to generate graphically the same emf as the generator, it must make three revolutions each time the rotor of the six-pole generator makes one revolution. The term *electrical degrees* is used in designating the angle θ turned through by the vector *op*, while the angle turned through by the generator rotor is measured in *mechanical degrees*. The number of electrical degrees may be obtained by multiplying the number of mechanical degrees by the number of pairs of poles.

246. Vector Representation of Alternating Voltages and Currents. It is generally assumed that these quantities vary according to a sine law and can therefore be represented by sine curves as shown in Fig. 201, where

$$i, \text{ current at any instant} = I_m \sin \theta$$
$$e, \text{ voltage at any instant} = E_m \sin \theta$$

For much of the work on a-c circuits and machines it is more convenient to represent alternating voltages and currents by the corresponding vectors E_m and I_m, Fig. 201, which, if rotated and projected upon the y axis, as was done in Fig. 200, would generate the sine curves of voltage and current.

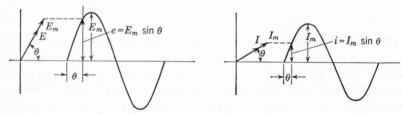

FIG. 201. Representation of an alternating voltage and current. e and i, instantaneous values of voltage and current; E_m and I_m, maximum values of voltage and current; E and I, effective values of voltage and current.

It is a standard convention that these vectors are always rotated counterclockwise, a convention that is in harmony with the general use of polar coordinates.

If the lengths of the vectors are made equal to the effective values E and I instead of to the maximum values E_m and I_m, these vectors will still represent the voltages and currents adequately in both magnitude and phase angle, although they will not generate the sine curves with proper amplitudes unless their lengths are first multiplied by $\sqrt{2}$.

In practice, effective values are nearly always used in drawing vector diagrams.

If two oscillographs are used as in Fig. 202, one of which, A, gives the voltage curve while the other, B, gives the current curve, it will be found that the current and the voltage do not necessarily reach their maximum values at the same instant but that curves such as those appearing in Fig. 202a, b, and c may be obtained, depending on the kind of load connected to the circuit. The reasons for the displacement of the current relative to the voltage are taken up in Chap 29; it is necessary, however, to take up at this point the method of representing such curves by vectors.

If two vectors such as E_m and I_m, Fig. 203, are rotated in the counterclock direction at the same rate, the angle α between them will remain unchanged, and their projections on the y axis, plotted on an angle base, will generate two sine curves displaced from one another by the angle α, as shown. The vectors E_m and I_m and the corresponding points on the sine curves are shown at three different instants, a, b, and c, in the rotation.

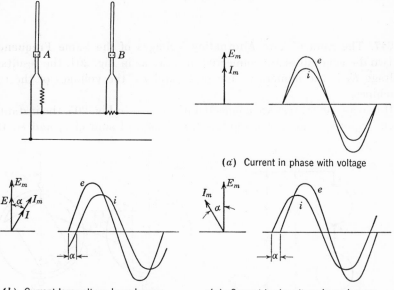

(a) Current in phase with voltage

(b) Current lags voltage by α degrees   (c) Current leads voltage by α degrees

FIG. 202. Phase relation between current and voltage.

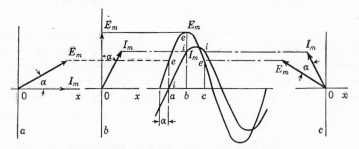

FIG. 203. Representation of a lagging current.

These curves are graphs of a voltage and a current of the same frequency, the voltage e reaching its maximum value α degrees before the current becomes a maximum.

When the current and voltage reach their maximum values at the same instant, they are said to be in phase with one another. When they reach their maximum values at different instants, they are out of phase and the current is said to be leading or lagging according as it becomes a maximum before or after the voltage has reached its maximum value.

The equations of the graphs of voltage and current in Fig. 203 will depend upon the axis of reference from which θ is measured. If, for example, θ is taken to be the angle between the vector I_m and the line ox, then the equations are

$$i = I_m \sin \theta$$
$$e = E_m \sin (\theta + \alpha)$$

247. The Sum of Two Alternating Voltages of the Same Frequency. If two d-c generators are connected in series as in Fig. 204, the resultant voltage E_3 is the numerical sum of E_1 and E_2, the voltages of the two machines.

If two a-c generators are connected in series as in Fig. 205, the instantaneous voltage e_3 at any instant is the numerical sum of e_1 and e_2, the

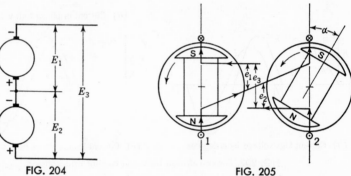

FIG. 204   FIG. 205

instantaneous voltages of the two machines at that instant. In the particular case shown, the voltage of the second machine lags or reaches its maximum value later than that of the first machine by the time required for the poles to pass through α degrees, and the sine curves representing the voltages of the two machines are e_1 and e_2, Fig. 206. The points on the resultant sine curve e_3 are obtained by adding together the values of e_1 and e_2 at different instants.

The voltages of the two machines may be represented by the vectors E_{1m} and E_{2m} drawn to scale with an angle α between them because, if these two vectors are rotated together in the counterclockwise direction with this fixed angle α between them, the vertical components e_1 and e_2, when plotted against the angle turned through by the vectors, will give the sine curves e_1 and e_2 in their proper phase relation.

Then if a parallelogram is drawn with E_{1m} and E_{2m} as the sides and α as the included angle, the diagonal E_{3m} of this parallelogram will represent the sum of the voltages of the two machines because, if rotated with the two other vectors, its vertical component, when plotted against the angle

θ, will give the sine curve e_3 correct in both amplitude and phase relation to the curves of e_1 and e_2.

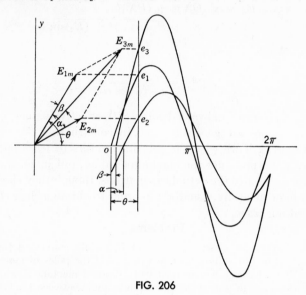

FIG. 206

That this is so may be seen from Fig. 206 in which it is evident that

$$E_{1m} \sin \theta = e_1$$
$$E_{2m} \sin (\theta - \alpha) = e_2$$
$$E_{3m} \sin (\theta - \beta) = E_{1m} \sin \theta + E_{2m} \sin (\theta - \alpha)$$
$$= e_1 + e_2$$
$$= e_3$$

These equations hold for all values of θ.

It follows therefore that two or more alternating voltages or currents may be added in the same way that forces are added, namely, by constructing parallelograms and either measuring or calculating the lengths of the diagonals and the magnitudes of the phase angles.

The parallelogram in Fig. 206 is called a vector diagram. It shows the maximum values of the voltages and

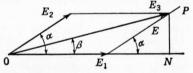

FIG. 207. Addition of alternating voltages by vectors.

their phase angles, but, since the effective values are equal to the maximum values divided by $\sqrt{2}$, it follows that, if the effective values are used in constructing the parallelogram instead of the maximum values, then every dimension of the parallelogram will be divided by $\sqrt{2}$ and the diagonal will be the effective value of the sum of the two voltages.

With reference to Fig. 207,

$$E_3 = \sqrt{(ON)^2 + (PN)^2}$$
$$= \sqrt{(E_1 + E_2 \cos \alpha)^2 + (E_2 \sin \alpha)^2}$$
$$\text{Angle } \beta = \tan^{-1} \frac{PN}{ON}$$
$$= \tan^{-1} \frac{E_2 \sin \alpha}{E_1 + E_2 \cos \alpha}$$

In practice, we are nearly always dealing with effective values, and therefore effective values are generally used in constructing the vector diagrams. Of course, if we wish the rotating vectors to trace out the sine curves to scale, we must use the maximum values, but in general the sine curves do not enter into the actual calculations, though they should either be sketched in or mentally visualized in order to obtain a clear conception of what is taking place.

Problems

28-1. Two six-pole a-c generators, A and B, rigidly connected to the same shaft, each generate 120 volts (effective value). If the poles of machine B are displaced by 20 mechanical degrees relative to those of machine A while the stationary armatures are in line, what is the phase angle between the two voltages and what is the resultant voltage (a) if the windings are in series as in Fig. 205 (b) if the connections of B are reversed? Show the result by sine curves and also by vector diagrams.

28-2. a. By means of a rotating vector, construct a sine wave of voltage having a maximum value of 100 volts. If the frequency of this voltage is 60 cycles per sec, indicate the scale of abscissas in seconds, fractions of a cycle, radians, and electrical degrees.

b. Assume that the generator generating the above emf has 14 poles. Through how many *mechanical* degrees will the shaft of this generator turn while the emf passes through 360 electrical degrees?

28-3. Two six-pole a-c generators are keyed to the same shaft and connected in series. Each machine generates 100 volts (effective). The poles of machine A are displaced 20 mechanical degrees behind those of B. Find the voltage at the terminals and its phase position relative to the two generator voltages as follows:

a. Plot to scale in their correct phase relation the waves representing the voltages of the two machines, and then find the resultant sine wave by adding the voltages of the two machines point by point.

b. Draw vectors representing the two voltages in their proper phase relation; find the geometric sum and show that it corresponds in magnitude and in phase relation with the corresponding curve found by method a.

28-4. If the terminals of generator B are reversed, show by means of a vector diagram the relative magnitudes and phase relations of voltages A and B and the terminal voltage.

29

ALTERNATING-CURRENT CIRCUITS

The student is strongly advised to master Arts. 85 to 90 before proceeding with this chapter.

248. Impedance. In d-c circuits the ratio of the volts impressed on a circuit to the amperes produced by that voltage is called the resistance R of the circuit and is expressed in ohms, whence

$$E = IR$$

In a-c circuits the ratio of the effective value of the voltage impressed on a circuit to the effective value of the current produced by that voltage is called the impedance Z of that circuit and is also expressed in ohms, whence

$$E = IZ$$

When the graph of the impressed voltage is a sine curve, the impedance can always be expressed as a function of the frequency and of the three fundamental circuit constants, namely, resistance, inductance, and capacitance.

We shall now proceed to investigate the simple special cases of circuits having inductance only, and resistance only, and from them can be built up the general case of circuits having both resistance and inductance. Circuits containing capacitance will be taken up later.

249. Alternating Currents in Inductive Circuits. Since any change in the current flowing in an inductive circuit sets up a counter emf of self-induction opposing that change, the sending of an alternating current through an inductive circuit results in the continuous generation of such counter emfs. We shall now proceed to show that, if the current is represented by the sine curve $i = I_m \sin \theta$, Fig. 208, then the emf of self-induction is represented by another sine curve e_{si} lagging 90° behind the current curve.

During the time interval from o to a the current i is increasing, and the emf of self-induction e_{si}, to oppose this increase, must be negative. From a to b the current i is decreasing and e_{si} must therefore be positive.

At the instant a, the current is neither increasing nor decreasing and e_{si} must be zero. Similarly from b to c the current is decreasing from zero to $-I_m$ and e_{si} must therefore be positive, while from c to d the current is increasing and e_{si} must be negative. At c the current is neither increasing nor decreasing and e_{si} must be zero. The magnitude of e_{si} is proportional to the rate of change of the current [Eq. (24)]. Therefore e_{si} is greatest when i is changing most rapidly, that is, at the instants o, b, and d.

We have now located the zero points and the maximum points of the curve of e_{si}. The entire curve may be plotted to scale as follows.

Divide the diagram of Fig. 208 up into narrow vertical strips of equal width. Let θ_1 and θ_2 be the values of θ at the two edges of any one strip.

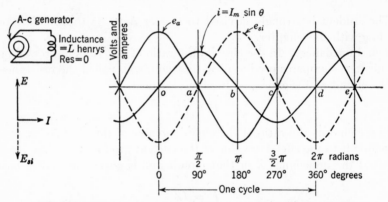

FIG. 208. Voltage and current relations in a purely inductive circuit.

Then the change in i that takes place during this change in angle is equal to $I_m \sin \theta_2 - I_m \sin \theta_1$. This change in i, divided by the time interval corresponding to the change in angle, gives the average rate of change of the current during that interval, and this rate of change, multiplied by the inductance L, gives the average value of e_{si} for the time interval.

If the average value of e_{si} is calculated in this way for each strip and is plotted on the center line of the strip, the points so obtained will form the sine curve e_{si}, Fig. 208, the amplitude of the curve, of course, depending upon the scale chosen. The narrower the strips, the more accurately will the points be obtained.

In order to make the above calculations, the frequency f in cycles per second must be known, as otherwise the time interval corresponding to $\theta_2 - \theta_1$ cannot be calculated.

Since the voltage of self-induction e_{si} is the emf with which the circuit opposes the changes in the current, it follows that the impressed emf which is causing the continuous variations in the current must at all times be greater than the opposing emf of self-induction by the amount of the emf required to drive the current through the resistance of the circuit.

So that, if e_a is the impressed emf, then at any instant $e_a = -e_{si} + iR$, where iR is the emf required to drive the current through the resistance of the circuit. In the extreme case of Fig. 208, where $R = 0$, $e_a = -e_{si}$, and the curve of impressed emf is simply the curve of e_{si} inverted.

In a circuit of pure inductance therefore the current lags behind the impressed emf by 90°.

250. Voltage and Current Relations. It has been shown in Art. 249 how the curves of the emfs may be plotted point by point in order to establish the fact that they are sine curves if the current curve is a sine curve, and that the graph of current lags 90° behind the graph of impressed emf when the circuit is pure inductance.

The same results may be obtained much more precisely and clearly with the aid of calculus,[1] as follows:

Given that the coil in Fig. 208 has an inductance of L henrys and that its resistance is zero, it is required to determine what the impressed emf must be in order to maintain an alternating current $i = I_m \sin \theta$ through the coil.

Let f = the frequency in cycles per second. At the end of one cycle,

$$\theta = 2\pi \text{ radians}$$

At the end of f cycles, that is, at the end of 1 sec,

$$\theta = 2\pi f \text{ radians}$$

At the end of t sec,

$$\theta = 2\pi f t \text{ radians}$$

hence

$$i = I_m \sin 2\pi f t$$

Let e = the value of the impressed emf at any instant. Then

$$e = L \frac{di}{dt} + iR \qquad \text{[Eq. (28), Art. 90]}$$

[1] Students who are unfamiliar with calculus may proceed to derive Eq. (51) as follows:

The current i in Fig. 208 changes from $-I_m$ to I_m in the time of half a cycle, or in $1/2f$ sec. Therefore the average rate of change is

$$2I_m \div \frac{1}{2f} = 4fI_m \text{ amp per sec}$$

The average voltage of self-induction is equal to the inductance in henrys multiplied by the average rate of change of the current. Therefore

$$\text{Average voltage } E_{av} = 4fLI_m$$

$$\text{Maximum voltage } E_m = \frac{\pi}{2} E_{av} \qquad \text{(Art. 239)}$$

$$= 2\pi fLI_m$$

and, since effective values are equal to maximum values divided by $\sqrt{2}$,

$$\text{Effective voltage } E = 2\pi fLI$$

but $$R = 0$$

therefore
$$e = L \frac{di}{dt}$$

$$= L \frac{d}{dt} (I_m \sin 2\pi ft)$$
$$= 2\pi f L I_m \cos 2\pi ft$$
$$= 2\pi f L I_m \cos \theta$$

$$= 2\pi f L I_m \sin \left(\theta + \frac{\pi}{2} \right) \tag{50}$$

which shows that the graph of impressed emf is a sine curve leading the current by 90°.

The maximum value that a sine can have is 1, hence

$$E_m = 2\pi f L I_n$$

and, dividing both sides by $\sqrt{2}$,

$$E = (2\pi f L) I \tag{51}$$

The group of factors $(2\pi f L)$ occurs so frequently in a-c work that it has been given a name and a special symbol. It is called the *inductive reactance* of the circuit and is denoted by X, so that Eq. (51) becomes

$$E = IX \tag{52}$$

where $X = 2\pi f L$.

From Eq. (52) and the definition of impedance, Art. 248, it follows that in a circuit of pure inductance only, the impedance is equal to the reactance. Note that from Eq. (52), if E is fixed in magnitude, the current I is inversely proportional to the frequency.

Example. A 60-cycle alternating emf of 110 volts (effective value) sends a current of 2.2 amp (effective value) through an inductive coil of negligible resistance. Find the reactance at 60 cycles and also the inductance. What would the current be if the frequency were 30 cycles?

$$\text{Reactance } X = \frac{E}{I} = \frac{110}{2.2} = 50 \text{ ohms}$$

$$\text{Inductance } L = \frac{X}{2\pi f} - \frac{50}{2\pi 60} = 0.133 \text{ henry}$$

At 30 cycles
$$X = 2\pi f L = 2\pi 30 \times 0.133 = 25 \text{ ohms}$$

and
$$I = \frac{E}{X} = \frac{110}{25} = 4.4 \text{ amp}$$

251. Power in an Inductive Circuit. The power in a circuit at any instant in watts is the product of e and i, the voltage and current at that instant. In an inductive circuit of negligible resistance the current lags the applied voltage by 90° and the curves representing e and i are as shown in Fig. 209.

At the instants a and b the voltage is zero, so that the power is zero at these instants; it is also zero at instants g, d, and f when the current is zero. Between g and a the voltage and current are in the same direction, so that the power is positive and energy is being put into the circuit, while between a and d the current and voltage are in opposite directions, so that the power is negative and energy is being taken from the circuit; the average power in the circuit is zero. The energy that is put into the coil

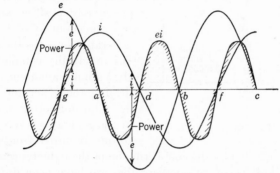

FIG. 209. Voltage, current, and power in an inductive circuit.

during the quarter cycle g to a is stored in the growing magnetic field and is returned again when the magnetic field collapses.

252. Mechanical Illustration. The curves and associated theory of Figs. 208 and 209 are not peculiar to alternating currents. They apply to all forms of reciprocating motion whether electrical or mechanical. For example, consider a mass M on a smooth horizontal plane with spiral springs attached as shown in Fig. 210. If the mass M is moved to the left so as to compress one spring and extend the other and is then released, it will oscillate back and forth with simple harmonic motion, and its velocity is then represented by the current curve i of Fig. 209. The force exerted on the mass by the springs is represented by the curve of impressed emf e and is zero at the center of travel of M, at which position the velocity of M is greatest, and is greatest at the ends of the travel of M, at which positions the velocity of M is zero, so that the curves of force and velocity are 90° out of phase as shown. The force which the mass exerts on the springs is represented by the curve e_{si}, Fig. 208, and is, of course, equal and opposite to the force which the springs exert upon the mass.

The power at any instant is equal to the force exerted by the springs multiplied by the velocity of M and is represented by the power curve of Fig. 209. During the quarter cycle from g to a the springs are exerting force in the direction of motion and are therefore doing work upon the mass.   This work is stored in the mass in the form of kinetic energy. During the next quarter cycle from a to d the springs are opposing the motion and bringing M to rest.   The mass is therefore doing work upon the springs and this work is stored in the distorted springs.   Thus the energy is shifted back and forth between the mass and the springs and the average energy delivered in any one direction is zero.   Similarly in the a-c case, energy is stored in the magnetic field of the coil during the quarter cycle g to a and is returned to the generator during the next quarter cycle.   The power load on the generator is a pulsating one, being

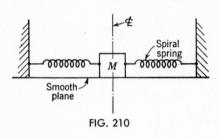

FIG. 210

alternately positive and negative, but the moment of inertia of the generator smooths these pulsations out practically completely, so that they are not apparent to the engine driving the generator.   The average retarding torque of the current i in the generator is zero, so that the torque required from the driving engine is not affected by the connecting on of the inductance coil L.

Note that this is not an analogy that we have been drawing.   It is merely another example illustrating the general theory of reciprocating motion. . The curves and fundamental equations of Figs. 208 and 209 apply as much to one example as to the other, although we are accustomed to using different symbols for the different cases.

253. Examples of Inductive and Noninductive Circuits.   The inductance $L = (n\phi/i)10^{-8}$ [Eq. (26)], so that, to have a large inductance, a circuit must be linked by a large flux ϕ for a given current i.   The inductance of coil b, Fig. 211, is much greater than that of the duplicate coil a because the flux ϕ has been greatly increased by the addition of the iron core C.

One form of adjustable inductance is shown in Fig. 212.   If the iron crosspiece mn is brought nearer to the poles pq, the reluctance of the magnetic circuit is decreased, so that a larger flux ϕ is produced by a given current i and the inductance is thereby increased.   Withdrawing the iron core is also a convenient way of reducing the inductance.   If the inductance is used for alternating current, the iron must be laminated.

An incandescent-lamp filament has an inductance that is negligible compared with its resistance.   The tungsten filament is wound into a tight little solenoid only a few hundredths of an inch in diameter, so that there is very little room for any magnetic flux.   In a long solenoid the flux produced by a given number of ampere-turns per inch is directly proportional to the cross-sectional area of the solenoid [Eq. (17), Art 63)].

Although a transmission line has only one turn, its inductance is not negligible because that one turn is usually many miles in length and is therefore linked by a large flux ϕ, particularly if the wires are spaced far

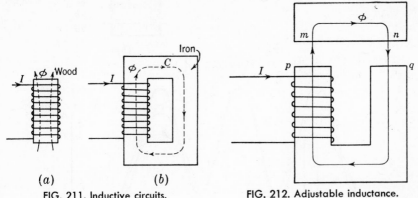

FIG. 211. Inductive circuits.   FIG. 212. Adjustable inductance.

apart, because then, as shown in Fig. 213, there is room for a large flux to pass between the wires.   If the two wires are brought closer together, the total amount of flux decreases, and as the center-to-center distance between the two wires approaches zero the flux approaches zero.   Since this distance can never actually be zero, the flux is never zero; but if the wires are small and are separated only by a thin film of insulation, the inductance is negligible.

Noninductive resistances are often made in the form of a long narrow loop of insulated resistance wire as indicated in Fig. 214a.   The loop may then be coiled up on a spool for convenience, as shown in Fig. 214b.   If the resistor must carry a large current the cross section of the metal must be large, but the center-to-center distance can still be kept small by changing the shape of the metal from cylindrical to a flat ribbon.

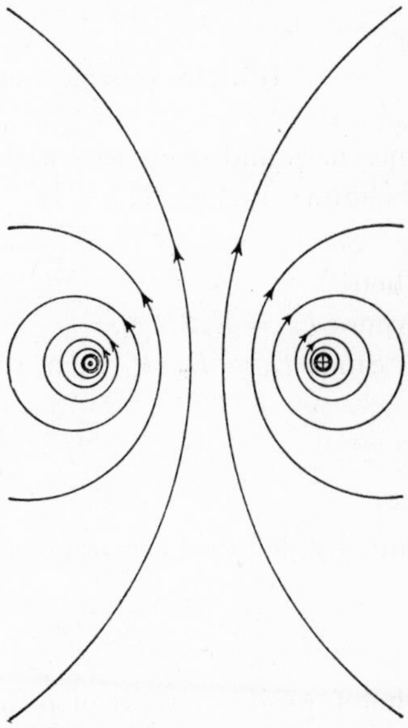

FIG. 213. Cross section of a two-conductor transmission line, showing the magnetic flux and the currents producing it.

254. Voltage, Current, and Power in Resistance Circuits. If an alternating voltage is applied to a noninductive circuit of resistance R, then, since there is no emf of self-induction opposing the change of current, the current i at any instant is equal to e/R and

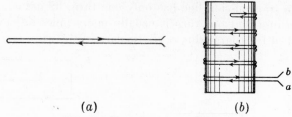

(a)   (b)

FIG. 214. Noninductive resistance.

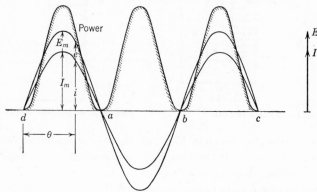

FIG. 215. Voltage e, current i, and power ei in a resistance circuit.

increases and decreases with the voltage, or is in phase with the voltage, as shown in Fig. 215.   If

$$e = E_m \sin \theta$$

then $$i = I_m \sin \theta$$

where $I_m = E_m/R$.

Since $I_m = E_m/R$, then, dividing both sides by $\sqrt{2}$, we obtain

$$I = \frac{E}{R} \quad \text{and} \quad R = \frac{E}{I}$$

but, by definition of impedance,

$$Z = \frac{E}{I}$$

therefore, in a circuit of pure resistance,

$$Z = R$$

The power in such a circuit is zero at the instants a, b, c, and d when both voltage and current are zero but is positive at all other instants; that is, energy is put into the circuit but none is taken out again.

Average power = average value of ei

= average value of $E_m \sin \theta \times I_m \sin \theta$

= $E_m I_m \times$ average value of $\sin^2 \theta$

= $\dfrac{E_m I_m}{2}$ (see footnote, Art. 241)

= $\dfrac{E_m}{\sqrt{2}} \times \dfrac{I_m}{\sqrt{2}}$

= EI and also = $I^2 R$

since $E = IR$, where E and I are effective values. Thus, in a noninductive circuit, the average power is the product of the effective values of the voltage and current.

255. Resistance and Inductance in Series. This is the case most generally met with in practice, nearly all circuits containing both resistance and inductance.

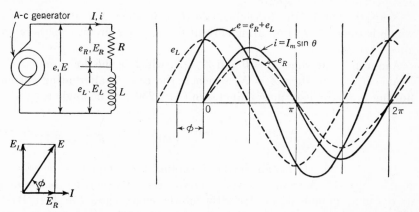

FIG. 216. Voltage and current in a circuit that has resistance and inductance in series. e, e_R, and e_L, instantaneous values of voltage; E, E_R, and E_L, effective values of voltage.

If an alternating current $i = I_m \sin \theta$ is flowing through a resistance R and an inductance L, connected in series as shown in Fig. 216, then the emf required to drive the current through the resistance R is given by the sine curve e_R in phase with i (Art. 254), and the emf required to drive the current through the inductance coil L is given by the sine curve e_L leading the current i by 90° [Eq. (50), Art. 250]. The total emf impressed upon the circuit by the generator at any instant is therefore $e = e_R + e_L$.

The curve e may be obtained by adding the corresponding values of e_R and e_L at various points on the cycle, but it has been shown in Art. 247 that, if a parallelogram is constructed with the adjacent sides equal to the effective values of the two sine curves, and the included angle equal to the phase angle between the two sine curves, then the diagonal will be equal to the effective value of the sum of the two sine curves. In this case the sine curves e_R and e_L are 90° out of phase; consequently the parallelogram is a rectangle as shown in Fig. 216. Therefore

$$E = \sqrt{E_R{}^2 + E_L{}^2} \qquad (53)$$

where E, E_R, and E_L are the effective values of e, e_R, and e_L, respectively.

Now $E_R = IR$, and $E_L = IX$, where $X = 2\pi fL$. Therefore

$$
\begin{aligned}
E &= \sqrt{(IR)^2 + (IX)^2} \\
&= I\sqrt{R^2 + X^2} \\
&= IZ
\end{aligned}
\qquad (54)
$$

where $Z = \sqrt{R^2 + X^2}$.

The *impedance* of a circuit is defined as being the ratio of the effective value of the impressed emf to the effective value of the resulting current and is denoted by the letter Z.

Note that if in the foregoing case $L = 0$, then $X = 0$ and $Z = R$, which is the case of alternating current flowing in a circuit of pure resistance (Art. 254).

Again if $f = 0$, then $X = 0$ and $Z = R$, which is the d-c case.

Also if $R = 0$, then $Z = X$, which is the case of alternating current flowing in a circuit of pure inductance (Art. 250). The angle is

$$\phi = \tan^{-1}\frac{E_L}{E_R} = \tan^{-1}\frac{IX}{IR} = \tan^{-1}\frac{X}{R}$$

The power at any instant in the foregoing case is equal to the product of the volts and the amperes, which is ei watts. By plotting this product at different points in the cycle the power curve shown in Fig. 217 is obtained. It is a sine curve of double frequency offset from the zero axis.

Since the curves are plotted on a time base ($\theta = 2\pi ft$ radians), the area under the power curve represents energy delivered or work done. During the time interval from a to b the impressed emf is in the same direction as the current and therefore the generator is putting energy into the circuit. From b to c the inductance coil is returning energy to the generator. The energy which is absorbed by the resistance R is converted into heat and is not returned.

The average power input to the inductance coil L is zero (Art. 251). The average power input to the resistance R is equal to $E_R I$ watts (Art. 254). Therefore the average power input to the circuit is

$$
\begin{aligned}
\text{Average power} &= E_R I \qquad \text{watts} \\
&= EI \cos\phi \qquad \text{watts}
\end{aligned}
\qquad (55)
$$

$\cos\phi$ is called the power factor of the circuit.

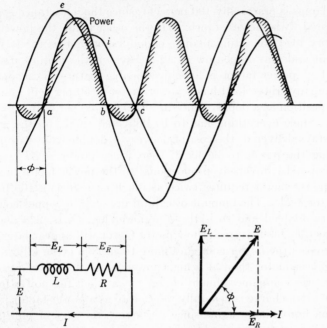

FIG. 217. Voltage, current, and power in a circuit that has resistance and inductance in series.

256. The Power Factor. In an a-c circuit the power factor is defined as the ratio $\dfrac{\text{actual power}}{\text{apparent power}}$ (AIEE Standards), where the apparent power is taken to be the product of the effective values of voltage and current.

The term *volt-amperes* is very often used instead of the term *apparent power*, partly because it is more descriptive and partly because the product of the effective values of the voltage and the current does not appear to be the power to anyone who is really familiar with the flow of alternating current.

In any circuit in which the phase angle between the sine waves of impressed voltage and current is equal to ϕ,

$$\text{Power factor} = \frac{\text{watts}}{\text{volt-amperes}}$$
$$= \frac{EI \cos \phi}{EI}$$
$$= \cos \phi$$

and can never be greater than unity. The power factor is generally expressed as a percentage in practice, 100 per cent being the maximum possible power factor. The power factor of a lighting load consisting of tungsten lamps is practically 100 per cent, since the inductance is negligible compared with the resistance. On the other hand, the power factor of a factory load consisting mainly of induction motors rarely exceeds 85 per cent and may be as low as 40 per cent if the motors are lightly loaded. Low power factor is an objectionable feature in any load. A power company whose load has a power factor of 50 per cent is in much the same position as a department store that has 50 per cent of its goods returned. Since everything has to be delivered twice, on the average, before it stays delivered, the cost of delivery is double what it should be.

Assuming the power to be fixed, then, since power $= EI \cos \phi$, the current required is inversely proportional to the power factor, and a 50 per cent power factor requires twice as much current as a 100 per cent power-factor load. The amount of capital invested in copper conductor is therefore doubled and so is the I^2R power loss (Arts. 228 and 229). Other objectionable features of low power factor will appear later.

Since it costs the power company more to carry a given kilowatt load at a low power factor than at a high power factor, it is only reasonable that the power companies should charge extra when the power factor is low. The extra charge is generally referred to as a power-factor penalty, which is an unfortunate name since it conveys the idea of punishment, whereas it is actually only a charge for an extra service rendered.

Example. If a resistance of 25 ohms and an inductive reactance of 50 ohms at 60 cycles are put in series, across 110 volts, find the current, the voltages across the two parts of the circuit, and the power in the circuit at 30, 60, and 120 cycles. The work is carried out in tabular form as follows:

Frequency	R, ohms	$X = 2\pi fL$	$\sqrt{R^2 + X^2}$	I	E_r	E_x	$\cos \phi$	Watts
30	25	25	35.4	3.10	78	78	0.71	240
60	25	50	56.0	1.96	49	98	0.44	96
120	25	100	103.0	1.07	27	107	0.24	29

257. The Wattmeter. The average power in an a-c circuit is measured by means of an electrodynamometer type of instrument called a wattmeter, constructed as shown in Fig. 199 and connected as shown in Fig. 218. The load current i is passed through the stationary coils A and produces a magnetic field, in which the moving coil C is mounted on jeweled bearings. The moving coil, in series with a high resistance r, is connected across the line, in parallel with the load. The small current i_e (about 20 ma) that passes through the moving coil C is proportional to the voltage e and is in phase with it, since the inductance of coil C is negligible compared with the high resistance r that is connected in series with it.

Since the moving coil C is carrying current and is in a magnetic field, its sides are acted upon by forces that produce a torque tending to turn it either clockwise or counterclockwise, depending on the directions of the current and the field, so as to line its axis up with that of the fixed coils.   The turning action is opposed by the two spiral springs that take the current in and out of the moving coil.   Only the top spring is shown in Fig. 218.

The magnitude of the turning or deflecting torque is proportional to the current in the moving coil and to the strength of the magnetic field. Now the current in the moving coil is proportional to the line voltage e, while the magnetic field is produced by the load current i and is therefore proportional to i.   Therefore in any given position of the coil the deflecting torque is proportional to the power $e \times i$.

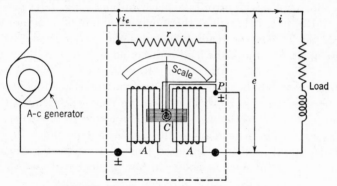

FIG. 218. Wattmeter connected into a circuit.

If the power is constant, as in the case of direct current, the coil takes up a position where the constant restraining torque of the spiral springs is equal to the constant deflecting torque of the electromagnetic reaction. The magnitude of the deflection is therefore a measure of the power, to some scale.

In the case of alternating current the instantaneous power pulsates in magnitude, as shown in Fig. 217, and goes negative twice per cycle unless the power factor is 100 per cent.   Therefore the deflecting torque also pulsates in the same way.   Owing to the inertia of the moving system, the coil takes up a position where the constant restraining torque of the spiral springs is equal to the average value of the deflecting torque.

Then since, in any given position of the moving coil, the average deflecting torque is proportional to the average power, it follows that, if the average value of an a-c power is equal to the constant value of a d-c power, they will produce the same average deflecting torque and therefore the same deflection.   Consequently a wattmeter can be calibrated on direct current and used on alternating current.   When calibrating or constructing the scale of a wattmeter, the d-c power is measured by means of a voltmeter and ammeter, the power being equal to the product EI. Suitable measured amounts of power are applied to the load, and the resulting positions of the wattmeter pointer are marked on the scale.

In practice, when calibrating a wattmeter, it is necessary to take two readings at each magnitude of power, in order to eliminate the effects of the earth's field. The second reading is taken with the current terminals reversed and the voltage terminals also reversed. The double reversal leaves the torque in the same direction, but, if the earth's field was adding to the deflection before the reversal, it must be subtracting from it after the reversal, and therefore the average of the two deflections is the true deflection due to the power alone. When measuring a-c power, the earth's field does not cause any error because then the reversals necessary for the elimination of this error take place automatically 120 times per sec.

It should be noted that since the moving-coil circuit is in parallel with the load, the wattmeter reading includes the power dissipated in the moving-coil circuit, and if the load is disconnected entirely the wattmeter will still read about 2 watts, on a 110-volt circuit. Whenever small amounts of power are being measured, the wattmeter reading is corrected by subtracting the power loss in its own moving-coil circuit. If the ± potential terminal P of the wattmeter is connected to the generator side of the current coils instead of to the load side, the power loss in the moving-coil circuit will be eliminated from the wattmeter reading, but the power loss in the current coils will now be included instead. Some wattmeters are provided with a third coil that compensates for the power loss in the potential circuit.

The sign ± on two of the wattmeter terminals signifies that the currents to or from these terminals must either both be entering or both leaving in order for the deflecting torque to be clockwise. This will be accomplished if the ± potential terminal P is connected to either side of the current coils in Fig. 218.

Example. If in the circuit shown in Fig. 218 the effective voltage $E = 100$ volts, the effective current $I = 50$ amp, and $W = 4,000$ watts, measured by a wattmeter, then

$$\text{Power factor of circuit} = \frac{\text{watts}}{\text{volts} \times \text{amperes}}$$

$$= \frac{4,000}{100 \times 50}$$

$$= 0.8$$

and the phase angle between current and voltage is the angle whose cosine is 0.8, or is 37°.

Thus the power factor may be measured by means of a wattmeter, voltmeter, and ammeter.

258. Switching Transients. The analyses of the flow of alternating current in inductive circuits, with and without resistance, Arts. 249 and 255, both began by assuming that the graph of current was a sine curve, $i = I_m \sin \theta$. In the case of pure inductance it was shown that the graph of the emf required to produce that current was also a sine curve, leading the current curve by 90°, as in Fig. 219.

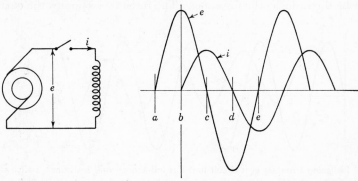

FIG. 219. Current in an inductive circuit when the resistance is zero and the switch is closed at the instant when e is a maximum.

If the switch connecting the generator to the inductance coil is closed at instant b or d, when e is a maximum and when i should be zero according to the theory in Art. 249, then the current curve assumed in Art. 249 and shown in Fig. 219 will be obtained. However, if the switch is closed at any other time in the voltage cycle, the current must still start from zero since the current is necessarily zero when the switch is open, and therefore, at the start at least, the current curve cannot agree with that obtained when the switch is closed at instant b or d.

In particular, if the resistance of the circuit is zero and the switch is closed at instant a when e is zero, then the current will start from zero at instant a, as shown in

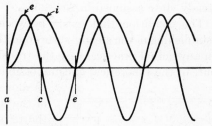

FIG. 220. Current in an inductive circuit when the resistance is zero and the switch is closed at the instant when e is zero.

Fig. 220, and will accelerate as long as e is positive, in accordance with the equation $di/dt = e/L$. Consequently, the current curve reaches its peak at instant c. The voltage then reverses, and the acceleration becomes negative and remains negative from c to e. Since the positive and negative halves of the voltage curve are identical, the decrease in current during the negative half cycle of the voltage must be equal to the increase in current during the positive half cycle, and therefore the current is zero again at instant e. This cycle repeats indefinitely. Thus the graph of current is a sine curve displaced vertically upward, so that it touches the x axis but does not cross it. In other words, the current is a pulsating unidirectional current, and each succeeding cycle is the same as the first one.

If, however, there is resistance in the circuit, each succeeding cycle will not be the same as the first one. The resistance opposes the current,

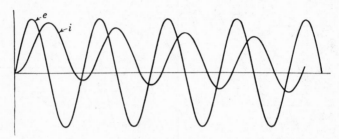

FIG. 221. Switching transient in a circuit that has inductance and resistance, switch closed when $e = 0$ ($R = 0.05X$). When the steady state is finally reached, i will lag e by $\tan^{-1}(X/R)$, that is, 87°.

with the result that it grows more slowly and therefore reaches a lower peak, as shown in Fig. 221. When the current is decreasing, the effect of the resistance is to assist in stopping the current, with the result that it decreases more rapidly and therefore crosses the x axis before reaching its bottom peak. Each succeeding cycle will approach more nearly to the steady state assumed in Art. 255.

The condition that exists between the closing of a switch and the establishing of the steady-state condition is called the switching transient. In any actual practical case the transient disappears within a few cycles, but, in the theoretical and impossible case of $R = 0$, it goes on forever,

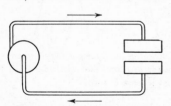

FIG. 222. Air being pumped from one tank to the other.

as shown in Fig. 220. The rate of decrease of the transient is a function of the ratio of the resistance to the inductance. In a circuit of pure resistance the current instantly jumps to the value e/R, and there is no transient.

259. Capacitors; Capacitance. Consider two tanks initially filled with air at atmospheric pressure and connected to each other through an air pump or blower as in Fig. 222. If the blower is started, air will be pumped from the lower tank to the upper tank until the pressure difference between the tanks is equal to the shutoff pressure difference of the blower, and the amount of air transferred will be proportional to this pressure difference, which can be varied by varying the speed of the blower.

Next consider two parallel metal plates separated by a layer of air or other insulating material and connected to the terminals of a direct-current generator, as in Fig. 223. Each metal plate normally contains billions of electrons that are as free to move about in the plates as the molecules of air are in the tanks. If the d-c generator is started up, with the polarity shown, electrons will be pumped from the lower plate to the upper plate, until the potential difference between the plates is equal to the no-load potential difference of the generator, and the amount of electricity transferred will be proportional to this potential difference, which can be varied by varying the speed of the generator.

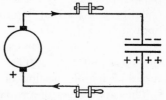

FIG. 223. Capacitor being charged by a d-c generator. Arrows show direction of flow of electrons.

Two conducting plates, separated by a layer of insulating material, and used for the storage of electricity, are called a **capacitor**. **The capacitance of a capacitor may be defined as the quantity of electricity, in coulombs, that must be transferred from one plate to the other in order to create a potential difference of one volt between the plates.** The quantity of electricity that is transferred is called the *charge*.

Although the natural way of expressing capacitance would be in coulombs per volt, it is actually expressed in **farads,** or **microfarads,** where a **farad is the capacitance of a capacitor in which a charge of one coulomb produces a potential difference of one volt between the plates.**

FIG. 224. Capacitor being discharged.

A microfarad = one-millionth of a farad.

If after charging the capacitor, as in Fig. 223, the generator is disconnected by opening the switches, then since no insulation is perfect the charge will gradually leak back to the lower plate through and along the surface of the insulation, but in dry weather it may be several days before the charge completely disappears. The capacitor can be completely discharged in a few microseconds by connecting the two ends of a short piece of wire to the two plates, as in Fig. 224.

So far the two pumping operations of Figs. 222 and 223 appear to be identical, but a striking difference is discovered if the distance between the two plates is varied, because it is then found that the capacitance is approximately inversely proportional to the distance between the plates. The explanation of this is to be found in the fact that the excess protons left behind in the lower plate exert a force of attraction on the electrons that are leaving this plate and so oppose the flow, while the excess electrons in the upper plate repel the electrons in the lower plate and so assist the flow.   Since the excess electrons in the upper plate are some distance away from the scene of the separations, while the excess protons are right on the spot, the repulsive forces assisting the flow are less than the attractive forces opposing the flow, and the generator must do work in removing electrons from the lower plate.   As the distance between the plates approaches zero, the forces of attraction and repulsion approach equality, and the emf required by the generator to transfer a given charge approaches zero.   Thus the capacitance approaches infinity.   We have concentrated on the forces acting on the flow of the electrons away from the lower plate.   A similar set of statements can be made concerning the forces acting on the flow of the electrons into the upper plate.

The capacitance of a capacitor also varies considerably with the nature of the insulating material between the plates.   This insulating material is generally called the dielectric, and the ratio of the capacitance of a given capacitor with a given dielectric between the plates, to the capacitance of the same capacitor with air or empty space between the plates, is called the dielectric constant.

Material	Dielectric constant
Air	1
Glass	5.4–9.9
Mica	2.5–6.6
Oil	2.2–4.7
Paraffined paper	2.0–2.6
Rubber	2.0–3.5
Shellac	2.9–3.7
Water	81

The reason why the capacitance changes with the dielectric is that the dielectrics themselves contain vast numbers of protons and electrons, which, although they cannot flow, can nevertheless move appreciably. That is, they are held elastically and not rigidly.   The distortion of the structure of the dielectric, caused by the charging of the capacitor, has a substantial effect on the forces of attraction and repulsion that assist or oppose the flow of the charge, and therefore has a substantial effect on the capacitance.

260. Capacitor Circuits with Direct and with Alternating Currents.   If a constant emf is applied across the terminals of the circuit shown in Fig. 225, then a momentary current will flow in the direction shown in Fig. 225a to charge the capacitor but current will not flow continuously since the circuit is broken by the insulating material between the plates.

If the applied voltage is now reversed, current will flow in the direction shown in Fig. 225b until the capacitor has given up its charge and will continue to flow in this direction until the capacitor is recharged in the opposite direction. The time required to reverse the charge will be approximately directly proportional to the resistance of the circuit. If then the applied voltage is alternating, a charging current will flow in and out of the wires x and y with a frequency which is the same as that of the applied voltage, and the lamps L will light up if sufficient current flows to heat the filaments.

The greater the capacitance of a capacitor, the more electricity it can hold, and the larger the charging current that passes through the connecting wires.

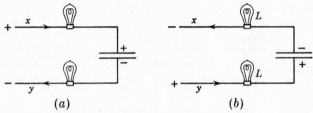

(a)   (b)
FIG. 225. Flow of current in a capacitor.

When a capacitor is connected across a source of alternating emf, the voltage across the capacitor is continually changing, and the charge changes with it in accordance with the equation

$$q = Ce \qquad (56)$$

where q = charge, coulombs (amperes $\times$ seconds)

  e = applied voltage

  C = a constant, called the capacitance of the capacitor, farads

In an actual capacitor, if e is changed suddenly, q cannot instantly adjust itself to the above equation, on account of the resistance and inductance of the leads and plates. In an idealized capacitor in which the resistance and inductance are assumed to be zero, so that there is no obstruction whatever in the way of the charge or discharge, the equation $q = Ce$ is rigidly correct no matter how fast e changes. However, since an average capacitor will discharge completely in something like one-millionth of a second if short-circuited by a good conductor, it follows that the equation $q = Ce$ holds quite accurately for actual capacitors for the comparatively slow changes of e that take place at frequencies met with in power and telephone circuits.

Since the capacitor is charged and discharged twice per cycle, it follows that the rate of charging must be proportional to the frequency. Hence the charging current is proportional to the frequency as well as to the emf and to the capacitance of the capacitor.

261. Phase Relation between Voltage and Current in a Capacitor. If the voltage applied to the capacitor in Fig. 226 is represented by the curve $e = E_m \sin \theta$, then the charge, which is proportional to the voltage, is represented by the curve q. The capacitor is charged alternately in opposite directions. Thus between the instants a and c the plate P_1 is positive, while between c and e the plate P_1 is negative.

At the instants b and d the charge in the capacitor is not changing and the current in the leads must therefore be zero.

Between a and b the voltage and the charge are increasing and the current is flowing in the direction of the impressed voltage e, as shown in

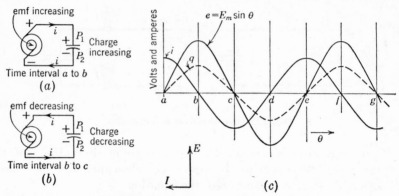

FIG. 226. Alternating current in a capacitor.

Fig. 226a, until, at the instant b, the charge is complete and the current has become zero; this gives the part of the current curve between the instants a and b (see Fig. 226c).

Between b and c the voltage and the charge are decreasing so that current must now be flowing out of the capacitor, or in the direction opposite to the impressed voltage e, as shown in Fig. 226b; this gives the part of the current curve between the instants b and c.

During the next half cycle between c and e the capacitor charges and discharges again but in the opposite direction, so that the current curve between c and e is the same as between a and c except that the sign is reversed.

From these curves it may be seen that the current leads the voltage by 90°.

262. Voltage and Current Relations in a Capacitor. The reasoning presented in Art. 261 can be expressed more precisely and clearly with the aid of calculus,[1] as follows: It is shown in Art. 260 that $q = Ce$. Now

---

[1] Students who are not familiar with calculus may proceed to derive Eq. (57) as follows: The charge in the capacitor shown in Fig. 226 changes from zero to $Q_m = CE_n$ coulombs in the time of one-quarter of a cycle, or in $1/4f$ sec, so that, since charge =

$$i = \frac{dq}{dt} = C \frac{de}{dt}$$

If the voltage applied to the capacitor is assumed to be a sine curve $e = E_m \sin \theta$, where the angle θ has the value of 2π radians per cycle, or $2\pi f$ radians per sec, the current flowing will be given by

$$i = C \frac{de}{dt}$$

$$= C \frac{d}{dt} (E_m \sin 2\pi ft)$$

$$= 2\pi fCE_m \cos 2\pi ft$$

which shows that the current curve leads the voltage curve by 90°, since a cosine curve is simply a sine curve shifted 90° to the left.

Now the maximum value that a cosine can have is unity. Therefore $I_m = 2\pi fCE_m$, and dividing both sides by $\sqrt{2}$

$$I = 2\pi fCE \qquad\qquad (57)$$

where I and E are effective values.

In a circuit of pure resistance, $E = IR$. In a circuit of pure inductance, $E = IX$. If we wish to have a similar expression for a circuit of pure capacitance, we must assign a name and symbol to the group of factors $1/2\pi fC$. It is called the condensive or capacitive reactance and is denoted by the letter X. If capacitive reactance and inductive reactance occur in the same circuit, X_c is used to represent the capacitive reactance. Thus Eq. (57) may be written

$$E = IX_c \qquad\qquad (58)$$

where $X_c = 1/2\pi fC$. From Eq. (58) and the definition of impedance, Art. 248, it follows that in a circuit of pure capacitance the impedance is equal to the reactance.

Example. An alternating emf of 110 volts sends 2.2 amp through a capacitor at 60 cycles. Find the reactance at 60 cycles and find also the capacitance of the capacitor.

---

average current $\times$ time,

$$Q_m = CE_m = I_{av} \times \frac{1}{4f}$$

and   Average charging current $I_{av} = 4fCE_m$ amp

Maximum charging current $I_m = I_{av} \times \frac{\pi}{2}$ (see Art. 239)

$$= \frac{\pi}{2} \times 4fCE_m = 2\pi fCE_m$$

therefore $I_{eff} = 2\pi fCE_{eff}$

$$X, \text{ reactance } = \frac{E}{I} = \frac{110}{2.2} = 50 \text{ ohms}$$

$$C, \text{ capacitance } = \frac{1}{2\pi fX} = \frac{1}{2\pi 60 \times 50} = 5.3 \times 10^{-5} \text{ farad} = 53\mu\text{f}$$

If the voltage applied to the above circuit is kept constant at 110, find the current that will flow through the capacitor at 30, 60, and 120 cycles.

$$X, \text{ reactance } = \frac{1}{2\pi fC}$$

This is inversely proportional to frequency, and is 50 ohms at 60 cycles from last problem.

$$I, \text{ current } = \frac{E}{X}$$

This is therefore proportional to frequency, and so has values of 1.1 amp at 30 cycles, 2.2 amp at 60 cycles, 4.4 amp at 120 cycles.

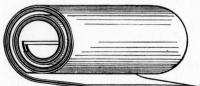

FIG. 227. One method of constructing capacitors.

263. Parallel-plate Capacitors. As shown in the last problem, a capacitor with a capacitance of 53 μf will take a current of 2.2 amp at 110 volts and 60 cycles. It is desirable to know the approximate dimensions of such a capacitor.

The capacitance of a parallel-plate capacitor is given by the formula

$$C = \frac{1}{4\pi} \times \frac{1}{9 \times 10^{11}} \times \frac{kA}{t} \qquad \text{farads} \qquad (59)$$

where A = area of active surface of one plate, sq cm
t = distance between plates, cm
k = dielectric constant (see Art. 259)

Example. A capacitor constructed as in Fig. 227 has plates of tin foil which are 40 ft long and 3 in. wide and which are separated by paraffined paper 0.0025 in. thick.

Since both sides of each plate are active,

$$A = 2 \times 40 \times 12 \times 3 = 2,880 \text{ sq in. } \doteq 18,600 \text{ sq cm}$$
$$t = 0.0025 \text{ in. } = 0.0063 \text{ cm}$$
$$k = 2.0$$

therefore

$$C = \frac{1}{4\pi} \times \frac{1}{9 \times 10^{11}} \times \frac{18,600}{0.0063} \times 2$$
$$= 0.53 \times 10^{-6} \text{ farad} = 0.53 \mu\text{f}$$

Such a capacitor will go into a tin case 1.75 in. square by 4 in. deep. It will require 100 of these capacitors, connected in parallel, to make up the 53 μf required.

264. Power in a Capacitor.   The power in a circuit at any instant is the product of e and i the voltage and the current at that instant.   In a capacitor the current leads the applied voltage by 90° and the curves representing e, i, and ei are shown in Fig. 228.   This last curve is obtained by multiplying together corresponding values of e and i at different instants; at a and c the voltage and therefore the power are zero; the

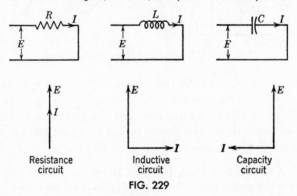

FIG. 228. Voltage e, current i, and power ei in a capacitor.

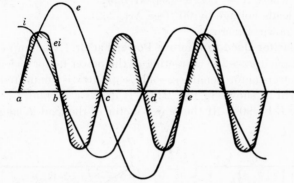

Resistance circuit   Inductive circuit   Capacity circuit

FIG. 229

power is also zero at instants b and d when the current is zero.   Between a and b energy is stored in the capacitor, while between b and c the same energy is given up by the capacitor, so that the average value of the energy used is zero and so also is the average power in the circuit.

265. Formulas Used in Circuit Problems

Resistance circuit (see Fig. 229):

$E = IR$
Current is in phase with voltage (see Art. 254)
Power $= EI$ watts (average power)

Circuit with inductive reactance (see Fig. 229):

$E = IX$ where $X = 2\pi fL$ (Art. 250).
Current lags voltage by 90° (Art. 249).
Average power is zero.

Circuit with capacitive reactance (see Fig. 229):

$E = IX$ where $X = 1/2\pi fC$ (see Art. 262).
Current leads voltage by 90° (see Art. 262).
Average power is zero.

266. Capacitor Used to Improve Power Factor. One important application of capacitors is the correcting of the power factor of loads in order to avoid power-factor penalties. The capacitor is connected in parallel with the load as shown in Fig. 230. It draws a current I_c, which leads the voltage E by 90°. If the power factor of the load is lagging so that

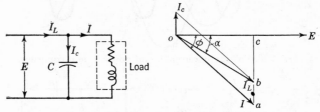

FIG. 230. Capacitor correcting power factor.

the load current I lags behind the voltage by the angle ϕ, then the line current I_L, which is the vector sum of I and I_c, is advanced in phase by the addition of the I_c component, and the power factor is increased. If I_c is made equal to ac, the power factor becomes 100 per cent. The power remains the same since $EI \cos \phi = EI_L \cos \alpha$.

Example. A certain load takes 10 kw at 75 per cent power factor. In their power contract the power-factor penalty is applied only to power factors below 85 per cent. What size of capacitor must be used in order to avoid the penalty? The voltage is 550 volts, 60 cycles.

In the vector diagram in Fig. 230, I is the load current and $\cos \phi = 0.75$. Therefore $\phi = 41°25'$.

I_L is the line current, and, if the penalty is to be avoided, then $\cos \alpha$ must not be less than 0.85. Therefore $\alpha = 31°47'$. $I_c = ab = ac - bc$, both of which are known if I is known. $EI \cos \phi = $ watts $= 10,000$. Therefore

$$I = \frac{10,000}{550 \times 0.75} = 24.2 \text{ amp}$$

$$ac = I \sin \phi = 24.2 \sin 41°25' = 24.2 \times 0.6615 = 16.0$$
$$oc = I \cos \phi = 24.2 \cos 41°25' = 24.2 \times 0.75 \quad = 18.15$$
$$bc = oc \times \tan \alpha = 18.15 \times \tan 31°47' = 11.25$$

therefore $I_c = ab = 16.0 - 11.25 = 4.75 \text{ amp}$

Now $I_c = E/X_c = 2\pi fCE$; therefore $C = I_c/2\pi fE$; therefore

$$C = \frac{4.75}{2\pi 60 \times 550} = 2.29 \times 10^{-5} \text{ farad} = 22.9 \ \mu\text{f}$$

267. Resistance and Capacitance in Series. Let us assume that a current $i = I_m \sin \theta$ is flowing through the resistance R and the capacitance C in series, Fig. 231, and let us determine the impressed emf e required to produce that current.

The emf e_r required to drive the current i through the resistance R is given by the sine curve e_r in phase with i, from Art. 254, and the emf e_c required to produce the current i in the capacitor part of the circuit is

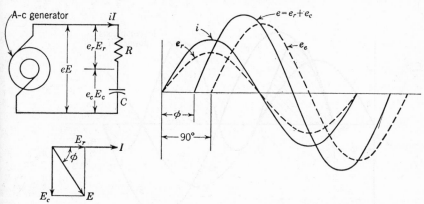

FIG. 231. Voltages and current in a circuit of resistance and capacitance in series. $e, e_r, e_c,$ and i are instantaneous values. $E, E_r, E_c,$ and I are effective values.

given by the sine curve e_c lagging 90° behind the current i, Art. 262. The total emf e impressed upon the circuit by the a-c generator at any instant is therefore $e = e_r + e_c$.

The curve e may be obtained by adding the corresponding values of e_r and e_c at various points on the cycle, or the two sine curves may be added by means of the parallelogram or vector method. Figure 231 shows both methods. Since the two sine curves to be added are 90° apart in phase, the parallelogram is a rectangle, with sides equal in length to the effective values E_r and E_c. The diagonal of this parallelogram is then equal to the effective value of the total impressed voltage. Therefore

$$E = \sqrt{E_r{}^2 + E_c{}^2}$$

but $E_r = IR$, and $E_c = IX_c$, where $X_c = 1/2\pi fC$; therefore

$$E = \sqrt{(IR)^2 + (IX_c)^2}$$
$$= I\sqrt{R^2 + X_c{}^2}$$
$$= IZ$$

where $Z = \sqrt{R^2 + X_c^2}$.

Angle $\phi = \tan^{-1}\dfrac{E_c}{E_r} = \tan^{-1}\dfrac{IX_c}{IR} = \tan^{-1}\dfrac{X_c}{R}$

The instantaneous power at any instant in the above case is equal to the product of the volts and the amperes and is ei watts. By plotting this product at different points in the cycle, the power curve shown in Fig. 232 is obtained. It is a sine curve of double frequency offset from the zero axis.

Since the curves are plotted on a time base ($\theta = 2\pi ft$ radians), the area under the power curve represents energy delivered or work done. During the time interval from a to b the impressed emf is in the same direction as

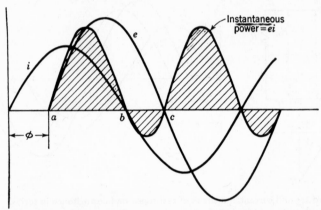

FIG. 232. Instantaneous values of voltage, current, and power in a circuit consisting of capacitance and resistance in series.

the current, and therefore the generator is putting energy into the circuit. From b to c the capacitor is returning energy to the generator. The capacitor returns as much energy as it receives, but, since it discharges through the resistance R, part of this energy is wasted as I^2R loss and does not get back to the generator. On the other hand, when the generator is charging the capacitor, it does so through the resistance R, and therefore the energy stored in the capacitor is less than that delivered by the generator by the amount of the I^2R loss. This accounts for the fact that the energy received back by the generator each cycle is so much less than the energy that it puts into the circuit each cycle.

Since the average power input to the capacitor is zero, while the average power input to the resistance is E_rI watts, it follows that the average power input to the entire circuit is E_rI watts. Since $E_r = E \cos \phi$, the average power is $EI \cos \phi$ watts.

268. Kirchhoff's Laws Applied to Effective Values of Alternating Voltages and Currents. Kirchhoff's laws, as stated in Art. 43, apply only to the actual instantaneous values of the currents and voltages. In Art. 255 we were tacitly applying Kirchhoff's second law when we said that $e = e_R + e_L$. However, in this article we also showed that the effective value of the total voltage E could be obtained by adding E_R and E_L vectorially. Similarly in Art. 267 we showed that the effective value E could be obtained by adding E_R and E_c vectorially. Moreover, it cannot make any difference to the rules for the addition of sine curves whether those since curves represent voltages or currents. Therefore we may say that Kirchhoff's laws apply to the effective values of current and voltage, provided that the addition is vectorial.

269. Resistance, Inductance, and Capacitance in Series. In the solution of such a circuit as that shown in Fig. 233a, the current vector should be taken as a basis for phase relation, since it is the same in all three parts of the circuit. The voltage E is the vector sum of E_r, E_l, and E_c, by Kirchhoff's second law (Art. 268), and is determined as follows:

A vector I is drawn in any direction.

A vector $E_r = IR$ is drawn to scale in phase with I.

A vector $E_l = IX_l$ is drawn to scale leading I by 90°.

A vector $E_c = IX_c$ is drawn to scale lagging I by 90°. Then

$$E = \text{vector sum of } E_r, E_l, \text{ and } E_c$$
$$= \sqrt{E_r^2 + (E_l - E_c)^2}$$
$$= \sqrt{(IR)^2 + (IX_l - IX_c)^2}$$
$$= I\sqrt{R^2 + (X_l - X_c)^2}$$

but $$E = IZ$$

therefore $$Z = \sqrt{R^2 + (X_l - X_c)^2} \tag{60}$$

If ϕ is the angle by which the voltage E leads the current I, then

$$\phi = \tan^{-1}\frac{E_l - E_c}{E_R} = \tan^{-1}\frac{IX_l - IX_c}{IR} = \tan^{-1}\frac{X_l - X_c}{R} \tag{61}$$

and the current will lead or lag the applied voltage according as X_c is greater or less than X_l.

When $X_c = X_l$, the capacitive and the inductive reactances exactly neutralize one another and the current has its maximum value and is equal to E/R. The circuit is then said to be in resonance.

The inductive reactance X_l is directly proportional to the frequency and is equal to $2\pi fL$, whereas the capacitive reactance X_c is inversely proportional to the frequency and is equal to $1/2\pi fC$. If then in Fig. 233a,

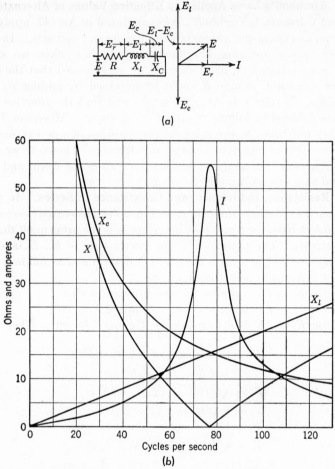

FIG. 233. (a) Resistance, inductance, and capacitance in series. (b) Curves showing the variation of inductive reactance, capacitive reactance, total reactance, and current with frequency, for the given example, where R, L, and C are connected in series.

the voltage E across the terminals is kept constant and the frequency is increased, X_l will increase and X_c will decrease until, when

$$X_l = X_c$$

or

$$2\pi f L = \frac{1}{2\pi f C}$$

and

$$f = \frac{1}{2\pi \sqrt{LC}}$$

(62

the circuit is said to be in resonance and the current has its maximum value.

The same problem is found in mechanics. An alternating force applied to a spring will cause the spring to oscillate. As the frequency of the applied force increases, the amplitude increases and reaches its maximum value when the applied frequency is the same as the natural frequency of vibration of the spring; with further increase of the frequency, the amplitude will decrease. This principle is made use of in the vibrating-reed frequency meter shown in Fig. 196.

The frequency $f = 1/(2\pi \sqrt{LC})$ is called the frequency of resonance and is also called the natural frequency of the circuit.

Example. If a resistance of 2 ohms, an inductive reactance of 12 ohms at 60 cycles, and a capacitive reactance of 20 ohms at 60 cycles are put in series across 110 volts, plot curves showing the variation with frequency of X_l, X_c, $X(= X_l - X_c)$, I, E_r, E_l, and E_c.

Several points for these curves are determined as follows:

Frequency	R	$X_l = 2\pi f L$	$X_c = \frac{1}{2\pi f C}$	$(X_l - X_c)$	$\sqrt{R^2 + (X_l - X_c)^2}$	$I = \frac{E}{\sqrt{R^2 + (X_l - X_c)^2}}$	$E_r = IR$	$E_l = IX_l$	$E_c = IX_c$
20.0	2	4.0	60.0	−56	56+	1.97	3.94	7.9	118
40.0	2	8.0	30.0	−22	22.1	4.98	9.96	40.0	150
60.0	2	12.0	20.0	−8	8.24	13.4	26.8	161.0	268
80.0	2	16.0	15.0	1	2.24	49.2	98.4	788.0	738
100.0	2	20.0	12.0	8	8.24	13.4	26.8	268.0	161
77.5	2	15.5	15.5	0	2.0	55.0	110.0	852.0	852

The frequency of resonance can be determined by Eq. (60) and is 77.5 cycles, because then $X_l = X_c = 15.5$ ohms. See Fig. 233b for plotted curves.

If the circuit is in resonance and the resistance is low, then a large current will flow, and if in addition the reactances are large, then the voltage drops across these reactances are large and may have several times the value of the applied voltage. This result is shown in the above problem. The inductance coil and the capacitor must be insulated to withstand 852 volts and not merely the applied 110 volts. The series RLC circuit should be regarded as a somewhat dangerous circuit, because unexpectedly high voltages may be obtained if resonance conditions are carelessly approached.

270. Resistance, Inductance, and Capacitance in Parallel. In the solution of such a circuit as that shown in Fig. 234a, the voltage vector should be taken as a basis for phase relation, since it is the same for all three parts of the circuit. The current I is the vector sum of I_r, I_l, and I_c, by Kirchhoff's first law (Art. 268), and is determined as follows:

A vector E is drawn in any direction (Fig. 234b).

A vector $I_r = \dfrac{E}{R}$ is drawn to scale in phase with E.

A vector $I_l = \dfrac{E}{X_l}$ is drawn to scale and lagging E by 90°.

A vector $I_c = \dfrac{E}{X_c}$ is drawn to scale and leading E by 90°. Then

$$I = \text{vector sum of } I_r, I_l, \text{ and } I_c$$
$$= \sqrt{I_r^2 + (I_l - I_c)^2}$$

and the current I will lead or lag the applied voltage E according as I_c is greater or smaller than I_l.

When $X_c = X_l$, the two currents I_c and I_l are equal in magnitude, and, since they are 180° out of phase with each other, their sum is zero at all

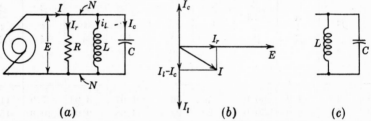

(a)   (b)   (c)

FIG. 234. Circuit with resistance, inductance, and capacitance in parallel.

times. Therefore when $X_c = X_l$, there is no current flowing in the line at the points NN, and the total line current is simply I_r. If the line were cut at points NN, so as to disconnect L and C from the line, as in Fig. 234c, the current in the circuit LC would continue to oscillate with undiminished amplitude since we have assumed an ideal resistanceless L and C. In any actual case the oscillations would gradually die down, owing to the resistance. The circuit is said to be in parallel resonance when the current input is in phase with the applied voltage, or when $X_c = X_l$, if both of these reactances are pure.

The physical picture of the oscillation may be described as follows.

In the first place it is important to realize that when the current at N is zero, then I_c and I_l are actually one and the same current. They would appear in the vector diagram to be equal and opposite currents because I_c is the clockwise current through L and C while I_l is the counterclockwise current through L and C.

Let us start at the instant when the capacitor is at its maximum charge and when the charging current is therefore zero and is about to reverse.

The capacitor now begins to discharge through the inductance, while the inductance opposes the growth of the discharge current. The discharge current continues to accelerate as long as there is any emf to make it accelerate, that is, as long as there is any charge left in'the capacitor. Therefore the current is at its maximum when the capacitor is completely discharged. All the energy that was stored in the capacitor is now stored in the magnetic field of the inductance coil. As the current continues flowing, the capacitor begins to be charged in the opposite direction, and the potential difference across its terminals accordingly opposes the current, with the result that the current begins to decrease. The inductance opposes the decrease, however, with the result that by the time that the growing potential difference across the capacitor terminals has finally reduced the current to zero, the capacitor is completely recharged, but with the opposite polarity. The capacitor then begins to discharge again, but only succeeds in becoming recharged in the original direction. This process of alternate discharge and recharge would continue indefinitely if there were no resistance in the circuit.

This electric oscillation is analogous to a car being allowed to coast down a dip in a railway. The momentum it acquires in rolling down the incline takes it up the other side, and, if there were no friction, the car would oscillate back and forth from side to side of the dip and could never get stopped at the bottom, unless it were equipped with brakes.

The circuit of Fig. 234a may be adjusted to resonance by varying either the inductance, the capacitance, or the frequency. In the following example the frequency is varied.

Example. A resistance of 20 ohms, an inductive reactance of 2.4 ohms at 60 cycles, and a capacitive reactance of 4.0 ohms at 60 cycles are put in parallel across 110 volts, as in Fig. 234a. Plot curves of the effective values of the currents I_l, I_c, I_r, and I, against frequency.

Several points for these curves are calculated in the following table and are plotted in Fig. 235. The curve of I_c is a straight line through the origin. The curve of I_l is a rectangular hyperbola and is tangent to both axes at infinity.

Frequency	R	$X_l = 2\pi fL$	$X_c = \dfrac{1}{2\pi fC}$	I_r	I_l	I_c	$I_l - I_c$	I
20.0	20	0.8	12.0	5.5	137	9	128	128+
40.0	20	1.6	6.0	5.5	69	18	51	51.2
60.0	20	2.4	4.0	5.5	46	28	18	18.8
77.5	20	3.1	3.1	5.5	35	35	0	5.5
80.0	20	3.2	3.0	5.5	34	37	− 3	6.2
100.0	20	4.0	2.4	5.5	28	46	−18	18.8

Resonance phenomena in a-c circuits play a very important part in radio, where circuits must be tuned to resonance in order to obtain sufficient selectivity and sensitivity, but have only a limited application in power engineering. Where a-c power circuits contain capacitors, as in power-factor correction, there is a possibility of a resonance condition existing in the circuit, with its attendant high voltages, which may puncture insulation, flashover insulators, or operate protective devices to shut down equipment. Fortunately such resonance conditions are comparatively rare.

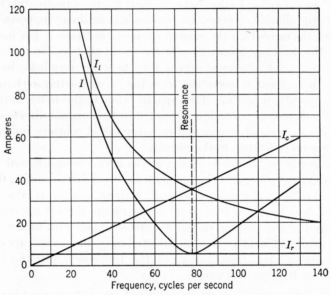

FIG. 235. Resistance, inductance, and capacitance in parallel.

271. Two Impedances in Parallel. In Fig. 236 the two impedances Z_1 and Z_2 are shown connected in parallel across the line. Both of these impedances consist of resistance and reactance in series. By definition of impedance,

$$I_1 = \frac{E}{Z_1} \quad \text{and} \quad I_2 = \frac{E}{Z_2}$$

Also $Z_1 = \sqrt{r_1^2 + x_1^2}$ and $Z_2 = \sqrt{r_2^2 + x_2^2}$ (see Art. 255)

Therefore $I_1 = \dfrac{E}{\sqrt{r_1^2 + x_1^2}}$ and $I_2 = \dfrac{E}{\sqrt{r_2^2 + x_2^2}}$

ϕ_1 (see Fig. 237) is the angle whose tangent is x_1/r_1 (see Art. 255) and ϕ_2 is the angle whose tangent is x_2/r_2.

$$I = \text{vector sum of } I_1 \text{ and } I_2$$
$$= \sqrt{(ON)^2 + (PN)^2} \quad \text{(Fig. 237)}$$
$$= \sqrt{(I_1 \cos \phi_1 + I_2 \cos \phi_2)^2 + (I_1 \sin \phi_1 + I_2 \sin \phi_2)^2}$$

And ϕ = the angle whose tangent is $\dfrac{PN}{ON}$

          = the angle whose tangent is $\dfrac{I_1 \sin \phi_1 + I_2 \sin \phi_2}{I_1 \cos \phi_1 + I_2 \cos \phi_2}$

Example. An electric heater that takes 1.5 kw at 100 per cent power factor and a motor that takes 1.75 kw at 75 per cent power factor are connected to a

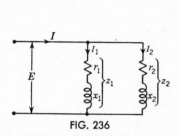

FIG. 236

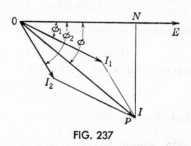

FIG. 237

115-volt line. What is the total current taken from the line, and what is the power factor of the total load?

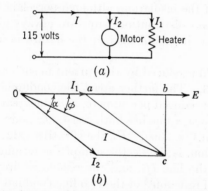

FIG. 238. Showing how to add the individual load currents on an a-c line.

Figure 238*a* shows the heater and motor connected to the line, while Fig. 238*b* shows the vector diagram. In any circuit the average power is given by the equation watts = $EI \cos \phi$ (Art. 255). Therefore

$$I = \frac{\text{watts}}{E \cos \phi}$$

Applying this formula to each load,

$$I_1 = \frac{1{,}500}{115 \times 1} = 13.04 \text{ amp in phase with } E$$

$$I_2 = \frac{1{,}750}{115 \times 0.75} = 20.29 \text{ amp lagging } E \text{ by angle } \alpha$$

where $\alpha = \cos^{-1} 0.75 = 41°24'$.

$$
\begin{aligned}
I &= \sqrt{ob^2 + bc^2} \\
&= \sqrt{(I_1 + I_2 \cos \alpha)^2 + (I_2 \sin \alpha)^2} \\
&= \sqrt{(13.04 + 20.29 \times 0.75)^2 + (20.29 \times 0.6613)^2} \\
&= \sqrt{28.26^2 + 13.42^2} \\
&= 31.28 \text{ amp}
\end{aligned}
$$

Power factor of total load $= \cos \phi = \dfrac{ob}{oc} = \dfrac{28.26}{31.28} = 90.3\%$

Total power $= 1,500 + 1,750 = 3,250$ watts

CHECK: Total power $= EI \cos \phi$
$$= 115 \times 31.28 \times 0.903$$
$$= 3,248 \text{ watts}$$

which checks to within better than one-tenth of 1 per cent.

272. Single-phase Transmission Line.

A single-phase transmission line usually consists of two parallel conductors, spaced a suitable distance apart and well insulated from each other. In the case of open-wire lines, air provides most of the insulation, although porcelain is required at the points of support and distribution wires are always given a coating of insulation to protect the public against the hazard of a fallen or broken wire.

The magnetic field produced by the current in such a transmission line is shown in Fig. 213. The farther apart the conductors are, the greater the amount of flux produced per ampere, and the greater the inductance of the line. Since such a line has both resistance and inductance, it may be represented as in Fig. 239a. E_g, the effective value of the voltage at the generating station, is the vector sum of the terminal voltage E_t, the resistance drop in the line IR, and the reactance drop in the line IX, where R is the total resistance of the two line conductors in series and X is the total reactance of the line.

Consider first the case of a load whose power factor is 100 per cent, as, for example, a resistance load. The phase relation between the voltages for 100 per cent power-factor load is shown in Fig. 239b.

A vector I is drawn in any direction.

A vector E_t is drawn to scale equal to the receiver voltage, and, since the power factor is 100 per cent, E_t and I are in phase.

A vector equal to IR is drawn to scale in phase with I.

A vector equal to IX is drawn to scale leading I by 90°.

The vector E_g is the vector sum of E_t, IR, and IX and may be scaled off or determined by calculation, as follows:

$$E_g = \sqrt{(E_t + IR)^2 + (IX)^2} \tag{63}$$

Since there is no power loss in the inductance of the line, the total loss is in the resistance and is equal to I^2R watts.

Values of line resistance and line reactance are generally given in ohms per mile of wire as in Table 3 on page 306.

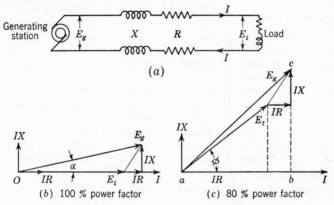

FIG. 239. Vector diagrams of a transmission line.

Example.   Seventy-five kilowatts at 2,200 volts and 60 cycles has to be delivered at the end of a 5-mile line, the size of wire being No. 0 B & S gauge copper and the spacing 48 in.   Find the voltage in the generating station and the power loss in the line when the power factor of the load is (*a*) 100 per cent and (*b*) 80 per cent, the current lagging.

a. One hundred per cent power-factor load:

$$E_t I \cos \phi = \text{watts} = 75{,}000 \qquad \text{and} \qquad \cos \phi = 1$$

Therefore
$$I = \frac{75{,}000}{2{,}200} = 34.1 \text{ amp}$$

Line resistance = 0.518 ohm per mile of wire   (from Table 3)
= 5.18 ohms for a 5-mile line

since there are 10 miles of wire in a 5-mile line.

Line reactance = 0.721 ohm per mile of wire   (from Table 3)
= 7.21 ohms for a 5-mile line
$IR = 34.1 \times 5.18 = 177$ volts
$IX = 34.1 \times 7.21 = 246$ volts
$E_g = \sqrt{(E_t + IR)^2 + (IX)^2}$ [from Eq. (63)]
$= \sqrt{(2{,}200 + 177)^2 + 246^2}$
$= 2{,}390$ volts

Power factor at generating station $= \cos \alpha = \dfrac{2{,}377}{2{,}390} = 99.5$ per cent

Power loss in line $= I^2R = 34.1^2 \times 5.18 = 6{,}023$ watts
Power delivered = 75 kw (given)
Power input to line $= 75 + 6.023 = 81.023$ kw

Efficiency of transmission $= \dfrac{\text{output}}{\text{input}} = \dfrac{75}{81.023} = 92.6$ per cent

TABLE 3. Copper Conductors

Size of wire		Resistance at 20°C, ohms per mile of wire	Inductive reactance per mile of wire at 60 cycles			
			Spacing, in.			
B & S gauge No.	Circular mils		24	48	72	96
0000	211,600	0.258	0.594	0.678	0.728	0.763
000	167,800	0.326	0.608	0.692	0.742	0.776
00	133,100	0.411	0.622	0.706	0.756	0.790
0	105,500	0.518	0.637	0.721	0.770	0.804
1	83,690	0.653	0.650	0.735	0.784	0.819
2	66,370	0.824	0.665	0.749	0.797	0.833
4	41,740	1.309	0.693	0.777	0.826	0.860
6	26,250	2.082	0.721	0.805	0.854	0.889

b. Eighty per cent power-factor load, lagging:

$$I = \frac{\text{watts}}{E_t \cos \phi} = \frac{75,000}{2,200 \times 0.8} = 42.5 \text{ amp}$$

Line resistance $R = 5.18$ ohms
Line reactance $X = 7.21$ ohms
$$IR = 42.5 \times 5.18 = 220 \text{ volts}$$
$$IX = 42.5 \times 7.21 = 307 \text{ volts}$$

A vector I is drawn in any direction (see Fig. 239c).

A vector $E_t = 2,200$ volts is drawn to scale at an angle $\phi = \cos^{-1} 0.8$ to the current vector I.

A vector $IR = 220$ volts is drawn to scale in phase with I.

A vector $IX = 307$ volts is drawn to scale leading I by 90°.

The vector E_g is the vector sum of E_t, IR, and IX and may be scaled off or calculated as follows:

$$\begin{aligned} E_g &= \sqrt{(ab)^2 + (bc)^2} \\ &= \sqrt{(E_t \cos \phi + IR)^2 + (E_t \sin \phi + IX)^2} \\ &= \sqrt{(2,200 \times 0.8 + 220)^2 + (2,200 \times 0.6 + 307)^2} \\ &= \sqrt{1,980^2 + 1,627^2} \\ &= 2,560 \text{ volts} \end{aligned}$$

Power loss in line $= I^2R = 42.5^2 \times 5.18 = 9,356$ watts

Efficiency of transmission $= \dfrac{75}{75 + 9.356} = 88.9$ per cent

The foregoing example shows how the voltage regulation and the efficiency of transmission on a given line are affected by a change in the power factor when the amount of the power is fixed.

At 100 per cent power factor,

$$E_g - E_t = 2,390 - 2,200 = 190 \text{ volts}$$

At 80 per cent power factor,

$$E_g - E_t = 2{,}560 - 2{,}200 = 360 \text{ volts}$$

So that dropping the power factor of the load from 100 to 80 per cent increases the line drop from 190 volts to 360 volts and reduces the efficiency of transmission from 92.6 to 88.9 per cent. Lowering the power factor therefore not only increases the line loss but also makes it more difficult for the power company to maintain the proper voltage at the consumer's premises.

273. Complex-quantity Method of Solving Alternating-current Circuits. When a circuit is made up of several branches, so that the vector diagram becomes rather more complicated than in the preceding examples, the task of solving the circuit can be considerably simplified by the use of the complex-quantity method of solution. In this method each vector is resolved into two components at right angles to each other.

For example, in Fig. 240 the vector V_1 may be resolved into the two components a_1 along the x axis and b_1 along the y axis, so that V_1 is the vector sum of a_1 and b_1, which is expressed by writing

$$V_1 = a_1 + jb_1$$

where the letter j, placed in front of the vector component b_1, is understood to mean that this vector component is at right angles to the x axis. The quantity $a_1 + jb_1$ is called a complex quantity.

274. Addition and Subtraction of Vectors. In accordance with the convention described in the preceding article, we write

$$
\begin{aligned}
V_1 &= a_1 + jb_1 \qquad \text{(see Fig. 240)} \\
V_2 &= a_2 + jb_2 \\
V_s &= \text{vector sum of } V_1 \text{ and } V_2 \\
&= a_s + jb_s \\
&= (a_1 + a_2) + j(b_1 + b_2)
\end{aligned}
$$

The length of V_s is $\sqrt{a_s^2 + b_s^2}$ and its phase angle ϕ is the angle whose tangent is b_s/a_s.

The vector difference $V_2 - V_1$ is obtained by reversing V_1 and then adding, as shown in Fig. 241. Thus the vector difference is

$$
\begin{aligned}
V_2 - V_1 &= V_3 \\
&= (a_2 - a_1) + j(b_2 - b_1) \\
&= a_3 + jb_3
\end{aligned}
$$

and in this particular illustration b_3 is negative, since b_1 is greater than b_2.

275. Multiplication of Vectors. The $a + jb$ method of representing a vector is particularly well suited to the processes of addition and subtraction, but it also lends itself readily to multiplication.

Consider the circuit shown in Fig. 242, the vector diagram of which is shown in Fig. 243. If the current vector I is drawn along the x axis, so that $I = I + j0$, then the voltage E_r required to drive this current through the resistance r also lies along the axis, since voltage and current are in phase in a resistance, and the voltage E_x required to drive the current through the reactance x is at right angles to the current and leads it

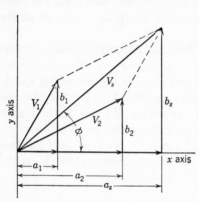

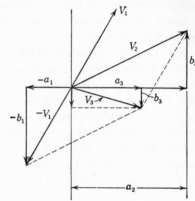

FIG. 240. Addition of vectors. V_s = vector sum of V_1 and V_2.

FIG. 241. Subtraction of vectors. V_3 = vector sum of V_2 and $-V_1$.

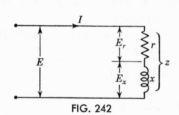

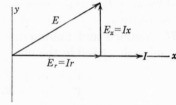

FIG. 242

FIG. 243

by 90° as shown. The total voltage E is the vector sum of E_r and E_x. Therefore

$$E = E_r + jE_x$$
$$= Ir + jIx$$
$$= I(r + jx)$$

But $E = IZ$, where Z = impedance of the circuit. Therefore

$$Z = r + jx$$

Thus impedance may be treated as a vector. In fact the impedance of a circuit may be regarded as the voltage required to drive a current of 1 amp, effective value, through that circuit and is then a vector the same as any other voltage. It is true that we measure resistance, reactance, and impedance in *ohms* but we could equally well measure them in *volts per ampere.*   Many people prefer to regard the impedance, $r + jx$, as an operator by which the current must be multiplied to give the voltage required to drive that current through the given impedance.

Now let us redraw the vector diagram for the circuit of Fig. 242, this time drawing I perpendicular to the x axis so that its components are given by the equation $I = 0 + jI$. The resulting vector diagram is shown in Fig. 244, and, since the location of the x axis cannot in any way affect the physical conditions of the circuit, it follows that the vector diagram of Fig. 244 is the vector diagram of Fig. 243 swung through 90°. In Fig. 244, E is made up of a negative x-axis component E_x and a positive y-axis component E_r, so that

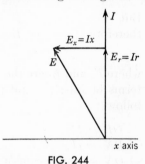

$$E = -E_x + jE_r$$

FIG. 244

In most cases a glance at the vector diagram is sufficient to determine which components are horizontal and which are vertical, and also whether the components are positive or negative, but, inasmuch as the vector diagram cannot be drawn accurately to scale until *after* the circuit is solved and the magnitudes and phase angles are known, it follows that in the more complicated diagrams there will often be some uncertainty as to signs.   It is therefore important to realize that, if we regard j as being an operator which turns a vector through 90° counterclockwise and then apply the ordinary rules of algebra, the signs will take care of themselves.   For example, in Fig. 244, $E = IZ$, but

$$I = 0 + jI \qquad \text{and} \qquad Z = r + jx$$
$$E = (0 + jI)(r + jx)$$
$$= jIr + j^2Ix$$

The j in front of Ir indicates that the vector Ir is turned 90° counterclockwise from the x axis, while the j^2 indicates that the vector Ix is turned through 90° twice, that is, through 180° from the x axis.   It accordingly still lies along the x axis but is negative.   Evidently performing the j operation twice is equivalent to multiplying by -1, or $j^2 = -1$.   Therefore $E = jIr - Ix$, which fits the vector diagram, Fig. 244.

Note also that j^3 turns the vector through $3 \times 90°$ counterclockwise, which is the same as turning it through 90° clockwise.   Therefore

$$j^3 = -j$$

Also j^4 turns the vector through 360°, which leaves it in the same position as before.   Therefore

$$j^4 = 1$$

Next let us again redraw the vector diagram for the circuit of Fig. 242, this time drawing I at any angle ϕ_1 to the x axis, so that

$$I = I_a + jI_b \qquad \text{(see Fig. 245)}$$

where $I_a = I \cos \phi_1$ and $I_b = I \sin \phi_1$.   Then

$$
\begin{aligned}
E &= IZ \\
&= (I_a + jI_b)(r + jx) \\
&= r(I_a + jI_b) + jx(I_a + jI_b) \qquad &(a) \\
&= I_a r + jI_a x + jI_b r + j^2 I_b x \qquad &(b)
\end{aligned}
$$

But $j^2 = -1$

therefore $E = (I_a r - I_b x) + j(I_a x + I_b r)$
$$= E_a + jE_b$$

where E_a and E_b are the x-axis and y-axis components of E.   The various terms of Eqs. (a) and (b) may be identified on the vector diagram as follows:

$OB = I_a r$
$BN = jI_b r$
$ON = $ vector sum of OB and BN
$\quad\;\; = I_a r + jI_b r = r(I_a + jI_b) = E_r$
$NM = jI_a x$
$MP = j^2 I_b x$
$NP = $ vector sum of NM and MP
$\quad\;\; = jI_a x + j^2 I_b x = jx(I_a + jI_b) = E_x$
$OP = $ vector sum of the four components OB, BN, NM, and MP
$\quad\;\; = E$

It is important to realize that in applying such an equation as $E = IZ$, if we merely multiply the numerical values of I and Z, we obtain only the

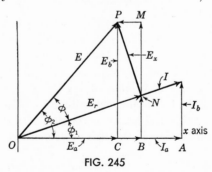

FIG. 245

numerical value of E; but if we write I and Z in the $a + jb$ form and thus obtain the vector product, we obtain E in the $a + jb$ form, which gives us the phase angle of E as well as its numerical magnitude.

Example. Given that, in Fig. 242, $r = 6$ ohms, $x = 3$ ohms, and $I = 10$ amp, determine the magnitude and phase angle of E when I is drawn at $36°52'$ to the x axis as in Fig. 245.

$$I = 10 \cos 36°52' + j10 \sin 36°52'$$
$$= 10 \times 0.8 + j10 \times 0.6$$
$$= 8 + j6$$
$$Z = r + jx$$
$$= 6 + j3$$
$$E = IZ$$
$$= (8 + j6)(6 + j3)$$
$$= 48 + j(24 + 36) + j^2 18$$

But $\qquad j^2 = -1$

therefore $\qquad E = (48 - 18) + j(24 + 36)$
$$= 30 + j60$$

Length of $E = \sqrt{30^2 + 60^2} = 67.08$ volts

$$\phi_2 = \text{angle whose tan is } \frac{60}{30} = 63°26'$$

$$\phi = 63°26' - 36°52' = 26°34'$$

NOTE: The work would, of course, have been very much simplified if the current vector I had been drawn along the x axis, but the object was to illustrate the general case.

276. Division of Vectors.   If the voltage E and the impedance Z of the circuit in Fig. 246 are known, then the current is given by the equation $I = E/Z$.

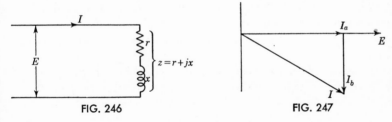

FIG. 246   FIG. 247

Let the vector E be drawn along the x axis as in Fig. 247.   Then

$$E = E + j0$$
$$Z = r + jx$$
$$I = \frac{E}{Z} = \frac{E + j0}{r + jx}$$

In order to reduce this expression for I to the standard $a + jb$ form, multiply by $(r - jx)/(r - jx)$, which, being equal to 1, will not change the value.

Then $\qquad$
$$I = \frac{E}{(r + jx)} \times \frac{r - jx}{(r - jx)}$$
$$= \frac{E(r - jx)}{r^2 + j(rx - rx) - j^2 x^2}$$

But
$$j^2 = -1$$

therefore
$$I = \frac{E(r - jx)}{r^2 + x^2}$$

$$= E\left(\frac{r}{r^2 + x^2}\right) - jE\left(\frac{x}{r^2 + x^2}\right) \qquad (c)$$

$$= I_a - jI_b$$

where I_a and I_b are the x-axis and y-axis components of I.

Note that in Eq. (c) the quantity $r/(r^2 + x^2)$ is the numerical factor by which the voltage E must be multiplied in order to obtain the component of current that is in phase with E, while $x/(r^2 + x^2)$ is the numerical factor by which the voltage must be multiplied in order to obtain the quadrature or 90° out of phase component of current. These two factors are used so frequently that they have been given names. They are called the *conductance* and the *susceptance* of the circuit.

277. Summary of Alternating-current Circuit Constants

Symbol	Circuit constant
r	Resistance
x	Reactance
Z	Impedance
g	Conductance
b	Susceptance
Y	Admittance

Definitions. The **resistance** of an a-c circuit may be defined as being the factor by which the effective value of the current must be multiplied in order to obtain the component of voltage that is in phase with the current.

The **reactance** of an a-c circuit may be defined as being the factor by which the effective value of the current must be multiplied in order to obtain the component of voltage which leads the current by ninety degrees.

The **impedance** of an a-c circuit may be defined as being the factor by which the effective value of the current must be multiplied in order to obtain the total voltage. And $Z = r + jx$.

The **conduct**ance of an a-c circuit may be defined as being the factor by which the effective value of the voltage must be multiplied to obtain the component of the current that is in phase with the voltage. When the circuit consists of an r and an x in series,

$$g = \frac{r}{r^2 + x^2} \qquad (64)$$

[as may be seen from Eq. (c), Art. 276].

The **susceptance** of an a-c circuit may be defined as being the factor by which the effective value of the voltage must be multiplied to obtain the component of current that lags behind the voltage by 90°. When the circuit consists of an r and an x in series,

$$b = \frac{x}{r^2 + x^2} \tag{65}$$

[as may be seen from Eq. (c), Art. 276].

When the reactance is capacitive, the current leads instead of lags, and therefore the susceptance b is negative. Equation (65) may be used for either inductive or capacitive reactances if the convention is adopted that all capacitive reactances shall be considered negative. This convention is used in the problem of Fig. 249.

The **admittance** of an a-c circuit may be defined as being the factor by which the effective value of the voltage must be multiplied to give the total current.

$$Y = g - jb$$

Also $Y = 1/Z$, as may be seen by comparing the two definitions.

Equations (64) and (65) express the g and b of a series circuit in terms of the r and x of that circuit. It will also be convenient to have equations expressing the r and x of a series circuit in terms of the g and b of that circuit. These equations are readily derived as follows: By definition of g and b,

$$I = E(g - jb)$$

Also, by definition of Z,

$$I = \frac{E}{Z}$$

Therefore

$$Z = \frac{1}{g - jb}$$

and on multiplying numerator and denominator by $g + jb$, we obtain

$$Z = \frac{g + jb}{g^2 + b^2} = \frac{g}{g^2 + b^2} + j\frac{b}{g^2 + b^2}$$

but for a series circuit,

$$Z = r + jx$$

Therefore

$$r = \frac{g}{g^2 + b^2} \tag{66}$$

$$x = \frac{b}{g^2 + b^2} \tag{67}$$

Example to Illustrate the Use of Conductances, Susceptances, and Admittances. Given the value of E in Fig. 248 and the values of the three impedances

$$Z_1 = r_1 + jx_1$$
$$Z_2 = r_2 + jx_2$$
$$Z_3 = r_3 + jx_3$$

determine the magnitude and phase angle of the total current I

$$I_1 = EY_1 = E(g_1 - jb_1)$$
$$I_2 = EY_2 = E(g_2 - jb_2)$$
$$I_3 = EY_3 = E(g_3 - jb_3)$$
$$I = \text{vector sum of } I_1, I_2, I_3$$
$$= E[(g_1 + g_2 + g_3) - j(b_1 + b_2 + b_3)]$$

in which the various values of g and b may be determined by means of Eqs. (64) and (65). Contrast this concise method of solution with the method used in Art. 271.

NOTE. If the inductive reactances of Fig. 248 were replaced by capacitors, the current would lead the voltage instead of lagging. This is best taken care of by considering a capacitive reactance as being negative, which makes b negative and thus reverses the sign of the j component of current.

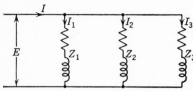

FIG. 248. Impedances in parallel.

Example. Determine the currents in all branches of the circuit shown in Fig. 249, and draw the complete vector diagram to scale.

The circuit would be much easier to solve if E_a had been given instead of E, because E_a is common to all three of the parallel impedances. Therefore assume E_a equal to 1 volt, use it as the x axis, and proceed. The proper correction can be applied later by simple proportion.

Let I_1', I_2', I_3', I', and E' be the values that I_1, I_2, I_3, I, and E would have if E_a were 1 volt. Then

$$I_1' = Y_1 = g_1 - jb_1$$

$$= \frac{r_1}{r_1{}^2 + x_1{}^2} - j\frac{x_1}{r_1{}^2 + x_1{}^2}$$

$$= \frac{4}{16 + 36} - j\frac{6}{16 + 36}$$

$$= 0.0769 - j0.1154$$

$$I_2' = Y_2 = g_2 - jb_2$$

$$= 0.1 - j0$$

$$I_3' = Y_3 = g_3 - jb_3$$

$$= \frac{7}{49 + 9} - j\frac{-3}{49 + 9}$$

$$= 0.1207 + j0.0517$$

$$I' = I_1' + I_2' + I_3'$$

$$= 0.2976 - j0.0637$$

Let $E_4' =$ voltage required to drive I' through Z_4. Then

$$E_4' = I'(r_4 + jx_4)$$

$$= (0.2976 - j0.0637)(2 + j2.5)$$

$$= 0.7544 + j0.6166$$

$$E' = E_a' + E_4'$$

$$= 1.7544 + j0.6166$$

$$= \sqrt{1.7544^2 + 0.6166^2}$$

$$= 1.860.$$

But $$E = 100 \text{ volts}$$

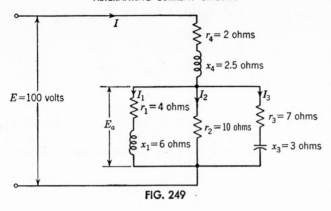

FIG. 249

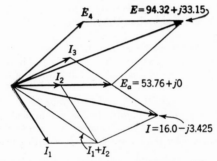

FIG. 250. Vector diagram for the circuit of Fig. 249.

Therefore multiply all the foregoing currents and voltages by $100/1.86$. Then

$$E_a = \frac{100}{1.86}(1+j0) = 53.76 + j0$$

$$I_1 = \frac{100}{1.86}(0.0769 - j0.1154) = 4.134 - j6.205$$

$$I_2 = \frac{100}{1.86}(0.1 + j0) = 5.376 + j0$$

$$I_3 = \frac{100}{1.86}(0.1207 + j0.0517) = 6.489 + j2.78$$

$$I = \frac{100}{1.86}(0.2976 - j0.0637) = 16.0 - j3.425$$

$$E_4 = \frac{100}{1.86}(0.7544 + j0.6166) = 40.56 + j33.15$$

$$E = E_a + E_4 = 94.32 + j33.15$$

Let ϕ be the phase angle by which I lags E. Then ϕ is the angle by which E

leads the x axis plus the angle by which I lags the x axis and

$$\phi = \tan^{-1}\frac{33.15}{94.32} + \tan^{-1}\frac{3.425}{16.0}$$
$$= 19°22' + 12°5' = 31°27'$$

Power factor of total circuit $= \cos 31°27' = 85.3\%$.

Problems

29-1. A circuit has an inductance of 0.1 henry and a noninductive resistance of 10 ohms in series. If the circuit is connected across a direct voltage of 120, what will be the voltage drop across the inductance and also that across the resistance (a) at the instant the switch is closed, (b) after the current has reached its maximum value, and what will be the maximum value of the current?

29-2. *a.* A coil of 200 turns, wound on a wooden ring that has a mean diameter of 12 cm and a circular cross section of 5 sq cm, is threaded by a flux of 134 lines of force when the current flowing is 4 amp. Find the inductance of the coil.

b. When the wooden ring is replaced by a steel ring of the same dimensions, the magnetic flux is 50,000 lines when the current is 1.32 amp. Find the inductance of the coil.

c. When the steel ring has an air gap of 0.2 cm length, the magnetic flux produced by a current of 9.32 amp is 50,000. What is the inductance of this coil?

29-3. A coil of negligible resistance has an inductance of 0.1 henry and is connected across a 120-volt line:

a. What current will flow at 30, 60, and 120 cycles?

b. What is the average power taken from the line in each case?

c. What is the maximum rate at which energy is given to the circuit during one quarter cycle and returned by the circuit to the line during the next quarter cycle (see Fig. 209)?

d. Explain without formulas why the current is inversely proportional to the frequency, the voltage being constant.

29-4. A coil with a noninductive resistance of 10 ohms is connected across a 120-volt line. (a) What current will flow when the frequency is 30, 60, and 120 cycles? (b) What is the average power taken from the line in each case? (c) What is the maximum rate at which energy is given to the circuit during each half cycle (see Fig. 215)?

29-5. An inductance of 0.1 henry and a noninductive resistance of 10 ohms are connected in series across a 120-volt line:

a. What current will flow when the frequency is 30, 60, and 120 cycles?

b. What is the average power taken from the line in each case?

c. What is the voltage drop across each part of the circuit at 60 cycles?

d. What is the power factor of the circuit in each case?

29-6. A certain coil is equivalent to a resistance and an inductance in series. The coil takes 20 amp from a 120-volt d-c line, and 12 amp from a 120-volt 50-cycle line. Determine the resistance of the coil, its inductive reactance, and its inductance.

29-7. How much current would the foregoing coil take from a 120-volt line having a frequency of only 25 cycles? Draw a vector diagram approximately to scale, and solve.

29-8. An electric circuit, supplied with 110-volt 60-cycle power, is made up of a resistance of 10 ohms and two inductive reactances, 20 ohms and 40 ohms, respectively, all three in parallel. (a) What is the total current supplied by the line? (b) What is the power factor of the circuit?

*29-9. A resistance, $R = 6$ ohms, and an unknown inductance L take 12 amp when connected in series across a 120-volt 50-cycle supply. Sketch complete vector diagram, approximately to scale, and determine the voltage drop across

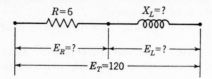

each part of the circuit. Compute the inductive reactance X_L and the inductance L. Determine the total power and the power factor of the combination. Check the total power with that taken by each part of the circuit. (Also check with the I^2R loss.)

*29-10. The series combination of the preceding problem is connected across a 120-volt supply having a frequency of 100 cycles per sec. Sketch complete vector diagram, approximately to scale, and determine the current, voltage drop, power, and power factor for each part and for the combination. Explain why the values in this case differ from those in the preceding problem.

29-11. *a.* An a-c 120-volt single-phase motor delivers 10 hp. The efficiency of the motor is 85 per cent and, on account of the reactance of the motor windings, the current lags behind the voltage and the power factor of the motor is only 80 per cent. What is the full-load current?

b. What is the full-load current of a 10-hp 120-volt d-c motor of 85 per cent efficiency?

c. What is the power taken from the line in each case?

29-12. The load on a single-phase 120-volt a-c generator consists of 150 incandescent lamps, each of which takes 0.5 amp, also some small motors delivering a total of 10 hp with an average efficiency of 85 per cent and an average power factor of 80 per cent. Find the current output of the generator, the kilowatt output of the generator, the power factor of the total load (the power factor of incandescent lamps is 100 per cent), and the horsepower of the engine if the generator efficiency is 90 per cent.

29-13. Seventy-five kilowatts at 2,200 volts and 60 cycles has to be delivered over a single-phase transmission line 5 miles long. Choose the size of wire so that the copper loss shall not exceed 8 per cent of the power delivered for the two following cases: (*a*) when the power factor of the load at the end of the line is 100 per cent; (*b*) when this power factor is 79 per cent, and the current is lagging. If the spacing of the wires is 48 in., what are the inductive reactance of the line, the resistance of the line, the voltage at the generating station, and the power lost in the line?

29-14. A wooden ring having a mean diameter of 12 cm and a rectangular cross section of 2 by 5 cm is wound with 200 turns of wire.

a. Find the flux per ampere.

b. Find the inductance of the coil $\left(\dfrac{N\phi}{I} 10^{-8} \text{ henrys} \right)$.

c. Find reactance of coil at 30 and 60 cycles.

d. Neglecting the resistance of the coil, find the current when connected across 100 volts with frequencies as in *c*.

e. If a second coil of 600 turns is wound on top of the 200 turns, what will be the inductance of this new coil?

f. How does the value of L vary with the number of turns of the coil?

g. If the two coils (600T and 200T) are connected in series, what will be the total inductance?

h. If the two coils are connected in series but their magnetic effects are in opposition, what will be the total inductance?

*29-15. The wooden ring of Prob. 29-14 is replaced by a laminated steel ring of the same dimensions.

a. What is the inductance of the coil of 200 turns? Assume the current to be less than 0.5 amp and therefore the permeability to be practically constant. Use Fig. 40.

b. Neglecting the resistance of the coil, find the voltage required to send 0.5 amp 60-cycle current through the coil.

*29-16. If a laminated iron core is moved into an a-c solenoid, the alternating current is decreased in magnitude. Explain why this is so.

*29-17. If a direct current were flowing through the foregoing coil, what effect would the insertion of the iron core have on the value of the current? Is there any permanent or momentary change in the current?

29-18 to 29-27. Draw a vector diagram approximately to scale, for each of the following circuits, and solve for the unknown quantities:

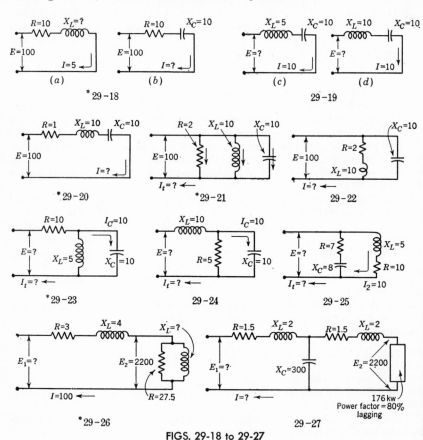

FIGS. 29-18 to 29-27

29-28. How many sheets of mica 0.1 mm thick, separating plates of 100-sq cm area, are required to construct a capacitor of 1-μf capacity? (The dielectric contant of mica is 6.) If plates are 0.1 mm thick, what are the dimensions of the apacitor?

29-29. A capacitor of 100-μf capacity is connected across a 120-volt line:

a. What current will flow at 30, 60, and 120 cycles?

b. What is the average power taken from the line in each case?

c. What is the maximum rate at which energy is given to the capacitor during one quarter cycle and returned by the capacitor to the line during the next quarer cycle (see Art. 264)?

d. What is the maximum charge in the capacitor on each half cycle?

e. What average current would this maintain in an external circuit for $\frac{1}{480}$ sec? What effective current if the current changes as a cosine function? (Compare with *a.*)

f. Explain without formulas why the current is directly proportional to the requency, the voltage being constant; the reverse is the case for an inductive circuit.

29-30. Two capacitors, A of 1-μf capacity and B of 2-μf capacity, are connected across 120-volt d-c mains. What is the charge in each capacitor, the total charge, and the voltage drop across each capacitor (*a*) when the capacitors are in parallel and (*b*) when the capacitors are in series?

29-31. A capacitor of 100-μf capacity and a noninductive resistance of 10 ohms are connected in series across a 120-volt line:

a. What current will flow when the frequency is 30, 60, and 120 cycles?

b. What is the average power taken from the line in each case? Explain why this is equal to I^2R.

c. What is the voltage drop across each part of the circuit at 60 cycles?

d. What is the power factor of the circuit in each case?

29-32. A circuit is made up of A, a noninductive resistance of 10 ohms, B, an inductance of 0.1 henry, and C, a capacitor of 100-μf capacity. Find the current in each, the total current, the voltage drop across each, and the resultant power factor:

a. When A, B, and C are connected in series across a 120-volt 120-cycle line.

b. When A, B, and C are connected in parallel across a 120-volt 120-cycle line.

c. When B and C in parallel are connected in series with A across a 120-volt 120-cycle line.

In case *a* what is the frequency of resonance and what is then the current in the circuit and the voltage drop across each part of the circuit? What must be the value of the resistance so that the voltage drop across the capacitor at resonance shall not exceed the value of 250 volts for which it was designed?

29-33. In Prob. 29-11 specify the capacitor to be placed in parallel with the 60-cycle motor so that the resultant power factor may be 100 per cent. What will then be the currents in the motor, the capacitor, and the line? What would this low-voltage capacitor cost at 50 cents per μf?

29-34. In Prob. 29-13 what would be the size of capacitor required to raise the power factor of the load from 79 per cent to 100 per cent? With 2,200-volt capacitors at $10 per μf, would it be cheaper to use capacitors and the small wire or to use the wire of larger cross section, the copper loss in the line to be the same in each case? Cost of wire is 40 cents per lb.

*29-35. A capacitor of a wireless receiving set has 40 plates each of 30-sq cm area and separated by air spaces of 0.1 cm. What is the capacitance of the capacitor in microfarads? If this capacitor is immersed in oil which has a dielectric constant of about 2.5, what is now the capacitance? What is the total capacitance of two such capacitors in parallel and what when they are in series?

*29-36. A capacitor of 50-μf capacitance is connected across a 240-volt line:

a. What current will flow at 30, 60, and 120 cycles?

b. What is the average power taken from the line in each case?

c. What is the maximum rate at which energy is given to the capacitor during one quarter cycle and returned by the capacitor to the line during the next quarter cycle (see Art. 264)?

d. What is the maximum charge in the capacitor on each half cycle?

e. What average current would this maintain in an external circuit for $\frac{1}{480}$ sec? What effective current if the current changes as a cosine function? (Compare with *a.*)

f. Explain without formulas why the current is directly proportional to the frequency, the voltage being constant; the reverse is the case for an inductive circuit.

*29-37. A capacitor of 50-μf capacitance and a noninductive resistance of 30 ohms are connected in series across a 120-volt line. (*a*) What current will flow when the frequency is 30, 60, and 120 cycles? (*b*) What is the average power taken from the line in each case? Explain why this is equal to I^2R. (*c*) What is the voltage drop across each part of the circuit at 60 cycles?

*29-38. Given $X_L = 12$ ohms, $R = 30$ ohms, $X_c = 40$ ohms, and $I_c = 3$ amp

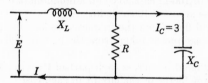

for the above circuit, draw a complete vector diagram and determine the following: (*a*) line current I, (*b*) terminal voltage E, (*c*) power factor of circuit.

29-39. For a transmission line supplying a load which has a leading power factor

$$E_2 = 2,000 \text{ volts}$$
$$I = 100 \text{ amp}$$

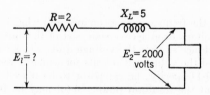

PF of load $= 80$ per cent leading
$f = 50$ cycles per sec
$R = 2$ ohms
$X_L = 5$ ohms

Determine the following: (*a*) input voltage E_l; (*b*) efficiency of transmission; (*c*) R and X_c in parallel equivalent to the load.

29-40. Determine the currents in all parts of the circuit shown in Fig. 29-40, and draw the complete vector diagram, with E_a along the x axis.

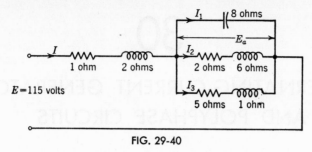

FIG. 29-40

30

ALTERNATING-CURRENT GENERATORS AND POLYPHASE CIRCUITS

278. Single-phase Generator. The essential parts of a revolving-field type of generator are shown in Fig. 251a. The stationary part which carries the conductors that are cut by the revolving field is called *the stator;* the revolving-field system is called *the rotor.*

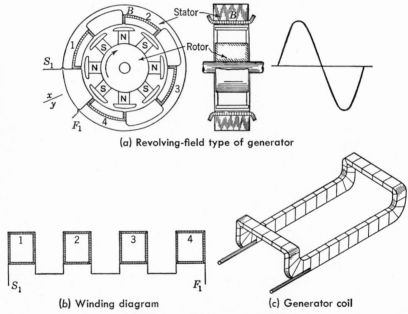

(a) Revolving-field type of generator

(b) Winding diagram   (c) Generator coil
FIG. 251. Single-phase generator.

The stator core B is built up of soft steel laminations and has slots on the inner periphery in which the stator coils are placed. One type of coil is shown in Fig. 251c and consists of several turns of copper wire, which are insulated from one another and are then taped with cotton and other insulating material. The machine shown in Fig. 251*a* has four of these coils which are connected in series so that their voltages add up.

Since a connection diagram such as Fig. 251*a* shows only one end of the machine, it is found desirable in practice to show the coils and connections by means of a developed diagram such as Fig. 251*b*, a diagram that shows what would be obtained if the winding in Fig. 251*a* were split at *xy* and then flattened out on a plane; the two diagrams are lettered similarly.

The voltage between the terminals S_1 and F_1 varies as shown in Fig. 251*a* and goes through four cycles per revolution.

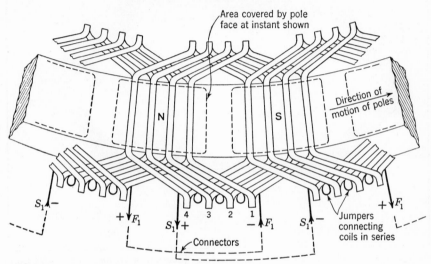

FIG. 252. Stator winding of a single-phase generator with the rotor removed. Winding distributed in four slots per pole. Viewpoint located on the axis of the machine, slightly offset from center.

Figure 251*a* illustrates the fundamental idea in the construction of a single-phase generator, but in actual practice the stator winding is seldom concentrated in one large slot per pole as appears in Fig. 251*a* and *b*. It is usually spread out into several smaller slots as shown in Fig. 252. This not only facilitates the ventilation of the coils to carry off the heat resulting from the armature copper loss but also provides more space for the copper and so increases the current-carrying capacity of the machine.

In Fig. 252 each coil group S_1F_1 consists of four coils connected in series. Figure 253 is a photograph of a single coil. With this type of winding there are two coil sides in each slot, one on top of the other, and the coils nest together very neatly. The terminal emfs of the successive coil groups are all equal and are alternately in phase and 180° out of phase with one another as shown by the plus and minus polarity signs; consequently they may be connected either in series or in parallel provided that alternate coil groups are connected reversed, so as to obtain the same polarity for all groups.   If they are connected in series, the total emf is equal to the emf of one coil group multiplied by the number of coil groups.

It should be noted, however, that the terminal emf of a single group of coils in Fig. 252 is not equal to four times the emf of a single coil, because

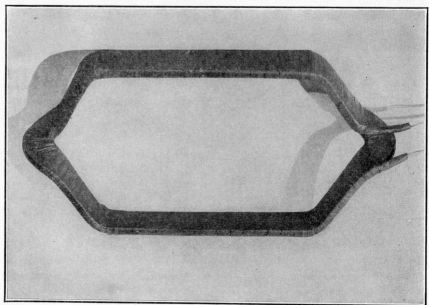

FIG. 253. Stator coil of an a-c generator or motor.   (*Courtesy of Westinghouse Electric Co.*)

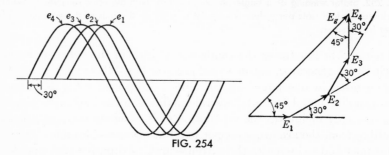

FIG. 254

these four emfs are not in phase with each other.   The phase angle between successive coils in Fig. 252 is 30 electrical degrees and the graphs of the emfs are therefore as shown in Fig. 254.   The total emf of the coil group is the vector sum of the four equal voltages E_1, E_2, E_3, and E_4.   Let E equal the numerical value of each of these equal voltages.   Then

$$E_q = 2(E \cos 45° + E \cos 15°) = 3.346E$$

instead of $4E$.   Thus a winding distributed in several slots per pole must have more turns than one that is concentrated in one slot per pole, in order to generate the same terminal voltage, but the cross-sectional area of the several slots is much greater than that of a single large slot, so that there is more than enough room for the extra turns, and in addition the ventilation is better.   Consequently, the net result of distributing the winding is to increase the capacity of the machine very substantially.

Another advantage of distributing the winding in several slots per pole is that it automatically improves the wave form.   This can readily be

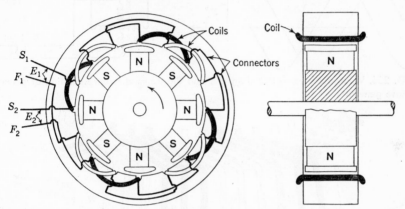

FIG. 255. Two-phase generator.   Stator or armature winding concentrated in one slot per phase per pole.

demonstrated by redrawing Fig. 254, using any type of nonsinusoidal curve, such as rectangular, triangular, or semicircular, and adding them up point by point.   The resultant wave will be much more nearly sinusoidal than the component waves.   In fact, the resultant wave approaches perfection as the number of component waves is increased.

279. Two-phase Generator.   Between the coil groups of Fig. 252 there is a considerable amount of stator surface that is not being utilized.   If we place a second entirely separate winding in this waste space and connect it to a separate load, we can then utilize this waste space and thereby considerably increase the total kilowatt rating of the machine.   A generator which has two separate circuits so arranged that their voltages are 90° out of phase with one another is called a two-phase generator.

Figure 255 shows the machine of Fig. 251 with a duplicate winding added at 90 electrical degrees to the first winding, and Fig. 256 shows the voltages generated by the two windings.   In this case we have evidently exactly doubled the rated capacity of the machine by making it two-phase. Usually, however, the windings are not concentrated in one slot per phase per pole and the rated capacity is not doubled by winding the machine two-phase.   Figure 257 shows the machine of Fig. 252 rewound two-phase.   In order to make room for the second phase, it was necessary to remove one coil from each coil group of the single-phase winding.   In this case changing from a single-phase winding to a two-phase winding increased the rated capacity of the machine by 63 per cent, with only a small increase in the capital cost.

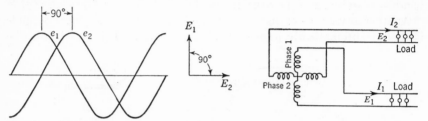

FIG. 256. Voltage curves, vector diagram, and diagrammatic representation of a two-phase generator.

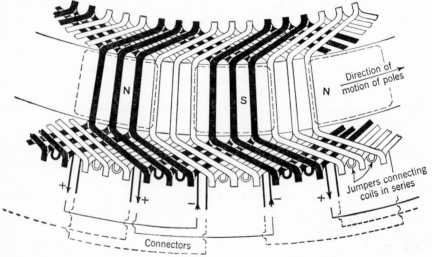

FIG. 257. Armature winding of a two-phase generator.   Winding distributed in three slots per phase per pole.   Viewpoint located on the axis of the machine, slightly offset from center.   The emf generated in the white phase is zero at the instant shown.

However the increase in the capacity of the generator was not the reason for the introduction of the two-phase system.   No one had succeeded in inventing a satisfactory a-c motor until someone had the brilliant idea of winding both the generator and the motor two-phase.   Two-phase induction motors were the first satisfactory a-c motors, and the two-phase system was introduced in order to supply power to these motors. Satisfactory single-phase motors have since been developed, but in general are used only in small sizes.

Figure 256 shows how lamps and small single-phase motors are connected to a two-phase system.   Large motors are wound two-phase and take power equally from both phases.

The only drawback to the two-phase system is that four wires are required for the transmission line.   This is not a very important drawback, however, and in distributing electrical energy in a city it is not necessary to carry both phases along every street; one street can be fed from one phase and the next street from the other phase, the two phases being carried along the same street only when there is a two-phase motor to be supplied.

280. Three-phase Generators.   If three separate armature windings are placed on the stator of a generator in such a way that the phase angles

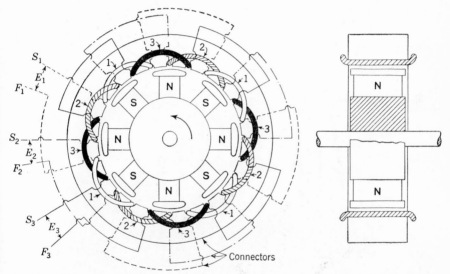

FIG. 258. Three-phase generator.   Armature winding concentrated in one slot per phase per pole.

between the voltages generated in the three windings are all 120 electrical degrees, the machine is called a three-phase generator.   Figure 258 shows the machine of Fig. 251 with two additional duplicate windings added, each winding being at 120 electrical degrees to each of the other two windings, and Fig. 259 shows the voltages produced by the three windings. The curves e_1, e_2, and e_3 show the instantaneous values of the voltages, while the effective values E_1, E_2, and E_3 are used in drawing the vector diagram.

Three-phase generators have been built with the armature windings concentrated in one slot per phase per pole as in Fig. 258, and a photograph of such a machine is shown in Fig. 260, but it is now the most general practice to use the type of coil shown in Fig. 261.   In this particular illustration the winding is distributed in two slots per phase per pole.

It will be noted that in Fig. 261 the coil groups are only 60 electrical degrees apart instead of 120.   The winding is therefore actually six-phase, and the vector diagram of the voltages generated in the successive coil

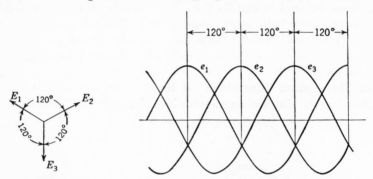

FIG. 259. Voltage curves and vector diagram of a three-phase generator.

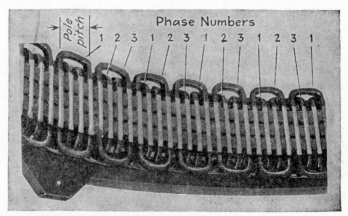

FIG. 260. Part of the stator of a large slow-speed three-phase generator.   Winding concentrated in one slot per phase per pole.

groups 1, 2, 3, 4, 5, 6 is as shown in Fig. 262a.   Now the voltage E_{gh} generated in coil group 4 is 180 deg out of phase with the voltage E_{ab} generated in coil group 1, as is indicated in both the vector diagram of Fig. 262a and the curves of instantaneous values of Fig. 262c.   Therefore if these two coil groups are connected in series, the resultant voltage will be either zero or $2E_{ab}$, depending on whether they are connected so that their voltages add or subtract.

Now E_{gh} is the voltage generated in coil group 4 in the direction through the coil group from g to h, and E_{hg} is the voltage generated in coil group 4 through the coil group in the reverse direction, from h to g.

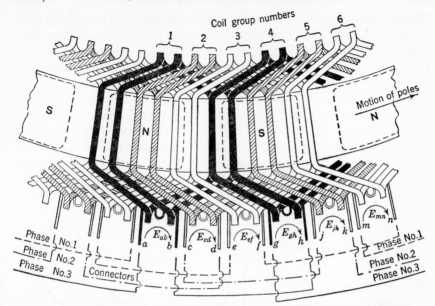

FIG. 261. Armature winding of a three-phase generator. Winding distributed in two slots per phase per pole.

FIG. 261A. Stator of a 57,500-kva 6,600-volt three-phase a-c generator in process of assembly at the factory. The rotor for this machine has 80 poles and turns at 90 rpm. The stator will be shipped in four sections, and the ten coils that are missing at each junction will be installed after shipment. (*Courtesy of General Electric Co.*)

Therefore $E_{hg} = -E_{gh}$. Now if coil end b is connected to coil end g, the resultant voltage of the two coils in series $= E_{ab} + E_{gh} = 0$, since E_{gh} is 180° out of phase with E_{ab}; but if coil end b is connected to coil end h, the resultant voltage of the two coils in series $= E_{ab} + E_{hg} = 2E_{ab}$, since E_{hg} is in phase with E_{ab}.

The winding of the machine in Fig. 261 therefore becomes three-phase if every second coil group of each phase is reversed when connecting up the coil groups. For example, in Fig. 261 the connectors for phase 3 take in coil group 1 by entering at the left-hand terminal a and leaving at the right-hand terminal b but take in coil group 4 by entering at the right-hand terminal h and leaving at the left-hand terminal g, thus connecting this coil group in reverse with respect to coil group 1. Reversing the

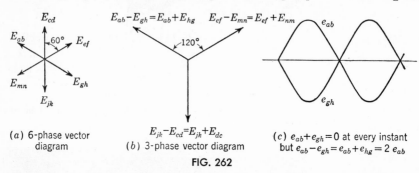

(a) 6-phase vector diagram

(b) 3-phase vector diagram $E_{jk}-E_{cd}=E_{jk}+E_{dc}$

(c) $e_{ab}+e_{gh}=0$ at every instant but $e_{ab}-e_{gh}=e_{ab}+e_{hg}=2\,e_{ab}$

FIG. 262

connections to coil groups 2, 4, and 6 in this way reverses the vectors E_{cd}, E_{gh}, and E_{mn} in the six-phase vector diagram of Fig. 262 by converting them into the vectors E_{dc}, E_{hg}, and E_{nm} and thus gives the three-phase vector diagram, Fig. 262 b.

It may be instructive at this point to look back to Fig. 257 and to note that the winding shown there is actually four-phase, since the successive coil groups are at 90 electrical degrees to each other all the way around the circle, and it is converted into two-phase in the same way that the six-phase winding of Fig. 261 is converted into three-phase. Also the winding shown in Fig. 252 might logically be called two-phase, with the phases at 180 electrical degrees to each other, and it is converted into single-phase in the same way that the six-phase and four-phase windings are converted, respectively, to three-phase and two-phase. However, the term two-phase has already been assigned to the arrangement of Fig. 256, in which the emfs of the two windings are at 90° to each other, and therefore must not be used to describe the winding of Fig. 252.

280A. Fractional-pitch Coils. The armature winding diagrams of Figs. 251 to 261 all show windings made up of full-pitch coils, so that when one side of a coil is under the center of a north pole the other side of that coil is under the center of a south pole. In practice, however, the distance between the two coil sides is usually less than full pitch. There are three advantages to be gained by using fractional-pitch coils: (1) The wave form is improved because the emfs generated in the two sides of each coil are slightly out of phase, and thus the number of components of emf to be added up is doubled, and this improves the wave form, as explained at the end of Art. 278.   (2) In the case of two-pole, four-pole, and six-pole machines the placing of the coils in the slots is greatly facilitated by the use of fractional-pitch coils.   In fact, it would often be practically impossible to force a full-pitch coil into a four-pole machine without

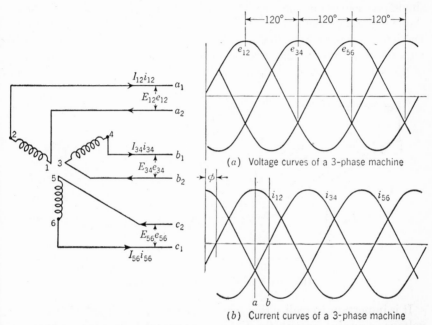

(a) Voltage curves of a 3-phase machine

(b) Current curves of a 3-phase machine

FIG. 263. Diagrammatic representation of a three-phase generator.   Small letters represent instantaneous values.   Capital letters represent effective values.   The symbol i_{12} is read "i one two" and signifies the current flowing through the winding from 1 to 2.

damaging the coil, because of the excessive deformation required.   (3) The V-shaped end connections are shorter for fractional-pitch coils than for full-pitch coils and this means a saving in weight and cost.

The only disadvantage of fractional-pitch coils is that the terminal voltage is somewhat less than with full-pitch coils.

281. Y Connection.   A three-phase machine is conveniently represented by a diagram such as that in Fig. 263, in which the three separate windings are arranged in the form of the vector diagram of Fig. 259. Such a machine has six terminals and six leads, two for each phase.

In order to reduce the number of leads, the three return wires a_2, b_2, and c_2 may be connected together to form a single common return wire n, as in Fig. 264.   The current in this wire at any instant is therefore the sum of i_{12}, i_{34}, and i_{56}, the currents in the three phases. (Note that i_{12} should be read i one two, not i twelve. It signifies the current flowing through the armature winding from 1 to 2.) Now it may be seen from Fig. 263b that if the three phases are equally loaded, then at any instant the sum of these three currents is zero: at instant a, for example, i_{12} is equal and opposite to $i_{34} + i_{56}$, while, at instant b, i_{34} is zero and i_{12} is equal and opposite to i_{56}. The wire n therefore carries no current back to the generator and the portion of it between the generator and the first single-phase load may be dispensed with. If the loads are all three-phase therefore, the common wire n disappears altogether. The resultant connection, shown in Fig. 265, is called the three-wire Y connection and requires only three conductors to supply the load, and at any instant one of the three conductors is always acting as the return for the other two.

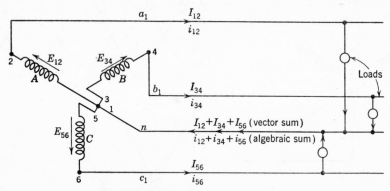

FIG. 264. Y connection, four-wire system.

It is important to realize that when an arrow is associated with a vector voltage or current, as with E_{12}, I_{12}, etc., in Fig. 264, it does not, and cannot, show the direction of the voltage or current, because the current flows in both directions, alternately. The arrow merely shows which direction is assumed to be positive when drawing the vector diagram or plotting the sine curves. When dealing with instantaneous voltages and currents, it may sometimes be desirable to have the arrows show the actual directions of the voltages and currents at some particular instant in the cycle, but unless it is expressly stated that they do so, it should be assumed that the arrows merely show which direction is taken as being positive.

The Y-connected three-phase four-wire system shown in Fig. 264 is widely used for distributing electrical energy in districts where the individual loads are mostly small and consequently single-phase, such as residential lighting and small motors. Such loads are never exactly evenly distributed among the three phases of the system and there is always current flowing in the *common*, or *neutral*, wire.

The three-wire three-phase system is the one generally used for the principal transmission lines, or wherever the loads are large and are consequently balanced three-phase.   In such cases the neutral wire would carry no current if it were present and it is consequently omitted.   The junction point of the Y is called the *neutral*.   Sometimes the neutrals at both ends of the line are grounded and the ground then takes the place of the common, or neutral, wire.   This is only done, however, if the loads are balanced so that very little current flows in the ground.

282. Δ-connected Loads on a Three-wire Three-phase Line. Although the three-wire three-phase system might be considered as fundamentally a system for feeding balanced three-phase loads, yet single-phase loads are readily connected to it, as shown in Fig. 265, and it is widely used

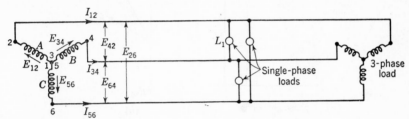

FIG. 265. Y-connected generator, three-wire system, Δ-connected and Y-connected loads. The vector sum of I_{12}, I_{34}, and I_{56} is zero. $E_{12} = E_{34} = E_{56} = E_n$, where E_n is the voltage to neutral. $E_{42} = E_{64} = E_{26} = E_l$, where E_l is the voltage between line wires.   It is shown in Art. 283 that $E_l = \sqrt{3} \, E_n$.

for feeding single-phase loads.   The current taken by any one single-phase load flows through two of the generator phases in series; for example, the current through the single-phase load L_1 flows through phase B from 4 to 3 and phase A from 1 to 2, and the voltage that drives the single-phase current is the sum of the voltages of the two phases.

The single-phase loads of Fig. 265 are said to be Δ-*connected* because, with a triangular configuration of the line, the three loads connected directly from line conductor to line conductor form the Greek letter Δ. The three single-phase loads of Fig. 264 are said to be *Y-connected*.

On a four-wire system the single-phase loads may equally well be connected either Y or Δ, but on a three-wire system they must be connected Δ since there is no neutral to connect them to.

Since single-phase loads can be connected to a three-wire system as readily as to a four-wire system, the question naturally arises why should the fourth wire ever be installed.   The answer to this question will be given in Art. 284.

283. Voltages, Currents, and Power in a Y-connected Generator. The voltage E_{64} that the three-phase generator impresses on the single-phase load L, Fig. 266a, is the vector sum of the voltages generated in phases C and B. That is, E_{64} is the vector sum of E_{65} and E_{34}. Now E_{56} is at $120°$ to E_{34}, as shown in Fig. 266b, and $E_{65} = -E_{56}$. Therefore E_{65} is at $60°$ to E_{34}, and, since E_{34} and E_{65} are equal in magnitude to the voltage to neutral, E_n, the vector sum of E_{65} and E_{34} is

$$E_{64} = 2E_n \cos 30° = \sqrt{3}\ E_n$$

In other words, the voltage between line conductors is $\sqrt{3}$ times the voltage between any one line conductor and neutral.

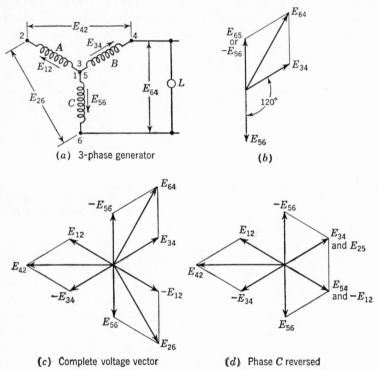

(a) 3-phase generator

(b)

(c) Complete voltage vector

(d) Phase C reversed

FIG. 266. Voltages in a Y-connected three-phase generator.

Figure 266c is the complete vector diagram of the voltages in a three-phase generator.

Note that, if the terminals of each phase were reversed, so as to bring terminals 2, 4, and 6 together to form the neutral instead of terminals 1, 3, and 5, then all the voltage vectors of Fig. 266c would be reversed, with the result that the arrangement would still be a symmetrical three-phase, with the line voltages E_{31}, E_{53}, and E_{15} all at $120°$ to each other. If, however, only one of the phases is reversed, the result is an unsymmetrical three-phase, as shown in Fig. 266d where phase C is reversed. Such a system could be used to transmit energy but it would be very unsatisfactory and inconvenient as compared with the symmetrical three-phase.

Since each phase of the generator can be connected to the neutral in two possible ways, it follows that there are eight possible ways of Y-connecting the three phases, and only two of them are correct. The test for correct phasing is the equality of the line-to-line voltages. If $E_{42} = E_{64} = E_{26}$, the machine must be correctly connected. Each one of the six possible wrong connections results in one line-to-line voltage being $\sqrt{3}$ times each of the other two line-to-line voltages, as in Fig. 266d.

Power. Refer to Fig. 264.

Let ϕ_a = angle by which I_{12} lags or leads E_{12} in phase A

  ϕ_b = angle by which I_{34} lags or leads E_{34} in phase B

  ϕ_c = angle by which I_{56} lags or leads E_{56} in phase C

These angles, and also the magnitudes of I_{12}, I_{34}, and I_{56}, are determined by the nature of the loads.

The average power in each phase is

$$W_a = E_{12}I_{12} \cos \phi_a \qquad \text{watts}$$
$$W_b = E_{34}I_{34} \cos \phi_b \qquad \text{watts}$$
$$W_c = E_{56}I_{56} \cos \phi_c \qquad \text{watts}$$
$$\text{Total average power} = W_a + W_b + W_c \qquad \text{watts}$$

If the loads are balanced, so that

$$I_{12} = I_{34} = I_{56} = I$$
$$E_{12} = E_{34} = E_{56} = E_n$$
$$\phi_a = \phi_b = \phi_c = \phi$$

then $$\text{Total power} = 3E_nI \cos \phi \qquad (68)$$

where E_n is called the voltage to neutral.

Let E be the voltage between line conductors. Then $E = \sqrt{3}\, E_n$. Substituting E in Eq. (68), we obtain

$$\text{Power} = \sqrt{3}\, EI \cos \phi \qquad (69)$$

Note that Eqs. (68) and (69) apply equally to both the three-wire and the four-wire system as long as the loads are balanced and that *they apply to neither system if the loads are not balanced.*

It has become customary to use the voltage E between phases as the voltage rating of machines and transmission lines, rather than the voltage of the individual phases, and consequently Eq. (69) is the one most generally used to represent the power.

284. Connection of Loads to a Three-phase Three-wire System. The loads on a three-phase line may be connected Y as in Fig. 267a, or Δ as in Fig. 267b and c, but a given load cannot in general be changed over from one connection to the other, because a change of voltage is involved. For example, suppose that three 120-volt 100-watt lamps are connected Δ as shown in Fig. 267b and c. The voltage across each lamp is 120 volts and the current taken by each lamp is $100/120 = 0.833$ amp. If now these lamps are reconnected Y, as in Fig. 267a, the voltage across each lamp will be only $120/\sqrt{3} = 69.3$ volts, and the lamps will glow a dull red and give off very little light.

If the lamps are to be connected Y, then they must be designed for the voltage $E_t/\sqrt{3}$, in this case 69.3 volts, and the current per lamp of 100 watts will be $100/69.3 = 1.44$ amp. If these lamps are then connected Δ, they will promptly burn out, since the voltage will be too high for them.

If one of the lamps in Fig. 267b burns out, the two remaining lamps will burn with their normal brilliancy; but if one of the lamps in Fig. 267a

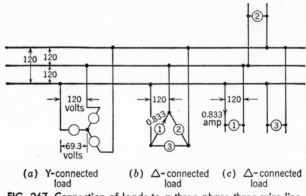

(a) Y-connected load   (b) Δ-connected load   (c) Δ-connected load

FIG. 267. Connection of loads to a three-phase three-wire line.

burns out, then the two remaining lamps will be in series across 120 volts and will be dim, since they are then operating at 60 volts instead of at the normal 69.3 volts.

From this it is evident that three individual loads Y-connected on a system which has no neutral wire cannot operate independently of each other, whereas they do operate independently of each other if connected delta, or if Y-connected on a line which has a neutral wire. For this reason, lamps are never Y-connected if there is no neutral wire. However, electric boilers and furnaces having three heating elements are Y-connected on three-wire systems. If one element failed, the whole unit would be shut down for repairs in any case, so the fact that the other two elements would not function properly, if left in service, is of no importance.

It is now convenient to answer the question propounded in Art. 282, namely: Why should the neutral wire ever be installed? The answer is to be found in the fact that, if loads which were originally connected Δ are changed to the Y connection, the line voltage must be raised to $\sqrt{3}$

times its previous value in order to obtain the proper voltage across each individual load.   Now, if the voltage of the line is raised to $\sqrt{3}$ times its previous value, the amount of power that can be transmitted over the line with a given current is multiplied by $\sqrt{3}$ also.   Consequently, if, when the growing loads on a Δ-connected system reach the maximum capacity of the lines, the neutral wire is strung in, the loads are reconnected Y, and the voltage is raised to $\sqrt{3}$ times its previous value, the situation is immediately relieved and considerable future growth taken care of.   This is the way in which the present four-wire three-phase city-distribution systems came into existence.

285. Δ-connected Generator.   Another method of connecting the three windings of a three-phase machine is shown diagrammatically in

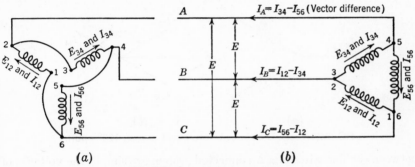

FIG. 268. Δ-connected generator.

Fig. 268, the windings being connected in series in the following order: 2 to 3, 4 to 5, and 6 to 1.   If the wires making these connections are shortened to zero length, Fig. 268a will be automatically converted into Fig. 268b.   On account of the appearance of this latter diagram, this three-phase connection is called the Δ connection.

Although the winding has been closed on itself, no current circulates around this closed circuit.   The resultant voltage in the closed circuit is the sum of the voltages in the three phases, but it may be seen from Fig. 263a that, at any instant, $e_{12} + e_{34} + e_{56}$ is zero, the voltage in one phase being always equal and opposite to the sum of the voltages in the other two phases.   If, however, an external circuit is connected between any two leads, then the voltage across that circuit will be E, the voltage of one phase, and current will flow through the circuit.

286. Voltages, Currents, and Power in a Δ-connected Generator.   The fundamental difference between the Y and Δ connections is that in the Y connection a single wire, called the neutral, is used in common by all three phases, while in the Δ connection each wire is used in common by two phases.   For example, if three similar single-phase loads are Δ-connected to the three leads in Fig. 268b, then the current I_{34} circulates through the top and middle wires and through the load connected from A to B, while the current I_{12} circulates through the middle and bottom wires and the load connected from B to C. Thus the middle wire is common to phases 1-2 and 3-4 and carries a current that is at all times the algebraic sum of the instantaneous currents i_{12} and i_{43}, or, since $i_{43} = -i_{34}$, we may write $i_B = i_{12} - i_{34}$ if we prefer.

If the graphs of current are sine curves, we may use vectors to perform the addition or subtraction, as shown in Fig. 269, where I_{12} and I_{34} are shown as two equal currents 120° apart in phase. It is evident that $I_B = 2I_{12} \cos 30° = \sqrt{3}\, I_{12}$. That is, when the loads are balanced, the currents in the line wires of a Δ-connected system are $\sqrt{3}$ times the currents in the individual phases or loads. On the other hand, the voltages

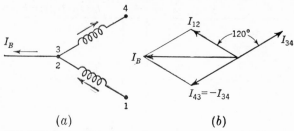

(a)   (b)

FIG. 269. Vector difference of two equal currents 120° apart.

between the line wires of a Δ-connected system are simply the voltages of the individual phases.

When the loads are unbalanced, it is not quite so simple to trace out the currents. For example, consider a single load connected between the top and middle wires of Fig. 268b. If ammeters are inserted in series with each of the phase windings of the generator, so as to measure I_{12}, I_{34}, and I_{56}, it will be found that I_{12} and I_{56} are not zero and that I_{34} is not equal to the current taken by the load. In fact.it is evident that the generator provides two parallel paths for the current taken by the single-phase load, one from 3 to 4 through phase 3-4 and the other from 2 to 5 through phases 2-1 and 6-5, in series. The first path carries approximately two-thirds of the total current and the second path the remainder, the current dividing in the inverse ratio of the impedances of the two paths.

Since the Δ-connected generator provides two parallel paths for the current taken by any single-phase load, it follows that any one of the three phase windings of the generator could be disconnected entirely without interfering with the operation of the generator, except that its rated capacity would be reduced. A generator operated with one phase disconnected is said to be operated *open* Δ. The open-Δ connection will be discussed more fully in Art. 329.

Incorrect Connections. If in Fig. 268b each of the phases is reversed, that is, if terminals 1 and 2 are interchanged, terminals 3 and 4 are interchanged, and terminals 5 and 6 are interchanged, the result will still be a symmetrical three-phase, and if the Δ is closed by a voltmeter, the voltmeter will read zero.   If, however, only one of the phases is reversed, as in Fig. 270 where phase 1-2 is reversed, the voltmeter will read twice the voltage of one phase, and if the Δ were closed by means of a low-resistance jumper instead of a high-resistance voltmeter, a very large current would circulate.   In fact, phase 1-2 would constitute a short circuit across the other two phases.

The test for correct phasing is to close the delta through a voltmeter as shown in Fig. 270.   The voltmeter will always read twice the voltage

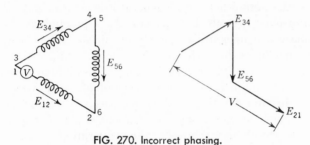

FIG. 270. Incorrect phasing.

of a single phase if the connections are incorrect and will read approximately zero if the connections are correct.   It will not read exactly zero in practice because the graphs of voltage are never absolutely pure sine curves.   It follows that in practice there is always some current circulating in the closed Δ.   This circulating current is sometimes large enough to have an appreciable effect on the temperature of the windings, in which case it is, of course, objectionable.   Most generators are Y-connnected. The Δ connection finds its principal application in transformer connections.

Power. Refer to Fig. 268b.

Let ϕ_{12} = angle by which I_{12} lags or leads E_{12}

ϕ_{34} = angle by which I_{34} lags or leads E_{34}

ϕ_{56} = angle by which I_{56} lags or leads E_{56}

These angles and also the magnitudes of the currents are determined by the nature of the loads.

The average power in each phase of the generator is

$$W_{12} = E_{12}I_{12} \cos \phi_{12} \qquad \text{watts}$$
$$W_{34} = E_{34}I_{34} \cos \phi_{34} \qquad \text{watts}$$
$$W_{56} = E_{56}I_{56} \cos \phi_{56} \qquad \text{watts}$$
$$\text{Total average power} = W_{12} + W_{34} + W_{56} \qquad \text{watts}$$

If the loads are balanced, so that

$$I_{12} = I_{34} = I_{56} = I'$$
$$E_{12} = E_{34} = E_{56} = E$$
$$\phi_{12} = \phi_{34} = \phi_{56} = \phi$$

then $$\text{Total power} = 3EI' \cos \phi$$

Let I be the current in the line conductors. Then $I = \sqrt{3}\, I'$. Substituting I in the above equation, we obtain

$$\text{Power} = \sqrt{3}\, EI \cos \phi$$

When this expression for power is compared with Eq. (69), it appears that with the same current in the line and the same voltage between lines the power is the same whether the generator is connected Y or Δ.

287. Three-phase versus Two-phase. It is pointed out in Art. 279 that two-phase machines utilize the stator surface more effectively than single-phase machines do. Three-phase machines utilize the stator surface still more effectively, since each phase is distributed over only one-third of the pole pitch instead of over one-half. (In Art. 278 it was shown that distributing the winding reduces the voltage somewhat.) Three-phase machines accordingly cost about 6 per cent less per rated kilowatt than two-phase machines of the same rating.

Another advantage of the three-phase system over the two-phase system is that only three wires are in general required for a three-phase transmission line, whereas the two-phase line requires four wires; or, if a common return wire is used for the two phases so as to reduce the number of wires to three, then since the two currents are at 90°, their vector sum is $\sqrt{2}$ times the current of one phase, so that the common wire must be 41 per cent larger than the other wires.

The superiority of the three-phase system over the two-phase system is not very great but it is enough to make three-phase the standard system, and the few comparatively small two-phase systems in operation at present are in general not being extended.

288. Power Measurement in Three-phase Four-wire Circuits. Since this system consists of three single-phase circuits using a common return wire, it follows that the power in each phase may be measured independently by a single-phase wattmeter connected in that phase (Art. 257) as shown in Fig. 271, and the total power is the sum of the three wattmeter readings.

$$W_1 = E_{01}I_1 \cos \phi_1 \qquad \text{watts}$$
$$W_2 = E_{02}I_2 \cos \phi_2 \qquad \text{watts}$$
$$W_3 = E_{03}I_3 \cos \phi_3 \qquad \text{watts}$$

If the load is balanced, the three wattmeters all read alike.

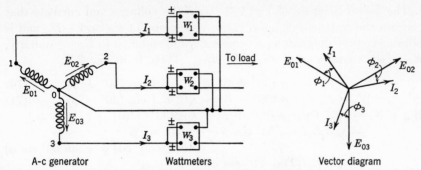

FIG. 271. Power measurement in a three-phase four-wire system. E_{01}, E_{02}, and E_{03} are determined by the generator. I_1, I_2, and I_3 are determined in both magnitude and phase angles (ϕ_1, ϕ_2, and ϕ_3) by the loads.

289. Power Measurement in Three-phase Three-wire Circuits with Balanced Load. When the neutral wire is not present, the power is measured by means of two wattmeters connected as shown in Fig. 272. The total power is equal to the sum of the two wattmeter readings $W_a + W_c$ whether the load is balanced or not and also regardless of whether the graphs of emf and current are sine curves or not.

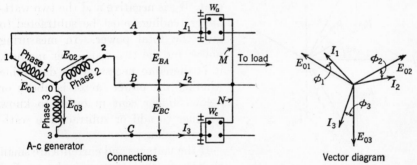

FIG. 272. Power measurement in a three-phase three-wire system.

Consider first the case where the graphs of emf and current are sine curves, and the load is balanced, the impedances of all three phases being equal, so that

$$I_1 = I_2 = I_3 = I$$
$$E_{01} = E_{02} = E_{03} = E_n$$
$$\phi_1 = \phi_2 = \phi_3 = \phi$$

and   Power $= 3E_n I \cos \phi = \sqrt{3}\, EI \cos \phi$ (Art. 283)

where E = voltage between wires = $E_{AB} = E_{BC} = E_{CA}$.

Now E_{BA} is the voltage applied to the wattmeter W_a and E_{BC} is the voltage applied to the wattmeter W_c.

The vector diagram of Fig. 273 shows the voltages and currents that concern the wattmeters. E_{BA} is the vector sum of E_{01} and $-E_{02}$ and is obtained on the diagram by reversing E_{02} and adding it to E_{01}. Similarly, E_{BC} is the vector sum of E_{03} and $-E_{02}$. Then, from Fig. 273,

$$W_a = E_{BA}I_1 \cos (30° + \phi) = \sqrt{3}\, E_n I \cos (30° + \phi) \qquad (70)$$
$$W_c = E_{BC}I_3 \cos (30° - \phi) = \sqrt{3}\, E_n I \cos (30° - \phi) \qquad (71)$$
$$W_a + W_c = \sqrt{3}\, E_n I [\cos (30° + \phi) + \cos (30° - \phi)]$$
$$= \sqrt{3}\, E_n I [\cos 30° \cos \phi - \sin 30° \sin \phi$$
$$+ \cos 30° \cos \phi + \sin 30° \sin \phi]$$
$$= \sqrt{3}\, E_n I [2 \cos 30° \cos \phi]$$

But $\qquad\qquad\qquad\qquad 2 \cos 30° = \sqrt{3}$
therefore $\qquad\qquad\qquad W_a + W_c = 3E_n I \cos \phi$
But $\qquad\qquad\qquad$ Total power $= 3E_n I \cos \phi$
therefore $\qquad\qquad\qquad W_a + W_c = $ total power

With reference to Eqs. (70) and (71), if the power factor of the load is 100 per cent, then ϕ is zero and the two wattmeter readings are equal. At 50 per cent power factor lagging, $\phi = 60°$ and the wattmeter W_a reads zero. For all lagging power factors below 50 per cent, W_a is negative and the two watt-meter readings must be subtracted to give the total power. In measuring power by the two-wattmeter method, it is therefore necessary to determine whether the power factor is above or below 50 per cent in order to know whether to add or subtract the watt-meter readings.

If the voltages and currents are small enough so that they may be applied directly to the meters, as in Fig. 272, and if the meters are connected into the circuit with due regard to the plus-minus ($\pm$) polarity marks, as shown, there will be no difficulty in determining whether the power factor is above or below 50 per cent, because the needle of W_a will be off scale to the left of zero if the power factor is below 50 per cent. It will then be necessary to reverse the current leads on W_a in order to obtain a reading, and all such readings must be considered negative.

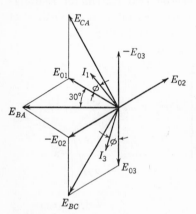

FIG. 273. Voltages applied to the two wattmeters of Fig. 272.

In the majority of practical applications the voltages and currents are too large to be applied directly to the meters, and it is necessary to insert instrument transformers between the meters and the line conductors, so as to reduce both voltages and currents by known ratios, as shown in

Fig. 334. It will still be possible to determine the proper connections if the polarity markings are complete, including polarity marking of the leads between the instrument transformers and the meters. If, however, the polarity markings are incomplete, there is a simple test that will show whether the power factor is above or below 50 per cent. This test consists in substituting E_{CA} for E_{BA} on wattmeter W_a, which in Fig. 272 is readily accomplished by shifting voltage lead M from line B to line C. If this substitution causes a reversal in the direction of the deflection of W_a, the power factor is below 50 per cent; otherwise it is above 50 per cent.

It does not matter which wattmeter is used in making this test. Shifting lead N from B to A has the same effect on W_c as shifting lead M from B to C has on W_a.

290. Watt-ratio Power-factor Chart for Balanced Three-phase Loads. With reference to Eqs. (70) and (71) it appears that $W_a = W_c$ only at

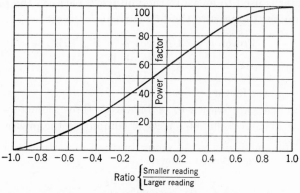

FIG. 274. Power-factor chart for balanced-load three-phase two-wattmeter method of power measurement.

100 per cent power factor and zero power factor, that is, when $\phi = 0°$ or is equal to plus or minus 90°. The ratio of W_a to W_c varies from 1 to 0 to -1 as the power factor changes from 100 per cent to 50 per cent to 0 per cent, as shown by the power-factor chart, Fig. 274, in which the power factor is plotted against the ratio of the two wattmeter readings, the smaller reading always being taken for the numerator. To obtain this curve, divide Eq. (70) by Eq. (71), which gives

$$\frac{W_a}{W_c} = \frac{\cos (30° + \phi)}{\cos (30° - \phi)} \tag{72}$$

The curve may now be plotted by assigning various convenient values to the angle ϕ in Eq. (72). For each value of ϕ assumed there is a corresponding value of the power factor $\cos \phi$ and of W_a/W_c. Conversely, if the ratio of the two wattmeter readings is known, the power factor can be read from the chart and this is a method of determining power factor in balanced three-phase circuits that is very widely used.

In order to use this chart, it is necessary to know whether the power factor is above or below 50 per cent so as to know whether the watt ratio is positive or negative. The chart does not show whether the power factor is leading or lagging.

Note that this power-factor chart gives correct results only if the load is balanced, and no customer should pay power-factor penalties that are based on power factors obtained from this chart without first checking up to see if his load is reasonably well balanced. It may be possible to reduce the penalty very substantially by rearranging the distribution of the single-phase loads among the three phases.

Another method of measuring the power factor of a three-phase load is to use a voltmeter and an ammeter in addition to the two wattmeters. The voltmeter is used to measure the voltage E between the phase wires and the ammeter to measure the line current I. Now

$$\text{Power} = \sqrt{3} \, EI \cos \phi = W_a + W_c$$

therefore
$$\cos \phi = \frac{W_a + W_c}{\sqrt{3} \, EI} \tag{73}$$

and $\cos \phi$ = power factor.

Unless the loads are known to be balanced, three ammeters should be used and the average value of I used in computing the power factor.

Example. In a measurement of power by the two-wattmeter method (Fig. 272) the meter readings were as follows:

$$W_a = 2,500 \text{ watts}$$
$$W_c = 5,000 \text{ watts}$$
$$E = 100 \text{ volts}$$
$$I = 50 \text{ amp}$$

and the power-factor test (Art. 289) showed that the power factor was above 50 per cent. Then

$$\text{Total power} = W_a + W_c = 7,500 \text{ watts}$$
$$\text{Power factor} = \frac{W_a + W_c}{\sqrt{3} \, EI} = \frac{7,500}{\sqrt{3} \times 100 \times 50} = 86.6\%$$

Checking with the watt-ratio power-factor chart,

$$\frac{W_a}{W_c} = \frac{2,500}{5,000} = 0.5$$

and the power factor corresponding to this ratio on the chart is 86.6 per cent.

$$\phi = \cos^{-1} 0.866 = 30°$$

291. General Case of Power Measurement in a Three-phase Three-wire Circuit. The treatment given in Art. 289 of the two-wattmeter method of power measurement in a three-phase three-wire circuit was limited to pure sine waves of current and emf and to balanced load.   The purpose of this treatment was to show how the wattmeter readings vary with the power factor, to introduce the power-factor chart, and to derive a rule for determining whether the wattmeter readings should be added or subtracted.   It will now be shown that the two-wattmeter method of Fig. 272 measures the power correctly whether or not the load is balanced, and whether or not the graphs of current and emf are sine curves.   It will of course be necessary to use instantaneous values of power, emf, and current, because vector diagrams apply only to sine curves.

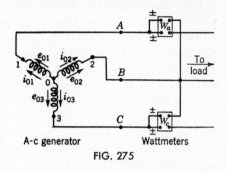

FIG. 275

With reference to Fig. 275, let w_a be the instantaneous power being measured by wattmeter W_a, and let w_c be the instantaneous power being measured by wattmeter W_c.   Then

$$w_a = e_{BA}i_{01} = (e_{01} - e_{02})i_{01} = e_{01}i_{01} - e_{02}i_{01}$$
$$w_c = e_{BC}i_{03} = (e_{03} - e_{02})i_{03} = e_{03}i_{03} - e_{02}i_{03}$$
$$w_a + w_c = e_{01}i_{01} + e_{03}i_{03} + e_{02}(-i_{01} - i_{03})$$

But i_{02} must be equal to $(-i_{01} - i_{03})$ since there is nowhere else for the current to go.   Therefore

$$w_a + w_c = e_{01}i_{01} + e_{02}i_{02} + e_{03}i_{03}$$
$$= \text{total instantaneous power}$$

and the inertia of the moving system of each wattmeter averages up the power being measured by that wattmeter as explained in Art. 257.

292. Δ-connected System.   A Y-connected generator has been used in the foregoing general proof of the two-wattmeter method of power measurement, but the proof works out just as simply if a Δ connection is used, and the student is advised to develop the proof for the Δ connection.

The generator maintains certain voltages between its terminals and the power is determined entirely by the external circuit, that is, by the load.   It cannot make any difference to the external circuit what the internal connections of the generator are, so long as it maintains the proper voltages between its external terminals.   In solving problems which deal only with the circuit external to the generator it is not necessary to know whether the generator is connected Y or Δ.   In the case of transmission-line problems, for example, the generator is always assumed to be Y-connected even if it is known to be Δ-connected; that is, the Δ-connected generators are replaced by equivalent Y-connected machines that would give the same terminal voltage. The reason for doing this is that it simplifies the calculation. Three-phase transmission-line problems are taken up in Chap. 39.

293. The Polyphase Wattmeter. The polyphase wattmeter consists of two single-phase wattmeters arranged one vertically above the other so that their moving coils may be mounted on the same shaft. There is only one pointer and its deflection is determined by the sum of the two deflecting torques, and is therefore a measure of the total power. One advantage of the polyphase wattmeter is that it is easier to read one pointer than to read two, especially if the load is fluctuating. The polyphase wattmeter is lighter and more compact than two single-phase watt-meters, but it is generally somewhat less accurate, due principally to mutual induction between the coils of the two component wattmeters, which are necessarily rather close together.

The two component wattmeters of the polyphase wattmeter may be read separately if it is desired to obtain the power factor from the watt-ratio power-factor chart. This is accomplished by disconnecting a volt-age lead from each component wattmeter in turn, while reading the deflection produced by the other wattmeter.

294. Kilovolt-Ampere Rating of Alternating-current Generators. A given generator can generate a certain voltage when driven at its rated speed and can carry a certain current continuously without overheating, but the power that it can deliver depends upon the power factor of the load. It therefore seems reasonable to rate a-c generators in terms of the volts and amperes that they can develop rather than in terms of power. Alternating-current generators are accordingly rated in kilovolt-amperes, abbreviated to kva. Kilowatts and kilovolt-amperes are equal at 100 per cent power factor, and at any other power factor kilowatts are equal to the product of the kilovolt-amperes and the power factor.

295. Equivalence between Y and Δ Loads. Figure 276 shows balanced Y and Δ loads, and a generator to which either of these loads may be considered to be connected. It is required that these two loads shall appear to the generator to be identical.

In the generator $E_{01} = E_{02} = E_{03} = E_n$, where E_n is the voltage to neutral of each line conductor. Also $I_{01} = I_{02} = I_{03} = I$, where I is the current in each line conductor.

a. Y Load. The impedance of each branch of the Y load is $z = \sqrt{r^2 + x^2}$.

$$ I = \frac{E_{01}}{z} = \frac{E_n}{\sqrt{r^2 + x^2}} $$

I lags E_{01} by the angle $\phi_s = \tan^{-1}(x/r)$.

b. Δ Load. Refer to Figs. 276 and 277.

$$I_a = \frac{E_{31}}{\sqrt{R^2 + X^2}} = \frac{\sqrt{3}\,E_n}{\sqrt{R^2 + X^2}}$$

I_a lags E_{31} by the angle $\phi_d = \tan^{-1}(X/R)$.

$$I_b = \frac{E_{12}}{\sqrt{R^2 + X^2}} = \frac{\sqrt{3}\,E_n}{\sqrt{R^2 + X^2}}$$

I_b lags E_{12} by the angle $\phi_d = \tan^{-1}(X/R)$.

$$I' = \text{vector sum of } I_a \text{ and } -I_b$$
$$= \sqrt{3}\,I_a = \frac{3E_n}{\sqrt{R^2 + X^2}}$$

It is required that I and I' shall coincide in both length and position in the vector diagram.

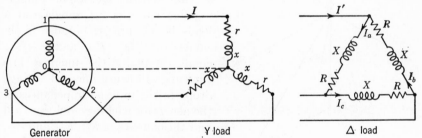

Generator   Y load   Δ load

FIG. 276. Equivalent Y and Δ loads.

Now in Fig. 277 it may be seen that I' leads I_a by 30°. Also E_{01} leads E_{31} by 30°. Therefore E_{01} leads I' by the angle ϕ_d. But E_{01} leads I by the angle ϕ_s, and, by hypothesis, I and I' are the same line, therefore

$$\phi_s = \phi_d$$

whence
$$\frac{x}{r} = \frac{X}{R} \tag{a}$$

Again
$$I' = I$$

or
$$\frac{3E_n}{\sqrt{R^2 + X^2}} = \frac{E_n}{\sqrt{r^2 + x^2}}$$

therefore
$$R^2 + X^2 = (3r)^2 + (3x)^2 \tag{b}$$

From Eqs. (a) and (b), $R = 3r$, and $X = 3x$.

Therefore a balanced Δ load can be replaced by a balanced Y load in which each resistance and reactance is one-third of the resistance and reactance of one branch of the delta load. Most engineers find the Y system easier to visualize, and to make calculations on, than the Δ system, and therefore it is the standard practice, in the case of balanced loads, to assume that the system is Y-connected, regardless of whether it is actually Y or Δ. If, however, the loads are not balanced and are Δ-connected, it is necessary to construct a vector diagram similar to Fig. 277, using the proper given values of R and X for each of the calculations of I_a, I_b, and I_c, with their phase angles ϕ_d. Then the line currents are obtained by combining I_a, I_b, and I_c in pairs as shown in Fig. 277 for I'. Note that

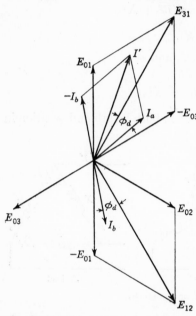

Fig. 277 as shown is not complete. It was drawn for a balanced-load condition, and since the three line currents are equal for a balanced load there was no point in obtaining more than one line current. With unbalanced Δ loads, Fig. 277 must be completed to give all three line currents.

Note that this method of computing line currents for unbalanced Δ loads is not precise because it assumes that E_{01}, E_{02}, and E_{03} are equal. Actually the unequal line currents will cause unequal voltage drops in the internal impedances of the generator windings and thus will mar the equality of E_{01}, E_{02}, and E_{03}. The error will not be important as long as the unbalanced portion of the load currents is small compared with the rated full-load current of the generator.

FIG. 277. Vector diagram showing some of the voltages and currents in the two equivalent circuits of Fig. 276.

296. The Addition of Balanced Three-phase Loads. This operation is probably most easily explained by working an actual example, as follows.

Example. The load on a 115-volt three-phase generator, as shown in Fig. 278, consists of (a) three groups of tungsten lamps, each group containing twenty 100-watt lamps, and (b) a motor operating at 82 per cent power factor and delivering 9 hp at 87 per cent efficiency. Find the power, power factor, and line current of the total load, and the readings on the two wattmeters.

Note that it is not stated whether the generator and motor are connected Y or Δ, because that information would be irrelevant. The lamps are shown connected Δ because they would be connected Δ on a 115-volt three-wire system, but that fact does not enter into the following computations.

The power in a balanced three-phase load $= 3 E_n I \cos \phi$ watts [Eq. (68)], where E_n is the voltage between each conductor and neutral, I is the line current to the

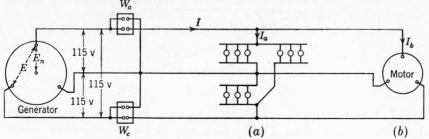

FIG. 278. Balanced loads on a three-phase generator.

load, and ϕ is the angle between E_n and I.   An alternative equation is

$$\text{Power} = \sqrt{3}\, EI \cos \phi \text{ watts [Eq. (69)]}$$

where E is the voltage between conductors.   In this problem $E = 115$ volts, and $E_n = 115/\sqrt{3} = 66.4$ volts.

a. The power taken by the lamps $= 3 \times 20 \times 100 = 6,000$ watts, and since tungsten lamps are practically pure resistance, $\phi_a = 0$.   Therefore

$$I_a = \frac{\text{watts}}{\sqrt{3}\, E} = \frac{6,000}{\sqrt{3} \times 115} = 30.1 \text{ amp}$$

b. The power taken by the motor $= (9 \times 746)/0.87 = 7,720$ watts, and $\cos \phi_b = 0.82$.   Therefore

$$I_b = \frac{\text{watts}}{\sqrt{3}\, E \cos \phi_b} = \frac{7,720}{\sqrt{3} \times 115 \times 0.82} = 47.25 \text{ amp}$$

Total power $= 6,000 + 7,720 = 13,720$ watts $= 13.72$ kw

The total current I is the vector sum of I_a and I_b.
From the vector diagram, Fig. 279,

$$
\begin{aligned}
I &= \sqrt{(ON)^2 + (PN)^2} \\
&= \sqrt{(I_a + I_b \cos \phi_b)^2 + (I_b \sin \phi_b)^2} \\
&= \sqrt{(30.1 + 47.25 \times 0.82)^2 + (47.25 \times 0.5725)^2} \\
&= \sqrt{68.8^2 + 27.05^2} \\
&= 74 \text{ amp}
\end{aligned}
$$

$$\text{Power factor} = \cos \phi = \frac{ON}{OP} = \frac{68.8}{74} = 93\%$$

$$\phi = \cos^{-1} 0.93 = 21°34'$$

Wattmeter W_a reads

$$
\begin{aligned}
\sqrt{3}\, E_n I \cos (30° + \phi) &= EI \cos (30° + \phi) \qquad \text{[Eq. (70)]} \\
&= 115 \times 74 \cos (30° + 21°34') \\
&= 5,290 \text{ watts} = 5.29 \text{ kw}
\end{aligned}
$$

Wattmeter W_c reads

$$
\begin{aligned}
EI \cos (30° - \phi) &= 115 \times 74 \cos (30° - 21°34') \\
&= 8,410 \text{ watts} = 8.41 \text{ kw} \\
W_a + W_c &= 5.29 + 8.41 = 13.7 \text{ kw}
\end{aligned}
$$

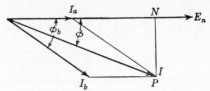

FIG. 279. Vector diagram for Fig. 278.

297. Power-factor Correction, Three-phase, with Capacitors. Capacitors are often used to correct the power factor of three-phase loads. Three capacitors are required and they may be connected either Y or Δ.

Example. The power load of a certain factory is 250 kw, three-phase, three-wire, 2,200 volts, 60 cycles, 70 per cent power factor. According to the terms of the power contract a power-factor penalty must be paid if the power factor is less than 85 per cent. Specify the capacitors required to reduce the penalty to zero, for both Y and Δ connections of the capacitors.

Since the load is balanced three-phase, whatever happens in one phase is duplicated in the other phases. Therefore only one phase need be considered. It is not stated whether the load and the generator are connected Y or Δ, because that information would be irrelevant. In the calculations they would be assumed to be connected Y, regardless of which connection was actually used.

Figure 280 shows the loads and capacitors Y-connected, and also the vector diagram for one phase.

$$\text{Load} = 250,000 \text{ watts} = 3E_nI_1 \cos \phi_1$$

where $E_n = 2,200/\sqrt{3} = 1,270$ volts. Therefore

$$I_1 = \frac{250,000}{3 \times 1,270 \times 0.70} = 93.7 \text{ amp}$$

and I_1 lags E_n by the angle ϕ_1 whose cosine is 0.70. I_c leads E_n by 90° and must be of such a magnitude as to make $\cos \phi = 0.85$. I is the vector sum of I_1 and I_c.

$$ON = I_1 \cos \phi_1 = 93.7 \times 0.70 = 65.6$$
$$PN = I_1 \sin \phi_1 = 93.7 \times 0.714 = 66.9$$
$$QN = ON \tan \phi = 65.6 \times 0.62 = 40.6$$
$$I_c = PQ = PN - QN = 66.9 - 40.6 = 26.3 \text{ amp}$$

But $\qquad I_c = \dfrac{E_n}{X_c} = 2\pi f C E_n$

therefore $\qquad C = \dfrac{I_c}{2\pi f E_n} = \dfrac{26.3}{2\pi 60 \times 1,270} = 55 \times 10^{-6}$ farad

$$= 55 \ \mu\text{f}$$

$$\text{kva per capacitor} = \frac{1,270 \times 26.3}{1,000} = 33.4$$

Therefore if the capacitors are to be connected Y, three capacitors will be required, each rated 33.4 kva at 1,270 volts, 60 cycles, and the capacitance of each capacitor will be 55 μf.

If the capacitors are to be connected Δ, they must still take the same current from the line, and the current to each capacitor will be $26.3/\sqrt{3}$

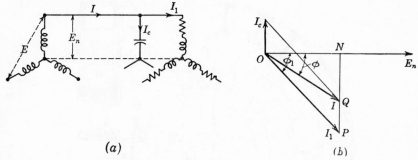

(a)   (b)

FIG. 280. Power-factor correction, three-phase.

amp, while the voltage across each capacitor will be $\sqrt{3}\, E_n$ volts. Thus the kilovolt-ampere rating of each capacitor at 2,200 volts 60 cycles is

$$\frac{\sqrt{3} \times 1,270 \times 26.3}{1,000 \times \sqrt{3}} = 33.4 \text{ kva}$$

The capacitance of each capacitor is

$$\frac{26.3}{\sqrt{3}\, 2\pi 60 \times 1,270 \sqrt{3}} = \frac{55}{3} \times 10^{-6} \text{ farad} = 18.3\ \mu\text{f}$$

The next step is to obtain quotations from the manufacturers in order to find out which is cheaper, 100 kva of capacitors at 2,200 volts 60 cycles or 100 kva at 1,270 volts 60 cycles.

298. Rotating-field Type of Alternating-current Generator. The construction of a rotating-field type of a-c generator is shown in Fig. 281.

The stator core B is built up of sheet-steel laminations, which are dovetailed into a cast-iron yoke A and clamped between two iron end heads E. These laminations have slots C on their inner periphery and in these slots are placed the armature conductors D which are insulated from the slots and are connected together to form a winding from which electric power is supplied to an external circuit. The stator core is divided into blocks by means of vent segments F and the ducts thereby provided allow air to circulate freely through the machine and keep it cool.

The rotor or revolving-field system consists of a series of N and S poles carrying exciting coils H and mounted on an iron field ring. An a-c generator has to be excited with direct current; it cannot therefore be self-exciting. The exciting current, generally supplied by a small d-c generator called an exciter, is led into the field coils through brushes M, which bear on slip rings insulated from the shaft.

The exciter voltage is independent of that of the a-c generator and is generally of the order of 120 volts, so that, in the case of high-voltage

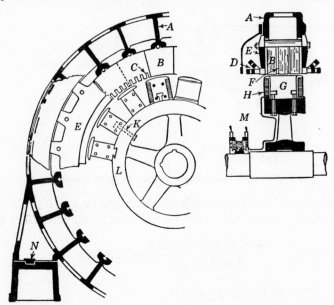

FIG. 281. Rotating-field type of generator with salient poles.

generators, the exciting current may be larger than the full-load current of the machine, as in the following example:

Example. A single-phase generator has an output of 1,000 kw at 13,200 volts and 100 per cent power factor. Find the current at full load. If the exciter voltage is 120 and the excitation loss is 2 per cent, find the output of the exciter and also the exciting current.

Watts = volts × amperes × power factor; therefore

$$1,000 \times 1,000 = 13,200 \times \text{amperes} \times 1.0$$

and at full load   Amperes = 76

Exciter output = 2 per cent of 1,000 kw = 20 kw

$$\text{Exciting current} = \frac{20 \times 1,000}{120} = 167 \text{ amp}$$

299. Steam Turbogenerators. The salient-pole type of rotor construction shown in Fig. 281 is used for the slow- and medium-speed generators that are designed to be driven by water turbines and diesel engines. The number of pairs of poles is equal to the frequency required divided by the speed in revolutions per second. A low-head water turbine is neces-

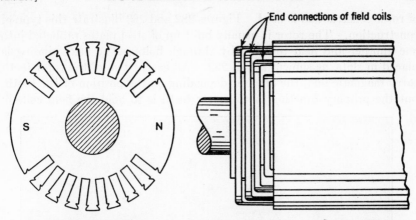

End connections of field coils

End view, field coils removed   Side view, field coils in place, end ring removed

FIG. 282. Rotor of a 3,600-rpm steam turbogenerator.

FIG. 283. Two-pole rotor of a 30,000-kva 3,600-rpm three-phase steam turbogenerator. (*Courtesy of General Electric Co.*)

sarily a low-speed unit and 60-cycle generators for low-head hydroelectric power plants have been built with as many as 128 poles. On the other hand, the steam turbine is inherently a high-speed unit and the generators that are to be directly coupled to steam turbines have either two or four poles. The centrifugal stress in these high-speed rotors is enormous, and, in order to obtain greater strength and at the same time to reduce the windage loss and to improve the flux distribution, a cylindrical type of rotor construction is used.   Figures 282 and 283 illustrate this type of construction.   The rotor is usually built up of steel plates rabbeted into one another and held together by through bolts.   The field winding is placed in slots, as shown in Fig. 282.   All except two of the rotor teeth carry magnetic flux, the amount depending on the position of the tooth, but the primary function of the rotor teeth is to hold the field coils in

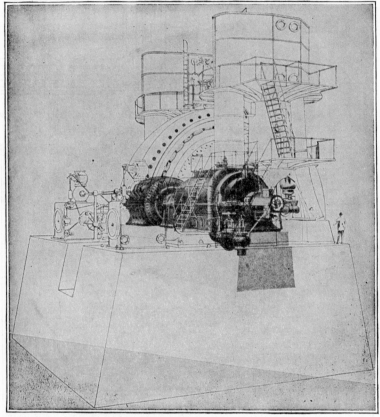

FIG. 284. Relative dimensions of an engine-driven generator and of a turbogenerator of the same capacity.

against the centrifugal forces.   Heavy steel wedges, beveled but not tapered, are forced into the grooves in the teeth above the field coils.   The end connections are held in by two bronze or steel sleeves, one of which can be seen in Fig. 283.   This figure also shows a twelve-bladed fan that is part of the cooling system.

All modern steam-power plants are equipped with turbogenerators. The steam turbine is considerably more efficient than the reciprocating engine and occupies less space.   Figure 284 gives an idea of the relative dimensions of the two types of power units. Turbogenerators have been built in sizes up to 200,000 kw. The cooling of such large machines has been one of the big problems encountered in their development. In order to keep a 30,000-kw generator reasonably cool, approximately 80,000 cu ft of air per minute must be driven through the machine.

300. Rotating-armature Type of Alternating-current Generator. This type is generally cheaper than the revolving-field type of machine for small outputs at low voltages. The armature is the same as that of a d-c generator, except that the commutator is removed and the armature

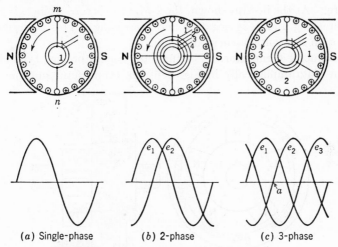

(a) Single-phase   (b) 2-phase   (c) 3-phase

FIG. 285. Rotating-armature type of a-c generator.

winding is tapped at suitable points, the taps being connected to the generator through slip rings and brushes. Each coil in a d-c generator generates alternating current. The commutator converts it into direct current. If the commutator is omitted, the result is necessarily alternating current.

A diagrammatic representation of single-phase, two-phase, and three-phase generators of this type is shown in Fig. 285.

To obtain single-phase alternating current, the winding is tapped at two diametrically opposite points m and n, which are connected to slip rings 1 and 2.

The emf between these slip rings is a maximum when the armature is in the position shown and is zero when the armature has moved through a quarter of a revolution from this position, because then half of the conductors between m and n are under the S pole and half under the N pole, so that the emfs neutralize each other. The emf again becomes a maximum after the armature has moved through half of a revolution from the position shown in Fig. 285 but the polarity of the slip rings is now reversed. The emf between the slip rings is therefore alternating and goes through one cycle per pair of poles passed.

If the armature is tapped at four points as shown in Fig. 285b, the voltage e_1 between the slip rings 1 and 2 is a maximum when the armature is in the position shown, while the voltage e_2 between the rings 3 and 4 is zero at the same instant, and e_2 lags e_1 by 90° so that the machine is now a two-phase generator.

To obtain three-phase currents, the armature must be tapped at three points as shown in Fig. 285c. It then becomes a three-phase Δ-connected armature. At the instant shown, the voltage e_2 is zero while e_1 is positive and decreasing and e_3 is negative and increasing. This corresponds to instant a on the voltage-curve diagram.

301. Inductor Generator. The inductor generator, one type of which is shown diagrammatically in Fig. 286, has been found suitable for the

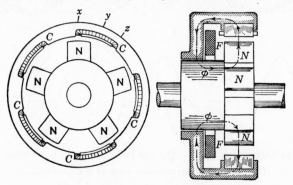

FIG. 286. Inductor generator.

generation of high-frequency emf, because of the simplicity of the rotor construction.

The stationary field coil F, when excited, produces a magnetic flux ϕ that causes all the inductors N to have the same polarity. The coils C are cut by the lines of force as the inductors rotate, and the generated voltage is a maximum when the inductors are in the position shown and one side of each coil is cutting lines of force. The voltage is zero when the poles are in position y and is a maximum again but in the opposite direction when the poles are in the position z and the other side of each coil is now cutting the lines of force. The voltage therefore passes through one-half cycle while the inductors move from x to z, or five cycles are passed through per revolution, so that a machine with five inductors is equivalent to a 10-pole revolving-field machine. Since only one side of each coil is active at any instant in the case of the inductor generator, it is heavier for a given output than the generators previously described, and is therefore used only when simplicity of construction is essential.

The ignition for aircraft engines is provided by permanent-magnet inductor-type magnetos.

Problems

*30-1. *a.* What are the essential parts of an a-c generator?

b. What are the main points of difference as compared with the d-c generator?

c. Are a-c generators separately or self-excited?

d. Why may the field current of a generator often be larger than the full-load armature current?

e. Why are large a-c generators usually of the revolving-field type?

*30-2. What is meant by a polyphase generator? Distinguish between a two-phase and a three-phase generator.

30-3. An a-c generator has three independent windings, and the six terminals are brought out to a connection board as shown in Fig. 30-3a. The induced voltages $E_{aa'}$, $E_{bb'}$, and $E_{cc'}$ have each an effective value of 100 volts and are respectively 120° out of phase as represented in the vector diagram, Fig. 30-3b. For

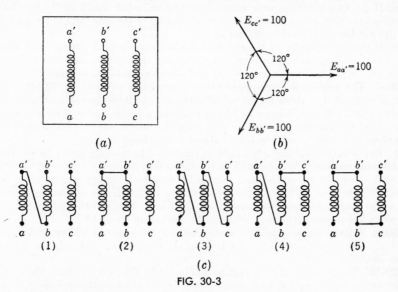

(*a*)   (*b*)

(1)   (2)   (3)   (4)   (5)

(*c*)

FIG. 30-3

each of the five terminal connections shown in Fig. 30-3c, draw a vector diagram and compute the magnitude of the resultant terminal voltage: (1) $E_{ab'}$, (2) E_{ab}, (3) $E_{ac'}$, (4) E_{ac}, (5) $E_{ac'}$. Label all vectors clearly.

30-4. For the terminal board in Fig. 30-3a, show diagram of terminal connections for interconnecting the three windings of the generator as follows: (*a*) three-phase Y connection; (*b*) three-phase Δ connection; and (*c*) all three windings connected in series so as to give the largest possible single-phase voltage at the terminals. Determine the value of this voltage. Show the line wires connected to the proper terminals in each case. If the rated current of each winding is 50 amp, designate the line voltages and the line currents for each of the above connections. What is the total kilovolt-ampere rating of the generator in each case?

*30-5. *a.* An eight-pole generator has 24 slots, is wound three-phase, and is

Y-connected.   Make a developed diagram such as that in Fig. 261 showing the coils and connections.

b. Show on another diagram how the coils would be Δ-connected.

c. If the voltage between terminals is 2,200 when the machine is Δ-connected, and the current in each line is 1,000 amp, what would be the terminal voltage and line current if the machine were reconnected Y?

d. What is the output if the power factor of the load is 80 per cent?

30-6. *a*. An eight-pole generator has sixteen slots and is wound two-phase. Make a developed diagram such as Fig. 257 showing the coils and the connections to the external circuit.

b. Draw a vector diagram showing the voltages and currents if the power factor of the load is 80 per cent.

c. If the voltage per phase is 2,400 and the current per phase is 800 amp, what is the output in kilowatts, the rating of the generator in kilovolt-amperes (Art. 294), and the horsepower of the driving engine if the generator efficiency is 94 per cent?

d. If the two windings were connected in series, what would be the resultant single-phase voltage and what would be the rating of the generator if the current in the winding is limited to 800 amp?

e. If the power factor of the external single-phase circuit is 86 per cent, show on a vector diagram the voltage of each phase, the current, and the resultant voltage.   What is the power factor of each phase considered separately?

30-7. The load on a three-phase 115-volt generator consists of 150 fifty-watt lamps connected in three groups of 50 each; also a 10-hp three-phase induction motor which has an efficiency of 85 per cent and a power factor of 80 per cent.

a. Find the current in each line supplying the motor, the current in each line supplying the lamps, and the total current drawn from the line.

b. Indicate how wattmeters should be connected to measure power by the two-wattmeter method.   What would be the indication on each wattmeter?

30-8. Three heater units each taking 1,000 watts at unity power factor are connected in Δ to a 115-volt three-phase line.   What is the resistance of each unit and what is the current drawn from the line?   Two wattmeters are used to measure the power supplied.   What is the indication on each?

30-9. A three-phase induction motor takes 3,000 watts at 80 per cent power factor.   Two wattmeters are used to measure the power.   What is the indication on each?

*30-10. Three heater units are connected in Y to a three-phase line.   Show how wattmeters are connected to measure power by (*a*) three-wattmeter method and (*b*) two-wattmeter method.   Prove that the sum of the two wattmeter readings will equal the sum of the three wattmeter readings.   Is this true for all power factors?

*30-11. What would happen if three heater units designed to be connected in Δ were connected in Y?   If three units designed for Y connection were connected in Δ?

30-12. In a certain three-phase generator the voltage generated in the windings of each of the three phases is 1,270.   The conductors have such a cross section that they will safely carry 100 amp.

a. If the machine has eight poles and 24 slots, make a developed diagram such as Fig. 261 showing the coils and their connections.

b. Show how the three phases would be connected together to make a Y-connected generator.   Show on another diagram how the machine would be Δ-connected.

c. What are the terminal voltage, the current per phase, the line current, and the output in kilovolt-amperes for the two connections?

30-13. If all three windings of the generator of Prob. 30-12 were connected in series so as to give the largest possible single-phase voltage at the terminals, what would then be the kilovolt-ampere rating of the machine? Show the connections of the coils under this condition.

***30-14.** Draw sine curves representing the voltages generated in the three phases of the generator of Prob. 30-12.

a. Let the machine be Y-connected and combine the curves so as to obtain the curves representing the terminal voltages.

b. Draw the vector diagram for the above six sine curves and show that the terminal voltage is equal to $\sqrt{3}$ times voltage per phase.

c. For the Δ-connected windings draw curves representing the currents per phase (100 amp); also resultant curves representing the line current which at any instant is the difference between the currents in the two phases connected to that line.

d. Show from the curves and corresponding vector diagram that the line current is $\sqrt{3}$ times the current per phase.

30-15. The load on a 230-volt three-phase line consists of three equal Y-connected impedances of $10 + j5$ ohms and three equal Δ-connected impedances of $20 + j30$ ohms. Compute the line current, power, and power factor for the total load.

30-16. It is required to raise the power factor of a 400 kw balanced three-phase load from 75 per cent lagging to 90 per cent lagging. The line voltage is 6,900 volts, 60 cycles. Specify the capacitors required for both Y and Δ connections of the capacitors.

30-17. *a.* Find the values of the currents I_1, I_2, and I_3 in Fig. 30-17 and also the angles by which they lag behind the voltages driving them.

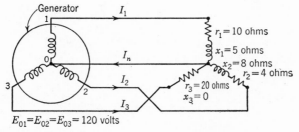

FIG. 30-17. Unbalanced Y-connected loads on a three-phase four-wire system.

b. Taking the voltage E_{01} as the vertical axis, draw the vector diagram to scale and express these three currents in the $a + jb$ form, in which a is the horizontal component and b is the vertical component.

c. Find the value of the neutral current I_n and show it on the vector diagram.

d. If three wattmeters were used to measure the power, as in Fig. 271, what would be the reading on each?

30-18. *a.* Find the values of the currents I_1, I_2, and I_3 in Fig. 30-18.

b. Taking the voltage E_{01} as the vertical axis, draw the vector diagram to scale and express I_1, I_2, and I_3 in the $a + jb$ form, in which a is the horizontal component and b is the vertical component.

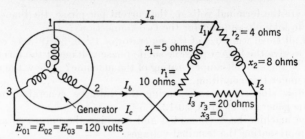

FIG. 30-18. Unbalanced Δ-connected loads on a three-phase system.

c. Find the values of I_a, I_b, and I_c, and draw them on the vector diagram.

d. Compute the total power consumption of the Δ-connected loads by adding the values of I^2r, and check by obtaining the sum of the wattmeter readings that would be obtained by the two-wattmeter method of power measurement (Fig. 272).

31

TRANSFORMERS

302. In order that electrical energy may be transmitted economically over long distances, high voltages must be used; but in order that electric circuits may be safely handled, low voltages are necessary for distribution. The a-c transformer is a piece of apparatus by means of which electrical energy can be received at one voltage and delivered at another voltage either higher or lower. Just as a pair of gears, in the mechanical transmission of energy, converts from one torque and speed to another torque and speed, so a transformer in the electrical transmission of energy converts from one voltage and current to another voltage and current.

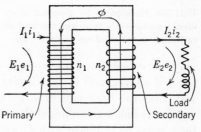

FIG. 287. The transformer. The arrows show merely which directions are assumed to be positive, and the choice is entirely arbitrary.

A transformer consists essentially of two separate windings on an iron core; one receives energy and is called the primary, and the other delivers energy and is called the secondary. Figure 287 shows a closed magnetic circuit of iron on which are placed the two windings having n_1 and n_2 turns, respectively. In an actual transformer of this type each of the two windings is distributed over both sides of the iron core, the high-voltage winding enclosing the low-voltage winding as shown in Fig. 294b. The symbols e_1 and i_1 denote the instantaneous values of the voltage and current impressed on the primary by the power supply system. The symbols e_2 and i_2 denote the instantaneous values of the output voltage and current of the secondary. The effective values are denoted by E_1, I_1, E_2, and I_2. The arrowheads merely show which directions are chosen to be regarded as positive when drawing the vector diagrams or plotting the sine curves. The actual instantaneous voltages, currents, and flux act alternately in both directions, each reversing twice per cycle. The phase angles between the various quantities remain to be investigated.

The small primary current that flows when the secondary is not connected to any load is called the *exciting current*, and the symbols i_0 and I_0 are used to represent its instantaneous and effective values.   Thus i_0 and I_0 are the no-load values of i_1 and I_1.

Let us first consider an ideal transformer in which there is no iron loss, in which the resistance of the windings is negligibly small, and in which all the flux links both windings.   Then when the secondary is not connected to any load but is left open circuited so that no current can flow in it, the primary winding is simply a coil of pure inductance, the theory of which has already been given in Arts. 249 and 250.   Figure 208 of Art.

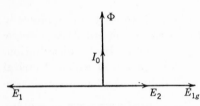

FIG. 288. No-load vector diagram of an ideal transformer with no iron loss and no resistance in the windings ($n_1/n_2 = 2$).

249 accordingly shows that when an alternating emf e_1 is applied to the primary winding of this ideal transformer the current i_0 that it produces will lag 90° behind e_1, and there will be an emf of self-induction e_{1g} exactly equal to e_1 and exactly 180° out of phase with e_1.   These phase relationships are also shown in the vector diagram, Fig. 288.   The voltage e_{1g} may be called the back voltage of the primary because it opposes the applied emf e_1, and in fact limits the primary current in much the same way that the back emf in a d-c motor limits the armature current.

Since it has been assumed that there is no iron loss, the flux ϕ produced by i_0 must be in phase with i_0, and this also is shown in Fig. 288.   In an actual transformer most of the flux follows the iron path and links with both windings as shown in Fig. 287.   Any flux that links with one winding only must complete its circuit through the air and is therefore relatively weak.   Such flux is called *leakage flux*.   For the ideal transformer under consideration it is assumed that there is no leakage flux, so that all the flux links with both windings.   This flux as it grows and dies generates the voltage e_{1g} and e_{2g} in the primary and secondary windings, respectively.   Therefore e_{2g} is in phase with e_{1g}.   If the graph of the applied emf e_1 is a sine curve, the graphs of e_{1g} and of the flux ϕ must also be sine curves, so that

$$\phi = \Phi_m \sin \theta = \Phi_m \sin (2\pi f t) \tag{74}$$

Now
$$e_{1g} = -n_1 \frac{d\phi}{dt} 10^{-8} \quad \text{volts} \tag{75}$$

where the minus sign is required because e_{1g} opposes the change in i_0 that causes the change in ϕ.   Similarly

$$e_{2g} = -n_2 \frac{d\phi}{dt} 10^{-8} \quad \text{volts} \tag{76}$$

where the minus sign may be considered conventional, although it is an obvious convention to give e_{2g} the same sign as e_{1g}, since they are produced by the same flux.

Substituting the value of ϕ from Eq. (74) in Eq. (75) gives

$$e_{1g} = -n_1\Phi_m \cos \theta \frac{d\theta}{dt} 10^{-8} \qquad \text{volts}$$

$$= -2\pi f n_1 \Phi_m \cos \theta \, 10^{-8} \qquad \text{volts} \qquad (77)$$

which incidentally shows that if the graph of flux is a sine curve the graph of e_{1g} is also a sine curve, and lags 90° behind the flux.

The maximum values of e_{1g} occur when $\cos \theta = +1$ and -1. Therefore

$$E_{1g(\max)} = 2\pi f n_1 \Phi_m 10^{-8} \qquad \text{volts}$$

and, dividing both sides by $\sqrt{2}$,

	$E_{1g} = 4.44 f n_1 \Phi_m 10^{-8}$	volts	(78)
Similarly	$E_{2g} = 4.44 f n_2 \Phi_m 10^{-8}$	volts	(79)
Dividing	$\dfrac{E_{2g}}{E_{1g}} = \dfrac{n_2}{n_1}$		(80)

In this ideal transformer, which has no leakage flux and whose windings have no resistance, the terminal voltage E_2 is equal to the generated voltage E_{2g}; also E_1 and E_{1g} are equal in magnitude, though opposite in sign. Therefore

$$\frac{E_2}{E_1} = \frac{n_2}{n_1} \qquad (81)$$

Equation (81) is exact for the ideal transformer at all loads, and is also accurate for an actual transformer at no load, because when I_2 is zero there can be no difference between E_2 and E_{2g}; and also when I_2 is zero I_1 is small, so that the difference in magnitude between E_1 and E_{1g} must be small. In the case of actual transformers at full load, Eq. (81) is usually in error by 2 or 3 per cent although the error may be somewhat larger if the power factor of the load is low. This completes the explanation of Fig. 288. Let us now take into account the iron loss. The flux in an air core is always in phase with the current that produces it, and there is no power loss in an air core. Similarly, in an ideal iron core having no iron loss the flux would be in phase with the exciting current as shown in Fig. 288. In any actual iron core, however, the flux lags behind the exciting current I_0, as shown in Fig. 289. Since E_{1g} is always exactly 90° behind Φ as shown by Eq. (77), and since E_1 is at 180° to E_{1g}, it follows that if the flux vector is shifted clockwise it will take E_{1g} and E_1 with it, and the net result of introducing iron loss is equivalent to shifting I_0 counterclockwise relative to the other vectors. There is now a power input to the transformer equal to $E_1 I_0 \cos \alpha$, and since the output is zero, the input is all loss.   Practically all this loss is iron loss.   There is a little primary copper loss $I_0{}^2R_1$, but since I_0 is small this copper loss is very small.

The exciting current I_0 may be regarded as made up of two components: (1) The magnetizing component $I_M = I_0 \sin \alpha$, which is required to produce the flux ϕ.   (2) The core-loss component $I_c = I_0 \cos \alpha$, which when multiplied by E_1 gives the hysteresis and eddy-current loss in the iron.   Both   components   vary widely with the maximum value of the flux density and with the grade of iron.

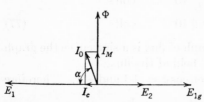

FIG. 289. No-load vector diagram of a transformer. (Ratio of primary turns to secondary turns equal to two.)

Now consider what happens when a load is connected to the secondary, as in Fig. 287, so that a current I_2 flows.   If the load contains no source of emf, but is merely an impedance Z made up of any combination of resistance, inductance, and capacitance, then $I_2 = E_2/Z$, and the angle by which I_2 lags E_2 may be anything from zero to plus or minus 90°, depending on the nature of Z.   The current I_2 flowing in the secondary winding exerts a magnetomotive force (mmf) of $I_2 n_2$ amp-turns, which acts on the same magnetic circuit as the primary mmf of $I_0 n_1$ amp-turns. Moreover, at full load $I_2 n_2$ is usually at least twenty times as large as $I_0 n_1$.   Unless this secondary mmf is neutralized by additional current flowing in the primary, the core flux will be greatly changed, and the balance between E_1 and E_{1g} in the primary will be completely upset. But in this ideal transformer there is nothing opposing the primary current except E_{1g}, and therefore if any unbalance is created between E_1 and E_{1g}, the primary current changes and continues to change until the balance

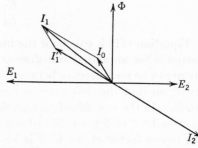

FIG. 290. Vector diagram of a transformer carrying a load. (Ratio of primary turns to secondary turns equal to two.)

is restored.   Now the balance can be restored only by neutralizing the secondary mmf $I_2 n_2$.   Let I_1' be the primary current required to neutralize $I_2 n_2$.   Then

$$I_1' n_1 = I_2 n_2 \qquad (82)$$

Moreover, I_1' must be 180° out of phase with I_2 so that their mmfs will be in opposition at all points in the cycle.   The total primary current I_1 is the vector sum of I_0 and I_1'.   Figure 290 shows the vector diagram for the ideal transformer when carrying an 86.6 per cent power-factor load so that I_2 lags E_2 by 30°.

At full load, I_1' is much larger than I_0, and for rough calculations we may neglect I_0 and substitute I_1 for I_1' in Eq. (82). Then

$$I_1 n_1 = I_2 n_2$$

or
$$\frac{I_1}{I_2} = \frac{n_2}{n_1}, \text{ approximately} \tag{83}$$

Due caution should be used in applying Eq. (83). It becomes hopelessly inaccurate at very light loads.

It might be noted here that if we had decided to drop the minus sign in Eq. (76), thus reversing the convention of signs in the secondary, the arrowheads associated with the secondary voltage and current in Fig. 287 would have been reversed, E_2 would have been in phase with E_1 in Figs. 288 to 290, and I_2 would have been in phase with I_1'. This alternative convention of signs is preferred by some people.

303. Leakage Flux. In the preceding theory, Art. 302, it was assumed that all the flux linked both windings. In actual practice, however, both the windings produce some flux that links only with the winding that produces it. Figure 291 shows the actual instantaneous currents and fluxes at a particular instant in the cycle when i_1 is positive and i_2 is negative. In general, these two currents are of opposite sign throughout most of the cycle, if we follow the convention of signs shown in Fig. 287.

The ampere-turns $n_1 i_1$ produce a flux ϕ_{1l}, called the primary leakage flux, which is proportional to i_1 and which threads the coil n_1 but does not thread n_2.

The ampere-turns $n_2 i_2$ produce a flux ϕ_{2l}, called the secondary leakage flux, which is proportional to i_2 and which threads the coil n_2 but does not thread n_1.

Now any coil in which a current i produces a flux ϕ which is proportional to the current is said to have self-inductance (see Art. 250) and the voltage to send an alternating current I through such a coil is IX, where X is the reactance of the coil; the current lags this voltage by 90°.

In Fig. 291, the flux ϕ_{1l} is proportional to the current i_1 and its effect is the same as if the coil n_1 had a reactance X_1, so that, instead of considering the effect of the flux ϕ_{1l}, the effect of the equivalent reactance X_1 may be considered. In the same way the leakage flux ϕ_{2l} may be represented by an equivalent reactance X_2. Figure 292 shows the diagram of an actual transformer in which the leakage fluxes ϕ_{1l} and ϕ_{2l} are replaced by the equivalent reactances X_1 and X_2 which, along with the resistances R_1 and R_2 of the coils, are placed for convenience outside the actual winding.

Between the terminals ab and cd, the transformer diagram in Fig. 292

is the same as the ideal diagram in Fig. 287. The vector diagram for this ideal transformer is shown in Fig. 290. It should be noted, however, that the terminal voltages of the ideal transformer in Fig. 292 are denoted by E_1' and E_{2g}, and not by E_1 and E_2 as in Fig. 290. Equation (81) therefore becomes

$$\frac{E_{2g}}{E_1'} = \frac{n_2}{n_1}$$

The actual terminal voltage E_2 is obtained by subtracting from E_{2g} the vectors I_2R_2 and I_2X_2, the voltages required to drive the current I_2

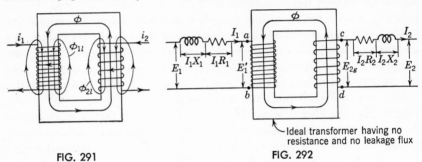

FIG. 291.

FIG. 292.

FIG. 291. The transformer, showing the actual instantaneous currents and fluxes during that part of the cycle in which i_1 is positive and i_2 is negative.

FIG. 292. An equivalent diagram of an actual transformer. It is made up of the ideal transformer of Fig. 287 plus the resistances R_1 and R_2 and the leakage reactances X_1 and X_2.

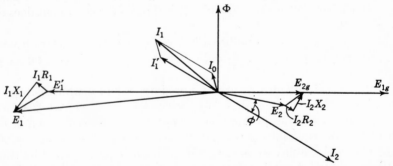

FIG. 293. Complete vector diagram of an actual transformer carrying a 95 per cent power-factor lagging load. The turns ratio is 2. In order to make a clear picture, the IR and IX drops have been made about three times their usual magnitude.

through the secondary resistance and reactance, respectively, where I_2R_2 is in phase with I_2, and I_2X_2 leads I_2 by 90°.

The applied primary voltage E_1 is obtained by adding to E_1' the vectors I_1R_1 and I_1X_1, where I_1R_1 is drawn parallel to I_1 and I_1X_1 leads I_1 by 90°. These subtractions and additions are shown graphically in Fig. 293.

When the power factor of the load on the secondary is lagging, E_2 is less than E_{2g}, and E_1 is greater than E_1', on account of the resistance and reactance drops, as shown in Fig. 293. These drops are proportional to the currents, so that the secondary voltage drops with increase of load. With leading power factors of secondary load, however, E_2 may be greater than E_{2g} and E_1 less than E_1', so that the secondary voltage may rise with increase of load. The student should satisfy himself on this point by drawing the vector diagram.

The calculation of the voltage drop in a transformer is identical with the calculation of the voltage drop in a transmission line (Art. 272), or rather in two transmission lines, since R_1 and X_1 are equivalent to one transmission line and R_2 and X_2 to another. There is no voltage drop in the ideal transformer left after R_1, R_2, X_1, and X_2 have been removed; there is only a voltage transformation, which is constant for all conditions of operation, and which is equal to the ratio of the turns.

304. Leakage Reactance in Standard Transformers. In transformers used in the distribution of electrical energy the leakage reactances X_1

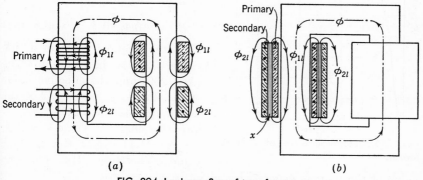

(a)											(b)

FIG. 294. Leakage flux of transformers.

and X_2 are kept small by constructing the transformer so that ϕ_{1l} and ϕ_{2l} are small. Figure 294a shows a transformer with a primary and a secondary coil on each leg and shows also the leakage fluxes. It may be seen from this diagram that, on each leg, ϕ_{1l} and ϕ_{2l} act in opposite directions, so that, if n_2 were interwound with n_1, then the leakage fluxes would neutralize and only the main flux ϕ be left. This result is approximated in practice by constructing the transformer as shown in Fig. 294b, where half of the primary and half of the secondary winding are placed over one another on each leg of the transformer core. The leakage fluxes have then to crowd into the space x between the windings, and the smaller the space x, the smaller the leakage fluxes and the smaller the leakage reactances.

As far as maintaining the proper voltage at the consumer's premises is

concerned, the lower the leakage reactances the better, but leakage reactance performs one valuable function in that it limits the short-circuit
current. This not only protects the transformer itself from destruction
during the time required for the protective devices to operate but also
lessens the rupturing duty on the circuit breakers, and the voltage disturbance on the rest of the system. In practice, therefore, transformers
are generally not built with the minimum possible leakage reactance but
usually have enough reactance to limit the short-circuit current to from
seven to thirty times full-load current, according to the service conditions.

305. Relation between Voltage and Flux Density in a Transformer.
During each cycle the flux grows to its maximum value Φ_m, decreases to

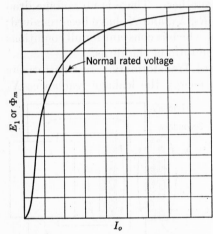

zero, grows to its maximum value
in the reverse direction, and again
decreases to zero. Therefore Φ_m
cuts the windings four times per
cycle or $4f$ times per sec. Therefore the average voltage E_{av} generated in a winding of n turns is

$$E_{av} = 4fn\Phi_m10^{-8} \quad \text{volts} \quad (84)$$

Now the average value of a sine
curve $= 2/\pi \times$ the maximum value
(Art. 239) and the effective value
of a sine curve $= 1/\sqrt{2} \times$ the
maximum value (Art. 241). Therefore the effective value $= \pi/2 \times$
$1/\sqrt{2} = 1.11$ times the average
value. Therefore the effective

FIG. 295. Saturation curve of a transformer.

value of the voltage generated is given by the equation

$$E = 4.44fn\Phi_m10^{-8} \quad \text{volts} \quad (85)$$

From this it appears that the flux Φ_m is proportional to the impressed
voltage. If the impressed voltage is increased step by step and readings
are taken of the corresponding values of the exciting current I_0, the
saturation curve may be plotted as in Fig. 295. It is evident from this
curve that, if a transformer is operated at a voltage considerably higher
than its rated voltage, the exciting current I_0 may be many times its
normal value, with the result that the primary copper loss will be abnormally high and the insulation may be damaged by overheating.

The height of the "normal rated voltage" line in Fig. 295 depends a
good deal upon the specifications under which the transformers are bought
and may be undesirably high if costs are being shaved to a minimum.

Let B be the maximum allowable flux density in lines per square inch and A be the cross-sectional area of the iron core in square inches, then $\Phi_m = BA$, and, substituting BA for Φ_m in Eq. (85),

$$E = 4.44 f n B A 10^{-8} \qquad \text{volts}$$

or
$$An = \frac{E10^8}{4.44fB} \qquad (86)$$

Equation (86) is the principal design equation for a transformer. For example, suppose that we wish to design a transformer to operate at a secondary voltage of 115 volts, 60 cycles. Turning to Fig. 41, page 63, we see that a suitable maximum value for B for sheet steel would be somewhere between 80,000 and 90,000 lines per sq in. Choosing 85,000, and substituting in Eq. (86), we get

$$An_2 = 508 \qquad (87)$$

If n_2 is made equal to 100 turns, then the core must have a cross section of 5.08 sq in. If $n_2 = 50$ turns, then $A = 10.16$ sq in. There is evidently an infinite number of combinations of A and n_2 that will satisfy Eq. (87). As the amount of copper is decreased, by decreasing the number of turns, the amount of iron increases. The designer finds out by trial what proportion of iron to copper results in minimum cost. However, if the transformer is to be used in an airplane, he will probably design for minimum weight rather than minimum cost.

The size of the conductor will be determined by the magnitude of the current that it will be required to carry.

Equation (86) also shows why 60-cycle transformers are both lighter and cheaper than 25-cycle transformers of the same rating. If E is fixed, then An is inversely proportional to f, so that, if the frequency is doubled, either the number of turns may be cut in half or the cross section of the iron may be cut in half, or both may be divided by $\sqrt{2}$.

306. Efficiency of a Transformer

$$\text{Efficiency} = \frac{\text{output}}{\text{input}} = \frac{\text{output}}{\text{output} + \text{losses}} \qquad (88)$$

where the losses are

Iron losses $\begin{cases} \text{Hysteresis loss} \\ \text{Eddy-current loss} \end{cases}$

Copper losses $\begin{cases} I_1{}^2 R_1 & \text{watts} \\ I_2{}^2 R_2 & \text{watts} \end{cases}$

There is no power loss in the primary and secondary reactances.

307. Hysteresis Loss.

Since the flux in a transformer core is alternating, power is required for the continual reversals of the elementary magnets of which the iron is composed. This power is called the hysteresis loss (see Arts. 71 and 72). The hysteresis loss in a transformer varies directly as the frequency, and approximately as $B^{1.6}$, where B is the maximum flux density.

308. Eddy-current Loss. If the transformer core in Fig. 296 is made of a solid block of iron, then the alternating flux ϕ threading this core

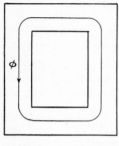

causes currents to flow as shown at a, in the same way as through a short-circuited secondary winding. Power is required to maintain these eddy currents. This power is called the eddy-current loss.

To keep these eddy currents small, a high resistance is placed in their path. This is accomplished by laminating the core, as shown at b, the laminations being separated from one another by varnish. The eddy-current loss varies as the square of the flux density and also as the square of the frequency.

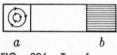

a b

FIG. 296. Transformer core.

309. Open-circuit Test. The hysteresis and eddy-current losses taken together constitute what is called the iron loss. Assuming that the input voltage E_1 is kept constant, the flux Φ_m will be practically constant, independent of the load, because Φ_m cannot change without upsetting the balance between E_{1g} and E_1, thus allowing additional primary current to flow to counteract the change in flux, as explained in Art. 302. Since the flux is practically independent of the load, the iron loss is assumed to be constant at all loads. The iron loss is readily determined by means of the connections shown in Fig. 297, in which rated voltage at rated frequency is applied to the primary winding while the secondary is left open-circuited. The power input under these conditions is equal to the iron loss plus a negligible amount of copper loss.

The wattmeter reading W_0 includes the power loss in its own potential circuit, as explained in Art. 257, unless the wattmeter is

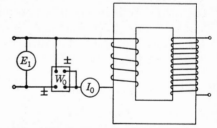

FIG. 297. Open-circuit test of a transformer (secondary open).

compensated. W_0 also includes the power loss in the ammeter. Therefore

$$\text{Iron loss} = W_0 - \frac{E_1{}^2}{R_p} - I_0{}^2 R_a - I_0{}^2 R_1 \qquad (89)$$

where R_p = resistance of potential circuit of wattmeter

R_a = resistance of ammeter

R_1 = resistance of transformer winding that is being used as primary in the test

The easiest way to eliminate the $I_0{}^2 R_a$ correction is to short-circuit the ammeter while reading the wattmeter. The $I_0{}^2 R_1$ correction is usually negligible, but the $E_1{}^2 / R_p$ correction may be quite important, especially if the transformer is small. The open-circuit test is always made on the low-voltage winding. The iron loss is the same, measured on either winding, so long as the rated voltage for that winding is applied, but if the measurement were made on the high-voltage winding, the current I_0 would be inconveniently small, and the voltage inconveniently large.

Example. The open-circuit test of a 50-kva 2,400- to 240-volt transformer, with the low-voltage winding connected to a 240-volt supply, as in Fig. 297, and with the high-voltage winding open-circuited, gave the following readings: $E_1 = 240$ volts, $I_0 = 8$ amp, $W_0 = 306$ watts with the ammeter short-circuited. The wattmeter was not compensated for the power loss in its own potential circuit and $R_p = 9,750$ ohms. The resistance of the low-voltage winding of the transformer is 0.005 ohm. What is the true iron loss?

Since the ammeter was short-circuited when reading the wattmeter, Eq. (89) becomes

$$\text{Iron loss} = W_0 - \frac{E_1{}^2}{R_p} - I_0{}^2 R_1$$

$$= 306 - \frac{240^2}{9,750} - 8^2 \times 0.005$$

$$= 306 - 5.9 - 0.3$$

$$= 300 \text{ watts}$$

310. All-day Efficiency. This is defined as the ratio of the total energy output during twenty-four hours to the total energy input for the same period. This efficiency is of especial importance when the transformer carries little or no load during the major portion of the 24 hr, but is always connected to the line. In the simplest case, where the output is constant for h hr and is zero for the remainder of the 24 hr,

$$\text{All-day efficiency} = \frac{\text{output} \times h}{\text{output} \times h + \text{iron loss} \times 24 + \text{copper loss} \times h} \quad (90)$$

In many cases, however, the load is variable, and it is then necessary to have the load curve on a time base in order to compute the energy wasted in copper loss during the 24 hr. In order to obtain the copper loss, read off the current values at suitable equal time intervals, say every half hour, and square each of these values. The sum of these squares, divided by the number of readings, in this case 48, gives the average value of I^2, which, when multiplied by the resistance of the winding, gives the average copper loss in watts for the 24-hr period. In practice the primary and secondary copper losses are obtained together by using the equivalent resistance (Art. 313). The kilowatthour output for the 24 hr may be obtained by means of a watthour meter, or by determining the area under the load curve.   Then

All-day efficiency

$$= \frac{\text{output, kwhr}}{\text{output, kwhr} + 24 \text{ (kw iron loss + kw average copper loss)}} \quad (91)$$

Example. In a 50-kva 2,400- to 240-volt transformer the iron loss is 300 watts, the primary resistance is 0.5 ohm, and the secondary resistance is 0.005 ohm. Find: (*a*) the efficiency when the load is 50 kw and the power factor 100 per cent; (*b*) the efficiency when the load is 5 kw and the power factor 100 per cent; (*c*) the efficiency when the load is 50 kva and the power factor 80 per cent; (*d*) the all-day efficiency in the last case if the load is constant and connected for 5 hr a day while the transformer is connected to the line for 24 hr a day.

a. I_2, secondary current $= \dfrac{50,000}{240} = 208$ amp

I_1, primary current $= \dfrac{50,000}{2,400} = 20.8$ amp, approximately

(This method of calculating I_1 assumes that the transformer is ideal, containing neither resistance nor reactance, and that $I_0 = 0$. The value of I_1 obtained in this way is used only in calculating the copper loss and is sufficiently accurate for the purpose.)

Copper loss $= 208^2 \times 0.005 + 20.8^2 \times 0.5 = 433$ watts
Iron loss $= 300$ watts
Total loss $= 733$ watts
Output $= 50,000$ watts
Input $= 50,733$ watts
Efficiency $= 98.5$ per cent

b. $I_2 = \dfrac{5,000}{240} = 20.8$ amp   and $I_1 = \dfrac{5,000}{2,400} = 2.08$ amp, approximately

Copper loss $= 20.8^2 \times 0.005 + 2.08^2 \times 0.5 = 4.33$ watts
Iron loss $= 300$ watts
Total loss $= 304$ watts
Output $= 5,000$ watts
Input $= 5,304$ watts
Efficiency $= 94.4$ per cent

c. $I_2 = \dfrac{50,000}{240} = 208$ amp   and $I_1 = \dfrac{50,000}{2,400} = 20.8$ amp, approximately

Copper loss $= 208^2 \times 0.005 + 20.8^2 \times 0.5 = 433$ watts
Iron loss $= 300$ watts
Total loss $= 733$ watts
Output $= 40,000$ watts
Input $= 40,733$ watts
Efficiency $= 98.2$ per cent

d.   All-day efficiency $= \dfrac{40,000 \times 5}{40,000 \times 5 + 300 \times 24 + 433 \times 5}$

$= 95.5$ per cent

311. Equivalent Resistance and Reactance of a Transformer. The calculation of the voltage drop in a transformer may be considerably simplified by ignoring I_0 and replacing R_1, R_2, X_1, and X_2 by a single

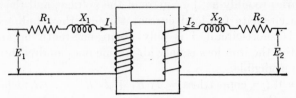

FIG. 298. Diagrammatic representation of a transformer.

equivalent resistance and reactance R_e and X_e that will give the same voltage drop.

If R_e and X_e are to be placed in the primary circuit, as shown in Fig. 299, then

$$R_e = R_1 + \left(\frac{n_1}{n_2}\right)^2 R_2 \tag{92}$$

and

$$X_e = X_1 + \left(\frac{n_1}{n_2}\right)^2 X_2 \tag{93}$$

That the foregoing equations are correct may be readily shown as follows: Let R_1' be the extra resistance that must be placed in the primary to give the same drop in E_2 that the resistance R_2 gave when placed in the secondary.

Then R_1' causes a voltage drop in the primary equal to I_1R_1' but all voltages applied to the primary winding produce secondary voltages equal to n_2/n_1 times those

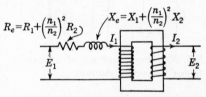

FIG. 299. The equivalent transformer.

primary voltages; therefore I_1R_1' causes a voltage drop in the secondary equal to $(n_2/n_1)I_1R_1'$, and this must be equal to the voltage drop originally caused by R_2 in the secondary. Therefore

$$\frac{n_2}{n_1} I_1R_1' = I_2R_2$$

and

$$R_1' = \frac{I_2}{I_1} \times \frac{n_1}{n_2} R_2 \quad \text{but } \frac{I_2}{I_1} = \frac{n_1}{n_2}$$

Therefore

$$R_1' = \left(\frac{n_1}{n_2}\right)^2 R_2$$

312. Short-circuit Test. The equivalent resistance and reactance are readily measured by means of a voltmeter, ammeter, and wattmeter, as shown in Fig. 300. The secondary is short-circuited and the voltage E_1

is adjusted until I_1 has its full-load value. Then I_2 also has its full-load value, since $I_2/I_1 = n_1/n_2$. There is no output; consequently the input is all loss, and this loss is almost entirely copper loss, because the iron loss varies roughly as the square of the voltage, and the value of E_1 required to circulate full-load current through the windings when the secondary is short-circuited is only about one-tenth normal voltage. Consequently, the iron loss is only about one one-hundredth normal and is therefore negligible.

Therefore W_s = copper loss = $I_1^2 R_1 + I_2^2 R_2 = I_1^2 R_e$; whence

$$R_e = \frac{W_s}{I_1^2} \tag{94}$$

Again, since the secondary is short-circuited, there is nothing opposing the flow of the primary current except R_e and X_e. Now

$$Z_e = \sqrt{R_e^2 + X_e^2}$$

and

$$Z_e = \frac{E_1}{I_1}$$

and

$$X_e = \sqrt{Z_e^2 - R_e^2} \tag{95}$$

One of the reasons for using equivalent reactance is that there is no way of measuring X_1 and X_2 separately.

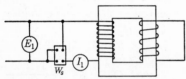

FIG. 300. Short-circuit test of a transformer (secondary shorted).

When making a short-circuit test, it is always the high-voltage winding that is used as the primary, while the low-voltage winding is shorted. If the measurement were made on the low-voltage winding, the voltage would be inconveniently low, while the current would often be inconveniently large. The equivalent resistance and reactance measured on the high-voltage side may be transferred to the low-voltage side by simply dividing their values by the square of the ratio of turns.

313. Equivalent Circuits of a Transformer. Problems concerning voltages and currents in transformers may be solved precisely by means of the vector diagram of Fig. 293, but this method is laborious, and therefore it is usual to substitute a simplified equivalent circuit in place of the transformer. The circuit shown in Fig. 301a may be made equivalent to any given transformer by assigning the proper values to R_0 and X_0 to make the current I_0 equal to the exciting current in both magnitude and phase angle. The resistance and reactance of the secondary winding have been transferred to the primary circuit as explained in Art. 311, and so has the load. If the load is expressed in kilovolt-amperes or kilowatts, it will not be affected by being transferred to the primary; but if it is expressed as an R and an X in series, then R and X must be multiplied by $(n_1/n_2)^2$ on transferring them to the primary. In any case the true secondary voltage $E_2 = E_2'(n_2/n_1)$, and the true secondary current $I_2 = I_1'(n_1/n_2)$.

The correct values of R_0 and X_0 are readily obtained from the open-circuit test. $I_0{}^2R_0$ must represent the iron loss; therefore

$$R_0 = \frac{\text{iron loss}}{I_0{}^2}$$

At no load, the difference between E_1 and E_1' is negligible. Therefore we may write $Z_0 = E_1/I_0$. Then

$$X_0 = \sqrt{Z_0{}^2 - R_0{}^2}$$

The so-called exact equivalent circuit of Fig. 301a may be simplified considerably by moving the R_0X_0 branch to the other side of R_1 and X_1,

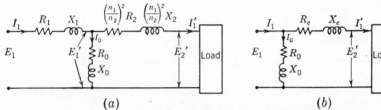

(a)   (b)

FIG. 301. (a) Equivalent circuit of a transformer. (b) Approximate equivalent circuit of a transformer.

as in Fig. 301b. In general, this introduces an error of from 1 to 3 per cent in I_0, but since I_0 is small compared with I_1, the resulting errors in the calculated values of I_1, I_1R_1, I_1X_1, and E_1 are negligible. R_1 and $(n_1/n_2)^2R_2$ may now be combined into the single resistance R_e, and X_1 and $(n_1/n_2)^2X_2$ may be combined into the single reactance X_e, to give the final simple equivalent circuit shown in Fig. 301b.

Example. A 50-kva 2,400- to 240-volt transformer gave the following readings on test:
Open-circuit test (Fig. 297):

$$\text{Iron loss} = 300 \text{ watts} \qquad E_1 = 240 \text{ volts} \qquad I_0 = 8 \text{ amp}$$

Short-circuit test (Fig. 300):

$$E_1 = 78 \text{ volts} \qquad I_1 = 20.8 \text{ amp} \qquad W_s = 433 \text{ watts}$$

1. Determine the equivalent circuit of Fig. 301b.
Solution. I_0 was measured on the low-voltage winding. If I_0 had been measured on the high-voltage winding, which happens to be the primary in this case, it would have been 0.8 amp, since the ratio is 10.

$$R_0 = \frac{\text{iron loss}}{I_0{}^2} = \frac{300}{0.8^2} = 469 \text{ ohms}$$

$$Z_0 = \frac{E_1}{I_0} = \frac{2,400}{0.8} = 3,000 \text{ ohms}$$

$$X_0 = \sqrt{Z_0{}^2 - R_0{}^2} = (3,000^2 - 469^2)^{\frac{1}{2}} = 2,960 \text{ ohms}$$

$$R_e = \frac{W_s}{I_1{}^2} = \frac{433}{20.8^2} = 1.00 \text{ ohm}$$

$$Z_e = \frac{E_1}{I_1} = \frac{78}{20.8} = 3.75 \text{ ohms}$$

$$X_e = \sqrt{Z_e{}^2 - R_e{}^2} = \sqrt{3.75^2 - 1} = 3.61 \text{ ohms}$$

2. If this transformer is carrying a load of 50 kva at 240 volts, 85 per cent power factor lagging, calculate the value of E_1 required to maintain E_2 at 240 volts and

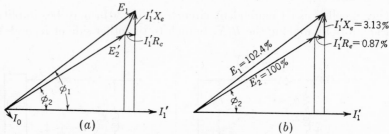

FIG. 302. (a) Vector diagram for the equivalent transformer circuit of Fig. 301b (not to scale). (b) Same diagram as (a) but with the values expressed in per cent.

also the power factor that would be measured at the input terminals of the transformer.

Solution. The vector diagram is shown in Fig. 302a. In the case of power transformers, the voltage ratio shown on the name plate is the same as the turns ratio. Therefore

$$E_2' = 240 \times 10 = 2,400 \text{ volts}$$
$$\phi_2 = \cos^{-1} 0.85 = 31°47'$$

$$I_1' = \frac{50,000}{2,400} = 20.8 \text{ amp}$$

$$I_1'R_e = 20.8 \times 1 = 20.8 \text{ volts}$$
$$I_1'X_e = 20.8 \times 3.61 = 75.1 \text{ volts}$$
$$\begin{aligned} E_1 &= [(E_2' \cos \phi_2 + I_1'R_e)^2 + (E_2' \sin \phi_2 + I_1'X_e)^2]^{\frac{1}{2}} \\ &= [(2,040 + 20.8)^2 + (1,264 + 75.1)^2]^{\frac{1}{2}} \\ &= (2,061^2 + 1,339^2)^{\frac{1}{2}} \\ &= 2,458 \text{ volts} \end{aligned}$$

$$\phi_1 = \cos^{-1} \frac{2,061}{2,458} = \cos^{-1} 0.838 = 33°0'$$

Ignoring the exciting current, the power factor measured at the input terminals of the transformer would be $\cos \phi_1 = 83.8$ per cent. If greater accuracy is desired in the determination of the power factor, it is necessary to take I_0 into consideration. $I_0 = E_1/Z_0$ and lags E_1 by the angle whose tangent is X_0/R_0.

Then I_1 is the vector sum of I_1' and I_0. If this is worked out, it will be found that I_0 lags E_1 by 81° and therefore lags I_1' by 48°. I_1 lags I_1' by 1°36', and the true input power factor is

$$\cos (33° + 1°36') = \cos 34°36' = 82.3\%$$

314. Reactance and Resistance in Per Cent. It has become common practice to express the equivalent reactance and resistance of a transformer in per cent. The reactance of a transformer is said to be 5 per cent if the full-load reactance voltage I_1X_e is equal to 5 per cent of the primary voltage, where X_e is the equivalent reactance in the primary circuit. For example, the per cent reactance and resistance of the transformer in Art. 313 are calculated as follows:

$$\text{Per cent reactance} = \frac{I_1X_e}{E_1} \times 100 = \frac{75.1}{2,400} \times 100 = 3.13$$
$$\text{Per cent resistance} = \frac{I_1R_e}{E_1} \times 100 = \frac{20.8}{2,400} \times 100 = 0.87$$

Of course the equivalent reactance and resistance may equally well be calculated to go in the secondary instead of in the primary. If X_e and R_e have been measured on the high-voltage side, as is usual, they may be transferred to the low-voltage side after multiplying each of them by $(n_2/n_1)^2$, where the subscript 2 refers to the low-voltage side. If this transfer of reactance is performed for the transformer in Art. 313, then X_e becomes $3.61/10^2 = 0.0361$ ohm. Now $I_2 = 10I_1 = 208$ amp, and

$$\text{Per cent reactance} = \frac{I_2X_e}{E_2} = 100 = \frac{208 \times 0.0361}{240} \times 100 = 3.13$$

as before.

One reason for expressing the equivalent reactance in per cent rather than in ohms is that when expressed in ohms it has two values, depending on whether it is placed in the primary or in the secondary, whereas when it is expressed in per cent it has only one value, any voltage drop in the primary being the same percentage of the primary voltage as the corresponding drop in the secondary is of the secondary voltage.

Per cent reactances and impedances are convenient for computing the currents that will flow in a transformer when the secondary is accidentally shorted. When the secondary is shorted, $I_1 = E_1/Z_e$, or $I_1Z_e = E_1$. Thus when the secondary is shorted, I_1Z_e is 100 per cent of E_1. Therefore the short-circuit current is given by the equation

$$\text{Short circuit } I_1 = \frac{100}{\text{per cent impedance}} \times \text{full load } I_1 \qquad (96)$$

Unless the transformer is quite small, R_e is negligible in Eq. (95), and per cent reactance may be substituted for per cent impedance in Eq. (96).

314A. Voltage Regulation. The voltage regulation of a transformer may be calculated either as the change in secondary voltage from no load to full load, expressed as a per cent of rated secondary voltage, with the primary voltage assumed constant, or as the change in primary voltage required to keep the secondary voltage constant from no load to full load, expressed as a per cent of rated primary voltage. The power factor of the load must always be specified when stating the voltage regulation because it varies widely with the power factor.

FIG. 303. Three-phase forced-air-cooled transformer, 66,000 kva, 215,000/60,000/12,000 volts. (*Courtesy of General Electric Co.*)

The equivalent transformer circuit of Fig. 301*b* and its vector diagram, Fig. 302*b*, are used to calculate the voltage regulation. At no load, $I_1' = 0$, the $I_1'Z_e$ drop is zero, and $E_1 = E_2'$. At full load, if E_2' is to remain constant, E_1 must be increased to be the vector sum of E_2' and $I_1'Z_e$. The arithmetical increase in E_1, expressed as a per cent of the rated E_1, is the per cent regulation. Therefore

$$\text{Voltage regulation} = \frac{E_1 - E_2'}{E_2'} \times 100\%$$

Example. A certain transformer has 3.13 per cent reactance and 0.87 per cent resistance. Calculate the voltage regulation with an 85 per cent power factor lagging load.

From Fig. 302b,

$$E_1 = [(E_2' \cos \phi_2 + I_1'R_e)^2 + (E_2' \sin \phi_2 + I_1'X_e)^2]^{1/2}$$
$$= [(100 \times 0.85 + 0.87)^2 + (100 \times 0.527 + 3.13)^2]^{1/2}$$
$$= 102.4$$

and   Voltage regulation = 102.4 − 100 = 2.4%

315. Cooling of Transformers.   Transformers become heated up owing to the losses.   This heat must be dissipated and the temperature of the

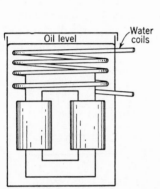

FIG. 304. Diagrammatic representation of a water-cooled transformer.

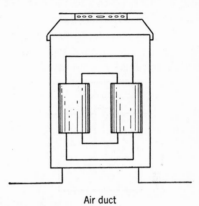

FIG. 305. Diagrammatic representation of an air-blast transformer.

transformer windings kept below the value at which the insulation begins to deteriorate.   Small low-voltage transformers can dissipate their heat by direct radiation.   Transformers for voltages over 600 volts are usually placed in steel tanks, which are then filled with insulating oil, or, if the fire hazard of the oil is not otherwise taken care of, with more expensive noninflammable liquids such as pyranol or inerteen.   The oil improves the insulation, and convection currents are set up in the oil by means of which the heat is carried away from the surfaces of the transformer windings and core.   It then becomes necessary to provide means for removing the heat from the oil.   For ratings up to 500 kva, corrugating the walls of

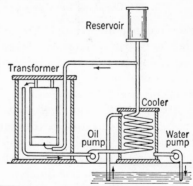

FIG. 306. Method of cooling a transformer by circulating the oil.

the tank provides sufficient radiating surface to cool the oil.   For ratings above 500 kva, there are three methods of cooling the oil:

1. The tank may be equipped with external radiators, as in Fig. 303,

in which case the rating may be considerably increased by providing fans to blow air against the radiators.

2. The oil may be cooled by circulating cold water through coils of copper tubing immersed in the oil above the transformer, as in Fig. 304.

3. The oil may be circulated through an external cooler by means of a pump, as in Fig. 306.

Method 2 was used quite extensively in the United States at one time, and is still used to some extent for large transformers, if water of suitable quality is readily available, but method 1 is in more general use.

The air-blast type of transformer is shown in Fig. 305. The transformer is well supplied with ducts so that the air can reach the points at which the heat is generated. One hundred and fifty cubic feet of air is

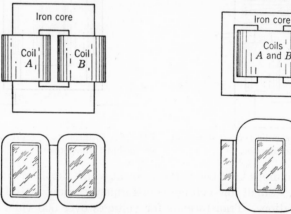

FIG. 307. Core-type transformer.

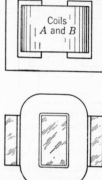

FIG. 308. Shell-type transformer.

required per minute per kilowatt loss. This type of transformer was developed partly in order to avoid the fire hazard of transformer oil, and partly to avoid the weight of the oil and the tank, for applications where weight is of special importance. Very few new installations of air-blast transformers are being made at the present time.

316. Core-type and Shell-type Transformers. The transformer shown in Fig. 307 is said to be of the core type. If coil B is removed and added to coil A, and if half of the iron core of coil B is moved around to the other side of coil A, as in Fig. 308, the resulting transformer is said to be of the shell type. The difference between the two types is shown more strikingly in Figs. 309 and 310. In general, the shell-type design is more economical for low-voltage transformers, while the core-type design is more economical for high voltage. However, the dividing line between the voltage ranges of the two types rises rapidly with the kva rating. Shell-type transformers have been built in large sizes for voltages up to 230 kv.

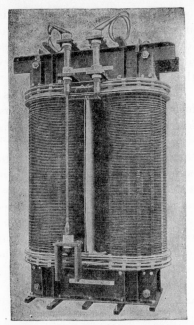

FIG. 309. Assembled core and coils for a single-phase core-type transformer, 16,667 kva, 110,000 volts, 60 cycles.

FIG. 310. Assembled core and coils for a single-phase shell-type transformer, 4,500 kva.

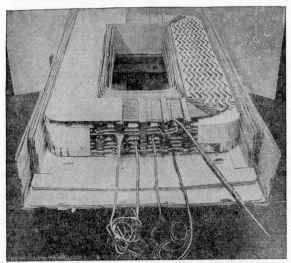

FIG. 311. A partially assembled high-voltage coil group for a large shell-type transformer showing the wavy strips that separate the pancake coils and provide channels through which the oil circulates to cool the coils. This particular coil group contains eight pancake coils.

The iron cores are built up of thin sheets of silicon steel, an alloy of iron usually containing 4 to 5 per cent silicon. The usual thickness of the sheets is 0.014 in. The silicon reduces the hysteresis loss and also increases the resistance of the iron, thus reducing the eddy currents.

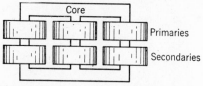

FIG. 312. Three-phase core-type transformer.

316A. Three-phase Transformers. A three-phase transformer consists essentially of three single-phase transformers with their three cores united into a single core assembly, as in Figs. 312 and 313. For three-phase circuits, there is a considerable saving in both cost and floor space when a three-phase transformer is used instead of three single-phase transformers, each in its own tank. The principal disadvantages of the three-phase transformer are that a breakdown in the winding of one phase puts the whole transformer out of commission, and also the repair job is more expensive.

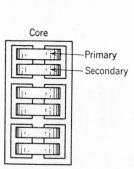

FIG. 313. Three-phase shell-type transformer.

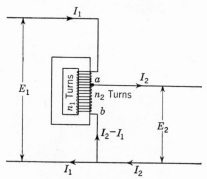

FIG. 314. Autotransformer.

317. The Autotransformer. If a reactance coil is placed across an a-c line, as shown in Fig. 314, the voltage E_2 obtained by tapping the coil as shown may have any value less than E_1, and, as in the ordinary transformer,

$$\frac{E_1}{E_2} = \frac{n_1}{n_2} = \frac{I_2}{I_1}$$

Since the primary and secondary currents oppose one another, the current in the section ab is the difference between the currents I_1 and I_2.

When the transformation ratio is comparatively small, the autotransformer, as this tapped reactance coil is called, is cheaper than the equivalent transformer with separate windings.

For example, consider the case where the ratio is 2, and where $I_2 = 100$ amp. Then $I_1 = 50$ amp, and the current in ab, the common part of the winding, is the difference between 50 and 100, which is 50 amp. Thus the current in both parts of the winding is 50 amp. If now we provide a separate secondary, the primary will still be carrying 50 amp, the only difference being that the 50 amp will now be flowing in the same direction throughout the entire primary, instead of being reversed in the lower part as it was before. The secondary winding which must carry 100 amp will be wound with a conductor having twice the cross section of the primary conductor but only half the length. Thus the secondary will have the same weight as the primary. Therefore, when the ratio is 2, changing from a two-winding transformer to an autotransformer effects a saving of 50 per cent in the amount of copper required, and also in the I^2R loss in that copper. For all ratios other than 2, the currents in the two parts of the winding of an autotransformer are unequal, and therefore the cross sections of the conductors are unequal. The saving decreases rapidly as the ratio is increased beyond 2.

Autotransformers are used extensively for ratios ranging from 1 to 2.5, particularly for reducing the voltage applied to a-c motors during the starting period.

318. Transformer Voltage Control. Transformers are usually provided with taps on one of the windings, so that the number of active turns on that winding can be varied. In order to change the tap, it is often necessary to take the transformer out of service and to remove the cover of the tank, and in that case the voltage adjustment is of rather a permanent nature. However, transformers may be obtained equipped with a switching device for changing taps without interrupting the load. The device is complicated by the requirement that it must make contact with the new tap before breaking contact with the old tap, and yet must not short-circuit the turns between the two taps. The basic principle

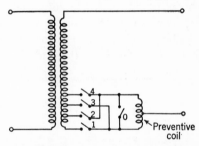

FIG. 315. Mechanism for changing taps on a transformer without interrupting the load.

of the tap-changing mechanism is shown in Fig. 315. A coil is practically noninductive to any current that enters at its center tap and divides equally each way. In normal operation switch 0 is always closed, and also one other switch. The maximum number of turns is obtained with switch 1 closed. When changing to tap 2, the sequence of switching operations is as follows: (1) open switch 0; (2) close switch 2; (3) open switch 1; (4) close switch 0.

The tap-changing mechanism is usually applied to the low-voltage winding, because of insulation difficulties at high voltages. Reducing the primary turns has the same effect on the secondary voltage as increasing the secondary turns. When neither voltage is really high, it will often be less expensive to place the tap-changing mechanism on the high-voltage winding, because of the smaller currents to be handled.

The **variac** is an autotransformer with an almost continuously variable ratio. It consists of a single-layer winding on a toroidal iron core. The tap changer is simply a carbon brush that rubs directly on the winding and so varies the ratio one turn at a time. The emf per turn is so low that it is possible to short a turn by means of a carbon brush without obtaining excessive current in the shorted turn. Variacs are made in sizes up to 40 amp at 115 volts or 20 amp at 230 volts.

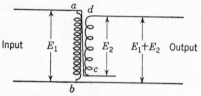

FIG. 316. Boosting transformer.

Boosting Transformer. If the voltage required is greater than that available on the highest-voltage tap of the transformer, the voltage may be raised by a small amount if a standard transformer is connected as shown in Fig. 316. The voltage of the line is boosted by the amount of the secondary voltage E_2.

When the secondary side of the transformer is tapped so that the boosting effect can be adjusted, the resulting piece of apparatus is the Stillwell feeder regulator. It is used to raise the feeder voltage above that of the powerhouse, so as to compensate for the voltage drop in the feeder and maintain the voltage at the load.

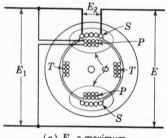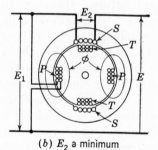

(a) E_2 a maximum   (b) E_2 a minimum

FIG. 317. Cross sections through a single-phase induction voltage regulator. PP = primary coil; SS = secondary coil; TT = tertiary coil.

Induction Voltage Regulator. A type of voltage regulator that gives a smooth continuous variation in voltage is shown in Fig. 317. It resembles a motor in that it consists of a stator and a rotor. The secondary coil is mounted on the stator. The primary coil is mounted on the rotor and produces a flux ϕ, part of which links with the secondary and induces the voltage E_2. The fraction of the flux ϕ that links with the secondary can be varied by turning the rotor. In the position shown in Fig. 317a, practically all the flux links with the secondary and E_2 is a maximum.

Figure 317*b* shows the rotor turned through 90°, in which position none of the flux ϕ links with the secondary. If the rotor is turned on through another 90°, E_2 will again be a maximum, but reversed in phase. Therefore by turning the rotor through 180°, E can be varied from $E_1 + E_2$ to $E_1 - E_2$.

The function of the tertiary coil TT is to reduce the leakage reactance of the secondary coil when the rotor is in the neighborhood of the position shown in Fig. 317*b*. If the tertiary coil were not present, the secondary SS would surround itself with a large flux, and the reactance drop would be very large. The tertiary coil, which is not connected to anything but is short-circuited, links with this flux, with the result that a large current is induced in the tertiary winding. This current opposes and greatly reduces the flux that produces it and hence greatly reduces the IX drop in the secondary. In Fig. 317*a* the tertiary coil is cutting no flux and carrying no current. It is not needed in this position because the primary and secondary are so close together that the leakage fluxes are small.

The induction voltage regulator is often arranged for automatic operation, in which case a small motor turns the rotor shaft slowly through a worm drive. The motor is started in either direction and stopped by means of a double-contact relay, which operates whenever the voltage E deviates from the desired value by more than a specified amount.

319. Induction Furnace. An electric furnace which operates as a transformer is shown diagrammatically in Fig. 318 and is called an

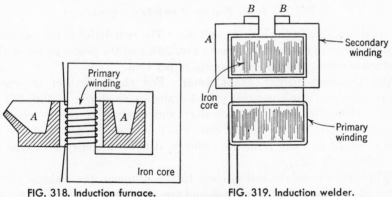

FIG. 318. Induction furnace.   FIG. 319. Induction welder.

induction furnace, the secondary winding in this case being the charge which is contained in the annular channel A and is heated by the secondary current. The amount of energy put into the secondary can be varied by varying the applied primary voltage.

Figure 319 shows diagrammatically an electric welder that operates on the same principle. The single turn A in this case is open and is closed by the two pieces to be welded. These pieces are held in the clamps B

and are forced together under pressure while the welding current passes across the contact and heats the ends to be joined.

It might seem that, since the secondary load in this case is a resistance load, the power factor of the transformer would be high at full load, and yet in practice it seldom exceeds 70 per cent. This is due to the fact that the distance between the primary and secondary windings cannot be made small, so that the leakage reactances are large.

The vector diagram for an induction furnace is shown in Fig. 320. The secondary winding is short-circuited since it consists of a ring of molten metal, so that E_2 the terminal voltage, is zero, and the secondary generated voltage E_{2g} is therefore made up of the two components I_2R_2 and I_2X_2, where R_2 is the resistance of the ring of molten metal and X_2

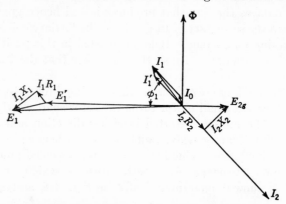

FIG. 320. Vector diagram of an induction furnace.

its reactance due to the leakage flux ϕ_{2l}. The remainder of this diagram is determined in the same way as in Fig. 293, and the power factor of the furnace is cos ϕ_1 and seldom exceeds 70 per cent.

320. Constant-current Transformer. For the operation of street lamps in series, the constant-current transformer shown in Fig. 321 is used. The primary coil is stationary and receives power at constant potential, while the secondary coil, which is suspended and is free to move toward or away from the primary, delivers a constant current to the lighting circuit.

When the secondary coil is close to the primary, the leakage reactances of the transformer are small and the secondary voltage is approximately equal to the primary voltage multiplied by the ratio of the number of turns. As the distance between the coils is increased, the leakage flux and the reactances increase and the secondary voltage drops, although the primary voltage remains constant.

The primary and the secondary currents are opposite in direction and, under these conditions, the primary and the secondary coils repel one another. The counterweight on the secondary coil is so adjusted that, when the desired current is flowing in this coil, the force of repulsion keeps the secondary coil suspended. If then some of the lamps in the circuit are cut out, the current tends to increase, but any increase in the current destroys the balance and the secondary coil rises until the current returns to its previous value, thus restoring the balance. The over-all power factor is high when the coils are close together but decreases as the distance between the coils is increased.

321. Saturable Reactor. The flow of alternating current to a load may be readily controlled by inserting a variable reactance in the line. One of the easiest ways to vary the reactance of an iron-cored coil is to superimpose a variable d-c component of magnetic flux in the iron core by means of a separate d-c control winding, as in Fig. 322. The polarities of the a-c coils are made such that the flux produced by them does not pass through the d-c control winding. The number of a-c turns and the cross section of the iron may be so chosen, by means of Eq. (86),

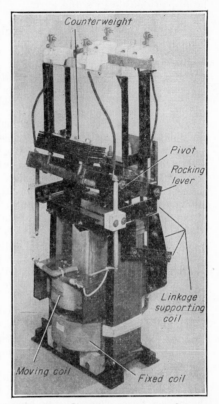

FIG. 321. Constant-current transformer.
(Courtesy of Westinghouse Electric Co.)

that the a-c supply voltage E will not saturate the iron, even if the load is short-circuited. Then when the d-c control current is zero, very little

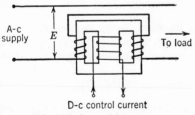

D-c control current
FIG. 322. Saturable reactor.

current will flow to the load, because the reactance of the a-c winding will be high. The application of a d-c current to the control winding superimposes a d-c flux in the iron cores of the a-c coils, and if the combined fluxes take the iron beyond the knee of the saturation curve, the a-c current will increase. If sufficient d-c current could be applied to produce complete saturation, the reactance of the a-c winding would be nearly zero. It should be noted, however, that this method of varying the reactance results in the alternating current being distorted very considerably from a sine curve, and this might be objectionable in some cases.

Problems

*31-1. Prove that the effective value of the secondary voltage of a transformer is given by

$$E_2 = 4.44fn_2\Phi_m10^{-8} \qquad \text{volts}$$

where n_2 is the number of secondary turns, Φ_m is the maximum value of the flux, and f is the frequency.

31-2. A 15-kva 2,400- to 240-volt 60-cycle lighting transformer has a cross-sectional core area of 10 sq in., of which 90 per cent is iron and 10 per cent is varnish. There are 1,440 turns on the primary winding. How many secondary turns are there? Find the flux through the core. Is this an average, effective or maximum value? What is the maximum flux density? How many ampere-turns per inch are required to produce the flux? (Use sheet-steel curve of Fig. 41 of text.) What will be the peak value of the no-load primary current if the length of the magnetic circuit is 40 in.? What percentage of full-load current is this?

*31-3. Why does the primary current increase as the impedance of the load circuit connected to the secondary is decreased?

31-4. What is meant by the leakage reactance of a transformer and why is it reasonable to assume that it is constant if the frequency is constant?

*31-5. What is meant by iron loss (or core loss) of a transformer? How does it vary with the load, and why?

*31-6. How would you measure the core loss of a transformer? Give diagram of connections and indicate the necessary readings to be taken.

*31-7. Upon what does the hysteresis loss of a transformer depend? Upon what does the eddy-current loss depend? Discuss how each of these losses may be kept down to a small value.

31-8. How does the flux through the magnetic circuit of a constant-voltage transformer vary with increase of load current from zero to full load? How do the leakage fluxes change during the same time?

31-9. A transformer has twice as many secondary turns as primary turns.

a. The primary resistance is equal to 0.3 ohm; the primary reactance is equal to 0.9 ohm; the secondary resistance is equal to 1.2 ohms; the secondary reactance is equal to 3.6 ohms. The transformer on no load takes 10 amp and 1,000 watts at 200 volts. Draw the vector diagram to scale for no-load conditions. These values are somewhat greater than in an actual transformer in order to give appreciable values for a vector diagram.

b. The load on the secondary is 50 amp at 400 volts and 80 per cent power factor lagging. Draw the complete vector diagram, assuming that $I_0 = 10$, and find the applied voltage and the primary current and power factor by scaling from the diagram.

c. Give in tabulated form the order in which you drew the vectors and the reasons for their directions and magnitudes.

d. Is the voltage regulation better or worse at 60 per cent than at 80 per cent power factor lagging? Draw an actual vector diagram for each case if you are not certain.

31-10. A 1,500-kva 63,500- to 13,200-volt 25-cycle transformer has a core loss of 20 kw. The primary resistance is equal to 16.2 ohms and the secondary resistance is equal to 0.53 ohm.   Find the efficiency of the transformer at full-load current, unity power factor.   What will it be at full-load current, 80 per cent power factor?   If this transformer is operated at full load and 100 per cent power factor for only 6 hr per day but is left connected to the line all day, what is its all-day or energy efficiency?

31-11. Is it safe to short-circuit a transformer?   What are the percentage resistance and reactance drops in the transformer of Prob. 31-9?

31-12. A welding transformer that operates from a 110-volt supply has 275 turns on the primary and a 1-turn secondary.   If the current taken from the line is 10 amp, approximately how much current is flowing in the secondary circuit, and at approximately what induced voltage?

***31-13.** What is the purpose of the constant-current transformer?   Explain its principle of operation.   How does it differ from the constant potential transformer?

31-14. Can a transformer designed for 60 cycles be used on 25 cycles and, if so, on what conditions?   How about using a 25-cycle transformer on 60 cycles?

31-15. The cross section of the iron core of a transformer is 4 in. by 4 in., and of this area 90 per cent is iron and 10 per cent is varnish or space.   The maximum allowable flux density is 75,000 lines per sq in. of iron.

a. How many primary and secondary turns are required if the transformer is to be rated 2,200 to 220 volts, 60 cycles?

b. If the transformer were being wound for 25 cycles, how many turns would be required?

c. If the cross section of the iron is doubled, how does this affect the number of turns required?

31-16. A 100-kva 2,200- to 220-volt transformer, on test, with connections as in Fig. 300, and with full-load current circulating in the windings, gave the following readings: $E_1 = 85$ volts; $W_s = 750$ watts.   Determine the equivalent resistance and reactance, and calculate the voltage regulation of the transformer with

a. 100 per cent power-factor load.

b. 50 per cent power-factor load, lagging.

c. 50 per cent power-factor load, leading.

d. Plot a graph of the voltage regulation on a power factor of load base from zero power factor leading to 100 per cent to zero power factor lagging.

31-17. The transformer in the preceding problem has an iron loss of 580 watts at rated voltage.   Calculate the full-load and one-tenth load efficiencies at 100 per cent and 50 per cent power factor.   Ignore the exciting current I_0 in calculating the copper loss.

31-18. An autotransformer is used to reduce the voltage of a line from 550 to 350 volts for motor starting.   If the secondary current is 80 amp, what are the currents in the two sections of the winding?

32

TRANSFORMER CONNECTIONS

322. Polarity of Transformers. A high-voltage winding terminal H_1 and a low-voltage winding terminal X_1 of a transformer are said to have the same polarity if the current entering the transformer at H_1 is approximately in phase with the current leaving the transformer at X_1. The word *approximately* is required because of the existence of the exciting current I_0, which flows only in the primary winding. The transformers

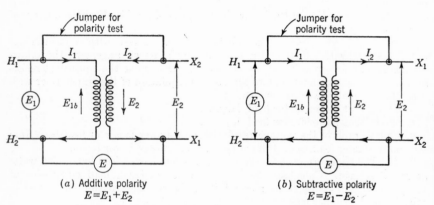

(a) Additive polarity
$E=E_1+E_2$

(b) Subtractive polarity
$E=E_1-E_2$

FIG. 323. Polarity test and terminal markings for transformers.

in Fig. 323 are shown undergoing a polarity test. The procedure is to jumper the two adjacent high-voltage and low-voltage terminals together, as in Fig. 323a and b, to connect a voltmeter E across the remaining two terminals, and to apply a convenient value of alternating voltage E_1, usually 115 volts, to the high-voltage winding. If the reading of the voltmeter is $E = E_1 - E_2$, the polarity is said to be *subtractive*, and the markings H_1, H_2, X_1, and X_2 are applied to the terminals, as shown in Fig. 323b. But if $E = E_1 + E_2$, the polarity is said to be *additive*, and the markings are then applied as in Fig. 323a. It is not necessary to measure E_2. It is only necessary to note whether E is larger or smaller than E_1.

The polarity of a transformer is merely a matter of the arrangement of the terminals, and it can be changed by crossing either the high-voltage or the low-voltage leads inside the tank. Polarity markings are very useful when connecting transformers into three-phase banks.

323. Single-phase Distribution Transformers. The transformers that serve residential and commercial areas generally transform from 2,300 to

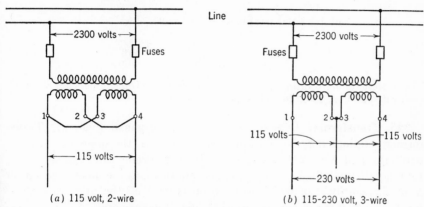

(a) 115 volt, 2-wire   (b) 115-230 volt, 3-wire

FIG. 324. Single-phase transformer connections.

115 or 120 volts. The secondary winding consists of two coils, each wound for 115 volts. These two coils may be connected either in parallel to provide a two-wire 115-volt supply, Fig. 324a, or in series to provide a three-wire 115- and 230-volt supply, Fig. 324b. If only the 230-volt supply is required, the middle wire of the three-wire system is omitted.

If a mistake is made in polarity when connecting the two secondary coils in parallel, Fig. 324a, so that 1 is jumpered to 4 and 2 to 3, the result will be a short-circuited secondary which will blow the fuses that are located on the high-voltage side. A mistake in polarity when connecting the coils in series, Fig. 324b, will result in the voltage across the outer conductors being zero instead of 230 volts.

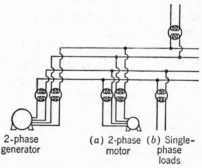

2-phase generator   (a) 2-phase motor   (b) Single-phase loads

FIG. 325. Connection of transformers to a two-phase line.

Taps for voltage adjustment, if provided, are located on the 2,300-volt winding.

324. Connections to a Two-phase Line. Figure 325a shows the method of transforming from high-voltage two-phase to low-voltage two-phase, for the operation of motors.

Example. Determine the rating of the transformers required for a 440-volt two-phase motor that delivers 50 hp with an efficiency of 90 per cent. The power factor of the motor is 88 per cent, and the line voltage is 2,300.

$$\text{Motor output} = 50 \text{ hp}$$
$$= 50 \times 0.746 = 37.3 \text{ kw}$$
$$\text{Motor input} = \frac{37.3}{0.9} = 41.4 \text{ kw}$$
$$\text{Motor input per phase} = \frac{41.4}{2} = 20.7 \text{ kw}$$
$$= \frac{20.7}{0.88} = 23.5 \text{ kva}$$

The nearest standard rating is 25 kva. Therefore two transformers are required, each rated 25 kva, 2,300 to 440 volts.

325. Transformer Connections to a Three-phase System. Transformer windings may be connected either Y or Δ, the same as generator windings, and Arts. 281 to 286 apply to transformer windings as well as to generator windings. Since the secondaries may be connected either Y or Δ, regardless of which connection is used on the primaries, there must be four ways of connecting the three transformers to form a three-phase bank, namely, Y-Y, Δ-Δ, Y-Δ, Δ-Y.

326. The Y-Y Transformer Connection. Figure 326 shows three transformers connected Y-Y on a typical three-phase four-wire system. This particular system provides a 208-volt three-phase supply for three-phase motors, and a 120-volt supply for lamps and other small single-phase loads, each of these loads being connected between the neutral N and any one of the three line or phase conductors a, b, or c. An attempt is made of course to distribute the single-phase loads resonably equally among the three phases.

The line voltage, which is the voltage between phase conductors a, b, and c, is $\sqrt{3}$ times the voltage of each phase conductor to neutral, that is $\sqrt{3}$ times the voltage across each individual transformer winding. The individual transformers are rated 2,300 to 120 volts.

As regards polarities, Fig. 326 shows one arrangement of the connections that will produce a set of balanced three-phase secondary voltages, but there is at least one other arrangement that will produce a similar result, because the three low-voltage terminals, $X_1 X_1 X_1$, can be connected to the neutral instead of the X_2 terminals, thus reversing all three secondary windings and all three secondary voltages. This is equivalent to turning the Y-shaped vector diagram upside down, which does not affect its operation in any way, except that it cannot operate in parallel with another transformer bank that has not been inverted. It may also be possible to make a similar interchange of terminals on the high-voltage side. That will depend upon whether the transformers are provided with two high-voltage bushing-type insulators, or only one. A transformer that is designed to be used only on systems with grounded neutrals is often provided with only one high-voltage bushing, and in that case the other terminal must be connected to neutral.

The Y-Y transformer connection can also be used on a three-wire three-phase system, but its use on a three-wire system is considered undesirable. Owing to the fact that the saturation curve is not a straight line, it follows that if a sine-wave emf is impressed on a transformer winding the graph of the exciting current cannot be a sine curve. Consequently, the three exciting currents, although equal and at 120° to each other,

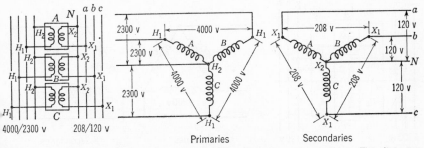

FIG. 326. Transformers connected Y-Y on a three-phase four-wire system. The diagram on the left is the plan of a typical arrangement. The diagram on the right shows the same connections, but the windings have been moved so as to make them form the vector diagrams of the voltages.

do not add up to zero, and therefore the neutral is needed to carry the resultant current. If the neutral is omitted, the three exciting currents are forced to add up to zero, but then the graph of the flux cannot be a sine curve, and therefore the voltages are distorted from the sine-wave form.

327. The Δ-Δ Transformer Connection. Figure 327 shows the transformers of Fig. 326 reconnected Δ-Δ. The line voltages are now simply the voltages across the individual transformer windings, and there is no visible neutral. A visible neutral can be created by Y-connecting three equal resistances, inductances, or capacitances to the three line conductors a, b, and c. The voltage between each line conductor and this neutral will then be $120/\sqrt{3}$ volts. Note that it was necessary to reduce the line voltage on the primary side from 4,000 to 2,300 volts when changing the primary transformer connections from Y to Δ. If the line voltage were not reduced the voltage impressed on the primary of each transformer would be $\sqrt{3}$ times the voltage rating of the transformer, and the resulting excessive exciting current and iron loss would soon overheat the transformer.

If the loads are balanced the line currents are $\sqrt{3}$ times the currents in the individual transformer windings, as explained in Art. 286.

As regards polarities, there are four different symmetrical arrangements of the connections that will produce a set of balanced three-phase secondary voltages. Figure 327 shows one of these arrangements; another can be obtained by reversing all six windings; a third can be obtained by reversing the three primary windings only; and a fourth by reversing the secondary windings only. If the transformer bank is to operate in parallel with an existing bank, only two of these arrangements will be correct, because the third and fourth arrangements produce secondary voltages that are in the opposite direction to those obtained

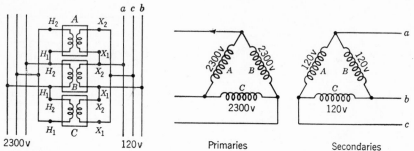

FIG. 327. Transformers connected Δ-Δ. The diagram on the left is the plan of a typical arrangement. The diagram on the right shows the same connections, but the windings have been moved so as to make them form the vector diagrams of the voltages.

with the first and second arrangements. If, however, the bank is to operate alone all four arrangements will supply the same service equally well. There are also three mechanically unsymmetrical arrangements that will produce the desired result, because both windings of any one transformer can be reversed simultaneously without altering the output voltages in any way, but anyone who uses unsymmetrical arrangements is deliberately doing it the hard way.

328. The Y-Δ Transformer Connection. Figure 328 shows the transformers of Fig. 326 with the secondaries reconnected Δ. The primary supply may be either three-wire or four-wire. In the case of the Y-Y connection it was stated that omitting the neutral on the primary side would cause the voltages to be distorted from the sine-wave form. In the case of the Y-Δ connection, if the neutral is omitted on the primary side the wave form of the voltage tends to distort, but this distortion causes currents to circulate in the Δ, and these currents act as magnetizing currents to correct the distortion. Therefore there is no objection to omitting the neutral. A detailed explanation of this action is outside the scope of this book.

Note that with the Y-Δ connection the voltage-transformation ratio of the bank is $\sqrt{3}$ times the voltage-transformation ratio of the individual transformers.   Each transformer is rated 2,300 to 120 volts, but the ratio of the line voltages is 4,000 to 120 volts.

With both the Y-Y and the Δ-Δ connections the line voltages on the secondaries are in phase with the line voltages on the primaries, but with the Y-Δ or Δ-Y connections the line voltages on the secondaries are at 30° to the line voltages on the primaries.   Consequently a Y-Δ or Δ-Y bank cannot be operated in parallel with a Δ-Δ or Y-Y bank.

As regards polarities, if the transformers are designed to be operated on a grounded-neutral system there are only two possible arrangements. All three Δ-connected windings may be reversed, but the Y-connected windings must not be reversed.   If, however, the transformers are

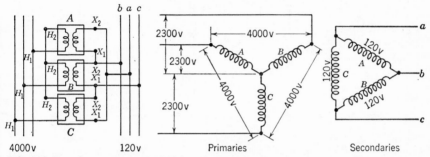

FIG. 328. Transformers connected Y-Δ.   The diagram on the left is the plan of a typical arrangement.   The diagram on the right shows the same connections, but the windings have been moved so as to make them form the vector diagrams of the voltages.

designed to be operated on an ungrounded system, then the Y-connected windings may also be reversed, giving four possible symmetrical arrangements.   If the transformer bank is to operate in parallel with an existing bank, the number of possible arrangements is reduced by one-half, because then it is not sufficient that the secondary voltages are equal and at 120° to each other; they must also be in phase with the secondary voltages of the existing bank.

329. Open-Δ, or V, Connection.   In a Δ connection the voltage of any one phase at any instant is equal and opposite to the sum of the instantaneous voltages in the two other phases, so that if, in Fig. 329, one transformer A of a bank of Δ-connected transformers is disconnected, the difference of potential between a and b is unchanged, being maintained by the transformers B and C in series, so that three-phase power can still be obtained from the lines a, b, and c.   This connection is called the V, or open-Δ, connection.

In Fig. 329, Δ-Δ connection (upper diagram), if the rated full-load secondary current of each transformer is I amp, then the full-load line current $I_l = \sqrt{3}\,I$ amp, being the vector difference of two currents which are each equal to I and which are 120° out of phase with each other (Art. 286).

The kilovolt-ampere rating of each transformer is $EI/1,000$ kva.

The total power transmitted by the line is $\sqrt{3}\,EI_l\cos\phi$ (Art. 286). But $I_l = \sqrt{3}\,I$ and therefore the kilovolt-ampere rating of the bank of three transformers is $\sqrt{3}\,EI_l/1,000 = 3EI/1,000$ kva = three times the rating of one transformer.

Now if one transformer is removed from the bank, each remaining transformer is still able to carry only its rated full-load current I, but

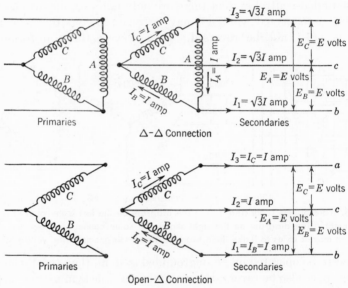

FIG. 329. Δ-Δ and open-Δ transformer connections.

the line current is now the current from a single transformer winding. Consequently, removing one transformer from the bank reduces the full-load current from $\sqrt{3}\,I$ to I amp, which is a reduction of 42.3 per cent instead of 33⅓ per cent as might be expected.

For example, if three transformers, each rated 33⅓ kva, are connected to form a closed-Δ bank, the rating of the bank is 100 kva; but if one of these transformers is removed, the rating of the resulting open-Δ bank is not 66⅔ kva but 57.7 kva. Thus when transformers are connected open Δ, the rating of the bank is approximately 13.4 per cent less than the sum of the individual ratings of the transformers. The reason for the loss of capacity is that transformers B and C must carry the current of the missing transformer A in addition to their own currents, and, since I_A is not in phase with either I_B or I_C, it follows that I_B and I_C are shifted in phase by removing transformer A. As a matter of fact, I_B

is shifted 30 deg in one direction and I_C 30° in the other direction.   Consequently, if the power factor of the load is 100 per cent, the transformers themselves are operating at cos 30°, that is, at 86.6 per cent power factor.   If the load power factor is 86.6 per cent, one transformer will be operating at 100 per cent and the other at 50 per cent.

This also explains how it is possible for I_2 to have different values in the two diagrams of Fig. 329, although in both it is the vector difference of I_B and I_C, and in both I_B and I_C have the same value, I amp.   In the closed Δ, I_B and I_C are 120° apart and their vector difference is $\sqrt{3}\ I$, but in the open Δ, I_B and I_C are only 60° apart and their vector difference is I.

The open-Δ connection is very extensively used on distribution systems.   There is usually a continuous growth of the power load on these systems and the capacity of the transformer banks must be increased from time to time.   It is not economical to install a bank whose capacity is very much in excess of the peak load.   What is done, therefore, is to install two transformers initially, connecting them open Δ and making them large enough to take care of the expected growth for the next 3 or 4 years.   Then when the load eventually exceeds the capacity of the bank, a third transformer is added to close the Δ.

330. Relative Advantages of the Y and Δ Connections.   The advantage of the Y connection is that it provides a neutral, which may be grounded.   If the neutral is solidly grounded, then the voltage between each conductor and ground is only $1/\sqrt{3}$ of the voltage between wires, and the cost of the insulation, on high-voltage lines, is considerably less than if the line had to be insulated for the full line voltage.   The transformers also are insulated for only $1/\sqrt{3}$ of the line voltage.   Transformers on high-voltage lines are accordingly generally connected Y on the high-voltage side, though they are generally connected Δ on the low-voltage side.

The advantages of the Δ connection are:

1. That the bank can originally be installed open Δ, thus saving the interest and depreciation on one transformer during the years while the load is small enough to be carried by two transformers.

2. That in the event of the failure of one transformer of a closed-Δ bank the two other transformers may remain in service, operating open Δ, and thus maintain the continuity of the service.

3. That transformers which are originally connected Δ-Δ at both ends of a transmission line may subsequently be reconnected Y on the line side, thus raising the line voltage by 73 per cent and increasing the amount of power that can be transmitted over the line.

With the three-wire three-phase system, which is the one generally used for transmission lines, the Y-connected bank acts as a unit and the entire bank must be taken out of service if one of the transformers fails, but with the four-wire system the other two transformers may remain in service.

From the foregoing brief summary it would appear that Y-connected transformer banks would be met with only on high-voltage lines or on lines where the connections had been changed from Δ to Y in order to raise the line voltage, and in general that is the case. For example, city

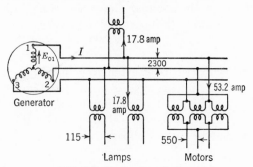

FIG. 330. Connection diagram.

distribution was at one time almost entirely three-phase, three-wire, 2,200 volts, with transformer banks Δ-Δ connected, but now in many cities these same transformers have been reconnected Y to operate on a line voltage of 4,000 volts, thus increasing the capacity of the distribution circuits. The secondaries are still delivering 115 to 120 volts to the lighting circuits. Since most of the city distribution load is single-phase, it was necessary to string in the neutral wire on changing over to the Y connection.

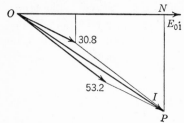

FIG. 331. Vector diagram.

Example. The load on a 2,300-volt three-phase three-wire line consists of (1) 1,200 fluorescent lighting units, each taking 92 watts at 115 volts, 90 per cent power factor lagging, and (2) 200 hp of 550-volt three-phase motors, with an average power factor of 80 per cent lagging and an average efficiency of 88 per cent. Specify the ratings of the transformers required, with connections as in Fig. 330, and find the total current I in the line, and the resultant power factor.

The kilovolt-ampere (kva) output of each lighting transformer is one-third of the kva input to the lamps, that is,

$$\frac{1,200 \times 92}{3 \times 1,000 \times 0.90} = 40.9 \text{ kva}$$

and the voltage rating of the lighting transformers is 2,300 to 115. The primary current in each lighting transformer is $40,900/2,300 = 17.8$ amp. These transformers form a Δ-connected load on the line and therefore the line current for them is $\sqrt{3} \times 17.8 = 30.8$ amp.

The kva output of each transformer of the bank feeding the motors is one-third of the kva input to the motors, that is,

$$\frac{200 \times 0.746}{3 \times 0.88 \times 0.80} = 70.6 \text{ kva}$$

and since the transformers are connected Δ-Δ, the voltage rating is 2,300 to 550. The primary current in each transformer is

$$\frac{70,600}{2,300} = 30.7 \text{ amp}$$

The line current for the motor transformers is

$$\sqrt{3} \times 30.7 = 53.2 \text{ amp}$$

The total current I in the line is the resultant of 30.8 amp at 90 per cent power factor and of 53.2 amp at 80 per cent power factor.

From the vector diagram, Fig. 331,

$$
\begin{aligned}
I &= \sqrt{(ON)^2 + (PN)^2} \\
&= [(30.8 \times 0.9 + 53.2 \times 0.8)^2 + (30.8 \times 0.436 + 53.2 \times 0.6)^2]^{1/2} \\
&= \sqrt{70.3^2 + 45.3^2} \\
&= 83.6 \text{ amp}
\end{aligned}
$$

$$\text{Power factor of total load} = \frac{ON}{OP} = \frac{70.3}{83.6} = 84\%$$

331. Scott Connection—Two-phase to Three-phase. Figure 332 shows the Scott connection used to transform from two-phase to three-phase, or vice versa. The primaries of the two transformers A and B

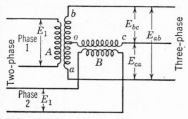

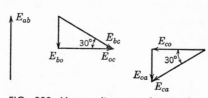

FIG. 332. Two-phase to three-phase Scott connection.

FIG. 333. Vector diagrams for the Scott connection.

are wound for the same voltage, namely, the voltage E_1 of the two-phase line. The secondary of transformer A is wound to give the desired three-phase voltage E_2, while the secondary of transformer B is wound to give a voltage equal to $(\sqrt{3}/2)E_2$. One end of the secondary of transformer B is connected to the mid-point o of the secondary of transformer A.

The vector diagrams in Fig. 333 show that the three line voltages on the three-phase side are equal and are at 120° to each other.

$$E_{ab} = E_2$$

as stated above.

$$E_{bc} = \text{vector sum of } E_{bo} \text{ and } E_{oc}$$

$$= \sqrt{E_{bo}^2 + E_{oc}^2} = \sqrt{\left(\frac{E_2}{2}\right)^2 + \left(\frac{\sqrt{3}}{2}E_2\right)^2} = E_2$$

$$E_{ca} = \text{vector sum of } E_{co} \text{ and } E_{oa}$$

$$= \sqrt{E_{co}^2 + E_{oa}^2} = \sqrt{\left(\frac{\sqrt{3}}{2}E_2\right)^2 + \left(\frac{E_2}{2}\right)^2} = E_2$$

It may be shown that a load which is balanced on the three-phase side is also balanced on the two-phase side.

332. Instrument Transformers. Wattmeters, ammeters, and voltmeters are not connected directly into a-c circuits if the voltage is over 550 volts, but are connected through special instrument transformers, as shown in Fig. 334, which is the same as Fig. 272 except that the instrument transformers have been added. The potential transformers, PT, are similar to small power transformers. The current transformers, CT, have their primary windings connected in series with the line, and their secondaries are practically short-circuited by the current coils of the wattmeters and ammeters. The impedances associated with the current transformers are so small that they have a negligible effect on the line currents I_1 and I_3. Normally there is very little magnetic flux in the iron of the current transformer, because the mmf of the secondary current almost completely neutralizes the mmf of the primary current, and the secondary voltage is generally less than 5 volts. Suppose for example that the line current $I_1 = 250$ amp, that the current transformer has two primary turns and 100 secondary turns, and that the combined impedance of the wattmeter and ammeter current coils is 0.5 ohm. The secondary current is

$$I_2 = \frac{I_1 n_1}{n_2}, \text{ approximately}$$

$$= \frac{250 \times 2}{100} = 5 \text{ amp}$$

The secondary voltage E_2 is equal to the I_2Z drop in the two meters and is

$$5 \times 0.5 = 2.5 \text{ volts}$$

If the total impedance of the secondary circuit of the current transformer is now doubled, the secondary current decreases by perhaps one quarter of 1 per cent, and that is enough to double the difference between $I_1 n_1$ and $I_2 n_2$, and therefore to double the flux, and also the secondary generated voltage, so that the secondary current is nearly independent of the secondary impedance over a fairly wide range of impedance. How ever, when precise measurements are required, the true current ratio is usually determined experimentally, with the same secondary burden (impedance) connected to the secondary that it will be carrying when in use.

Let N_c = current ratio of current transformers

N_p = voltage ratio of potential transformers

Then the power in the three-phase circuit of Fig. 334 is

$$\text{Power} = N_p N_c (W_a + W_c) \qquad \text{watts} \qquad (97)$$

Current transformers are generally designed to give a secondary current of 5 amp on full load. Potential transformers are generally designed for a secondary voltage of 115 or 120 volts.

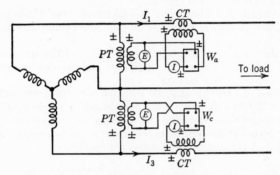

FIG. 334. Instrument-transformer connections for three-phase power measurement.

Note that if the secondary of a current transformer is open-circuited when the primary is carrying current, so that I_2 is reduced to zero, the mmf of the primary current will be completely unopposed, and will take the iron to saturation, with the result that dangerous voltages may be generated in the secondary.

Problems

32-1. Specify the transformers required for a 500-hp 2,300-volt three-phase motor of 90 per cent power factor and 93 per cent efficiency supplied from a 6,000-volt line.

32-2. If the foregoing transformers are connected Δ and one of the three burns out, to what value must the load on the motor be decreased to prevent overloading of transformers?

32-3. If the foregoing load had to be supplied from a two-phase line, specify the Scott-connected transformers required and give the current capacity of both primary and secondary windings.

32-4. Three transformers are connected Y on the high-voltage and Δ on the low-voltage side. If the total output is 300 kva, the primary voltage 2,200, and the secondary voltage 220, what are the voltage, the current, the rating of each transformer?

32-5. What would happen if you connected a transformer to a d-c circuit?

32-6. Two 250-hp 2,200-volt three-phase motors of 90 per cent power factor and 93 per cent efficiency are supplied from a 44,000-volt transmission line by three single-phase transformers connected Δ-Δ.   (a) Specify the kilovolt-amperes and voltage ratings of the transformers.   (b) One of the transformers fails and the remaining two transformers furnish power to one of the motors carrying full load.   What is the kilovolt-ampere load carried by each transformer in this case?

32-7. A three-phase 66,000-volt transmission line supplies three loads A, B, and C.   Load A consists of 400 hp of motors, 2,200 volt, 85 per cent efficiency, 80 per cent power factor.   Load B supplies a transmission line at 13,000 volts to a substation where delta-delta transformers lower the voltage to 2,200 volts.   The voltage is then stepped down to 115 by Δ-Δ connected transformers for an a-c incandescent lighting load of 500 kw.   The loss in the lines is 8 per cent.   Load C supplies four hundred 60-watt lamps at 115 volts for local lighting near the power house.   The 66,000-volt transformers are all connected Y-Δ.

a. Make a diagram of the system.

b. Find currents in all line wires and all transformer windings.

c. Find kilovolt-ampere ratings of all individual transformers, also the voltage ratio.

d. Find the current in the 66,000-volt lines and the resultant power factor. (Note that transformer losses are neglected and primary power factor assumed equal to secondary power factor.)

32-8. A load of 2,000 kw at 2,200 volts, 75 per cent power factor, is to be supplied from a 33,000-volt three-phase line through a single bank of transformers. Sketch the connections and give the primary and secondary voltages and currents of the transformers for the following cases: (a) Δ-Δ connection; (b) Y-Y connection; (c) Y-Δ connection; (d) open-Δ connection.

33

POLYPHASE INDUCTION MOTORS

333. Induction Motor. This motor is the most extensively used a-c motor in power work. The essential parts of such a machine are shown in Figs. 335 and 336. The stator or stationary part is exactly the same as that of an a-c generator. The rotor, however, is entirely different and the type most generally used, called the squirrel-cage type, consists

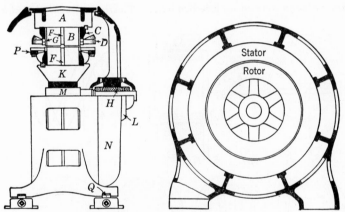

FIG. 335. Squirrel-cage induction motor.

of a cylindrical core that carries a large number of copper bars on its periphery. These bars are all joined together at the ends by two brass rings, as shown in Fig. 336. The action of this machine will be explained in detail.

334. Rotating Field. In Fig. 337p are represented the essential parts of a two-pole two-phase induction motor. The stator carries two windings M and N, which are spaced 90 electrical degrees apart, and, in the actual machine, are bent back so that the rotor may readily be inserted. These windings are connected by wires to two-phase mains and the currents which flow at any instant in the coils M and N are given by

403

FIG. 336. Squirrel-cage rotor of an induction motor.   (*Courtesy of General Electric Co.*)

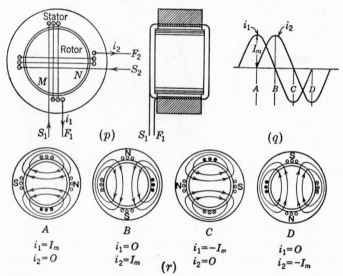

FIG. 337. Revolving field of a two-pole two-phase induction motor.

the curves in Fig. 337q; at instant A, for example, the current in phase $1 = +I_m$ while that in phase 2 is zero.

The windings of each phase are marked S and F at the terminals and these letters stand for start and finish, respectively; a plus current is one that goes in at S and a minus current one that goes in at F.

The magnetic fields produced by windings M and N at instants A, B, C, and D, Fig. 337q, are shown in diagrams A, B, C, and D. That the field actually rotates in passing from diagram A to diagram B may be seen by considering some intermediate instant between A and B. If we measure θ from instant A, then $i_1 = I_m \cos \theta$ and $i_2 = I_m \sin \theta$. Therefore phase 1 produces a horizontal component of mmf $M_1 = i_1 n = I_m n \cos \theta$ amp-turns, while phase 2 produces a vertical component $M_2 = i_2 n = I_m n \sin \theta$ amp-turns, where n = turns per phase. These components and their resultant M_R are shown in Fig. 339 for $\theta = 30°$ and for $\theta = 45°$.

$$M_R = \sqrt{M_1{}^2 + M_2{}^2} = [(I_m n \cos \theta)^2 + (I_m n \sin \theta)^2]^{1/2}$$
$$= I_m n (\cos^2 \theta + \sin^2 \theta)^{1/2} = I_m n \qquad (98)$$

Thus the resultant mmf is of constant strength and rotates at constant speed. Figure 338 shows the magnetic field produced by the resultant mmf when $\theta = 45°$.

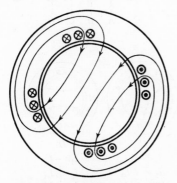

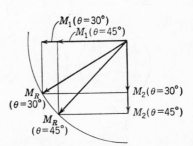

FIG. 338. Magnetic field when $\theta = 45°$. $i_1 = I_m \cos 45° = I_m/\sqrt{2}$; $i_2 = I_m \sin 45° = I_m/\sqrt{2}$.

FIG. 339. Components of mmf produced by the stator currents of a two-phase induction motor.

Note that reversing the connections to either phase reverses the direction of rotation of the magnetic field.

335. Rotating Field of a Three-phase Motor. In Fig. 340p is represented the winding of a two-pole three-phase motor. M, N, and Q, the windings of the three phases, are spaced 120 electrical degrees apart. These windings are connected to the three-phase mains and may be connected either Y or Δ. In either case the currents that flow at any instant in the coils M, N, and Q are given by the curves in Fig. 340r; at instant A, for example, the current in phase 1 is $+I_m$, that in phase 2 is $-(I_m/2)$, and that in phase 3 is also $-(I_m/2)$.

The resultant magnetic field produced by the windings at instants A, B, C, and D is shown in Fig. 340s, from which it may be seen that, just as in the case of the two-phase machine, a revolving field is produced which is of constant strength and which goes through one revolution while the current in one phase passes through one cycle.

The three coil terminals F_1, F_2, and F_3 are generally connected together to form a neutral, while the three terminals S_1, S_2, and S_3 are connected to the three wires of a three-phase three-wire line. If the connections to any two of these S terminals are interchanged, the direction of rotation of

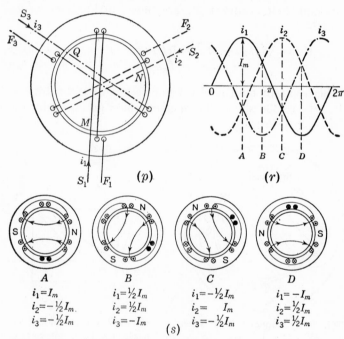

FIG. 340. Revolving field of a two-pole three-phase induction motor.

the magnetic field is reversed, and this is the method used to reverse the motor.

336. Multipolar Machines. The revolving fields of the two-pole machines shown in Figs. 337 and 340 turn at 3,600 rpm on a 60-cycle system and 1,500 rpm on a 25-cycle system; and the rotor, as will be shown later, turns at approximately the same speed. In order to obtain motors with lower speeds, it is necessary to increase the number of magnetic poles produced by the stator winding.

Figure 341 shows part of the stator winding of an eight-pole three-phase induction motor. This winding is identical with the stator winding of the three-phase generator shown in Fig. 258. Figure 341a and b shows the directions of the currents in the various coils at instants A

and B and also the positions of the magnetic field of one pair of the poles, N and S, produced by those currents.

The distance between the centers of two adjacent poles, measured along the circumference at the air gap, is called the pole pitch. In comparing Fig. 341b with Fig. 341a it is evident that the magnetic field has shifted one-third of a pole pitch in one-sixth of a cycle. It therefore shifts two pole pitches per cycle, and its speed in revolutions per second

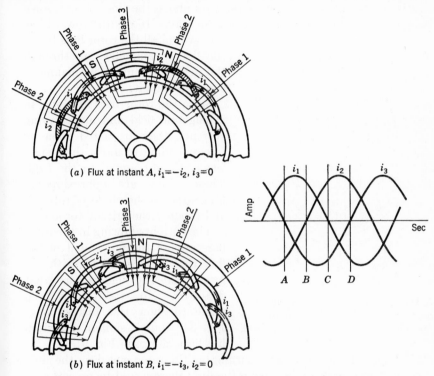

(a) Flux at instant A, $i_1=-i_2$, $i_3=0$

(b) Flux at instant B, $i_1=-i_3$, $i_2=0$

FIG. 341. Revolving field of an eight-pole three-phase induction motor.

is equal to the frequency divided by the number of pairs of poles or, the speed being expressed in revolutions per minute,

$$\text{Speed of revolving field} = \frac{120f}{p} \quad \text{rpm} \tag{99}$$

where p = number of poles.

The speed of the revolving field is called the synchronous speed of the motor. It is also the speed at which a generator with the same number of poles must run in order to give the same frequency as that applied to the motor. The table of possible speeds on page 258 therefore applies to induction motors as well as to generators.

337. Driving Torque. Let the rotating field of a two-pole induction motor, produced by either a two-phase or a three-phase stator, be represented by a pair of north and south poles rotating about the common axis o, as shown in Fig. 342. The moving field cuts the rotor bars and generates in them emfs which are shown by crosses and dots. The circuit through the bars is completed by the two brass end rings to which each bar is welded at each end. Consequently, current flows. It flows away from the observer in the rotor bars above the line xx and down through the far end ring, half going each way. It returns toward the observer in all the rotor bars below the line xx and flows up through the near end ring, thus making a complete circuit.

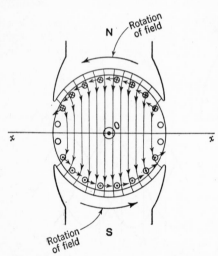

Since the rotor bars are lying in a magnetic field and are carrying currents, they are acted upon by forces tending to move them sideways at right angles to the field. These forces are approximately tangential to the circle of rotation and produce the driving torque.

The currents flowing in the rotor bars oppose the movement of the flux that induces them, with the result that the field is somewhat distorted. No attempt has been made to show this distortion in Fig. 342, but a similar distortion has been shown in Fig. 91c.

FIG. 342. Cross section showing the voltages, currents, and torque produced in the rotor of an induction motor by the rotating field.

338. Slip. If the rotor were turning at the same speed as the flux, the rotor bars would not be cut by the flux; there would be no emf generated in them; and the rotor current would be zero. Consequently, the driving torque would also be zero. Therefore the rotor will never turn quite so fast as the flux.

The speed of the flux is called the synchronous speed. The rotor would eventually attain this speed if the windage and friction could be reduced to zero. The difference between the rotor speed and the flux speed is called the *slip*. It is usually expressed as a percentage of the synchronous speed and is represented by the symbol s.

$$\text{Slip} = \frac{\text{synchronous speed} - \text{rotor speed}}{\text{synchronous speed}}$$

The slip at no load of a standard 5-hp 1,200-rpm squirrel-cage induction motor, equipped with ball-bearings, is about one-twentieth of 1 per cent, or 0.6 rpm. The slip of the same motor at full load is about 4 per cent or 48 rpm.

Between no load and full load the slip of an induction motor is directly proportional to the brake torque. If the brake torque is doubled, the motor will begin to slow down and will continue to slow down until the driving torque is doubled. Now the force on each rotor bar is directly proportional to the current in the bar and to the flux density. The total flux is maintained nearly constant by the stator currents, as will be explained in Art. 346, and therefore, in order to double the driving torque, the rotor current must double. Therefore the emf induced in the rotor bars must be doubled. But this emf is proportional to the slip, and therefore the slip must be doubled. Hence the slip is directly proportional to the brake torque.

The foregoing simple line of reasoning gives results that are quite accurate for all loads from no load to full load, but leads to incorrect results if extended to loads much in excess of full load, because it ignores one factor that begins to be important at about full load. This factor is the fact that, since the emfs and currents in the rotors bars are alternating and since the bars have an appreciable self-inductance, being embedded in iron, the currents in the rotor bars will not be in phase with the emfs driving them but will lag by some phase angle ϕ_2. The frequency of the emfs generated in the rotor bars is directly proportional to the slip, and is equal to sf, where f is the line frequency. On a 60-cycle system sf will be 60 cycles per sec when the rotor is stationary, the slip then being 100 per cent, and may be as low as 0.03 cycle per sec when the rotor is running at no load. The leakage reactance of the rotor circuit is $2\pi sfL_2 = sX_2$, where X_2 is the leakage reactance when the rotor is stationary. The term *leakage* has the same meaning here as when applied to a transformer, that is, it refers to flux that links only with the winding that produces it. If R_2 is the resistance of the rotor circuit, then

$$\phi_2 = \tan^{-1} \frac{sX_2}{R_2}$$

At all loads up to full load the slip is so small that ϕ_2 is too small to have any appreciable effect on the torque, but at overloads, or when starting, ϕ_2 becomes important. Its effect is to decrease the driving torque, as will be shown in Art. 339.

339. Starting Torque. Let the rotating field of a two-pole induction motor be replaced by a pair of imaginary poles rotating about the armature axis, as in Figs. 343, 344, and 345. The dots and crosses in Fig. 343 show the directions of the emfs generated in the rotor bars by the rotating field. In an actual machine, with the stator winding distributed in several slots per phase, the flux density will be greatest at the center of the pole, and the graph of the emf generated in any one bar will be approximately a sine curve. In Fig. 343 the relative magnitudes of the instantaneous emfs being generated in the rotor bars are indicated roughly by the varying sizes of the dots and crosses. The emf is, of course, a maximum in that conductor that is cutting the strongest field.

At start, when the rotor is stationary, the frequency of the emfs generated in the rotor bars by the rotating field is equal to the frequency of the emfs applied to the stator winding, so that when the rotor is stationary the currents in the rotor and stator have the same frequency.

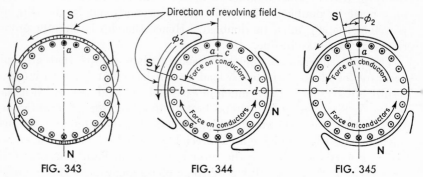

FIG. 343   FIG. 344   FIG. 345

FIG. 343. Direction of the emf in the rotor bars.
FIG. 344. Direction of the currents in the bars of a low-resistance rotor at standstill.
FIG. 345. Direction of the currents in the bars of a high-resistance rotor at standstill or of a low-resistance rotor at about 20 per cent slip.

Now the resistance of the copper bars of the squirrel-cage rotor winding is very low; but since these bars are embedded in iron, they have considerable self-inductance, and their reactance is large compared with their resistance. The rotor current in each bar therefore lags considerably behind the emf in that bar. In conductor a, for example, Fig. 343, the emf has just reached its maximum value, but the current in that conductor lags the emf by an angle ϕ_2 which is here assumed to be 75° and thus does not become a maximum until the poles have moved into the position shown in Fig. 344, which is 75° from the position shown in Fig. 343.

Since the conductors in Fig. 344 are carrying current and are in a magnetic field, they are acted on by forces, the direction of which may be determined by the distorted-field rule, Art. 25, from which it is found that, while the forces in the belts bc and de tend to make the rotor follow the revolving field, those on the conductors in the belts cd and be act in the opposite direction. The former forces are the larger, so that the rotor tends to follow the rotating field. The effective value of the current in the rotor conductors at standstill is

$$\frac{\text{Rotor voltage at standstill}}{\text{Rotor impedance at standstill}} = \frac{E_2}{\sqrt{R_2{}^2 + (2\pi f L_2)^2}}$$

and the rotor impedance at standstill in the low-resistance general-purpose type of induction motor is large enough to limit the starting current to about six times the full-load value. The starting torque, however, is only about 1½ times the full-load value. The loss of starting torque is due partly to the fact that some of the conductors produce torque which opposes the starting of the motor, as shown in Fig. 344, and

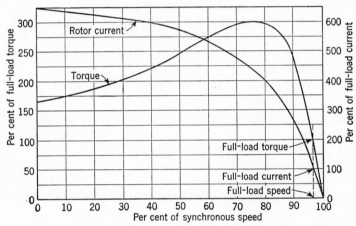

FIG. 346. Variation of torque and rotor current with speed in a low-resistance general-purpose type of squirrel-cage induction motor.

partly to the fact that the bars carrying the large currents are in relatively weak fields, while the strong field is occupied by bars carrying relatively small currents.

The magnitude and the frequency of the emfs generated in the rotor bars are proportional to the speed of the revolving field relative to the rotor. Consequently, as the rotor speeds up, the rotor emfs and frequency decrease. For example, if the emf generated in each rotor bar when stationary is 10 volts, 60 cycles, then, when the rotor is running at one-half synchronous speed, the emf in each bar is 5 volts, 30 cycles. The reactance is also cut in half, but the impedance is not cut quite in half because it contains a resistance component R_2. The rotor current accordingly is reduced slightly. Since the reactance is reduced to one-half, the phase angle ϕ_2 between the rotor emf and the rotor current is reduced approximately to one-half, with the result that more of the bars are producing torque in the forward direction (see Fig. 344). The total resultant driving torque therefore increases as the rotor speeds up, and, when the rotor speed is up to 75 per cent of the synchronous speed, the rotor emf is 2.5 volts, 15 cycles, and the driving torque has approximately doubled, although the rotor current has decreased about 30 per cent.

The variations of torque and rotor current with speed, for a low-resistance general-purpose type of squirrel-cage induction motor, are shown in Fig. 346. The motor develops its maximum torque at about 75 per cent of synchronous speed. At that speed the rotor reactance is low enough so that the torque of nearly all of the rotor bars is in the forward direction, and the rotor current is still large. As the speed increases further, the rotor current and the torque decrease, until at synchronous speed the rotor emf, current, and torque are all zero.

340. Torque and Rotor-current Equations

Let Φ = number of lines of rotating flux per pole

E_2 = voltage generated in the rotor circuit at standstill, by the rotating flux

X_2 = leakage reactance of rotor circuit at standstill

R_2 = resistance of rotor circuit

f = line frequency

s = slip

I_2 = current in rotor circuit at any slip s

ϕ_2 = phase angle by which I_2 lags sE_2

T = electromagnetic torque

Then sE_2 = voltage generated in rotor circuit at any slip s, assuming that Φ is constant

sf = frequency in rotor circuit

sX_2 = leakage reactance of rotor circuit at any slip s

$$I_2 = \frac{sE_2}{\sqrt{R_2^2 + s^2X_2^2}} \tag{100}$$

$$\cos \phi_2 = \frac{R_2}{Z_2} = \frac{R_2}{\sqrt{R_2^2 + s^2X_2^2}} \tag{101}$$

It is evident from Fig. 344 that if the current in the rotor lagged behind the rotor voltage by a phase angle of 90°, then ϕ_2 would be 90°, and exactly half the rotor conductors would be trying to turn the rotor clockwise, while the other half would be trying to turn it counterclockwise, and the resultant torque would be zero. Let us therefore resolve I_2 into two components, one, $I_2 \cos \phi_2$, in phase with sE_2, and the other, $I_2 \sin \phi_2$, lagging 90° behind sE_2. Now the component $I_2 \sin \phi_2$ produces no resultant torque, and therefore the total resultant torque is

$$T = K\Phi I_2 \cos \phi_2 \tag{102}$$

Substituting Eqs. (100) and (101) in Eq. (102) gives the torque directly in terms of the slip, as follows:

$$T = \frac{K\Phi s E_2 R_2}{R_2{}^2 + s^2 X_2{}^2} \tag{103}$$

The operating curves of Fig. 346, at constant line voltage, may be plotted by means of Eqs. (100), (101), and (102), or (103), provided that it is possible either to measure or to calculate the five constants, K, Φ, E_2, R_2, and X_2. The curves so obtained will not be precise because Φ is not actually a constant. It decreases slightly with increasing load, as will be explained in Art. 346. Also R_2 increases somewhat with frequency.

Note that from no load to full load the slip is so small that sX_2 is negligible compared with R_2, and Eqs. (100) and (103) may be simplified to

$$I_2 = \frac{sE_2}{R_2} = K_1 s \tag{104}$$

$$T = \frac{K\Phi s E_2}{R_2} = K_2 s \tag{105}$$

Thus the rotor current and the torque are both directly proportional to the slip from no load to full load.

341. Variation of Starting Torque with Rotor Resistance. If the resistance of the rotor circuit of an induction motor were zero, then the rotor current at standstill would lag 90° behind the rotor voltage, since $\phi_2 = \tan^{-1}(sX_2/R_2)$, and in Fig. 344 ϕ_2 would be 90°. Consequently, the clockwise components of torque would be equal to the counterclockwise components of torque. Therefore an induction motor would develop no starting torque if the resistance of its rotor circuit were zero.

Again, if the rotor resistance were infinitely large, there would be no rotor current, and therefore no torque. Since the starting torque is zero when $R = 0$, and also when R is equal to infinity, it follows that there must be some intermediate value of rotor resistance that will give a maximum value of starting torque. Figure 347 shows the variation of starting torque and rotor current with rotor resistance. These curves may be plotted by means of Eqs. (103) and (100), with $s = 1$.

As the rotor resistance is increased from zero, the angle of lag ϕ_2 of the rotor current decreases, thus increasing the number of rotor bars contributing to the driving torque (see Figs. 344 and 345) and also shifting them into a stronger field, while decreasing the number of bars that oppose the driving torque and shifting them into a weaker field. Thus the net torque increases rapidly as the rotor resistance is increased from zero.

On the other hand, increasing the rotor resistance increases the rotor impedance and decreases the rotor current and thus tends to reduce the torque.

When the rotor resistance is quite low, the first effect is much larger than the second, and the torque increases as the rotor resistance is increased, but a value of rotor resistance is soon reached at which all the rotor bars are on the driving side and none are opposing, as in Fig. 345. Beyond this point the first effect soon becomes negligible; hence the torque becomes approximately proportional to the current, and the torque therefore decreases as the rotor resistance is increased.

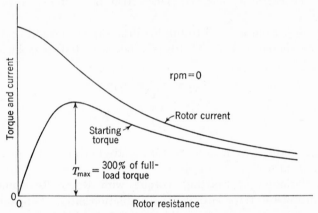

FIG. 347. Variation of starting torque with rotor resistance for a squirrel-cage induction motor.

In order to find the value of rotor resistance that gives maximum starting torque, differentiate Eq. (103) with respect to R_2, and equate to zero. It will be found that the value of rotor resistance for maximum torque, at any slip s, is given by

$$R_2 = sX_2 \qquad (106)$$

Therefore if it is desired to have maximum starting torque, and also maximum acceleration throughout the accelerating period, we should start with a rotor resistance equal to the rotor reactance at standstill, and decrease R_2 continuously as the motor gains speed, always keeping the rotor resistance equal to the rotor reactance.

342. High-resistance Rotor. The low-resistance general-purpose squirrel-cage induction motor draws about 6 times full-load current at standstill and develops a starting torque of about $1\frac{1}{2}$ times full-load torque, as shown in Fig. 346. Increasing the rotor resistance to about three times the normal value doubles the starting torque and reduces the current by about 25 per cent. The rotor is then called a high-resistance rotor, although its resistance is still a small fraction of 1 ohm.

The starting characteristics of a high-resistance rotor are decidedly superior to those of the low-resistance rotor, but its running characteristics are decidedly inferior, and therefore its field of application is limited to services that consist chiefly of starting and stopping, or other intermittent loads.

The chief reason why the running characteristics of the high-resistance rotor are so inferior to those of the low-resistance rotor is that the

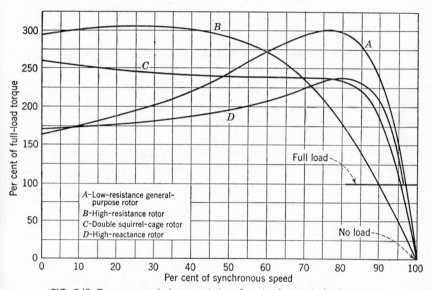

FIG. 348. Torque-speed characteristics of squirrel-cage induction motors.

I^2R loss in the rotor is about three times as great. This not only wastes power but would also make it necessary to increase the size of the rotor in order to provide sufficient cooling surface if the motor were used for anything but intermittent service.

A comparison between the torque-speed and current-speed characteristics of low-resistance and high-resistance rotors is shown in Figs. 348 and 349. It will be noticed that for all brake torques from no load to the breakdown point the slip of the high-resistance rotor is considerably greater than that of the low-resistance rotor. In fact from no load to full load the slip is practically directly proportional to the rotor resistance, because doubling the rotor resistance requires that the voltage generated in the rotor bars be doubled in order to provide the necessary rotor current, and, since this emf is produced by the slip, it follows that the slip must also be doubled.

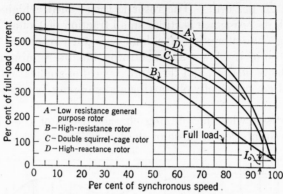

FIG. 349. Current-speed characteristics of squirrel-cage induction motors, stator current plotted against speed.

343. Wound-rotor Induction Motor. There are many motor applications in which it is desirable to combine the superior starting torque of the high-resistance rotor with the superior running characteristics of the low-resistance rotor. In order to do this, it is necessary to be able to vary the rotor resistance. This could be accomplished by removing one end ring and connecting the free end of each rotor bar to a separate slip ring, as is shown for one bar only in Fig. 350. Each slip ring would be

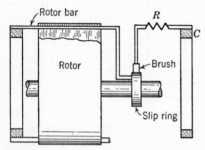

FIG. 350. Squirrel-cage rotor with bars that have an adjustable resistance.

connected through a stationary brush and a variable resistance R to the common stationary end ring C. This particular construction would permit the variation of the rotor resistance but would require the use of as many slip rings as there are rotor bars; consequently it is modified in practice so as to reduce the number of slip rings.

The standard practice is to connect the bars in series in three groups so as to form a three-phase winding, as shown diagrammatically in Fig. 351. The circuits of the three phases are completed through slip rings and a three-phase rheostat. The three sliding contacts on the rheostat move together so that the three resistances are always equal. All the resistance is in the circuit at the start, and, as the motor comes up to speed, the resistances are gradually cut out and are finally reduced to zero. This type of motor is called the wound-rotor type of induction motor, and it very successfully combines the best features of the high-resistance and low-resistance rotors. It is, however, more expensive than the squirrel-cage motor, especially in the smaller sizes.

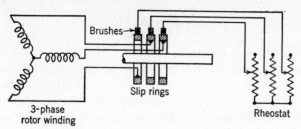

FIG. 351. Wound-rotor and variable resistances.

344. Adjustable-speed Operation.   The squirrel-cage motor is essentially a constant-speed machine.   For adjustable-speed operation the wound-rotor motor may be used.   If such a motor is operating with a load having a constant torque and a resistance is inserted in the rotor circuit, as shown in Fig. 351, the rotor current will decrease, thus decreasing the driving torque, and the motor will slow down.   As the speed drops, however, the rotor slips more rapidly through the revolving field, so that a greater emf is generated in the rotor conductors, the current increases, and, at some lower speed, is again sufficient for the load.   Any

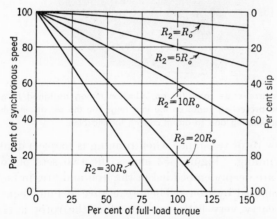

IG. 352. Effect of rotor resistance on the speed of an induction motor. R_0 = minimum ɔtor resistance.

peed from zero to about 96 per cent of synchronous speed can be obtained n this way, but with this type of speed reduction the speed varies widely ʋith the brake torque, especially at the lower speeds.   This is shown in ʼig. 352, in which R_0 is the resistance of the rotor circuit when the ʰeostat resistance has been reduced to zero.

The curves of Fig. 352 may be plotted with sufficient accuracy by ʱeans of Eq. (105), which may be rearranged as follows:

$$s = \frac{TR_2}{K\Phi E_2} = K_3 TR_2 \qquad (107)$$

where $K_3 = 1/K\Phi E_2 =$ a constant.

This method of speed control is similar to the armature-resistance speed control of d-c shunt motors (Art. 140). In both cases the speed varies widely with the brake torque, and the efficiency is reduced in the same proportion as the speed. Therefore in both cases the practical application is limited to short-time operation at the reduced speeds. It is, however, an excellent and widely used method of speed control in its own particular field.

345. Double Squirrel-cage Rotors for High Starting Torque. Another less expensive method of obtaining a comparatively high rotor resistance

FIG. 353. Double squirrel-cage rotor for an induction motor, designed to give a high starting torque. The projecting vanes on the end rings fan the air against the end connections of the stator winding and so aid in cooling the machine.

at start and a low rotor resistance when running is to use a double squirrel-cage rotor winding. Figure 353 shows the two sets of rotor bars. The heavy bars are deeply embedded in the iron and are, in fact, almost completely surrounded by iron. Their reactance at line frequency is so high that they carry very little current when the rotor is stationary. The smaller bars are near the surface and are not completely surrounded by iron; consequently they have low reactance, and since they are small in cross section their resistance is relatively high. At start, therefore, only the high-resistance rotor bars are carrying much current, and the starting characteristics are therefore those of a high-resistance rotor.

As the motor comes up to speed, however, the reactance of the heavy bars decreases and the proportion of the total rotor current that they carry increases, until at running speed they are carrying practically the same current per square inch of cross section as the smaller bars are. Thus the resistance is low under running conditions.

A comparison between the torque-speed and current-speed character-istics of the double squirrel-cage motor and those of the other types of squirrel-cage motors is shown in Figs. 348 and 349. Curves are not shown for the wound-rotor motor because separate curves would be required for each step on the variable rotor resistance. When the wound-rotor motor is starting, its torque and current are generally the same as those of the high-resistance rotor. When running with all the resistance cut out, the curves for the low-resistance rotor apply. Note that the double squirrel-cage method of obtaining a high rotor resistance at start is not quite so effective as the wound-rotor method. The start-ing torque of the double squirrel-cage motor is about 2.6 times full-load torque, while the wound rotor develops 3 times full-load torque at start. Note also that the pull-out torque[1] of the double squirrel-cage motor is less than that of the general-purpose low-resistance rotor, which is practically the same as that of the wound rotor. However, in many high-starting-torque applications the starting and pull-out torques of the double squirrel-cage motor are entirely adequate, and, since this motor is considerably cheaper and more rugged than the wound-rotor motor, it is extensively used.

346. Vector Diagrams for the Three-phase Induction Motor. The three-phase induction motor in its simplest form consists of a squirrel-cage rotor and three stator coils set at 120° to each other, as shown in Fig. 340. As far as the stator winding is concerned, the transfer of energy from the stator to the rotor is fundamentally the same as the transfer of energy from the primary to the secondary of a transformer. In fact a wound-rotor induction motor may be used as a three-phase transformer if the rotor is locked in place.

a. No-load Conditions. Let us assume that the rotor is running at synchronous speed, a condition which could be achieved theoretically by reducing the friction and windage to zero, or experimentally by driving the rotor mechanically by means of another type of motor. Since the rotor is turning at the same speed as the flux, its conductors are not being cut by the flux, and therefore there is no emf or current in the rotor.

The vector diagram for one phase of the motor, for this no-load condi-tion, is shown in Fig. 354. Three-phase alternating emfs, E_1, applied to the three stator windings, cause alternating currents I_0 to flow in them and produce the rotating flux. The no-load stator current I_0 is called the exciting current. It lags nearly 90° behind E_1, because the rotor conductors may be ignored when they are not carrying any current, and then the circuit consists simply of three coils, or coil groups, of high

---

[1] The pull-out torque of a motor is the minimum brake torque that will stall the motor.

inductance and low resistance. I_0 lags less than 90° because of the iron loss in the stator and the resistance of the stator winding. The exciting current of an induction motor is considerably greater than that of a transformer because of the air gap. The air gap is made as small as is feasible, but I_0 is still about one-third of the full-load current.

The rotating flux cuts the stator coils and generates an emf E_{1g} in each phase of the stator winding. If E_{1g} were exactly equal and opposite to E_1, as it is shown to be in Fig. 354, there would be no emf left over to drive I_0 through the resistance R_1 and the leakage reactance X_1 of the stator winding. Therefore the vector sum of E_1 and E_{1g} cannot be zero, but must in fact be equal to I_0Z_1, where I_0Z_1 is the vector sum of I_0R_1 and I_0X_1. However, I_0Z_1 is only about 3 per cent of E_1 and therefore would be almost invisible if drawn to scale in Fig. 354. Consequently, it has been ignored and E_{1g} has been shown as exactly equal and opposite to E_1.

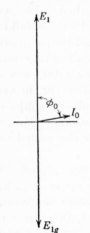

If E_1 is increased, the balance between E_1 and E_{1g} is upset and I_0 increases, thus increasing the flux and consequently E_{1g}, so that the balance is restored. Consequently, I_0, Φ, and E_{1g} are all proportional to E_1, except that as saturation is approached, I_0 increases faster than E_1.

b. *Motor Loaded.* When a brake load is applied to the motor, the rotor slows down slightly. Its conductors are then cut by the rotating field; emfs are generated in them, and currents flow. These rotor currents produce powerful mmfs that would greatly alter the rotating flux Φ if it were not for the fact that any alteration in Φ upsets the balance between E_{1g} and E_1, with the result that additional stator currents flow to restore the balance, and this balance can be restored only if the additional stator currents neutralize the mmfs of the rotor currents. Note that this reaction is fundamentally the same as in the transformer. Let us examine it in greater detail. In Fig. 343 the emfs generated in the rotor conductors by the rotating field are represented by a pattern of crosses and dots, and this pattern rotates in perfect synchronism with the rotating field that produces it. In Figs. 344 and 345 the rotor currents lag behind the rotor emfs by the angle ϕ_2 which varies with the operating condition but is constant for any given load and line voltage. Therefore the pattern of crosses and dots for the rotor currents also rotates at exactly the same speed as the rotating field, and so does the mmf produced by those rotor currents. Thus the rotor currents tend to produce a rotating field the same as the stator currents do. These

FIG. 354. No-load vector diagram for one phase of an induction motor, ignoring the I_0R_1 and I_0X_1 voltage drops in the stator winding.

two fields always rotate in the same direction at exactly the same speed.
The angle between them, however, varies with the operating condition.
In Fig. 344 the rotor mmf lags 165° behind the main field, while in Fig.
345 this angle is 105°.

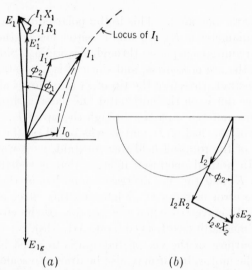

(a)   (b)

FIG. 355. (a) Full-load vector diagram for one phase of an induction motor.   (b) Vector
diagram for the rotor of an induction motor.

Figure 355a shows the vector diagram for one phase of the stator of an
induction motor when it is carrying a load.

E_1 = voltage impressed on one phase of the stator winding
   = line voltage divided by $\sqrt{3}$, assuming a Y connection
E_1' = $E_1 - I_1 Z_1$ (vector subtraction)
E_{1g} = $-E_1'$
I_1' = component of stator current required in each phase to neutralize
      the mmf of the rotor currents
I_1 = vector sum of I_1', I_0
ϕ_2 = phase angle by which I_2 lags sE_2
   = phase angle by which I_1' lags E_1'

That these two phase angles are equal is a basic feature of transformer
action.   The power factor of a load remains unchanged when it is transferred from the secondary to the primary.
   In order to determine how I_1' varies with change of brake load, it is
necessary to examine the variation of I_2 and ϕ_2.   Figure 355b shows the
vector diagram for the rotor.   The rotor voltage sE_2 is equal to the vector

sum of I_2R_2 and I_2sX_2, and from this triangle it is evident that

$$I_2sX_2 = sE_2 \sin \phi_2 \tag{108}$$

or

$$I_2 = \frac{E_2}{X_2} \sin \phi_2 \tag{109}$$

where E_2 and X_2 are constants. This is the polar equation [Eq. (109)] of a circle whose diameter is E_2/X_2, whose center lies on the horizontal axis, and whose circumference passes through the origin. Since the locus of the tip of I_2 is the arc of a circle, and since I_1' is a constant times I_2, and since I_0 is constant, therefore the tip of I_1 also moves along the arc of a circle whose center is on the horizontal line passing through the tip of I_0 and whose circumference passes through the tip of I_0.

The derivation of the loci of I_2 and I_1 was based on the assumption that the strength of the rotating field was constant, as it would be if E_1' were constant. In normal operation it is E_1 that is constant, not E_1', and consequently E_1' and the flux decrease somewhat as the brake load is increased. The error introduced by ignoring this effect is small, and in any case is partly corrected when the location of the circle for I_1 is determined experimentally (see Locked Test, Art. 348).

The principal purpose of the vector diagram is to assist in explaining the operation of the motor, but it may also be drawn to scale if sufficient test data are available, and it may then be used to obtain operating characteristics. The essential data for locating the circle for I_1 may be obtained from two tests, known, respectively, as the no-load test and the locked test. These tests are described in Arts. 347 and 348.

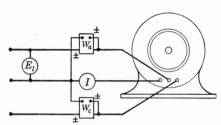

FIG. 356. Connections for measuring the power input to a three-phase motor.

347. No-load Test. Figure 356 shows the connections for measuring the power input to a three-phase motor. For the no-load test, rated line voltage E_l is impressed and the rotor is allowed to run free. The power factor will be less than 50 per cent, which will be indicated by one of the wattmeters being off-scale to the left. In order to read this wattmeter, it will be necessary to reverse either the current leads or the potential leads. Then W_0, the no-load power input to the motor, is equal to the difference between the two wattmeter readings. But the power input is also equal to $\sqrt{3}\ E_lI_0 \cos \phi_0$. Therefore $\sqrt{3}\ E_lI_0 \cos \phi_0 = W_0$ and

$$\cos \phi_0 = \frac{W_0}{\sqrt{3}\ E_lI_0} \tag{110}$$

The ammeter reads the magnitude of I_0, which should be the same in all three phases. Thus the no-load test determines both the magnitude and phase angle of I_0, and thus locates one point on the circle that is the locus of I_1. Note that when I_0 is measured in this way it includes a small power component to supply the friction and windage losses, which was not included in the theoretical I_0 of Art. 346. The magnitude of I_0 is not appreciably affected by the inclusion of this power component, but its phase angle ϕ_0 is decreased somewhat. It is standard practice to include the friction and windage when measuring the magnitude and phase angle of I_0.

Now since there is no power output, the input is all loss. The rotor copper loss is negligible at no load; but the stator copper loss is not negligible, and is equal to $3I_0{}^2R_1$. Then $W_0 - 3I_0{}^2R_1$ is equal to friction, windage, and iron loss, all three of which are assumed to be independent of load. The resistance of the stator winding is measured between any two terminals, using direct current. This gives the resistance of two phases in series, which must be divided by two to obtain R_1.

348. Locked Test. The rotor is locked in place by any convenient means, such as a brake. With meter connections as in Fig. 356, reduced voltage is impressed. Suppose for example that the applied voltage is made equal to one-quarter of the rated line voltage E_l. The meters are read, not forgetting to note whether the power factor is below 50 per cent, so that the wattmeter readings must be subtracted. Now when the rotor is locked the current varies directly as the voltage, while the power input varies as the square of the voltage. Therefore I_L, the stator current at rated voltage with the rotor locked, is equal to four times the current measured at one-quarter of rated voltage. And W_L, the power input at rated voltage with the rotor locked, is equal to sixteen times the power input at one-quarter of rated voltage. Now

$$\sqrt{3}\ E_l I_L \cos\phi_L = W_L$$

therefore
$$\cos\phi_L = \frac{W_L}{\sqrt{3}\ E_l I_L} \tag{111}$$

Thus both the magnitude and the phase angle of the locked stator current at rated voltage are obtained from the locked test.

Since two points on the circular locus of I_1, namely, I_0 and I_L, have been obtained and since it is known that the center of this circle is located on a horizontal line drawn through the tip of I_0, the circle diagram may be drawn to scale, as shown in Fig. 357. The vector diagram is now ready for use, as far as the stator quantities are concerned, but first let us note that the copper losses may also be obtained from the locked test, in the same way that they are obtained from the short-circuit test in the case of a transformer. The applied voltage is adjusted to give whatever stator currents are desired.   The watts input for any one stator current is then equal to the sum of the stator and rotor copper losses for that particular stator current, the iron loss being practically negligible during a locked test because of the low flux density.   It is important to note that in the locked test the frequency of the rotor currents is equal to the line frequency, usually 60 cycles, but when the

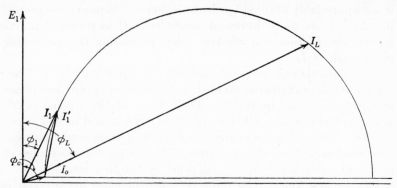

FIG. 357. Circle diagram for an induction motor, as obtained from the no-load and locked tests.

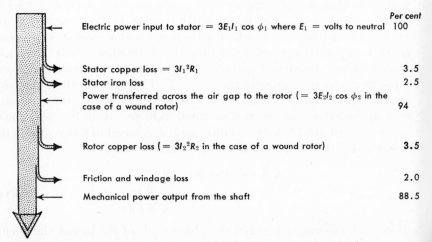

	Per cent
Electric power input to stator $= 3E_1I_1 \cos \phi_1$ where $E_1 =$ volts to neutral	100
Stator copper loss $= 3I_1^2R_1$	3.5
Stator iron loss	2.5
Power transferred across the air gap to the rotor ($= 3E_2I_2 \cos \phi_2$ in the case of a wound rotor)	94
Rotor copper loss ($= 3I_2^2R_2$ in the case of a wound rotor)	3.5
Friction and windage loss	2.0
Mechanical power output from the shaft	88.5

FIG. 358. Power-flow diagram for an induction motor, showing typical values for a 15-h 1,800-rpm three-phase motor when carrying full load.

motor is in normal operation the frequency of the rotor currents is onl 2 or 3 cycles.   Now in the case of a double squirrel-cage rotor, or of rotor with deep narrow slots, the rotor resistance at 60 cycles may b two or three times what it is at 3 cycles.   In such cases the locked tes which must be carried out at rated line frequency when determining I and starting torque, should be repeated at as low a frequency as is feas ble for the determination of the copper losses. A frequency of 15 cycles will usually give a reasonably accurate measurement of the copper losses. This completes the measurement of the power losses in the motor. Figure 358 is a power-flow diagram for a typical induction motor. As usual the assumption that the iron loss is independent of the load is not strictly correct, and the true efficiency may be appreciably less than the conventional efficiency obtained by ignoring the increase of iron loss with load. The difference should not be more than about 1 per cent if the design is good.

348A. Calculation of Characteristics. Let I_1 be any chosen stator current drawn to scale to meet the circle on the vector diagram, Fig. 357. The phase angle ϕ_1 is scaled from the diagram. Then

$$\text{Power factor} = \cos \phi_1$$
$$\text{Power input} = 3E_1I_1 \cos \phi_1$$
$$\text{Power output} = \text{power input minus losses}$$
$$\text{Efficiency} = \frac{\text{power output}}{\text{power input}}$$

An expression for the slip may be obtained by multiplying both sides of Eq. (100) by I_2R_2, as follows:

$$I_2{}^2R_2 = \frac{sE_2I_2R_2}{\sqrt{R_2{}^2 + s^2X_2{}^2}} = sE_2I_2 \cos \phi_2$$

Therefore
$$s = \frac{I_2{}^2R_2}{E_2I_2 \cos \phi_2} \tag{112}$$

Now $I_2{}^2R_2$ is the rotor copper loss per phase, and $E_2I_2 \cos \phi_2$ is the power per phase that is transferred across the air gap to the rotor. Hence if both numerator and denominator of Eq. (112) are multiplied by the number of phases, we obtain

$$\text{Slip} = \frac{\text{rotor copper loss}}{\text{power transferred to rotor}}$$
$$= \frac{\text{rotor copper loss}}{\text{power input to stator minus stator copper and iron loss}}$$

349. Power Factor of Induction Motors. It may be seen from Fig. 355 or 357 that the power factor $\cos \phi_1$ of the induction motor is quite low at light loads but increases as the load is increased. At no load it may be less than 10 per cent, while at full load it rarely exceeds 88 per cent. The greatest weakness of the induction motor is that it is apt to incur power-factor penalties. Since the power factor increases as the load is increased, it follows that, whenever the power contract contains a power-factor penalty clause, care should be taken not to install motors that are any larger than is necessary. The variation of power factor with load is shown in Fig. 359.

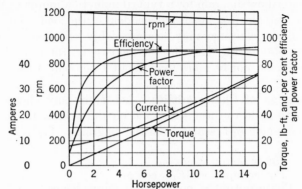

FIG. 359. Operating characteristics of a three-phase 60-cycle 230-volt 10-hp squirrel-cage induction motor with a low-resistance general-purpose rotor.

349A. Equivalent Circuit of an Induction Motor. The easiest way to calculate the operating characteristics of an induction motor is by means of an equivalent circuit. The derivation of this circuit will probably be clearer if we consider the specific case of a three-phase wound-rotor motor in which the ratio of stator turns to rotor turns is n_1/n_2. Considering one phase only,

$$I_2 = \frac{sE_2}{\sqrt{R_2{}^2 + s^2 X_2{}^2}} \tag{100}$$

Dividing both numerator and denominator by s, we obtain

$$I_2 = \frac{E_2}{\sqrt{(R_2/s)^2 + X_2{}^2}}$$

where E_2 and X_2 are the rotor voltage and rotor reactance per phase when the rotor is stationary. Hence if we lock the rotor and insert in the rotor circuit an additional resistance R_3 sufficient to make the total rotor resistance equal to R_2/s the rotor current I_2 will be the same as it was when the rotor was running normally at slip s, and the stator will not be affected in any way by this change.

Since $R_3 + R_2 = R_2/s$,

$$R_3 = \frac{R_2}{s} - R_2 = R_2\frac{1-s}{s}$$

The next step is to transfer R_2, X_2, and R_3 from the rotor or secondary to the stator or primary, as was done in the case of the transformer. The resulting circuit is shown in Fig. 360a, in which

$$R_2' = \left(\frac{n_1}{n_2}\right)^2 \times R_2 \qquad X_2' = \left(\frac{n_1}{n_2}\right)^2 \times X_2$$

$$R_L = \left(\frac{n_1}{n_2}\right)^2 \times R_3 \qquad I_1' = \frac{n_2}{n_1} \times I_2$$

The values of R_0 and X_0 must be such that I_0 will be correct in both magnitude and phase angle, and these values are readily obtained from the no-load test.

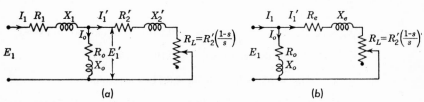

FIG. 360. (a) Equivalent circuit of one phase of an induction motor. (b) Approximate equivalent circuit for one phase of an induction motor.

The labor involved in solving the equivalent circuit is greatly reduced if R_0 and X_0 are shifted to the other side of R_1 and X_1 as in Fig. 360b, in which $R_e = R_1 + R_2'$ and $X_e = X_1 + X_2'$. Note that this approximate equivalent circuit of the induction motor is identical with that of the transformer, Fig. 301b. R_e and X_e are obtained from the locked test.

Example. A 50-hp 440-volt three-phase 60-cycle induction motor on test gave the following data:

1. Resistance of stator winding between terminals is 0.22 ohm. Therefore the resistance R_1 per phase is 0.11 ohm.

2. *No- load test.* Connections as in Fig. 356.

$$f = 60 \text{ cycles} \qquad E_l = 440 \text{ volts} \qquad I_0 = 24 \text{ amp}$$
$$W_c = 5{,}150 \text{ watts} \qquad W_a = -3{,}350 \text{ watts}$$
$$W_0 = 5{,}150 - 3{,}350 = 1{,}800 \text{ watts}$$

$$E_1 = \frac{440}{\sqrt{3}} = 254 \text{ volts}$$

$$Z_0 = \frac{E_1}{I_0} = \frac{254}{24} = 10.6 \text{ ohms}$$

$$I_0{}^2 R_0 = \frac{1{,}800}{3} = 600 \text{ watts per phase}$$

$$R_0 = \frac{600}{24^2} = 1.04 \text{ ohms}$$

$$X_0 = \sqrt{Z_0{}^2 - R_0{}^2} = \sqrt{10.6^2 - 1.04^2} = 10.5 \text{ ohms}$$

3. *Locked test.*   Connections as in Fig. 356.

$$f = 15 \text{ cycles} \qquad I_L = 65 \text{ amp (rated full-load current)}$$
$$E_l = 33.6 \text{ volts} \qquad W_c = 2{,}150 \text{ watts} \qquad W_a = 766 \text{ watts}$$
$$W_L = 2{,}150 + 766 = 2{,}916 \text{ watts}$$

$$E_1 = \frac{33.6}{\sqrt{3}} = 19.4 \text{ volts}$$

$$Z_e = \frac{E_1}{I_1'} = \frac{E_1}{I_L} \text{ (approx.)} = \frac{19.4}{65} = 0.298$$

$$I_L{}^2 R_e = \frac{2{,}916}{3} = 972 \text{ watts per phase}$$

$$R_e = \frac{972}{65^2} = 0.23 \text{ ohm}$$

$$X_e = \sqrt{Z_e{}^2 - R_e{}^2} = \sqrt{0.298^2 - 0.23^2} = 0.19 \text{ ohm at 15 cycles}$$

$$X_e \text{ at 60 cycles} = \frac{60}{15} \times 0.19 = 0.76 \text{ ohm}$$

$$R_2' = R_e - R_1 = 0.23 - 0.11 = 0.12 \text{ ohm}$$

4. *Illustrating the use of the equivalent circuit.*   Points on the characteristic curves are obtained by choosing various convenient values of s and solving the equivalent circuit for each value of s, as follows:
Take $s = 3$ per cent.   Then

$$R_L = R_2' \frac{1 - s}{s} = 0.12 \frac{1 - 0.03}{0.03} = 3.88 \text{ ohms}$$

$$I_1' = \frac{E_1}{(R_e + R_L) + jX_e} = \frac{254}{4.11 + j0.76} = \frac{254(4.11 - j0.76)}{4.11^2 + 0.76^2}$$
$$= 59.8 - j11.0 = \sqrt{59.8^2 + 11.0^2} = 60.7 \text{ amp}$$

In the foregoing calculation, E_1 has been represented by a horizontal vector that is, $E_1 = 254 + j0$, whereas in the circle diagram of Fig. 357 E_1 is vertical that is, $E_1 = 0 + j254$. If the I_1' of the equivalent circuit is turned counterclockwise 90°, it becomes $11.0 + j59.8$ and fits the circle diagram.

$$I_0 = \frac{E_1}{R_0 + jX_0}$$

or may be taken directly from the no-load test, as follows:

$$3E_1 I_0 \cos \phi_0 = W_0 = 1{,}800 \text{ watts}$$

$$I_0 \cos \phi_0 = \frac{1{,}800}{3 \times 254} = 2.36$$

$$I_0 \sin \phi_0 = \sqrt{I_0{}^2 - 2.36^2} = \sqrt{24^2 - 2.36^2} = 23.9$$

Therefore
$$I_0 = 2.36 - j23.9 \text{ (when } E_1 = 254 + j0)$$
$$I_1 = I_1' + I_0 = (59.8 + 2.36) - j(11.0 + 23.9)$$
$$= 62.2 - j34.9 = \sqrt{62.2^2 + 34.9^2} = 71.2 \text{ amp}$$

$$I_1 \text{ lags } E_1 \text{ by } \tan^{-1} \frac{34.9}{62.2} = \tan^{-1} 0.561 = 29°18'$$

Power factor $= \cos 29°18' = 87.2$ per cent

Power input $= \sqrt{3} \times 440 \times 71.2 \times 0.872 = 47,400$ watts

Power output $= 3(I_1')^2 R_L = 3 \times (60.7)^2 \times 3.88 = 42,900$ watts

$\qquad\qquad\qquad = 57.5$ hp

$\qquad$ Efficiency $= \dfrac{42,900}{47,400} = 90.6\%$

e slip at full load would be

$$\frac{50}{57.5} \times 3 \text{ per cent} = 2.65\%$$

350. High-reactance Squirrel-cage Induction Motors. The low-resist-
ce general-purpose induction motor draws a starting current of about

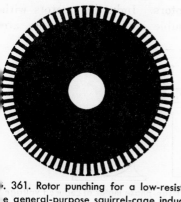

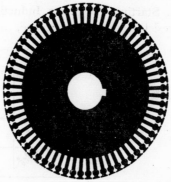

. 361. Rotor punching for a low-resist-
e general-purpose squirrel-cage induc-
 motor. (*General Electric Company.*)

FIG. 362. Rotor punching for a high-
reactance type of squirrel-cage induction
motor. (*General Electric Company.*)

times full-load value if switched directly onto the line. Moreover,
s current is at a low power factor. In the case of large motors, this
normal current may momentarily pull down the voltage of the system
ally enough to be objectionable in its effects on the operation of other
uipment. In such cases, the usual practice is to reduce the voltage
ring starting by inserting a transformer bank between the motor and
 line. The transformer bank is removed as soon as the motor attains
 speed.

Another method of reducing the starting current is to design the rotor
have a higher reactance. This is very easily done. All that is neces-
y is to bury the bars a little more deeply in the iron. Figures 361 and
 show cross sections of the rotor slots of the low-resistance general-
rpose and the high-reactance squirrel-cage rotors, and Figs. 348 and
 show a comparison of the operating characteristics.

The effect of increasing the reactance of the rotor is (1) to decrease the
rting current and therefore the starting torque and (2) to increase

the angle of lag ϕ_2 of the rotor current, and thus still further reduce the starting torque, as explained in Art. 339. Yet Fig. 348 shows that the high-reactance rotor develops a slightly higher starting torque than the low-resistance general-purpose rotor. The explanation of this paradox is to be found in the peculiar shape of the rotor slots. In fact the high-reactance rotor of Fig. 362 partakes of the characteristics of the double squirrel-cage rotor of Fig. 353. The heavy conductors of the inner circle are more deeply embedded in the iron than the smaller conductors of the outer circle and consequently have a higher inductance. Therefore the current distribution at start is not uniform, and the effective resistance of the rotor circuit is higher than that of the general-purpose rotor. Increasing the rotor resistance increases the starting torque, as explained in Art. 341.

351. Starting Polyphase Induction Motors. Induction motors with high-resistance, high-reactance, and double squirrel-cage rotors are

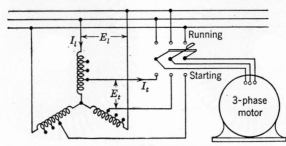

FIG. 363. Autotransformer connections for starting a three-phase motor at reduced voltage. Standard taps give 50, 65, and 80 per cent of line voltage.

always started at full-line voltage, by simply switching them directly on to the line. The wound-rotor induction motor is started in the same way, except that the variable rotor resistance is always set at its maximum value before switching the motor on to the line. The rotor resistance is then gradually cut out as the motor comes up to speed.

Small general-purpose induction motors with low-resistance rotors are also started at full-line voltage, but the larger sizes are usually started at reduced voltage, in order to lessen the disturbance caused on the supply system by the large, low-power-factor starting current of this type of motor. The voltage is reduced by means of a transformer bank that is inserted between the motor and the line and is removed as soon as the motor attains full speed. The transformers used for this purpose are always autotransformers, as in Fig. 363, because the ratio is never more than 2, and, when the ratio is small, autotransformers are considerably cheaper than two-winding transformers.

Reducing the voltage not only reduces the current, but also reduces the starting torque, and this sets the upper limit for the transformer ratio in any given case.   The rotating field Φ is proportional to the applied voltage E_t which produces it, while the rotor current I_2 is proportional to Φ (when the rotor is stationary), so that the starting torque, which is proportional to $\Phi \times I_2$, is proportional to Φ^2 and therefore to E_t^2.   But $E_t = E_l/N$, where N is the transformer ratio.   *Therefore the starting torque is directly proportional to the square of the applied voltage and is inversely proportional to the square of the transformer ratio.*

Again, in a transformer that steps the voltage down, the primary current is approximately equal to the secondary current divided by the transformer ratio.   Therefore $I_l = I_t/N$, where I_t = current to motor (see Fig. 363).   Now I_t is directly proportional to E_t, that is to E_l/N. *Therefore the starting current drawn from the line is inversely proportional to the square of the transformer ratio.*

Example.   A certain motor at standstill takes 5 times full-load current with normal applied voltage and develops 1.5 times full-load torque.   What must the applied voltage be to obtain full-load torque and what will be the starting currents in the motor leads and in the line?

$$\left(\frac{E_t}{E_l}\right)^2 = \frac{\text{full-load torque}}{1.5 \times \text{full-load torque}} = \frac{1}{1.5}$$

Therefore
$$E_t = \sqrt{\frac{1}{1.5}} \times E_l$$
$$= 0.815 E_l$$

or 81.5 per cent of normal voltage.

$$\text{Starting current in motor} = 5 \times \text{full-load current} \times \frac{E_t}{E_l}$$
$$= 4.1 \times \text{full-load current}$$
$$= I_t \quad \text{(Fig. 363)}$$

Ignoring the exciting current of the autotransformer,

$$\text{Starting current in line} = 4.1 \times \text{full-load current} \times \frac{E_t}{E_l}$$
$$= 3.3 \times \text{full-load current}$$
$$= I_l \quad \text{(Fig. 363)}$$

The other types of induction motors are never started on reduced voltage because to do so would nullify the very reason for their existence.

352. Comparison of the Fields of Application of the Different Types of Squirrel-cage Induction Motors.   *a. High-resistance Rotor.*   This is a special-service rotor and is used only where the service consists chiefly of starting and stopping, or where intermittent loads of short duration are to be smoothed out by means of a flywheel.   Its high slip causes it to slow down and allow the flywheel to carry the peak of the load.

b. Low-resistance General-purpose Rotor. This rotor has the highest efficiency, power factor, and pull-out torque and the smallest slip of all the squirrel-cage rotors and is therefore generally used wherever its starting torque is adequate.

c. High-reactance Rotor. In cases where the size of the motor is large enough so that, if a low-resistance rotor were used, it would be necessary to employ starting transformers, a high-reactance rotor may be substituted in order to save the weight, cost, or space, of the starting transformers.

The high-reactance rotor also develops a higher starting torque than the low-resistance rotor when starting transformers are used with the latter, and this may be an important factor.

d. Double Squirrel-cage Rotor. This rotor is used wherever a starting torque of over $1\frac{1}{2}$ times full-load torque is required, provided that the driven mechanism is such that it will not be injured by the sudden application of $2\frac{1}{2}$ times full-load torque. If the torque must be applied gradually, a wound-rotor motor must be used.

It might appear that, since the double squirrel-cage rotor develops an even larger starting torque than the high-reactance rotor and yet costs practically the same and draws the same starting current, it might very well take the place of the high-reactance rotor. It must be realized, however, that an extra-high starting torque, when not required, can be very objectionable, especially with belt drives, and the high-reactance rotor is deliberately designed to have a lower starting torque than the double squirrel-cage rotor, so that it will start more gently.

The four particular designs of squirrel-cage rotors discussed in this chapter will take care of almost any load that can be taken care of by a squirrel-cage motor. However, as many intermediate characteristics as are desired can be obtained by suitable modifications of the shape, size, and depth of the rotor slots, and different manufacturers provide somewhat different selections of starting torque and current in their standard lines.

The full-load efficiencies of the low-resistance, high-reactance, and double squirrel-cage motors generally differ by less than 1 per cent. Hence efficiency is not an important factor in deciding between them, but the efficiency of the high-resistance motor is substantially lower.

353. Induction Generator. Suppose that an electric car driven by an induction motor is operating on a road where there is a long pull up followed by a long coast down. When on the upgrade, the motor runs at about 4 per cent less than synchronous speed, at which speed the rotor slips fast enough through the revolving field to cause full-load current to flow.

Starting on the down grade, the car begins to drive the motor and the speed of the motor first becomes equal to the synchronous speed, at which speed the rotor current is zero, and then runs at a speed which is greater than synchronous so that the rotor is again slipping through the revolving field. But since it is now running faster than the field, the direction of motion of the conductors relative to the field has been reversed. Therefore the rotor emf and current have been reversed, and the torque which was a driving torque now becomes a retarding torque so that the machine is now acting as a generator and delivering power to the line. When the speed is about 4 per cent above synchronous speed, the machine will be delivering full load as a generator. Figure 364 shows the vector diagram for this condition. The electric power input to the machine, per phase, is still $E_1 I_1$ cos ϕ_1, but cos ϕ_1 is now negative.

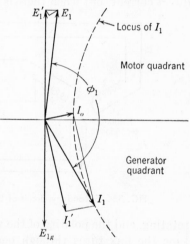

FIG. 364. Vector diagram of an induction motor operating as a generator.

The locomotives of the electrified section of the Virginian Railway are equipped with three-phase induction motors and obtain regenerative braking on the long heavy grades of the mountain division as explained above.

354. Brush-shifting Polyphase Induction Motor. The demand for an adjustable-speed polyphase motor with good speed regulation and reasonably high efficiency at all speeds has led to the development of a commutator type of motor, the speed of which may be adjusted by shifting the brushes.

The reason why the efficiency of the wound-rotor motor is so low at low speeds is that the rotor current is controlled by inserting resistance in the rotor circuit. The $I^2 R$ loss in this resistance can be avoided if the resistance is replaced by a counter emf to oppose the current. This counter emf must, of course, have the same frequency as the emf in the rotor bars and its magnitude must be adjustable. The generation and application of this counter emf are obtained as follows:

First, the rotor and stator windings are interchanged. That is, the primary is wound on the rotor and is fed through three slip rings, while the secondary is wound on the stator. This does not change the operation of the motor in any way, but it does mean that the rotating flux which is produced by the primary winding, and which rotates at synchronous speed relative to that winding, rotates at slip speed relative to stationary objects, such as the secondary winding. For example, in a 60-cycle two-pole motor operating with 5 per cent slip, the rotor, carrying the primary winding, rotates at 95 per cent of 60, or 57 rps, while the flux produced by that primary winding rotates at 3 rps in the opposite direction. The frequency of the emf generated in the secondary winding on the stator is accordingly 3 cycles per sec.

A separate d-c drum winding is placed in the same slots as the primary winding on the rotor and is connected to a commutator. Now if the rotor were running at synchronous speed, the field would be stationary and the voltage across a pair of brushes on the commutator would be direct current, but when there is any load on the motor the flux is slowly

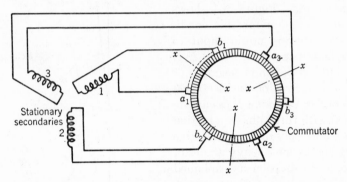

FIG. 365. Secondary circuit of brush-shifting polyphase induction motor.

rotating, and the polarity of the voltage across the brushes reverses every time the flux turns through one-half a revolution. Thus the voltage across the brushes is alternating and its frequency is the same as that in the secondary winding on the stator.

Each phase of the secondary is connected to a pair of brushes on the commutator, as shown in Fig. 365. The brushes $a_1a_2a_3$ are carried on one rocker arm, and the brushes $b_1b_2b_3$ on another rocker arm. When the a brushes are set to coincide with the b brushes on the x-x axes, then each pair of brushes a_1b_1, a_2b_2, a_3b_3 is short-circuited by a commutator bar and the motor runs as an ordinary wound-rotor induction motor with the rotor resistance cut out. But if the brushes are separated as in Fig. 365, a counter emf is obtained from the commutator for each phase. This counter emf may be either positive or negative, depending upon which set of brushes is moved clockwise. Thus a range of speeds above and below synchronous speed may be obtained, and, since this counter emf is practically independent of the load, the speed of the motor is reasonably independent of the load.

The brush-shifting induction motor is more expensive than the wound-rotor motor but its efficiency is higher at all speeds except synchronous speed and is very much higher at the lower speeds. It is, of course, used only where adjustable speed is required, as in bakery machinery, stokers, printing machines, calenders, etc.

Problems

*33-1. Explain how a revolving magnetic field may be produced by currents in stationary windings. Derive a formula for speed of the revolving field in terms of number of poles and frequency.

*33-2. What determines the value of the current in the rotor conductors at standstill? Under running conditions?

*33-3. Why does the reactance of the rotor vary greatly between starting and running conditions? What effect does this have on the power factor of the rotor current?

*33-4. In starting a squirrel-cage induction motor, why is the starting torque relatively low though the current drawn from the line may be very high? (For example, only 1.5 times full-load torque at starting with 5 times full-load current.)

*33-5. What is the effect of inserting resistance in the rotor circuit? In what type of induction motor can we insert resistance in the rotor circuit?

*33-6. What is meant by slip in an induction motor? How is the percentage slip computed?

33-7. The speed of a four-pole 60-cycle induction motor at full load is 1,710 rpm. What is the percentage slip? If the voltage induced in the rotor windings at starting (standstill) is 130 volts, the rotor resistance is 5 ohms, and the rotor reactance at starting is 12 ohms, determine the rotor current at starting and also at full load.

33-8. The following data were obtained by test on a 5-hp 220-volt three-phase 60-cycle squirrel-cage induction motor:

Terminal voltage	Amperes per line	Rpm	Wattmeter readings		Torque, lb at 1 ft
220 (no load)............	5.2	1,200	+ 690/−	390	0.0
220....................	6.6	1,192	+ 1,280/+	50	5.5
220....................	8.5	1,180	+ 1,810/+	540	11.2
220 (full load)............	13.2	1,150	+ 2,910/+1,490		23.0
220....................	19.5	1,110	+ 4,260/+2,340		36.0
220 (at standstill)........	72.0	0	+13,000/−1,400		35.0

a. How many poles has the motor and what is the span of the stator coils?

b. If a 900-rpm motor is wanted, what changes must be made?

c. What is the no-load loss and what is the input at full load?

d. Plot power factor and efficiency on a horsepower output base.

e. If an autotransformer is used to reduce the starting current, what is the secondary emf for full-load torque and what are then the current in the motor, the current in the line, and the power factor?

f. What would have been the starting current for full-load torque if the motor had been of the wound-rotor type with a suitable resistance in the rotor circuit?

g. Since the wound-rotor motor gives full-load torque at starting with full-load current, what must be the power factor at starting?

33-9. When the voltage applied to a motor carrying full-load brake torque is reduced to 90 per cent of the normal value, what happens (*a*) to the strength of the rotating field, (*b*) to the rotor current, and (*c*) to the speed? Efficiency and power factor are not much changed.

*33-10. Draw a diagram similar to Fig. 341 for a six-pole three-phase 60-cycle induction motor with one slot per phase per pole (18 total). Plot the resulting magnetic field for the four instants *A*, *B*, *C*, and *D*, Fig. 341, and from these diagrams find the speed of the revolving field in revolutions per minute and derive the speed formula in terms of the number of poles and the frequency. (Be sure that you get the starts of the three phases 120 and not 60 electrical degrees apart.)

*33-11. On what does the starting torque of an induction motor depend? Why does the starting torque vary as the square of the applied emf?

*33-12. What must be the frequency of the line if a six-pole induction motor runs at 1,125 rpm on full load? Tabulate the various possible synchronous speeds of induction motors used on 25- and 60-cycle lines.

*33-13. What is the effect upon the slip of an induction motor of introducing resistance into the rotor circuit? Explain.

*33-14. What is the distinct disadvantage of controlling the speed of an induction motor by inserting resistance into the rotor circuit?

33-15. A certain induction motor at standstill takes 5 times full-load current with normal applied voltage and develops 1.5 times full-load torque. (*a*) What must be the applied voltage to obtain 0.8 full-load torque at starting? (Express in terms of normal voltage.) (*b*) What will be the starting current in the line? (Express in terms of full-load current.)

33-16. A 20-hp 220-volt 855-rpm three-phase 60-cycle squirrel-cage induction motor with 220 volts applied takes a current of 6 times full-load current at standstill and develops 1.8 times full-load running torque. Full-load current is 60 amp.

a. What voltage must be applied to produce full-load torque at starting?

b. What current will this voltage produce?

c. If this reduced voltage is obtained by autotransformers, what will be the line current?

d. If the starting current is limited to full-load current, what will be the starting torque as a percentage of full-load torque?

e. If the applied voltage is reduced 10 per cent while the motor is running, what will be the speed in rpm and the torque in per cent at full-load current? (Neglect change in exciting current.)

f. If, while running at full load, the frequency is increased 10 per cent and the voltage is increased 10 per cent while the torque is 10 per cent above full-load value, what will be the current and speed?

33-17. A manufacturing plant, which is supplied with 50-cycle power at 440 volts, three-phase, requires a 40-hp squirrel-cage induction motor. They are offered a 1,710-rpm 50-hp 60-cycle 550-volt squirrel-cage motor (secondhand) that has a starting torque of 1.5 times full-load torque with 5 times full-load current at 550 volts, 60 cycles. If this machine is used at 50 cycles, 440 volts, determine the following:

a. What will be the change in flux?

b. What will be the approximate change in starting torque?

c. What will be the approximate change in iron loss?

d. Can it be used to deliver 40 hp continuously?

e. What will be the speed at the maximum continuous horsepower?

33-18. The voltage generated in each phase of the rotor winding of a 60-cycle wound-rotor induction motor at standstill is 80 volts. The impedance of each phase of the rotor winding is 0.1 ohm resistance and 0.5 ohm reactance at 60 cycles. Full-load rotor current is 30 amp.

a. How much resistance must be inserted in each phase of the rotor to limit the starting current to full-load value?

b. How much resistance must be inserted in each phase of the rotor to reduce the speed to 25 per cent of synchronous speed at (1) full load (2) one-tenth load?

c. Plot curves of starting torque and rotor current, in per cent of full-load values, on a rotor resistance base, and determine the value of rotor resistance for maximum starting torque.

NOTE. The rotor current may be resolved into two components, one lagging the rotor voltage by 90° and producing no torque (Art. 339) and the other in phase with the rotor voltage and producing approximately the same torque per ampere as is produced under full-load running conditions.

33-19. A 440-volt 25-hp three-phase 60-cycle six-pole squirrel-cage induction motor on test gave the following results:

1. Resistance between any two terminals of the Y-connected stator winding is 0.48 ohm.

2. No-load test: Input to stator at rated voltage is 12 amp, 850 watts.

3. Locked test at 60 cycles: Input to stator at one-fourth rated voltage is 45.7 amp, 4,380 watts; torque is 18 lb-ft.

4. Locked test at 20 cycles: Input to stator at one-eighth rated voltage is 47.7 amp, 3,410 watts.

a. From tests (2) and (4) determine the equivalent circuit of Fig. 360*b*.

b. From this circuit calculate and plot curves of stator current, power factor, efficiency, and speed or slip, on a horsepower output base.

c. From test (3) calculate the starting torque and stator current when the motor is switched directly on to a 440-volt line.

34

ALTERNATING-CURRENT-GENERATOR CHARACTERISTICS

355. Armature Reaction. As long as the armature conductors of an a-c generator are carrying no current, the only magnetic flux present is that produced by the direct current in the field coils. This flux is carried around by the rotation of the rotor, cuts the stationary armature conductors, and generates emfs in them. When however, the generator is delivering current to a load, this current, flowing in the armature conductors, produces a magnetic field also.

Now it was shown in Art. 336 that, when three-phase current is supplied to the stator of an induction motor, magnetic fields are produced which glide from coil to coil, the whole field rotating about the axis of the machine; but the stator of the generator is identical with the stator of the induction motor, and consequently the magnetic field produced in the generator by these same alternating currents must also be a rotating one.

Figure 366A shows the flux produced by the armature currents in a three-phase generator when the power factor of the load is 100 per cent. The crosses and dots show the directions of both the voltages and the currents, since the voltage and the current are in phase at 100 per cent power factor. The voltage generated in phase 2 by the flux produced by the field current is zero at the instant shown because the conductors of phase 2 are midway between the poles and are therefore not being cut by the flux from these poles. The current in phase 2 is also zero because voltage and current are in phase when the power factor of the load is 100 per cent. The armature reaction is cross-magnetizing as in the d-c generator, the flux produced in the poles by the armature currents being at right angles to the axes of the poles. The pole tips on the left are weakened, while those on the right are strengthened. The net result is that the flux is crowded to the right-hand pole tips and is somewhat reduced by the crowding action. The distorted flux, pulling back on the poles, creates the opposing torque with which the rotor resists being turned when current is flowing in the armature.

Figure 366*B* shows the flux produced by the armature currents alone, when the power factor of the load is zero lagging. The crosses and dots show the directions of the armature currents but not of the emfs. The currents are shown the same as in Fig. 366*A* but, since they now lag 90°

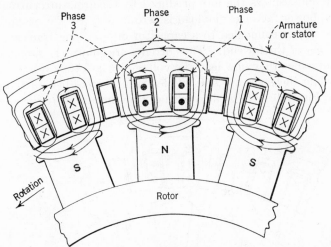

FIG. 366A. Flux produced in a three-phase generator by the armature currents only, when the power factor of the load is 100 per cent. (Armature winding concentrated in one slot per phase per pole.)

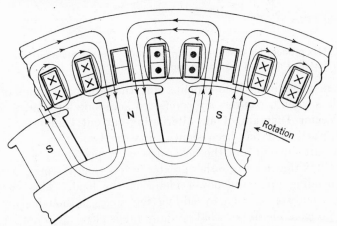

FIG. 366B. Flux produced in a three-phase generator by the armature currents only, when the power factor of the load is zero lagging.

behind the voltage, they do not reach the values shown until the poles have moved on 90 electrical degrees from the position shown in Fig. 366*A*. The flux produced by the armature currents is now directly demagnetizing and, since it rotates at the same speed as the poles, it is continuously demagnetizing throughout the complete revolution.   It follows that with loads of low lagging power factor, such as lightly loaded induction motors, the terminal voltage of the generator drops off rapidly as the load is increased.   This is one more drawback of low power-factor loads.

Figure 366C shows the flux produced by the armature currents alone when the power factor of the load is zero leading, as, for example, when the generator is connected to a capacitor or to a long transmission line that is open at the far end.   The currents are shown the same as in Fig. 366A, but, since they now lead the voltage by 90°, they reach the values shown while the poles are still 90 electrical degrees behind the position shown in Fig. 366A.   The flux produced by the armature currents is now

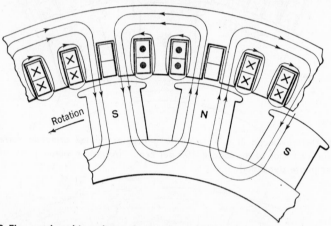

FIG. 366C. Flux produced in a three-phase generator by the armature currents only, when the power factor of the load is zero leading.

directly magnetizing, which explains why the terminal voltage of a generator rises when capacitors are connected across its terminals.

356. Vector Diagram of an Alternating-current Generator.   In the preceding article it has been shown how the two fluxes, produced by the armature current and the field current, respectively, add to give a resultant flux that may be either greater or less than the original no-load flux, depending upon the power factor of the load.   This method of treating armature reaction by adding the fluxes, although it gives the clearest possible picture of what actually takes place, does not lend itself readily to the obtaining of numerical results.   When it is desired to calculate what the terminal voltage will be under a given load condition, it is better to consider the two fluxes separately, to calculate the two voltages generated by these two fluxes, and then to add these two voltages to obtain the resultant voltage.

Now the voltage generated in the armature conductors by the flux produced by the armature currents is fundamentally a reactance voltage, in that it (1) is produced by the armature currents themselves, (2) is roughly proportional to the armature current, and (3) is at 90° to the current.   That this voltage is at 90° to the current may be seen from any one of Figs. 366A, B, and C, where phase 2 is carrying zero current but is at the centers of the magnetic poles produced by the armature flux and is therefore having a maximum emf induced in it by that flux.

Thus the voltage generated by the flux produced by the armature current is IX_s, where X_s is a constant called the *synchronous reactance* of the generator.   It is called *synchronous* because its flux rotates in synchronism with the main field.

Now the flux produced by the field current alone is constant, as long as the field current is constant, and therefore the voltage E_0 generated by

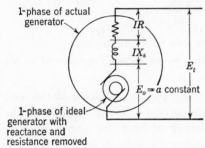

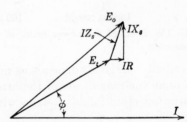

FIG. 367. Diagrammatic representation of an a-c generator.

FIG. 368. Vector diagram of an a-c generator (power factor of load equal to 86 per cent lagging).

this flux is constant.   All changes in terminal voltage therefore are due entirely to changes in the magnitude and phase angle of IX_s and IR.

Figure 367 shows one phase of a conventionalized a-c generator in which the resistance and synchronous reactance have been separated from the generator proper.

Let E_t = terminal voltage of one phase of the generator

E_0 = voltage generated in one phase by the field flux only

= a constant as long as field current I_f is constant

IX_s = voltage consumed by the synchronous reactance of generator

IR = voltage consumed by armature resistance

Z_s = synchronous impedance of the generator, per phase

= $\sqrt{R^2 + X_s{}^2}$

cos ϕ = power factor of external load

Then E_0 is the vector sum of E_t, IX_s, and IR.   Figure 368 shows the vector diagram drawn for one phase only.

$$E_0 = \sqrt{(E_t \cos \phi + IR)^2 + (E_t \sin \phi + IX_s)^2} \qquad (113)$$

an equation which can be solved for any one quantity if the remaining quantities are given.

357. Voltage Characteristic Curves and Voltage Regulation of an Alternating-current Generator. It may be seen from Fig. 369a, b, c that the difference between the terminal voltage E_t under load and the no-load

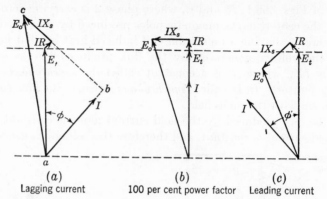

(a)   (b)   (c)
Lagging current   100 per cent power factor   Leading current

FIG. 369. Effect of the power factor of the load on the voltage regulation of an a-c generator.

terminal voltage E_0 depends as much upon the power factor of the load as upon the magnitude of the armature current. Figure 370 shows the variation of terminal voltage with change of load, for three different power factors of load, when the field current is kept constant.

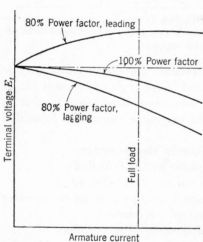

FIG. 370. Voltage characteristics of an a-c generator. (Field current and speed constant.)

The voltage regulation of an a-c generator is defined as being the rise in terminal voltage when the load is reduced from rated full-load kilovolt-amperes to zero, speed and field current remaining constant. It is expressed as a percentage of the full-load voltage. Thus

$$\text{Voltage regulation} = \frac{E_0 - E_t}{E_t}$$

the subtraction being algebraic, not vector.

As may be seen from Fig. 369, the voltage regulation is different for every different power factor of load and becomes negative if the power factor is leading considerably.

The voltage regulation for any given power factor of load may be calculated by means of Eq. (113), if the synchronous reactance and the armature resistance are known, as follows:

Example. A single-phase generator with a full-load output of 416 amp at 2,400 volts has a resistance of 0.1 ohm and a synchronous reactance of 3 ohms. Find the regulation at 100 per cent power factor, and also at 80 per cent power factor with a lagging current, the full-load voltage being 2,400 volts in each case.

$$\text{Full-load current} = 416 \text{ amp}$$
$$\text{Resistance drop } IR = 416 \times 0.1 = 41.6 = 42 \text{ volts}$$
$$\text{Synchronous reactance drop } IX_s = 416 \times 3 = 1,248 \text{ volts}$$

At 100 per cent power factor (see Fig. 369b),

$$E_0{}^2 = (E_t + IR)^2 + (IX_s)^2$$
$$= 2,442^2 + 1,248^2$$
and
$$E_0 = 2,740$$
$$\text{Regulation} = \frac{E_0 - E_t}{E_t} = \frac{340}{2,400} = 14.2\%$$

At 80 per cent power factor with lagging current (see Fig. 369a),

$$E_0{}^2 = ab^2 + bc^2$$
$$= (E_t \cos \phi + IR)^2 + (E_t \sin \phi + IX_s)^2$$
$$= (2,400 \times 0.8 + 42)^2 + (2,400 \times 0.6 + 1,248)^2$$
and
$$E_0 = 3,328$$
$$\text{Regulation} = \frac{3,328 - 2,400}{2,400} = 38.6\%$$

358. Experimental Determination of the Synchronous Impedance of an Alternating-current Generator. The no-load saturation curve for one

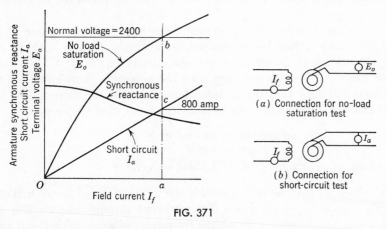

FIG. 371

phase of an a-c generator is shown in Fig. 371. It is obtained by driving the generator at rated speed, varying the field current I_f in suitable steps, and measuring the corresponding values of E_0. In the case of a single-phase generator, E_0 is the no-load terminal voltage, and the connections are as in Fig. 371a. In the case of a three-phase generator, the connections are as in Fig. 372, and $E_0 = E/\sqrt{3}$. If the neutral is accessible, E_0 may be measured directly.

The short-circuit armature-current curve for a single-phase generator is obtained by reducing the field current to a small value, or interrupting it entirely, short-circuiting the generator terminals through an ammeter, as in Fig. 371b, and then gradually increasing the field current in suitable steps. The armature current I_a is then plotted against I_f. In the case of a three-phase generator, all three phases must be shorted, as in Fig. 372, but since the three currents will be equal, only one of them need be measured. In general, it will not be possible to obtain the complete

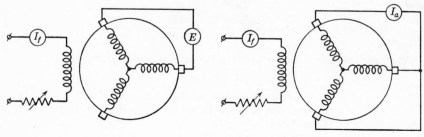

No-load saturation test   Short-circuit test

FIG. 372. Obtaining the synchronous impedance of a three-phase generator.

short-circuit curve experimentally without overheating the generator, but since the graph is a straight line, it may be produced as far as is desired.

From these two curves, the synchronous impedance per phase of the generator may readily be determined, for example, with $I_f = oa$, in Fig. 371, the voltage E_0 generated in one phase at no load is $ab = 2{,}400$ volts. With the same field current and with the armature short-circuited, the terminal voltage is zero and E_0 is used up in driving the current $ac = 800$ amp through the synchronous impedance of the winding, so that

$$\text{Voltage } ab = \text{current } ac \times Z_s$$

or

$$2{,}400 = 800\,Z_s$$

therefore

$$Z_s = 3 \text{ ohms} = \sqrt{R^2 + X_s{}^2}$$

from which X_s may be determined if the value of R is known; and R is readily measured by passing a direct current through the winding and measuring the current and voltage by means of an ammeter and voltmeter. In general, R is so much smaller than X_s that X_s is practically numerically equal to Z_s.

It may be seen from Fig. 371 that the synchronous reactance decreases as the field current is increased. This is a magnetic saturation effect. As the field current is increased, the armature current also increases, and the components of flux produced by these two currents both increase. As long as the resultant flux density is below the knee of the saturation curve, the flux produced per ampere of armature current is approximately constant, and therefore the synchronous reactance is approximately constant. For higher flux densities, the flux produced per ampere is less, and consequently the synchronous reactance is smaller.

The fact that the synchronous reactance is not actually a constant but varies considerably with both saturation and power factor makes it difficult to obtain accurate results in the type of calculation illustrated in this chapter, because there is no way of knowing what value of X_s to insert in the formula. For rough calculations, one may use the value of X_s corresponding to rated no-load voltage, Fig. 371. A more precise method of calculation has been developed and is used by designers, but it is too involved to be described here.

Example 1. A three-phase Y-connected generator has a full-load output of 240 amp at 2,400 volts. With a certain field excitation the no-load voltage between terminals was 2,400 volts, and the current in each line on short circuit was 465 amp. The resistance of each phase is 0.1 ohm. Find the synchronous reactance per phase.

$$E_t, \text{ terminal voltage at no load} = 2,400 \text{ volts}$$

$$E, \text{ voltage per phase at no load} = \frac{2,400}{\sqrt{3}} = 1,390 \text{ volts}$$

$$I_t, \text{ line current on short circuit} = 465 \text{ amp}$$
$$I, \text{ current per phase on short circuit} = 465 \text{ amp}$$

$$Z_s, \text{ synchronous impedance per phase} = \frac{1,390}{465} = 3 \text{ ohms}$$

$$X_s, \text{ synchronous reactance per phase} = \sqrt{Z^2 - R^2} = \sqrt{3^2 - 0.1^2} = 3-$$

Find the regulation of this machine at full load and 100 per cent power factor, the full-load voltage between terminals being 2,400 volts.

$$\text{Full-load current in line} = 240 \text{ amp}$$
$$\text{Full-load current per phase} = 240 \text{ amp}$$
$$\text{Resistance drop } IR \text{ per phase} = 240 \times 0.1 = 24 \text{ volts}$$
$$\text{Reactance drop } IX_s \text{ per phase} = 240 \times 3 = 720 \text{ volts}$$
$$\text{Full-load voltage between terminals} = 2,400 \text{ volts}$$

$$\text{Full-load voltage per phase} = \frac{2,400}{\sqrt{3}} = 1,390 \text{ volts}$$

Then at 100 per cent power factor (see Fig. 369b),

$$E_0^2 = (1,390 + 24)^2 + 720^2$$
and
$$E_0 = 1,586 \text{ volts per phase}$$
and   No-load voltage between terminals $= 1,586 \times \sqrt{3} = 2,740 \text{ volts}$

$$\text{Regulation} = \frac{2,740 - 2,400}{2,400} = 14.2\%$$

Example 2. A three-phase Δ-connected generator has an output of 240 amp at 2,400 volts. With a particular field excitation the no-load voltage between terminals was 2,400 volts and the current in each line on short circuit was 600 amp. The resistance of each phase was 0.2 ohm. Find the synchronous reactance per phase.

$$E_t, \text{ terminal voltage at no load} = 2,400 \text{ volts}$$
$$E, \text{ voltage per phase at no load} = 2,400 \text{ volts}$$
$$I_l, \text{ line current on short circuit} = 600 \text{ amp}$$
$$I, \text{ current per phase on short circuit} = \frac{600}{\sqrt{3}} = 346 \text{ amp}$$
$$Z_s, \text{ synchronous impedance per phase} = \frac{2,400}{346} = 6.9 \text{ ohms}$$
$$X_s, \text{ synchronous reactance per phase} = \sqrt{6.9^2 - 0.2^2} = 6.9-$$

Find the regulation of this machine at full load and 100 per cent power factor, the full-load voltage between terminals being 2,400 volts.

$$\text{Full-load current in line} = 240 \text{ amp}$$
$$\text{Full-load current per phase} = \frac{240}{\sqrt{3}} = 139$$

Resistance drop IR per phase $= 139 \times 0.2 = 28$ volts
Synchronous reactance drop IX_s per phase $= 139 \times 6.9 = 960$ volts
Full-load voltage between terminals $= 2,400$ volts
Full-load voltage per phase $= 2,400$ volts

At 100 per cent power factor (see Fig. 369*b*),

$$E_0^2 = (2,400 + 28)^2 + 960^2$$
$$E_0 = 2,615 \text{ volts}$$
$$\text{Regulation} = \frac{2,615 - 2,400}{2,400} = 9\%$$

359. Automatic Regulators. To maintain the voltage of an a-c generator constant, the field excitation must be increased as the armature current increases and as the power factor decreases. This cannot be done by adding series-field coils as in the case of the d-c generator, because the line current is alternating and not suitable for excitation purposes.

The field current is supplied by a small shunt-excited d-c generator called an exciter, and the alternator voltage is controlled by varying the resistance of a rheostat which is in series with the field of the exciter. This may be done in various ways. One method is to provide the rheostat with a large number of taps and contact studs, mounted in a circle, and to have a small d-c motor operate the contact arm through a worm drive. The d-c motor is driven by a storage battery and is controlled by a contact-making voltmeter or relay which is connected, through a transformer, across the terminals of the alternator, and which starts the d-c motor up in one direction if the voltage exceeds a certain maximum value, and in the opposite direction if the voltage is less than a certain minimum value. Thus the voltage is automatically held between two fixed limits, which may be set as close together as is desired.

360. Rating of Alternating-current Generators. An a-c generator is designed so as to give normal voltage and normal current without overheating, but the output in kilowatts will depend entirely on the power factor of the connected load. It is usual to specify the output at 100 per cent power factor and then, to emphasize the fact that this output cannot be obtained from the machine at lower power factors, the unit of output is taken as the kilovolt-ampere (kva) and not as the kilowatt, where kilovolt-amperes × power factor = kilowatts.

Example. A single-phase generator can give 100 amp at 2,400 volts. What is the output of the machine in kilovolt-amperes and also in kilowatts if the power factor of the load is 80 per cent?

$$kva = \frac{2,400 \times 100}{1,000} = 240$$
$$kw = 240 \times 0.8 = 192$$

A three-phase generator can give 100 amp from each terminal with a voltage between terminals of 2,400; then

$$Output = \frac{1.73 \times 2,400 \times 100}{1,000} = 415 \text{ kva}$$

At 80 per cent power factor, the output would be

$$415 \times 0.8 = 332 \text{ kw}$$

361. Efficiency. The losses in an a-c generator are the same as in a d-c generator and consist of the mechanical and iron losses, the armature copper loss, and the field-excitation loss. These losses are determined in the same way as for the d-c machine (see Art. 153). It must be noted, however, that the efficiency depends on the power factor of the load, as may be seen from the following example:

Example. A 2,400-volt 500-kva 60-cycle three-phase Y-connected generator on test gave the following data:

> Mechanical and iron losses = 12 kw
> Field current at full load, 100% power factor = 53 amp
> Field current at full load, 80% power factor = 65 amp
> Resistance of each phase of armature winding = 0.38 ohm

The exciter voltage is constant at 125 volts, and voltage control is accomplished by means of a rheostat in the generator field circuit. Calculate the full-load efficiency when the power factor of the load is 100 per cent, and also when the power factor is 80 per cent lagging.

$$\text{Full-load armature current} = \frac{500,000}{\sqrt{3} \times 2,400} = 120 \text{ amp}$$

	At 100 % power factor	At 80 % power factor
Output.................	$\sqrt{3} \times 2,400 \times 120 = 500$ kw	$\sqrt{3} \times 2,400 \times 120 \times 0.8 = 400$ kw
Mechanical and iron losses	12 kw	12 kw
Excitation loss..........	$125 \times 53 = 6.6$ kw	$125 \times 65 = 8.1$ kw
Armature copper loss....	$120^2 \times 0.38 \times 3 = 16.4$ kw	$120^2 \times 0.38 \times 3 = 16.4$ kw
Total loss..............	35.0 kw	36.5 kw
Input..................	535 kw	436.5 kw
Efficiency.............	$500/535 = 93.5\%$	$400/436.5 = 91.6\%$

362. Short-circuit Current of a Three-phase Generator. If all three phases of a Y-connected generator are shorted to the neutral, the only impedance left in the circuit of each phase is the synchronous impedance

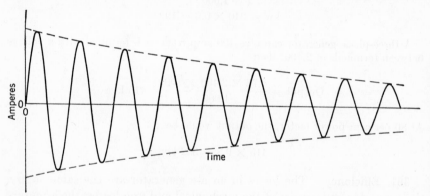

FIG. 373. Short-circuit current in a three-phase a-c generator. Short applied at the instant when the terminal emf is a maximum.

of the generator. Therefore the short-circuit current, after the transient has died out, is given by the equation

$$I = \frac{E_0}{Z_s} \qquad \text{or} \qquad I = \frac{E_0}{X_s}$$

since R is relatively small.

It is found, however, that the current during the first few cycles, after suddenly applying the short, is much larger than the value given by the foregoing equation. Figure 373 shows how the short-circuit current in one phase gradually dies down to the value E_0/Z_s. In this figure the phase has been shorted at the instant when the emf was a maximum, so as to avoid superimposing the type of switching transient discussed in Art. 258.

The explanation of the large initial value of the short-circuit current is to be found in Fig. 366B. This figure applies because Z_s is chiefly reactance, and the short-circuit current therefore lags nearly 90° behind E_0. Figure 366B shows that part of the flux produced by the armature coils links with the field coils also, and part does not. Let us split the synchronous reactance X_s into two components x and x', where x is the reactance corresponding to the flux ϕ that links the armature coils only, and x' is the reactance corresponding to the flux ϕ' that links both armature coils and field coils. If now a short is suddenly applied, so that a large current I flows in the armature coils, the flux ϕ grows simultaneously with the current and is immediately effective in generating a voltage Ix to limit the current. The flux ϕ', however, cannot grow quickly because, as it grows, it cuts the field coils and generates voltage in them, which by Lenz's law causes additional current to flow in the field coils to oppose the growth of ϕ'. Therefore ϕ' grows comparatively slowly. Thus during the first cycle ϕ' is negligible, and the short-circuit current is given approximately by the equation $I = E_0/x$. Later, when ϕ' has grown to its final value, $I = E_0/(x + x')$, and is much smaller. This type of transient may be called an *armature reaction transient*.

If the short is applied at the instant when the emf is zero, a switching transient of the type shown in Fig. 221 will be superimposed on the armature reaction transient, with the result that the peak value of the first half wave of current will be doubled. Peak values up to thirty times full-load current have been obtained in this way from steam turbogenerators. Such currents produce dangerous stresses in the generator, and designers now take care that x is large enough to protect the machine. Partly closing the slots above the coils increases x.

Problems

34-1. A single-phase generator has an output of 1,000 kva at 6,600 volts. When rotating at normal speed, the no-load voltage with a certain field excitation was 6,600 and the current on short circuit with the same field excitation was 380 amp. The resistance of the winding is 1.5 ohms.

a. Find the reactance of the winding.

b. Find the regulation at 100 per cent power factor, also at 80 per cent and at zero power factor with lagging current, the full-load voltage being 6,600 volts in each case.

34-2. A three-phase generator has an output of 1,000 kva at 2,400 volts and is Y-connected. The mechanical and iron loss is 20 kw, the exciting current is 125 amp at 100 per cent power factor and 160 amp at 80 per cent power factor, while the exciter voltage is 120. The resistance of each phase of the armature winding is 0.5 ohm. Find: (*a*) the armature copper loss; (*b*) the full-load efficiency at 100 per cent and at 80 per cent power factor.

34-3. The following data were taken on no-load saturation and short-circuit runs of a 220-kva 2,200-volt 60-cycle 600-rpm single-phase generator.

Field current, amp	No-load volts	Short circuit, amp
20	740	65
40	1,460	130
60	2,100	198
80	2,600	260
100	2,930	325
120	3,190	385
140	3,380	460
160	3,520	525

The resistance of the armature is 1.1 ohms.

a. Plot the no-load saturation and short-circuit current curves from the above data.

b. Find the reactance of the armature at various field currents and plot on the same sheet as the curves in *a.*

c. Assuming a constant value of reactance of 10 ohms, what is the resistance drop and what the reactance drop with full-load current?

d. Find the regulation at 100 per cent power factor, also at 80 per cent power factor with leading current, and 60 per cent power factor with lagging current, the terminal voltage being 2,200 at full load in each case.

e. If the terminal voltage has to be kept constant at all loads by means of a voltage regulator, what range of excitation must be taken care of by the regulator for all loads from no load to full load at 60 per cent power factor lagging?

f. Why is the field current of the machine so large compared with the armature current?

g. Why is it safe to short-circuit an a-c generator even with full field excitation while a d-c generator would burn up with the same treatment?

h. If the core loss, windage, and friction of this generator at normal voltage are 6 kw and if the excitation voltage is 110 volts, what are the losses at full load with 100 per cent power factor and with 60 per cent power factor and lagging current and what are the efficiencies under these two conditions of operation?

34-4. An a-c generator of 1,000-kva capacity has a full-load efficiency of 93 per cent at 100 per cent power factor and of 91 per cent at 80 per cent power factor with lagging current.

a. What size of engine would you use if the machine is used entirely for incandescent lighting load?

b. What size of engine would you use if it were to be used for motor load and it was known that the power factor would never exceed 80 per cent?

35

POLYPHASE SYNCHRONOUS MOTORS
AND PARALLEL OPERATION OF
ALTERNATING-CURRENT GENERATORS

363. Principle of Operation of Synchronous Motors. The stator of the synchronous motor is identical with that of the a-c generator and induction motor, but the rotor, as shown in Fig. 374, is a combination of

Leads for
field current

Slip rings for
field current

FIG. 374. Rotor of a synchronous motor. (*Courtesy of General Electric* Co.)

the rotors of the generator and the induction motor. It consists of an ordinary salient pole generator rotor with a squirrel-cage winding carried in slots cut in the pole faces.

No field current is supplied to the poles when starting, and the motor therefore starts as an ordinary induction motor (Art. 339); that is, the armature currents produce a revolving magnetic field which cuts the squirrel-cage rotor bars and generates emf in them. The resulting currents in the bars create the driving torque.

As soon as the rotor has come up to speed and is running with a slip of, say, 2 or 3 per cent, a d-c field current is gradually applied to the field windings on the rotor poles, the magnetized poles lock with the revolving field produced by the armature currents, and the rotor then runs at synchronous speed.

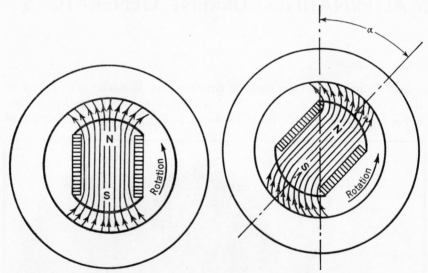

FIG. 375. Magnetic field and rotor position of a two-pole synchronous motor when the brake torque is zero.

FIG. 376. Magnetic field and rotor position under load. The rotor lags by the angle α behind the magnetic field produced by the armature currents.

The torque which holds the rotor poles in synchronism with the revolving field produced by the armature currents is the same torque that swings an ordinary magnetic-compass needle into line with the earth's magnetic field. If the rotor, or the compass needle, is exactly lined up with the magnetic field, as in Fig. 375, there is no torque, and this represents the condition of zero brake load; but if the rotor, or the compass needle, is deflected away from the line of the field by some mechanical means, as in Fig. 376, a torque is developed, which increases as the deflection is increased, becoming a maximum at a deflection of 90° from the line of the field. Any further increase of brake torque will cause the rotor to pull out of synchronism and stop.

Once the rotor has pulled into synchronism, the squirrel cage takes no further part in the steady-state operation of the motor, because it is not being cut by the flux and therefore carries no current. However, any sudden change in the brake load causes the rotor to oscillate about its position of dynamic balance in the rotating field. This oscillation induces emfs in the squirrel-cage bars and thus causes currents to flow in them, with the result that electromagnetic forces act on the bars to oppose the oscillation. Thus the squirrel cage acts to stabilize the position of the rotor relative to the rotating field. This is an important function of the squirrel cage, as otherwise the oscillations would sometimes be large enough to cause the rotor to pull out of synchronism.

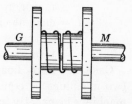

364. Mechanical Analogy. The transmission of power by means of an a-c generator and a synchronous motor is similar in many ways to the transmission of power by means of a flexible spring coupling such as that shown in Fig. 377.

FIG. 377. Mechanical analogy to a synchronous motor.

If the load on the side M is increased, the spring stretches and M drops back through a small angle relative to G, but both continue thereafter to rotate at normal speed.

365. Vector Diagrams of a Synchronous Motor. The easiest way to investigate the operation of a synchronous motor is to begin with two a-c generators operating in parallel, being driven in perfect synchronism and generating equal voltages, but not carrying any load. One of them may then be allowed to lag behind the other by a few degrees and thus automatically to become a motor.

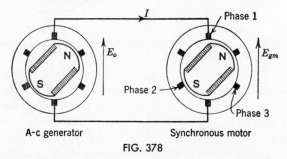

FIG. 378

Two identical two-pole machines are shown in Fig. 378. We shall refer to one of them as a generator and to the other one as a motor, even though they are both functioning as generators in Case 1. Only one phase need be considered, because from the symmetry of the machines it is evident that whatever happens in one phase will be duplicated in the other two phases, only delayed by 120 and 240 electrical degrees, respectively. Figure 379 shows the circuit of one phase of the two machines, broken down into its component parts, as was done in Fig. 367.

Let E_0 = voltage generated in one phase of generator by flux produced
by its field current

E_{gm} = voltage generated in one phase of motor by flux produced by
its field current

E_r = vector sum of E_0 and E_{gm}

X_g, X_m = synchronous reactances per phase of armature windings of
generator and motor, respectively.

R_g, R_m = resistances per phase of armature windings of generator and
motor, respectively

I = current circulating through one phase of armature windings
of the two machines

E = terminal or line voltage

Case 1. Zero Load, and $E_{gm} = E_0$. Let the field currents of the
two machines be equal so that $E_{gm} = E_0$, and let the rotors of the two
machines be exactly in step, as in Fig. 378, so that E_{gm} and E_0 are exactly
180° out of phase with each other with reference to circulating current,
that is, when E_0 is trying to circulate current clockwise E_{gm} is trying to

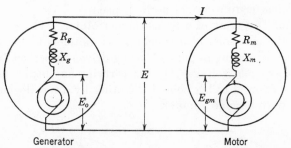

Generator   Motor

FIG. 379. Showing the component circuit elements of one phase of a three-phase generator
driving a three-phase synchronous motor.

circulate it counterclockwise. Then since E_{gm} and E_0 are equal and
opposite, their vector sum $E_r = 0$, and $I = 0$. The vector diagram is
as shown in Fig. 380a. This is the case of absolutely zero load. In
order to obtain this case experimentally, it would be necessary to supply
a mechanical torque to the synchronous motor shaft of sufficient magnitude to take care of the windage, friction, and iron losses of the synchronous motor. This could be done by means of an auxiliary motor.

Case 2. Motor Carrying a Brake Load, and $E_{gm} = E_0$. Let a brake
torque be applied to the shaft of the synchronous motor of Fig. 378, so
that the rotor is pulled back an angle α behind the revolving field. E_{gm}
now lags behind its no-load position by the angle α, as shown in Fig.
380b. E_r is now no longer zero, and the current I is equal to E_r divided
by the impedance of the circuit through the two machines in series.

That is,

$$I = \frac{E_r}{\sqrt{(R_m + R_g)^2 + (X_m + X_g)^2}} \qquad (114)$$

Since the resistances are generally small compared with the reactances, the effect of the resistances is often neglected and then

$$I = \frac{E_r}{X_m + X_g} \qquad (115)$$

The current I lags the voltage E_r by the angle whose tangent is $(X_m + X_g)/(R_m + R_g)$, and since the ratio of reactance to resistance in synchronous motors and generators is rarely less than 15, the angle between E_r

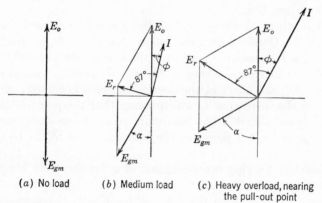

| (a) No load | (b) Medium load | (c) Heavy overload, nearing the pull-out point |

FIG. 380. Vector diagrams for the synchronous motor at various loads, but with constant excitation and with $E_{gm} = E_0$.

and I is rarely less than 86°.   It varies from about 86° to 89° and is shown as 87° in Figs. 380 and 381.

The line voltage E, Fig. 379, is not shown in Fig. 380.   It differs from E_0 by the amount of the IR_g and IX_g voltage drops; but since it is vector subtraction, E is not necessarily smaller than E_0.   In fact, if the IR_g and IX_g voltage drops are drawn in Fig. 380, it will be found that in this special case where E_0 and E_{gm} are equal, E and E_0 are approximately equal in magnitude though differing considerably in phase angle.

R_g and X_g are approximately inversely proportional to the kva rating of the generator.   Consequently, if the generator is very much larger than the motor, the IR_g and IX_g drops are negligible, and then Eqs. (114) and (115) become

$$I = \frac{E_r}{\sqrt{R_m{}^2 + X_m{}^2}} \qquad \text{or, approximately,} \qquad I = \frac{E_r}{X_m} \qquad (116)$$

Also E_0 in Fig. 380 may then be replaced by E.   Even if the generator is not large, if its terminal voltage E is kept constant by a voltage regulator that adjusts the field current to compensate for the IR_g and IX_g drops, then E must be substituted for E_0 in Fig. 380, and R_g and X_g must be dropped from Eqs. (114) and (115), giving us Eq. (116).

The electric power developed in the generator is $E_0 I \cos \phi$.   The electric power output of the generator is less than this by the amount of the $I^2 R_g$ copper loss.   Similarly, the electric power developed in the motor must be $E_{gm} I \cos (180° - \alpha + \phi)$, but $\cos (180° - \alpha + \phi)$ is negative, and thus the power is actually absorbed, not developed.   This absorbed electric power is less than the power input to the motor by the amount of the $I^2 R_m$ copper loss, while the mechanical power output of the motor is less than the absorbed electric power by the amount of the windage, friction, and iron loss.

Note that when the brake load on the motor is increased the rotor is pulled back in the field and the angle α in Fig. 380 increases.   This causes E_r and I to increase, and for values of α less than 90° the power $E_0 I \cos \phi$ also increases, although $\cos \phi$ is decreasing.   However, as α approaches 90°, the effect of the decreasing $\cos \phi$ becomes greater than the effect of the increasing I, which means that the point of maximum power has been passed.   The maximum power is generally more than twice the normal rated power of the motor as fixed by its temperature rise.

366. Effect of Varying the Excitation of a Synchronous Motor.   The three diagrams of Fig. 381 show the effect of varying the field current of a synchronous motor when the line voltage E is kept constant, so that E replaces E_0, as explained in Art. 365.   In Fig. 381b the field current of the motor has been increased so as to make E_{gm} considerably larger than the line voltage E.   It is evident from a comparison of Fig. 381a, b, and c that as E_{gm} is increased, E_r, the vector sum of E_{gm} and E, turns counterclockwise, and that as E_{gm} is decreased, E_r turns clockwise.   Since the angle between E_r and I is constant, it follows that I also turns counterclockwise as E_{gm} is increased and clockwise as E_{gm} is decreased.   The power factor can therefore be controlled over a wide range by varying the field current of the motor.   This is a valuable characteristic of the synchronous motor because it provides an inexpensive means of avoiding power factor penalties.

In drawing the vector diagrams of Fig. 381, it was assumed that the brake torque was kept constant.   Therefore the power output of the motor would be constant, since the speed of a synchronous motor is always constant.   Therefore the power input $EI \cos \phi$ would also be constant except for almost negligible changes in armature copper loss.   This means that $I \cos \phi$ must be the same for all three diagrams.   Hav-

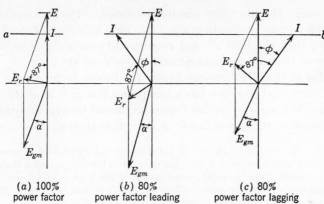

(a) 100%
power factor

(b) 80%
power factor leading

(c) 80%
power factor lagging

FIG. 381. Showing the effect of varying the excitation of a synchronous motor.   The line
voltage E and the brake load are both assumed to be constant.

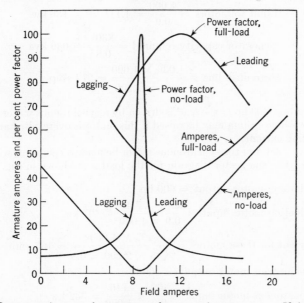

FIG. 382. Current and power-factor curves for a synchronous motor, 50 hp, 550 volts,
60 cycles, three phase.

ing chosen a suitable value of $I \cos \phi$, the horizontal line ab is drawn as
the locus of the tip of the vector I.   Then, for example, Fig. 381b, the
vector diagram for 80 per cent power factor leading, may be constructed
as follows: The current I is drawn leading E by the angle $\phi = \cos^{-1}$
0.80 = 37°.   The voltage E_r is then drawn leading I by the angle whose
tangent is X_m/R_m, 87° in the illustration given.   The length of E_r is
given by Eq. (116).   Now E_r is the diagonal of a parallelogram of which

E is one side.   It is therefore possible to complete the parallelogram, and this completes the vector diagram. E_{gm} may now be scaled off the diagram, and then the field current required to produce this value of E_{gm} may be read from the no-load saturation curve of the motor.

367. Use of the Synchronous Motor for Power-factor Correction.   If the load connected to a line has a low power factor, it is often advisable to arrange that some of the load shall be carried by synchronous motors so as to improve the power factor of the whole system.

Example.   If 1,000 hp of 2,200-volt three-phase induction motors are operating at the end of a transmission line, find the current in the line and also the generator capacity required if the average power factor of the load is 80 per cent and the average efficiency is 90 per cent.   (The induction motor, see Chap. 33, takes a lagging current, and its power factor cannot be controlled.)

$$\text{Output of motors} = 1,000 \text{ hp}$$

$$\text{Input to motors} = \frac{1,000}{0.9} = 1,111 \text{ hp} = 830 \text{ kw}$$

$$\text{Generator capacity required} = \frac{830}{0.8} = 1,036 \text{ kva}$$

$$\text{Current in line} = \frac{1,036 \times 1,000}{\sqrt{3} \times 2,200} = 272 \text{ amp}$$

If, for example, 400 hp of the load is driven by a synchronous motor, the power factor of the whole system may be raised if this motor is overexcited and made to draw a leading current.

If the power factor of the synchronous motor be made 85 per cent, with the current leading, then the vector diagram for the load is as shown in Fig. 383*b*.

$$\text{Induction-motor output} = 600 \text{ hp}$$

$$\text{Induction-motor input} = \frac{600}{0.9} \times \frac{746}{1,000} = 497 \text{ kw}$$

$$\text{Current for these motors} = \frac{497 \times 1,000}{\sqrt{3} \times 2,200 \times 0.8} = 163 \text{ amp}$$

$$\text{Synchronous-motor output} = 400 \text{ hp}$$

$$\text{Synchronous-motor input} = \frac{400}{0.9} \times \frac{746}{1,000} = 332 \text{ kw}$$

$$\text{Synchronous-motor current} = \frac{332 \times 1,000}{\sqrt{3} \times 2,200 \times 0.85} = 102 \text{ amp}$$

The line current I is the vector sum of the induction-motor current I_1 and the synchronous-motor current I_2, as shown in Fig. 383*b*.

$$
\begin{aligned}
I &= \sqrt{(I_1 \cos \phi_1 + I_2 \cos \phi_2)^2 + (I_1 \sin \phi_1 - I_2 \sin \phi_2)^2} \\
&= \sqrt{(163 \times 0.8 + 102 \times 0.85)^2 + (163 \times 0.6 - 102 \times 0.527)^2} \\
&= \sqrt{(217)^2 + (44.1)^2} \\
&= 221 \text{ amp}
\end{aligned}
$$

Thus the substitution of the synchronous motor for 400 hp of induction motors reduced the line current from 272 to 221 amp, reduced the kilovolt-ampere demand from 1,036 to 840 kva, and raised the power factor of the total load from 80 per cent to 98 per cent. The line current I lags the voltage by the angle ϕ, where $\phi = \tan^{-1} (44.1/217) = 11.5°$. The vector diagram, as usual, is drawn for one phase only, and the synchronous motor is assumed to be Y-connected, for the sake of simplicity, although it makes no difference which way the motor is connected as long as it is designed to give the proper terminal voltage with the connection used.

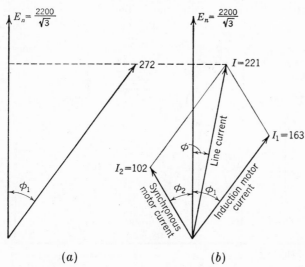

FIG. 383. Vector diagrams showing how an overexcited synchronous motor corrects power factor.

368. Synchronous Capacitors. If a synchronous motor is used only for controlling power factor and is never coupled to any mechanical load, it is usually called a *synchronous capacitor*, as it actually does the work of an electric capacitor and yet runs as a synchronous machine. When a synchronous capacitor is carrying full rated leading kva, the current leads the line voltage by 88 to 89°, depending on the size of the machine. These angles correspond to power factors of 3.5 and 1.75 per cent, respectively. The ordinary capacitor has a power factor of about 0.5 per cent at 60 cycles.

369. Parallel Operation of Alternating-current Generators. In general, electrical transmission and distribution systems are fed by several generators connected in parallel. In order that two generators may operate in parallel and share the load equally between them, their generated voltages must be equal, of the same frequency, and in phase, with reference to the load. Note that, if the two voltages are in phase with reference to the load, they are 180° out of phase with reference to currents circulating between the two machines. For example, in Fig. 384, which shows one phase only of two three-phase generators, if the voltages e_1 and e_2 of phase a of the two machines both act in the direction shown by the arrows for one-half cycle, and reverse together, they are in phase with reference to the load, since they both act to circulate current the same way through the external circuit; but if the two machines are considered alone, then e_1 is acting to circulate current clockwise through the two machines while e_2 is acting to circulate current counterclockwise through the two machines. Therefore e_1 and e_2 are 180° out of phase as far as currents circulating through the two machines only

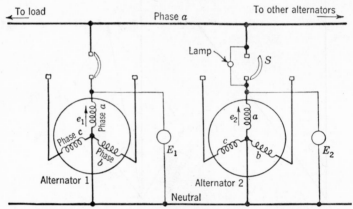

FIG. 384. Parallel operation of alternators (a-c generators).

are concerned. If $e_1 = e_2$ at all times, there is no current circulating between the two machines.

Suppose that generator 1 of Fig. 384 is carrying the entire load upon the system, and that, as the load increases beyond the capacity of one generator, it is required to start up generator 2 to help carry the load. The prime mover of generator 2, usually either a steam turbine or a water wheel, is started and the generating unit is brought up to speed. The d-c field current is then applied to the generator and its generated voltage E_2 is adjusted to be equal to E_1, but before switch S can be closed it is necessary to have the two voltages in "synchronism," that is, in phase with reference to the load. For example, if E_2 were 180° out of synchronism, then each machine would constitute a short circuit on the other machine. A very large current would circulate through the two machines but there would be no current or voltage supplied to the load.

370. Synchronizing. The phase relationship between E_1 and E_2 can be determined approximately by connecting a lamp across the switch contacts as shown in Fig. 384. This completes the path for the circulating current but limits it to a very small value, since the lamp has a high

resistance.   When E_2 is 180° out of synchronism, the voltage across
the lamp is equal to $E_1 + E_2$ and the lamp burns brightly; but when E_2
is in perfect synchronism, the voltage across the lamp is $E_1 - E_2 = 0$
and the lamp goes black.   If the frequency of generator 2 is one-half a
cycle per sec greater or less than the frequency of generator 1, then generator 2 passes through synchronism once every 2 sec, and the lamp
flashes on and off every 2 sec.   The speed of the prime mover of the
incoming machine is adjusted until the frequency of the flashing is very
low, and switch S is closed while the lamp is black.

In all modern plants the lamp is replaced by a synchroscope, which
not only indicates the actual phase angle in degrees between E_2 and E_1,
at every instant, but also shows by the direction of motion of its pointer
whether the incoming machine is running too fast or too slowly.

In actual practice, the incoming machine is rarely in perfect synchronism at the instant the switch is closed, but it quickly pulls into synchronism.   For example, if E_2 is a few degrees behind E_1, then the vector
diagram of Fig. 380b applies, substituting E_1 for E_0 and E_2 for E_{gm}.   A
circulating current I therefore flows, which drives machine 2 as a synchronous motor and which is a load on machine 1.   Thus the circulating
current creates a driving torque in the machine which is behind, and a
retarding torque in the machine which is ahead, and once a generator is
synchronized and connected to the powerhouse bus bars it cannot be
pulled out of synchronism by any torque smaller than its pull-out torque
when running as a synchronous motor.

The first time a generator is synchronized, it is necessary to syn-
chronize all three phases simultaneously in order to make sure that the
phases have been connected to the switches in the proper order.   For
instance, if phases 2 and 3 have become interchanged, the three phases
cannot be brought into synchronism simultaneously, nor can the two
machines operate in parallel until the error has been rectified.

**371. Load and Power-factor Control in the Operation of Alternating-
current Generators.**   If two d-c generators are operating in parallel, and
the field excitation of one of the machines is increased, then the voltage
of that machine will be raised and it will take a larger portion of the load.
An increase in load makes the engine and generator slow down and
allows the engine to draw the additional amount of steam required for
the additional load.

If two a-c generators are operating in parallel, an increase in the excitation of one generator raises the internal voltage E_0 of that generator, but
this only turns its current vector clockwise, as will be demonstrated in
the following paragraphs, and does not increase its proportion of the total
power output.

Consider the case of two a-c generators operating in parallel in a powerhouse as in Fig. 384, and let E_{01} and E_{02} be the voltages generated in phase a of the machines by the fluxes produced by their field currents. If there is no load connected to the generators, the only current that can flow is a circulating current through the two machines. For such a condition it is natural to draw the vector diagram from the viewpoint of the circulating current, in which case E_{01} and E_{02} are always approximately 180° out of phase. The vector diagrams for the synchronous motor, Figs. 380 and 381, are drawn with reference to the circulating current because there is no other current; but when generators are sharing an external load, it is probably clearer to draw the vector diagram from the viewpoint of the load current, in which case E_{01} and E_{02} are always approximately in phase.

Figure 385 is the vector diagram for two similar generators, perfectly in phase and equally excited, so that they share the external load current $2I$ equally, each supplying the current I. The phase angle of I is of course determined by the nature of the external load. The common terminal voltage to neutral E is less than E_{01} and E_{02} by the IZ_s drop in each machine. Figure 386 is the vector diagram for the two generators when they are perfectly in phase but are unequally excited and are not carrying any load. E_r is the vector difference between E_{02} and E_{01}. The circulating current I_c lags behind E_r by about 87°, but this same current returns through generator 1. That is, when i_c is positive in generator 2, it is negative in generator 1. Therefore in the vector diagram the current through generator 1 is $-I_c$. Now let us combine the two cases of Figs. 385 and 386. Figure 387 shows what happens to Fig. 385 when the excitation of generator 2 is suddenly increased 5 per cent while the excitation of generator 1 is decreased 5 per cent, thus keeping the common terminal voltage constant. The circulating current I_c now flows in addition to the load current, so that

$$I_2 = \text{vector sum of } I \text{ and } I_c$$

and $I_1 = \text{vector sum of } I \text{ and } -I_c$

also $E = E_{02} - I_2 Z_{s2} = E_{01} - I_1 Z_{s1}$ (vector subtraction)

In this particular illustration $Z_{s1} = Z_{s2}$, but they need not be equal. The power outputs of the two generators are, respectively, $EI_1 \cos \phi_1$ and $EI_2 \cos \phi_2$. It is clear from Fig. 387 that these two powers are no longer equal, although they were equal before the excitations were changed. The load shift introduced by the sudden change in excitation is, however, of very short duration. The extra load on generator 2 causes it to drop back a few degrees, while generator 1 gains a few degrees. If Fig. 386 is redrawn for this condition, it will be seen that the effect is to turn E_r and I_c clockwise a few degrees. This process continues only until I_c in Fig. 387 is at right angles to E, and then the power outputs of the two generators are again equal. Figure 388 shows the final steady-state condition.

To change the distribution of load between two a-c generators operating in parallel, the governors of the driving engines must be manipulated so as to change the distribution of the steam supply.

As the total load on the two generators increases, they both slow down, and the engine governors automatically allow the necessary amount of steam to flow, while the frequency of the generated emf decreases slightly. In order that the two machines may divide the load properly, the engines

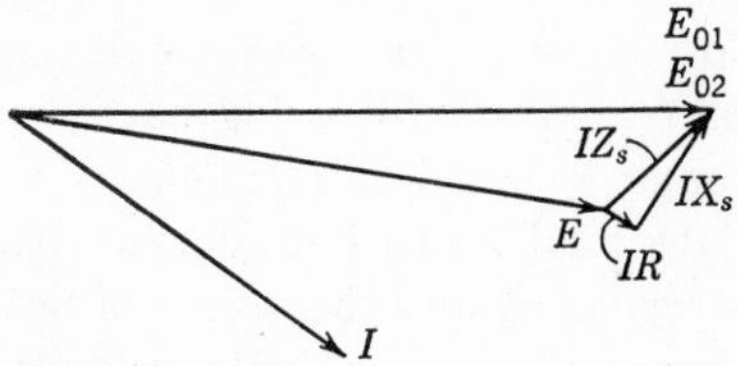

FIG. 385. Generators equally excited and perfectly in phase so that they share the load perfectly.

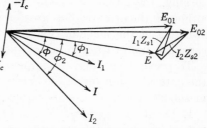

FIG. 386. Generators perfectly in phase but unequally excited and carrying no load.

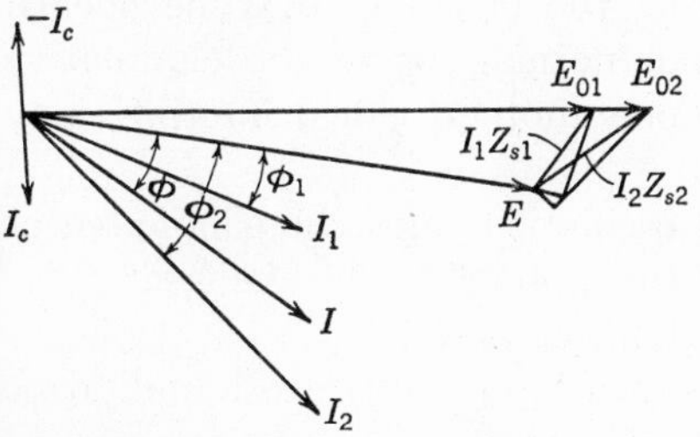

FIG. 387. Showing what happens to Fig. 385 when the excitations of the two generators are suddenly made unequal (transient condition).

FIG. 388. Generators unequally excited but supplied with equal powers by their prime movers (steady-state condition).

FIGS. 385, 386, 387, and 388. Vector diagrams for one phase of two similar generators operated in parallel.

should have the same percentage drop in speed between no load and full load.

The same applies to generators driven by water wheels. To make any one of a number of turbine-driven a-c generators take a larger portion of the total load, the governor of that machine must be manipulated to allow the turbine to take more water.

372. Hunting. In the case of an engine-driven a-c generator, and particularly if the engine is of the reciprocating type, the angular velocity is not uniform but consists of a uniform angular velocity with a superimposed oscillation. The frequency of the generated emf therefore is not constant but rises and falls regularly.

If this emf is applied to a synchronous motor, the synchronous speed of the motor tends to rise and fall regularly with the frequency, and the motor tends to have a superimposed oscillation similar to that of the generator. If the natural period of oscillation of the motor has the same frequency as this forced oscillation, then the effect will be cumulative and the motor will oscillate considerably.

A similar result would be found with the model shown in Fig. 377. If the torque applied to G is not uniform, then G will oscillate about its position of mean angular velocity and M will have an oscillating force impressed on it by the spring. If the moment of inertia of the flywheel M is such that its natural frequency of oscillation is the same as the frequency of the impressed oscillation, then G and M will swing backward and forward relative to one another through a considerable angle.

As the two machines M and G oscillate relative to one another, the angle α, Fig. 380, increases and decreases regularly, and the values of both E_r and of the current I vary above and below the average value required for the load. This surging of current is of comparatively low frequency and is indicated by an ammeter placed in the circuit. Owing to this surging, the circuit breakers protecting the machines may be opened although the load is not greater than normal, while the cumulative swinging of the machines relative to one another, called hunting, may cause the motor to drop out of step.

To prevent hunting, the impressed oscillations must be eliminated or the natural frequency of oscillation of the motor must be changed. The methods used in practice to minimize hunting are:

1. Damp the governor if the impressed oscillations are found to be caused by a hunting governor.

2. Change the natural period of oscillation of the machine by changing the flywheel; the larger the moment of inertia of the rotating part of the motor, the longer is its natural period of oscillation.

3. The squirrel-cage winding carried in the slots in the pole faces acts to damp the oscillations. These oscillations generate voltages in the bars and the resulting currents develop torque to oppose the oscillations. The damping action of this squirrel-cage winding is usually sufficient to prevent hunting.

Alternating-current generators are often provided with *partial squirrel cages*, or *damping grids*, which are carried in slots in the pole faces and are not interconnected between poles.

Problems

*35-1. Describe the construction of a synchronous motor, naming its principal parts. How is the field of a synchronous motor excited? Explain, briefly, the principle of operation of the synchronous motor.

*35-2. Can the speed of a synchronous motor be varied by varying the field current? Explain concisely what does happen when the field excitation is (a) strengthened and (b) weakened.

35-3. What is the effect on the speed of a synchronous motor of increasing the brake load? Explain why the speed remains constant. Why cannot the load be increased indefinitely?

35-4. How can a synchronous motor be made to draw a leading current from the line? Give a brief physical explanation of how this is accomplished.

35-5. How can a polyphase synchronous motor be built so as to be self-starting, without the use of a separate starting motor?

35-6. What is meant by "hunting" in a synchronous machine? Discuss several ways in which hunting may be prevented.

35-7. What is the purpose of dampers on a synchronous motor? Explain fully.

35-8. The load of a plant consists of 1,200 hp of 2,300-volt 60-cycle three-phase motors with an average efficiency of 90 per cent and an average power factor of 75 per cent. Find the current in the lines and the rating of the generator required.

a. Determine the rating of the overexcited synchronous motor required to raise the power factor to 100 per cent, also that required to raise the power factor to 90 per cent, the synchronous motor running without mechanical load in both cases.

b. Determine the capacity of three Y-connected capacitors required to raise the power factor of the load to 100 per cent. Which is cheaper in capital cost, capacitors at \$10 per μf or a synchronous motor at \$12 a kilovolt-ampere?

c. If 500 hp of the load may suitably be driven by a synchronous motor, what must be the input rating of this motor so that the power factor of the load may be 90 per cent, the efficiency being 92 per cent?

d. What effect has the power factor of the load on the size of generators, the loss in the transmission line, the size of engines and boilers?

35-9. A 200-hp 2,200-volt 1,200-rpm 60-cycle three-phase Y-connected synchronous motor has the following constants: synchronous reactance per phase = 10 ohms; resistance per phase = 1.0 ohm; full-load current = 41.5 amp. If this motor is driven by an identically similar machine operating as a generator and if both are excited to generate rated voltage at no load, how many mechanical or space degrees must the motor rotor lag behind the generator rotor in order that the motor carry full-load current? What will the power and power factor be? Draw the vector diagram for one phase accurately to scale. A graphical solution by trial is the easiest solution.

35-10. If the motor of Prob. 35-9 is connected to a line of such large kilovolt-ampere capacity that the line voltage is practically unaffected by the motor current,

a. How many space degrees must the motor rotor lag behind its no-load position in order that it may carry full-load current, and what is the maximum power that the motor can take from the line, the motor being excited to generate rated voltage at no load?

b. For what no-load voltage must the motor be excited in order that its power factor at full load may be (1) 100 per cent and (2) 90 per cent leading?

36

POLYPHASE-MOTOR APPLICATIONS AND CONTROL

373. The Synchronous Motor. The principal advantage of the synchronous motor is that its power factor can be controlled. It may be operated at 100 per cent power factor, or it may be overexcited and made to draw a leading current from the line so as to compensate for the lagging

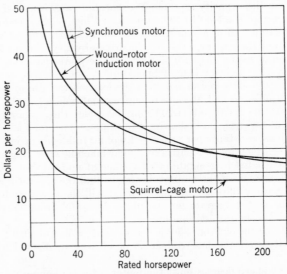

FIG. 389. Relative capital costs of three-phase motors.

power factor of induction motors in the same plant. This is a very important property of the synchronous motor, because power-factor penalties may become rather a large item in the cost of power if no attention is paid to the power factor.

In certain very special applications the fact that the speed of the synchronous motor is absolutely independent of both the load and the voltage may be of importance.

The efficiency of the synchronous motor is slightly greater than that of the induction motors, particularly at partial loads. The chief disadvantage of the synchronous motor is that direct current must be provided for its excitation. A small exciter is usually mounted on the same shaft to provide this. Other minor objections are (1) that a disturbance on the system may throw the motor out of synchronism and cause it to stop, whereas an induction motor will continue running; (2) that the control of a synchronous motor is not so simple as that of an induction motor, in that the field must be applied after the motor has come up to speed and must be adjusted to give the desired power factor; (3) in sizes up to about 300 hp it is more expensive than the squirrel-cage induction motor (Fig. 389). Because of these disadvantages the synchronous motor is not used in small sizes. It is very extensively used in large sizes, however, and it may be laid down as a general principle in selecting large motors for constant-speed work, that wherever power factor is of importance a synchronous motor should be chosen if the starting-torque requirements are not too severe and the brake-load fluctuations are not so violent as to throw the motor out of synchronism.

TABLE 4. Synchronous Speeds of Polyphase Motors

Poles	Revolutions per minute		
	60 cycles	50 cycles	25 cycles
2	3,600	3,000	1,500
4	1,800	1,500	750
6	1,200	1,000	500
8	900	750	375
10	720	600	300
p	$\dfrac{120 \times 60}{p}$	$\dfrac{120 \times 50}{p}$	$\dfrac{120 \times 25}{p}$

The standard synchronous motor does not develop so high a starting torque as the wound-rotor induction motor or the double squirrel-cage induction motor, and, although the synchronous motor can be designed to give almost any desired starting torque by increasing the diameter, the cost also increases. For very severe starting duty, therefore, the synchronous motor will cost more than either the wound-rotor or the double squirrel-cage induction motor, and whether this extra capital cost is justified or not depends entirely upon the particular power contract and the power factor of the rest of the plant load. For light starting duty the synchronous motor, in the larger sizes, is somewhat cheaper than the induction motor of the same rating. Synchronous motors are available only with the speeds shown in Table 4.

374. Single-phase Motors. The single-phase motors described in the next chapter are more expensive than polyphase motors of the same output and are not used for general power work. They are used in small sizes where polyphase current is not available. Practically the only large single-phase motors in use are the alternating-current series motors used in electric traction. A single-phase traction system requires only one trolley wire, since the steel rails can be used for one conductor, but with three-phase three conductors are required and therefore two trolley wires must be provided; consequently single-phase is generally used in a-c traction in spite of the greater cost of the single-phase motor. In Italy, however, three-phase induction motors are used on their electric railways and two trolleys are provided.

375. Induction Motors. Induction motors always take a lagging current, and have a full-load power factor of about 80 per cent for a 1-hp 1,800-rpm motor, 90 per cent for a 100-hp 1,200-rpm motor, and 84 per cent for a 100-hp 600-rpm motor. The power factor decreases with the load and may be less than 20 per cent at no load.

The induction motor is available with the same synchronous speeds as the synchronous motor. The full-load speed may be anywhere from about 1.7 to 4.2 per cent lower than the synchronous speed, depending on the size and synchronous speed.

Squirrel-cage Induction Motors. Squirrel-cage induction motors are available with four standard types of rotor:

1. Low resistance (requires starting compensator for higher ratings)
2. High resistance (often called high slip)
3. Double squirrel cage (high starting torque, low starting current)
4. High reactance (normal starting torque, low starting current)

These four types have been compared in Art. 352. Amongst them they are able to take care of every kind of constant-speed application there is, and there is no motor that provides better service in the constant-speed field. When the synchronous motor is selected in preference to an induction motor, as it often is in the large sizes, it is usually power-factor considerations that have determined the choice, or some minor difference in cost or efficiency, and not service considerations.

Wound-rotor Induction Motors. These motors are now used only where starting control or speed control is required or where the service consists chiefly of starting and stopping or reversing. For example, they are used for hoists, cranes, conveyers, rolling mills, etc., and also where it is desired to use a flywheel to smooth out intermittent loads of short duration. In order that a flywheel may store and give up energy, its speed must change. The normal slip of an induction motor is not large enough to permit the flywheel to function effectively, but with the wound rotor resistance may be cut into the rotor circuit automatically as the load comes on to the machine, so as to increase the slip and allow the flywheel to carry as much of the load as is desired. High-resistance squirrel-cage rotors are also used for this type of service.

376. Speed Control of Wound-rotor and Squirrel-cage Induction Motors. With the wound-rotor induction motor it is possible to obtain any speed from about 96 per cent of synchronous speed down to zero speed by varying the resistance in the rotor circuit. However, the efficiency is reduced in the same proportion as the speed, and at all reduced speeds the speed varies widely with the load, as explained in Art. 344. Therefore it is not economical to operate at reduced speed for any great length of time, and in general an operator is required continuously at the controls in order to obtain the desired speed.

The speed of any induction motor or synchronous motor may be varied by varying the speed of the generator that supplies the electric power, but this method is obviously limited to special cases where each motor or group of motors has a private power supply, as in the case of electric drive on ships.

The stator coils of an induction motor can be reconnected in such a way as to double the number of poles and so cut the speed in half. It does not add a great deal to the cost of the motor to provide the necessary switching arrangements for making this change, and the result is a motor with efficient operation at two speeds. However, it does not provide for any intermediate speeds, unless of course a wound rotor is used, in which case the rotor coils also must be reconnected. Stators can also be constructed with two complete sets of windings. For example, one winding might be six-pole to give 1,200 rpm and the other four-pole to give 1,800 rpm. Each of these windings can then be reconnected for half the speed thus giving four speeds, namely, 600, 900, 1,200, and 1,800 rpm. This type of motor is considerably more expensive than a single-speed motor.

Another method of speed control that is applicable to squirrel-cage induction motors is to vary the applied voltage. The flux is directly proportional to the applied voltage, and therefore to generate a given rotor voltage the slip must double every time the applied voltage is cut in half. Unfortunately the torque per ampere is also cut in half when the flux is halved, and therefore when using this method of speed control care must be taken to see that the motor is not burnt out by drawing excessive currents at the reduced speeds. It may be necessary for example to use a 3-hp motor to drive a mechanical load that never exceeds 2 hp. In general, this method of speed control is used only on loads where the torque required drops off considerably as the speed is reduced. The applied voltage may be varied by means of either saturable reactors, variacs, or tap-changing transformers.

377. Brush-shifting Polyphase Induction Motor. This motor, described in Art. 354, is the only a-c motor that has a speed control at all comparable with that of the shunt or separately excited d-c motor. Its speed is continuously adjustable over a range of about 3 to 1, it will stay reasonably well at whatever speed the brushes are set, and its efficiency is quite good at all speeds. It is a relatively expensive motor, and its method of speed control is not so convenient as that of the d-c shunt motor. Its great virtue is that it provides a good speed control without necessitating the installation of a d-c power supply.

378. Starting Compensator. Synchronous motors, and large low-resistance squirrel-cage motors, are usually started on reduced voltage by means of a bank of autotransformers, as explained in Art. 351.

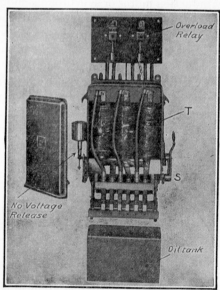

FIG. 390. Starting compensator for a three-phase induction motor.

The combined autotransformers and switches constitute what is called a starting compensator. One type is shown in Fig. 390 and consists essentially of three autotransformers T and a double-throw switch S by means of which the motor is connected to low-voltage taps for starting and is then connected directly to the line when nearly up to full speed.

The complete connections of this compensator are shown in Fig. 391a.

Figure 391b shows the connections during the starting period; normal voltage E_1 is applied to the lines a, b, and c, while a reduced voltage E_2 is tapped off from the autotransformers and is applied to the motor.

Figure 391c shows the connections during the running period. The voltage applied to the motor is now normal and the overload relays O

are connected in the circuit while the no-voltage-release coil M is connected across one leg of the circuit.

The no-voltage-release feature is similar in principle to that used on starters for d-c motors and consists of a latching solenoid which holds the starting arm against the tension of a spring. When the line voltage fails, the solenoid M is deenergized and the starting handle then returns to the off position.

In the case of a heavy overload, the plungers of the overload relays O are raised and open the circuit of the no-voltage release M; the starting handle then returns to the off position.

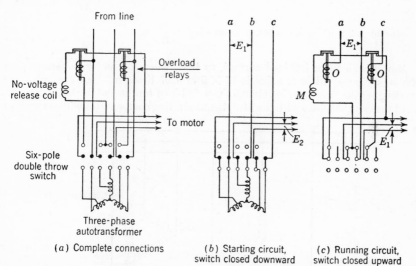

(a) Complete connections   (b) Starting circuit, switch closed downward   (c) Running circuit, switch closed upward

FIG. 391. Diagram of connections of a three-phase starting compensator.

Thermal overload relays are also used extensively, especially up to 50 hp.

379. Y-Δ Method of Starting. This method is sometimes used for three-phase motors. The windings of the three phases are kept separate from one another and six leads are brought out from the machine. Under normal running conditions the windings are Δ-connected, as shown in Fig. 392b, and the voltage per phase is E_1 volts. During the starting period the windings are Y-connected, as shown in Fig. 392a. In this case the voltage per phase is equal to $E_1/1.73$, or 58 per cent of normal voltage.

Example. If a Δ-connected motor at standstill takes 5 times full-load current with normal applied voltage and develops 1.5 times full-load torque, what is the starting current in the motor and also in the line, if the motor is Y-connected, and what is the starting torque under these conditions? (The student should make a diagram of connections showing the double-throw switch required to change from Y to Δ.)

Starting torque $= 1.5$ (full-load torque) $\times (1/\sqrt{3})^2$
         $= 0.5$ (full-load torque)

Starting current in line when Δ-connected $= I_s$

Starting current in each phase of motor when Δ-connected $= \dfrac{I_s}{\sqrt{3}}$

Starting current in each phase of motor when Y-connected $= \left(\dfrac{I_s}{\sqrt{3}}\right) \times \dfrac{1}{\sqrt{3}}$

$ = \dfrac{I_s}{3}$

Starting current in line when Y-connected $= \dfrac{I_s}{3}$

Now I_s is 5 times full-load current, so that, when the motor is Y-connected, the starting current in the line is ⅓ × 5 or 1.67 times full-load current. The starting torque, however, is only 0.5 times full-load torque and, if this is not sufficient to start the motor with the load, then a starting compensator will be required.

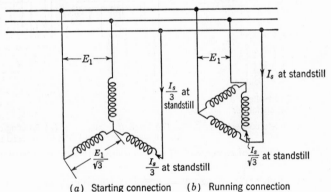

(a) Starting connection   (b) Running connection

FIG. 392. Voltage and current relations with Y-Δ starting.

380. Starter for a Wound-rotor Motor. To start up a motor of this type, the main switch is closed and then the resistance R in the rotor circuit is gradually cut out as the motor comes up to speed.

Since the rotor is wound in three sections (see Art. 343), three sets of contacts are required, which for small motors may be mounted on a faceplate as shown in Fig. 393. This starter may be used as a speed regulator if the resistance has sufficient current-carrying capacity.

The drum type of controller, shown in Fig. 143, is generally used for wound-rotor motors above 25 hp and often for the smaller motors as well. Contactor switches are used for motors above 300 hp and also for smaller motors if the control is automatic.

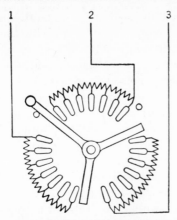

FIG. 393. Three-phase sliding-contact rheostat for starting and speed control of a wound-rotor induction motor (cover removed).   (*Courtesy of General Electric Co.*)

381. Starting Synchronous Motors. Synchronous motors are generally started up as squirrel-cage induction motors and are then converted into synchronous motors by applying a field current after they have come up to speed; but if they are starting up under zero load, they are sometimes brought up to speed by a small motor with a high starting torque, which is mounted on the same shaft, and they are then synchronized in on to the line as if they were generators (Art. 370).   The starting motor is then disconnected from the line.

The advantage of this method of starting is that it causes the least possible disturbance on the supply system.

382. Dynamic Braking of Induction Motors. A direct current of suitable magnitude applied to any two terminals of the stator winding of a three-phase induction motor will produce a stationary magnetic field that is identical with that normally produced by the three-phase supply, except that it is not rotating. Therefore if an induction motor that is running with a slip of, say, 4 per cent is suddenly switched from the a-c supply to a d-c supply the effect is to reduce the synchronous speed to zero, so that the motor is now running with a *negative* slip of 96 per cent. Now the torque developed with a *negative* slip of 96 per cent is equal in magnitude and opposite in direction to the torque developed with a *positive* slip of 96 per cent, provided that the stator currents are the same in both cases. A low-resistance squirrel-cage induction motor when switched directly onto the line draws about 6 times full-load current and develops about 1.5 times full-load torque. Consequently, if when running at full speed it is switched to a direct current, whose magnitude is equivalent to 6 times full-load alternating current, it will develop a retarding torque equal to 1.5 times full-load torque. The magnitude of this retarding torque may be controlled by varying the direct current.

Dynamic braking is particularly effective when applied to wound-rotor induction motors, because then the torque may be controlled by varying the rotor resistance, thus avoiding the complication of having to provide means of varying the direct current. Also larger retarding torques can be obtained with smaller currents.

The main drawback to dynamic braking is that it requires a large direct current at a low voltage. The least expensive way of obtaining this d-c supply is by means of transformers and selenium rectifiers. Motor-generator sets are sometimes used, however, because of the greater ease of control.

37

SINGLE-PHASE MOTORS

383. Single-phase Induction Motors. If one of the phases of a two-phase induction motor is opened while the motor is running, the machine will continue to rotate and carry the load.

A two-pole single-phase induction motor at standstill is shown diagrammatically in Fig. 394. When an alternating current flows in the winding A, an alternating flux ϕ is produced. Since this magnetic field is not rotating, there is no tendency for the rotor to turn, so that the machine is not self-starting. The fact that this motor can develop torque

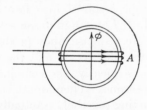

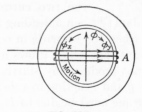

FIG. 394. Diagrammatic representation of a single-phase induction motor.

FIG. 395

when running but not when stationary will be demonstrated in the following article.

384. Running Torque of a Single-phase Induction Motor. If, as in Fig. 396, two equal vectors P rotate with the same speed but in opposite directions, the resultant vector R alternates between the values $R = 2P$ and $R = -2P$ and always lies in the line joining these two points.

An alternating magnetic flux ϕ, such as that in Fig. 395, is therefore equivalent to two rotating fields ϕ_x and ϕ_y, which are of equal strength and rotate in opposite directions with the same speed. These fields tend to turn the rotor in opposite directions, so that the resultant starting torque is zero.

Suppose that the rotor has been started by some external means and is rotating in the same direction as the field ϕ_x but with a speed that is 5 per cent less than synchronous speed. The rotor bars will then be

475

cutting the field ϕ_x, and an emf will be induced that will send through these bars a current I_x of frequency sf, where s is the percentage slip and f is the applied frequency. Since this rotor frequency is low, the current lags by only a small angle, and the torque due to this current is large.

The rotor bars, however, are also cutting the field ϕ_y, and, since this field is moving in a direction opposite to that of the rotor, the frequency of the resulting rotor current I_y is almost equal to $2f$. This frequency is high, and the current I_y lags by a large angle, so that the torque due to this current is small (see Art. 339). The characteristics with respect to slip, efficiency, and power factor are therefore similar to those of a polyphase induction motor.

FIG. 396

385. Split-phase Method of Starting Single-phase Induction Motors. One of the methods used to obtain a rotating field from a single-phase supply is shown diagrammatically in Fig. 397. The motor is wound two-phase, and a resistance R is added to winding A. In practice, this is generally accomplished by using finer wire for phase A rather than by adding an external resistance. Because of the higher ratio of resistance to reactance in phase A, I_a does not lag so much as I_b and there is an angle β between the two currents. I_a may be resolved into two components: (1) $I_a \sin \beta$, leading I_b by 90°, and (2) $I_a \cos \beta$, in phase with I_b. Now when the currents in coils A and B are in phase, they produce a resultant flux which grows and dies but does not rotate and therefore does not produce any starting torque. Consequently, the combination $I_a \cos \beta$ and I_b acting together produces no torque. Therefore the starting torque must be due to $I_a \sin \beta$ and I_b acting together. Actually the starting torque is given by the equation[1]

$$T_s = k I_a I_b \sin \beta \qquad (117)$$

General-purpose split-phase induction motors develop starting torques ranging from 0.75 to 2.0 times full-load torque. **High-torque** split-phase induction motors develop starting torques up to 2.5 times full-load torque, but these larger starting torques are obtained at the expense of larger starting currents and lower running efficiencies. The high-torque motors are intended only for infrequent service.

The high-resistance winding, phase A, is generally referred to as the auxiliary winding. At about 75 per cent of synchronous speed a centrifugal switch operates and disconnects the auxiliary winding from the

[1] A rigid proof of this equation is given by B. F. Bailey and J. S. Gault, "Alternating-current Machinery," pp. 299–301, McGraw-Hill Book Company, Inc., New York, 1951.

line. It is important that this should be done because otherwise the auxiliary winding would generally be burned out due to its high resistance.

386. Capacitor-start Induction Motors. Better starting conditions can be obtained by inserting a capacitor in series with the auxiliary winding as in Fig. 398, where R represents the resistance of the auxiliary winding.

The phase angle β between I_a and I_b depends upon the size of the capacitor C and can be made exactly 90° at start, if desired. As the motor speeds up, the rotor and stator currents decrease, and the angle β changes. In order to keep β equal to 90°, it would be necessary to decrease the capacitance C continuously as the motor gained speed. This

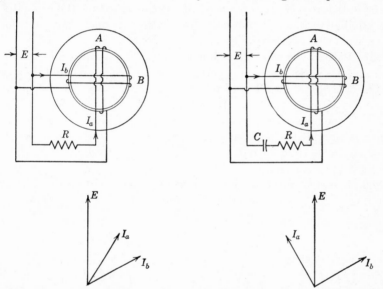

FIG. 397. Resistance R in series with one winding.

FIG. 398. Capacitor C in series with one winding. Here R represents the resistance of winding A.

is not feasible, nor is it necessary, because a single fixed capacitor of the proper magnitude will give a starting torque that is greater than 3.5 times full-load torque at all speeds from zero to 70 per cent of synchronous speed. At about 75 per cent of synchronous speed a centrifugal device disconnects winding A from the line, and the motor then runs single phase.

There are two reasons for disconnecting the capacitor as the motor comes up to speed. In the first place the capacitance that gives the largest starting torque is about four times too big for the best running conditions, and in the second place if the capacitor is used only for starting it can be an electrolytic type of capacitor which is much smaller and cheaper than the paper capacitors required for continuous operation.

387. Capacitor-start Capacitor-run Induction Motor. In this type of motor winding, A is never disconnected from the line, and the motor always runs two-phase. But the capacitance C is provided by two capacitors in parallel, and at about 75 per cent of synchronous speed a centrifugal device disconnects one of these capacitors. Although ideal operation requires a continuous reduction in C from zero speed to full speed, a two-stage variation in C gives almost as good results. The capacitor-run motor has a higher efficiency and a higher pull-out torque than the motor that uses split phase for starting only, and its power factor is nearly 100 per cent. A capacitor-start induction motor should not be operated as a capacitor-run motor, because neither the capacitor nor the auxiliary winding is designed for continuous operation, and both of them would be overheated by continuous operation.

388. Permanent-split Capacitor Motors. In applications where the motor starts under practically zero load, it is possible to avoid the expense of the centrifugal switch and of one of the capacitors of the capacitor-start capacitor-run motor. In that case the running capacitor is permanently connected in series with one winding and no additional capacitance is provided when starting. The starting torque is poor, chiefly because the starting current in winding A is strictly limited by the small value of the capacitance.

389. Speed Control of Single-phase Induction Motors. The stator winding of a single-phase induction motor can easily be arranged to give

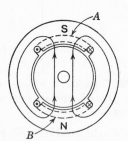

FIG. 399. Two-pole connection.

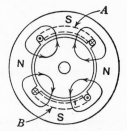

FIG. 400. Consequent-pole connection.

two synchronous speeds, one double the other. In Fig. 399 the two coils A and B are connected in series with their mmfs adding, which results in a two-pole motor. In Fig. 400 the two coils are again in series but the connections to coil B have been reversed so that the mmfs are in opposition, with the result that four poles are produced and the synchronous speed is cut in half. Similarly, a four-pole motor can be reconnected to produce eight poles. The change from one speed to the other is easily and quickly accomplished by means of a two-pole double-throw switch. The north poles of Fig. 400 are often called *consequent poles;* and a two-speed motor that obtains its lower speed by producing consequent poles is said to have a *consequent-pole* winding.

Speed can also be controlled by varying the applied voltage and thus varying the slip. The most common method of varying the applied voltage is by means of a transformer with taps on its secondary. A variac provides the maximum possible number of taps and therefore gives the finest speed adjustment.

390. Universal or Single-phase Series Motor. This motor is wound and connected like a d-c series motor, the field coils being in series with the armature winding, but a few structural changes are necessary to

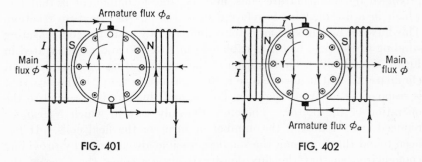

FIG. 401 FIG. 402

make a machine that will operate in a satisfactory manner with alternating current.

In Fig. 401 the current is flowing through such a motor in one direction, while in Fig. 402, half a cycle later, the current is flowing in the opposite direction, in both the armature and the field coils, but the reversal of both flux and current leaves the direction of the torque unchanged. The instantaneous torque is $K\phi i$, where i is the instantaneous current flowing in both armature and field coils and ϕ is the instantaneous flux produced in the poles by the mmf of the field coils. The graphs of ϕ and i on a time base are both sine curves and ϕ is practically in phase with i because of the air gaps. Neglecting saturation and also the tendency of the flux ϕ to lag slightly behind i, we may say that the instantaneous torque is $K_1 i^2$. Since i passes through zero twice per cycle, the motor develops 120 pulsations of torque per second on a 60-cycle system and 50 pulsations per second on a 25-cycle system. The moment of inertia of the armature smooths out these pulsations quite effectively. The average torque is $K_1 I^2$, where I is the effective value of the alternating current.

If an ordinary d-c series motor is connected to an a-c power supply, and is not coupled to any mechanical load, it will run; but the current will be small, the power factor will be low, the torque will be feeble, there will generally be sparking at the commutator, and the poles and yoke will soon become quite hot. In order to obtain satisfactory operation on alternating current, certain modifications are necessary, as follows:

The most important modification is that the poles and yoke must be laminated, as otherwise the eddy currents produced in them by the alternating flux will be large and will quickly overheat the motor.

The next most important modification is to reduce the reactance of the circuit through the motor so as to allow more current to flow, and also so that the power factor will be higher. The reactance of the motor circuit is $X_a + X_f$, where X_a is the reactance of the armature winding and X_f is the reactance of the field coils. Now X_a includes all the flux produced by the armature coils, and its largest component is that flux which in a d-c machine is referred to as the flux of armature reaction. This flux can be almost completely eliminated by adding a compensating winding in the pole faces, as explained in Art. 196 and as illustrated in Figs. 157 and 158. The addition of the compensating winding does not eliminate X_a, but it does reduce it to a reasonable value. The flux that is responsible for X_f is the main flux ϕ, and this flux is essential to the operation of the motor. Therefore the only way in which X_f can be reduced is by reducing the number of turns in the field coils. It has been found that by using the smallest feasible air gap, and by providing enough iron so that the flux density is always below the knee of the saturation curve, it is possible to reduce the number of field turns to about one-third of the number usually provided on d-c series motors.

A vector diagram of the single-phase series motor is shown in Fig. 403, in which

I = current through motor

Φ = flux through the poles

E_g = voltage generated in armature winding due to its rotation and consequent cutting of flux Φ

$X = X_a + X_f$ = reactance of armature winding plus reactance of field coils

$R = R_a + R_f$ = resistance of armature winding plus resistance of field coils.

IX = voltage required to drive current through the reactance of the motor circuit

IR = voltage required to drive current through the resistance of the motor circuit

E_a = voltage required to overcome E_g, E_a must be equal and opposite to E_g

E = line voltage = vector sum of E_a, IR, IX

$\cos \alpha$ = power factor of motor

Since Φ is produced by I, and since there are two air gaps, Φ has been shown in phase with I, although it actually lags by an amount too small

to be important. The phase angle of E_g in the vector diagram is most
easily determined by considering instantaneous values. The instantaneous voltage e_g is generated in the armature conductors due to their
motion through the flux ϕ, and $e_g = Kn\phi$, where n is the speed. Therefore when $\phi = 0$, $e_g = 0$. In other words voltage cannot be generated

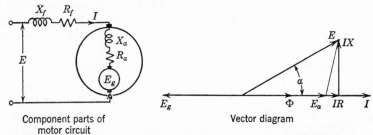

Component parts of   Vector diagram
motor circuit

FIG. 403. Circuit and vector diagrams of the single-phase series motor.

by rotating an armature in a field of zero strength. Also when ϕ is a
maximum e_g is a maximum. Since the graphs of ϕ and e_g pass through
zero at the same instant, and also through maximum at the same instant,
the vector E_g must be either exactly in phase with the vector Φ or exactly
180° out of phase. The first possibility is readily eliminated by noting
that in Fig. 401 the voltage generated
by the rotation is in opposition to
the direction of flow of the current,
the same as in the d-c motor, and
therefore E_g must be at 180° to Φ.

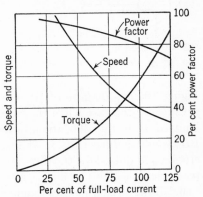

FIG. 404. Characteristics of a single-phase
series motor.

If the frequency of the power
supply is reduced, the reactance X
reduces in the same proportion, and
the vector IX in Fig. 403 becomes
shorter, with the result that the
power factor $\cos \alpha$ is increased. E_a
also becomes larger as IX is decreased, assuming that E is fixed, and
therefore the speed increases. Commutation, power factor, and effi-
ciency are all improved by lowering the frequency of the power supply,
and the motor operates best on direct current.

When operating on direct current, the speed and torque characteristics
are of course those of a d-c series motor. Changing to alternating current does not alter the general shape of these curves, but the speed drops
somewhat faster with increase of load. Typical characteristic curves
are shown in Fig. 404.

Approximately one-third of the electric locomotives of the world are
driven by large single-phase a-c series motors. The speed and torque

characteristics are well suited to such a service and the speed is easily and efficiently regulated by varying the applied voltage. The voltage maintained between the trolley and the track is usually somewhere between 11,000 and 22,000 volts, and this is stepped down to a suitable voltage by means of a transformer that is provided with a number of secondary taps, so that the voltage applied to the motor can be varied.

In the United States 25 cycles is the standard frequency for a-c electric traction, while 15 and 16⅔ cycles are used in Europe. Alternating-current series railway motors are always provided with commutating interpoles, which function the same as with the d-c motors.

The a-c series motor is also used quite extensively in fractional-horse-

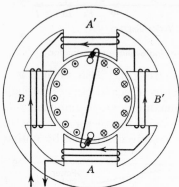

power sizes on both 25 and 60 cycles, wherever speed control or variation of speed with load is required, as in the operation of sewing machines, portable machine tools, desk fans, vacuum cleaners, etc. It is often called the universal motor because it runs on direct current as well as on alternating current.

391. The Repulsion-start Induction Motor. In construction the repulsion-start induction motor resembles a single-phase series motor. The armature, however, is not connected in series with the field coils but is short-circuited.

FIG. 405. Diagrammatic representation of a repulsion-start induction motor.

Figure 405 is a diagrammatic representation of a repulsion motor.

Consider the case when the rotor is stationary. If the coils AA' were omitted, as in Fig. 406, the alternating flux ϕ produced by the field coils BB' would induce emfs in the armature conductors. In Fig. 406 the crosses and dots show the directions of the induced emfs during the quarter cycle in which the flux is growing, the directions being obtained by Lenz's law. Each of these emfs will be in the reverse direction during the next quarter cycle, but at all times in tracing through the armature winding from one brush to the other, by either of the two paths, the number of crosses encountered will be equal to the number of dots, and therefore there is no resultant emf across the brushes, and no current flows in the short-circuiting conductor x or in the armature winding. Therefore the conclusion may be drawn that any current that flows in the armature when the rotor is stationary must be due solely to the action of the coils AA'.

Figure 407 shows coils AA' acting alone, and is drawn for the quarter cycle during which the flux is growing, the same as Fig. 406. These two figures are identical except for the position of the brushes relative to the poles. In tracing through the armature winding from one brush to the other in Fig. 407, the emfs encountered are all in the same direction and therefore a large current flows through the armature and the short-circuiting conductor x. The reaction between this current and the poles AA' does not produce any net torque, however, because under each pole half the conductors carry current in one direction while the other half carry current in the opposite direction.

If both sets of coils are acting, as in Fig. 405, then the current produced in the armature by coils AA' develops a powerful torque by reacting with

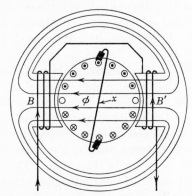

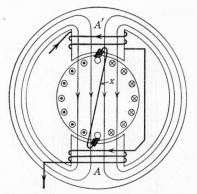

FIG. 406. Showing the directions of the emfs induced in the armature conductors by the coils BB' while the flux is growing; rotor stationary.

FIG. 407. Showing the directions of the emfs and currents induced in the armature conductors by the coils AA' while the flux is growing; rotor stationary.

the magnetic field of poles BB'. As the motor comes up to speed, a centrifugal device operates and pushes a ring against the ends of the commutator bars, thus short-circuiting every armature coil. The motor then runs as a single-phase squirrel-cage induction motor.

In another arrangement of the repulsion-induction type of motor the rotor carries a regular squirrel cage in addition to the drum winding and commutator. This arrangement makes it unnecessary to provide a device for short-circuiting the commutator bars. The starting torque of the repulsion-induction motors is at least 3.5 times full-load torque.

In Fig. 405 the stator apparently has four salient poles, but at the instant shown, A' and B' are both north poles, while A and B are both south poles. The resultant field is therefore at 45° to the vertical line through the two brushes. This resultant field could equally well be produced by a single pair of poles with their common magnetic axis at 45°, and in fact that is the way in which the stator is actually constructed. Moreover, in practice, the poles are not salient. They are produced by a single-phase winding distributed in the slots of a stator core that is the same as the core of any other induction motor. It is the rotor that is different, and the essential feature is that the line passing through the two brushes must be at approximately 45° to the field produced by the stator coils.

The motors of Figs. 397, 398, 399, and 405 are all two-pole and have a synchronous speed of 3,600 rpm on a 60-cycle system. To obtain 1,800 rpm, four poles are required. The universal motor of Fig. 401 may also have more than two poles, but in the case of this motor it is economy of construction and commutation difficulties that decide the number of poles, not the speed. The universal motor can be wound for any speed that is desired. Every time the number of armature conductors is reduced by one half the speed is doubled.

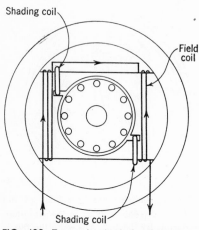

FIG. 408. Two-pole shaded-pole motor.

392. The Shaded-pole Motor. The shaded-pole motor is a single-phase squirrel-cage induction motor that obtains its starting torque by placing a coil of one or more short-circuited turns around a portion of each pole, as in Fig. 408. These short-circuited coils are called shading coils. The circuit that is connected to the line consists simply of the field coils in series. Transformer action between the field coils and the shading coils produces current in the shading coils, and this current opposes the growing and dying of the flux, with the result that the flux in the shaded portions of the poles is retarded considerably in phase angle behind the main flux. Now in the standard two-phase motor the two fluxes are at 90° to each other in both phase and space. In the shaded-pole motor the main flux and the shaded flux are at considerably less than 90° to each other in both phase and space. Nevertheless, the resultant flux actually does rotate, although it varies widely in magnitude as it does so, and also rotates with a nonuniform angular velocity. Since the flux rotates, the motor develops a starting torque, although only about 60 per cent of full-load torque.

The shaded-pole motor has the usual speed characteristic common to all induction motors and is generally regarded as a constant-speed motor, although its slip at full load may be 15 per cent or more. It is the standard general-purpose constant-speed a-c motor for applications requiring $\frac{1}{20}$ hp or less. Its efficiency is low, but since the power is so small, the efficiency is of little interest. The efficiency could be improved by arranging to open-circuit the shading coils after the motor has come up to speed, but the centrifugal switch would add more weight and cost to the miniature motor than could be justified by the small saving in power. The shaded-pole motor is available in synchronous speeds of 1,800 rpm and 3,600 rpm at 60 cycles.

393. Comparison of the Methods of Starting Single-phase Induction Motors. In the following list the various methods of starting fractional-horsepower single-phase induction motors are arranged in ascending order of capital cost:

1. Shaded pole
2. Phase splitting by resistance
3. Permanent-split capacitor
4. Capacitor-start
5. Capacitor-start capacitor-run
6. Repulsion-start

If methods 2 and 3 are interchanged in the foregoing list, the methods are then in ascending order of starting torque, except that methods 4 and 5 should be equal.

The repulsion-start motor was at one time the most widely used single-phase induction motor, but it has now been almost completely replaced in the fractional-horsepower field by the capacitor motors. However, as the horsepower rating of the motor is increased, the cost of the repulsion-start motor increases less rapidly than that of the capacitor motors, and above 1 hp the repulsion-start motor is cheaper than either the capacitor-start or the capacitor-start capacitor-run motors. The repulsion-start motor is therefore still used in sizes above 1 hp, although it has the disadvantage of being somewhat noisier than the capacitor motors.

394. Single-phase Synchronous Motor. A single-phase a-c generator may be made to operate as a motor. When an alternating emf is applied to the winding of the single-phase machine shown in Fig. 409, an alternating current flows through that winding. The conductors a, b, c, and d are then carrying current and are in a magnetic field so that force acts on each conductor, while an equal and opposite force acts on the poles and tends to turn the rotor. The current, however, is alternating, so that the force on the rotor is alternating in direction unless the polarity of the poles is changed when the current reverses.

This would be the case if the machine were already running at such a speed that, during the time of half a cycle or in $1/2f$ sec, the rotor moves through the distance between two adjacent poles or through $1/p$ of a revolution. This speed, called the synchronous speed, is therefore

$$\text{Synchronous speed} = \frac{1}{p} \times 2f \quad \text{rps}$$

$$= \frac{120f}{p} \quad \text{rpm}$$

and is the speed at which the machine would have to run as a generator in order to generate an emf of f cycles per sec.

The motor-generator set that converts the a-c power into d-c power in the Great Northern Railway type of electric locomotive is driven by a 3,600-hp single-phase synchronous motor. An a-c series motor, mounted on the same shaft, is used to start the synchronous motor and bring it up to speed. As soon as the synchronous motor is synchronized, the a-c series motor is disconnected from the line and is subsequently used as a d-c generator to provide field current for regenerative braking. This is the only application of large single-phase synchronous motors that is known to the authors. Fractional-horsepower single-phase synchronous motors are used extensively for driving clocks and other devices where timing is important. They are usually made self-starting by phase splitting, the same as with induction motors, and they take advantage of the fact that a synchronous motor will operate without any field current, although at a low power factor. An unexcited single-phase synchronous motor with soft-iron salient poles is generally called a **reluctance motor.** If the rotor is simply a cylinder of hard steel, the starting and running torques will both be due chiefly to hysteresis, and it will accelerate to synchronous speed. This type of synchronous motor is called a **hysteresis motor.**

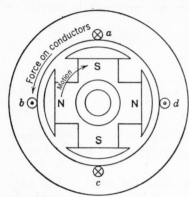

FIG. 409. Single-phase synchronous motor.

Problems

37-1. A 110-volt 0.5-hp two-phase 60-cycle squirrel-cage induction motor is to be operated from a single-phase line. When the rotor is stationary and either winding is connected across the line, the current is 20 amp at 15 per cent power factor.

a. What capacitance must be connected in series with one of these windings to obtain 20 amp in both windings at start?

b. If the phase is split by means of resistance inserted in series with one winding, find by trial the value of resistance for maximum starting torque, and express the starting torque as a per cent of that obtained with the capacitor.

*37-2. *a.* Why do a-c series motors operate better on 25 cycles than on 60 cycles?

b. What are the two advantages gained by using a compensating winding to compensate for armature reaction in an a-c series motor?

c. In what ways must the d-c series motor be modified in order that it may operate satisfactorily on alternating current?

d. Is the driving torque of an a-c series motor constant throughout the cycle?

38

CONVERTING AND RECTIFYING APPARATUS

395. Converting Requirements. It frequently happens that electric power cannot be applied directly to a particular service in the form in which it happens to be available and must therefore be converted into some other form before it is utilized. For example, electric power is usually available only in the form of alternating current at 60 or 25 cycles, but electrochemical plants, street railways, high-speed elevators, reversing mill drives, etc., require direct current, and apparatus must therefore be installed to convert from alternating current to direct current. Again, when an electric railway operating on alternating current buys power from a 60-cycle system, it is necessary to convert it to 25 cycles.

The following six types of conversion are required in practice:

1. Alternating current to direct current
2. Direct current to alternating current
3. Direct current to direct current of a different voltage
4. Alternating current to alternating current of a different voltage
5. Alternating current to alternating current of a different frequency
6. Two-phase to three-phase

Of the above conversions, 4 and 6 are cheaply and efficiently performed by transformers (Chap. 31), 2, 3, and 5 are performed by motor-generator sets, while 1, which is by far the most common, is performed by a variety of devices, such as motor-generator sets, rotary converters, mercury-arc rectifiers, dry-disk rectifiers, and thermionic tubes.

396. Motor-generator Sets. A motor-generator set consists of two rotating machines mechanically coupled together, one of which, running as a motor, takes electric power from the source of supply and drives the other machine as a generator.

The motor-generator set is the most flexible type of converting apparatus. It can perform any of the six conversions listed in Art. 395 and lends itself most readily to control.   It costs several times as much as a transformer, requires much more attention, and is less efficient, especially at light loads.   It is widely used, never-theless, to perform conversions that cannot at present be performed satis-factorily in any other way.

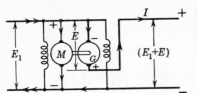

FIG. 410. Booster motor-generator set.

397. Booster Motor-generator Set.

Figure 410 shows how a motor-gen-erator set may be used to boost or otherwise control the voltage obtained from a d-c supply line.   The generator in this case is connected in series with the line and its voltage E may either add to or subtract from the line voltage E_1.

If 10 kw at 220 volts is required from a 110-volt line and a booster set is used, then

$$\text{Booster output} = EI$$
$$= 5 \text{ kw at } 110 \text{ volts}$$
$$\text{Output of driving motor} = \frac{5 \times 1{,}000}{746} \times \frac{1}{0.85}$$
$$= 8 \text{ hp at } 110 \text{ volts}$$

where $0.85 =$ efficiency of the generator.

398. The Synchronous Rotary Converter.

The emf generated in each coil of a d-c generator is an alternating emf, and any d-c generator can be converted into an a-c generator of the type described in Art. 300 by installing two or more slip rings and connecting them permanently to suitable points on the armature winding.   Figure 411 shows a two-pole d-c generator of the Gramme-ring type converted into a single-phase a-c generator by the addition of two slip rings a and b permanently connected to diametrically opposite points x and y on the armature winding or the commutator.   When brushes are mounted to rub on the slip rings, the machine can be made to operate in quite a variety of ways, as follows:

1. As a d-c generator.

2. As an a-c generator.

3. As a generator simultaneously supplying two different loads, one direct current and the other alternating current.

4. As a d-c motor.

5. As a synchronous motor.

6. It can be run as a d-c motor while supplying alternating current to a load, thus converting d-c power to a-c power.

7. It can be run as a synchronous motor while supplying direct current to a load, thus converting a-c power to d-c power.

When performing this last function, which is by far the most important commercially, the machine is called a rotary converter.

When operating as a rotary converter, the current in the armature winding at any instant is the difference between the direct current and the alternating current at that instant. The armature copper loss is therefore considerably less than it would be in a motor-generator set of the same output.

There is a fixed ratio between the d-c voltage and the a-c voltage of a rotary converter. The voltage between the slip rings a and b of Fig. 411 is a maximum when x and y are in the neutral position, that is, under brushes c and d, but this is also the voltage between the d-c brushes c and d. Therefore the d-c voltage E_d is equal to the maximum value of the alternating voltage, and is equal to $\sqrt{2}$ times the effective value of the alternating voltage.

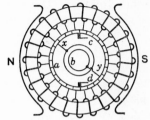

FIG. 411. Diagrammatic representation of a rotary converter.

The single-phase rotary converter of Fig. 411 can be converted into a three-phase machine by adding a third slip ring and spacing the three taps x, y, and z 120° apart instead of 180°, as shown in Fig. 412, in which case the effective value of the alternating voltage between slip rings is $\sqrt{3}/2 \sqrt{2}$ times the d-c voltage; or it can be converted into a six-phase

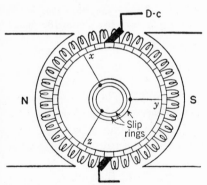

FIG. 412. Three-phase rotary converter.

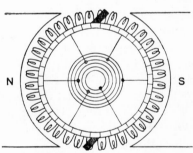

FIG. 413. Six-phase rotary converter.

machine by providing six slip rings and spacing the taps 60° apart, as in Fig. 413.

The advantage of the six-phase rotary over the three-phase is that the copper loss is appreciably less. The proof of this statement is rather too long and complicated to be given here. Most of the larger rotary converters are six-phase. The a-c power is received three-phase and is converted into six-phase by means of the transformer connection shown in Fig. 414, in which the mid-points of the three secondaries are connected together, so that each secondary forms two phases 180° apart. The conversion from three-phase to six-phase costs practically nothing because the transformers are needed in any case to step down the voltage.

It is impossible to change the d-c voltage of a rotary converter without changing the a-c voltage. Varying the field current does not change either voltage. The rotary converter is driven as a synchronous motor and it reacts to a change in the field current in exactly the same way as any other synchronous motor. A change in the field current merely changes the power factor on the a-c side, as explained in Art. 366. If it is desired to raise the voltage of the d-c terminals of the machine, then the applied alternating voltage must be raised. One method of doing this is to supply the rotary converter through a transformer that is provided with an adequate number of taps and with a mechanism for tap

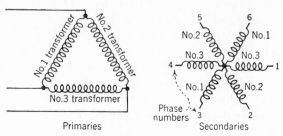

FIG. 414. Transformer connections, three-phase to six-phase. The mid-points of the secondaries are connected together so that each secondary forms two phases 180° apart.

changing under load. Another method is to insert a booster, generally on the a-c side of the machine. This booster is simply a small three-phase a-c generator, mounted on the shaft of the rotary converter and connected in series with the three-phase supply. The voltage is controlled by varying the field current of the booster, and the booster voltage may be either added to or subtracted from the line voltage.

The machine in Fig. 411 is shown with a Gramme-ring winding for the sake of simplicity, but all modern rotary converters have drum windings such as that shown in Fig. 73. In Figs. 412 and 413 the coils are merely indicated conventionally by loops joining the commutator bars and may be considered as representing any type of winding.

Rotary converters are provided with grids carried in slots in the pole faces. The grids constitute partial squirrel cages and not only make the the rotary converter self-starting on the a-c side, but also act to damp out any hunting.

399. Motor-generator Sets versus Rotary Converters. A polyphase rotary converter weighs and costs approximately half as much as a motor-generator set of the same power rating. The saving in weight and cost is due to the fact that in the rotary converter a single machine is performing simultaneously the functions of both motor and generator.

Moreover, the power losses in a rotary converter are less than half those in a motor-generator set of the same rating.   The copper loss in a six-phase rotary converter that is operating at 100 per cent power factor is only about 15 per cent of the copper loss in the equivalent motor-generator set.   This is due to the fact that the current in the armature winding is the difference between the a-c and d-c currents.   All the other losses in the rotary converter are about the same as those in the generator of the motor-generator set.   The efficiency of a large rotary converter is about 95 per cent, compared with 88 per cent for the equivalent motor-generator set.   As a natural consequence of the difference in cost and efficiency the motor-generator set is used for conversion of alternating current to direct current only in applications where the control of the d-c voltage is of major importance, as for example in the Ward Leonard system of speed control.

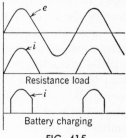

FIG. 415

400. Thermionic Rectifiers.   The fundamental idea of a rectifier is to provide a path which is conducting in one direction only, so that when the path is connected in series with an a-c generator it will act as a check valve and allow current to flow during one-half of each cycle only.   The resultant current will be an intermittent, or pulsating, direct current, as shown in Fig. 415, which can be used to charge batteries or capacitors.

The thermionic rectifier, as shown in Fig. 416, consists of a tungsten filament f and a nickel or molybdenum plate p enclosed in an evacuated glass bulb.   The filament is heated by the passage of a current, called the filament current, which is driven by the battery b, and the temperature of the filament can be controlled by varying the resistance r.

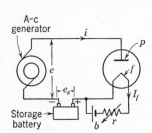

FIG. 416. Thermionic-tube rectifier being used to charge a storage battery from an a-c supply.

When the filament is cold, the space between the filament and the plate is nonconducting, regardless of polarity, but when the filament is red-hot electrons can flow through this space from the filament to the plate but cannot flow in the opposite direction.   The explanation is as follows: The atoms of any body that is not at absolute zero temperature are in a state of more or less violent agitation, depending upon the temperature of the body.   As the temperature of the filament f is raised, the agitation becomes more and more violent, until, at a red heat, electrons are shot out through the surface of the filament into space, in much the same way that molecules would be shot out if the temperature were

raised to the boiling point of the metal.   But just as bullets shot into the
air from a machine gun are eventually brought back to the earth by the
force of gravity, so are the electrons brought back to the filament by
the force of attraction between them and the protons in the filament.
The action is somewhat complicated by the mutual repulsion between the
electrons, but the net result is that the hot filament is surrounded by a
regular snowstorm of billions of electrons, half of which are traveling
away from the filament with a diminishing velocity, and the other half
toward the filament with an increasing velocity.

If now we give the plate p a positive charge, it will exert a force of
attraction on these electrons, and those which are nearest to the plate
will be attracted to it.   The greater the positive charge on the plate,
that is, the greater the emf e_p impressed between the plate and the filament, the greater will be the number of the electrons attracted to the
plate, until, at an emf that is called the saturation emf, every electron
emitted by the filament is sucked in by the plate.   Any further increase
in e cannot increase the current i.

When e is reversed, the charge on the plate becomes negative and the
flow of electrons to the plate ceases.   The plate is not hot enough to
emit electrons and therefore there can be no flow of electrons in the
reverse direction.   Thus the thermionic tube is conducting in one direction only.

In dealing with what happens inside the tube it is customary to speak
of the "flow of the electrons" rather than of the "electric current"
in order to avoid the confusion which arises from the fact that the conventional direction of current is in the opposite direction to the actual
flow.

The filament current may be either alternating or direct current.

401. Full-wave Rectification Using Two Rectifiers.   When only one
rectifier is used, the current is intermittent, as shown in Fig. 415, but if
two rectifiers are connected, as shown in Fig. 417, one will carry current
during one half cycle, and the other will carry current during the other
half cycle, and the average value of the total current will be doubled.   In
practice, the two plates are usually placed inside a single glass bulb, one
on each side of the filament.   Thus the two plates use the same filament
and only one tube is required.   In some applications it may be necessary
to smooth out the pulsations in the d-c output.   This can be done by
means of a filter of the type shown in Fig. 455.

402. Efficiency of Thermionic Rectifiers.   An ideal rectifier would be
one that would offer zero resistance to the flow of current in one direction
and infinite resistance to the flow of current in the opposite direction.
The thermionic rectifier offers practically infinite resistance to the flow
of current in one direction, but the resistance in the opposite direction is

by no means zero, and there is accordingly a power loss in the tube, the instantaneous value of which is equal to $e_p i$ watts, where e_p is the volts drop between the plate and the filament, and i is the plate current. The energy lost in this way is converted into heat, and the plates of the larger thermionic rectifiers are water cooled so as to carry this heat away and keep the plates from getting hot enough to emit electrons and thus spoil the rectifying properties of the tube. The power input to the filament to keep it hot is also a power loss and is constant. In practice, the power input to the filament is generally alternating current.

With reference to Fig. 416, if the voltage e_s of the storage battery is increased by adding more cells, and the alternating emf e is increased just

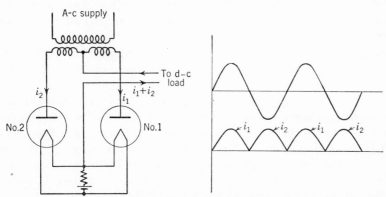

FIG. 417. Full-wave rectification produced by two thermionic rectifiers.

sufficiently to give the same value of i as before, then the losses in the tube are unchanged but the power output $e_s i$ is increased and therefore the efficiency of the rectifier is increased. Thus the higher the voltage of the circuit, the greater the efficiency of the rectifier, up to the voltage at which the tube breaks down. This is true of every type of rectifier and is also true of a transmission line. In fact, a rectifier may be regarded as a special type of one-way transmission line.

403. Field of Application of Vacuum-type Thermionic Rectifier. The highly evacuated thermionic rectifier is essentially a high-voltage rectifier. The resistance of its plate circuit is too high to enable it to be used efficiently on low voltages. It is, however, sometimes used on low voltages where the amount of power to be handled is so small that the efficiency is of minor importance, as in radio receiving sets.

The vacuum-type thermionic rectifier has been built in sizes up to 30 kw and for voltages up to 150,000 volts. Its field of application is at present chiefly limited to supplying direct current for smoke and dust precipitators, X-ray machines, and the plate circuits of radio transmitters and receivers, and for testing and research purposes.

404. Gas-filled Thermionic Rectifiers.   The voltage required to drive the plate current through a thermionic rectifier is greatly reduced, and its current-carrying capacity increased, if the tube is filled with mercury vapor or argon gas at a low pressure.   This makes the rectifier suitable for low-voltage operation—and incidentally makes it unsuitable for high-voltage operation.

The Tungar and Rectigon rectifiers made by the General Electric Company and the Westinghouse Electric and Manufacturing Company, respectively, are of this type and are manufactured in sizes up to 12 amp at 100 volts or 6 amp at 200 volts.   They are used principally for charging small storage batteries.

The way in which the gas increases the flow of the electrons is explained as follows: When gas is present at a low pressure, the electrons collide with the gas molecules with sufficient force to knock electrons out of them, thus converting them into positively charged ions.   The additional electrons so obtained join the stream flowing to the positive plate, while the heavy positive ions move slowly toward the hot cathode.   Now the hot cathode is surrounded by a cloud of electrons, called the *space charge*, and this negative charge opposes the emission of the electrons and drives many of them back into the cathode.   The positive ions mingle with the negative space charge and largely neutralize it, thus greatly increasing the flow of electrons away from the cathode.   The voltage drop between the plate and the hot cathode in a thermionic rectifier containing mercury vapor is normally about 10 to 20 volts, and is practically independent of the current.   Consequently, excessive current will flow if the d-c load is short-circuited.

405. Mercury-arc Rectifiers.   The mercury-arc rectifier is a special type of gas-filled thermionic rectifier in which the hot filament is replaced by a pool of mercury, and the plate is replaced by iron or graphite anodes, as shown in Fig. 418, where P_1 and P_2 are the anodes.   The main body of the bulb contains only mercury vapor.

In order that the rectifier may function, the surface of the mercury pool must be hot enough to emit electrons.   Under operating conditions the plate current, or arc current as it is generally called in this type of rectifier, keeps the surface of the mercury hot enough to emit electrons; but if the d-c output current is reduced below a certain minimum value, the mercury will drop below the electron-emission temperature and the arc will go out.   There is thus for every mercury-arc rectifier a minimum load below which it cannot operate, and artificial loads are frequently supplied to be used in keeping the rectifier operating during momentary periods of very light load.

In order to start the rectifier, the bulb is tilted until the mercury comes in contact with the starting electrode P_3.   The bulb is then tilted back to the vertical position and, as the mercury breaks contact with the starting electrode, a temporary arc is formed that heats a spot on the surface of the mercury pool to the electron-emission temperature.

The mercury-arc rectifier shown in Fig. 418 cannot be operated as a half-wave rectifier with a single anode to give the intermittent direct current shown in Fig. 415, because the temperature of the surface of the mercury pool would drop below the electron-emission temperature during the half cycle in which no current was flowing.   In fact, the mercury-arc rectifier will not operate as a full-wave rectifier using two electrodes

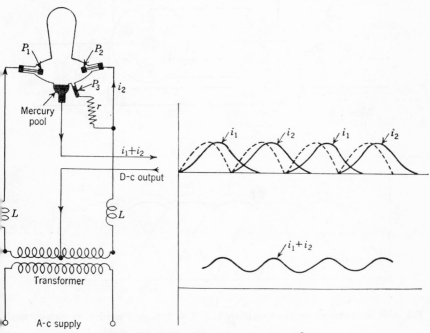

FIG. 418. Single-phase mercury-arc rectifier.

unless some inductance is inserted in one or both of the leads to the anodes P_1P_2.   With no inductance and with a pure resistance d-c load the rectified current would have the form shown in Fig. 417, and during the time that the current was nearly zero the mercury would cool and the arc go out.   The inductances LL spread out the current waves so that they overlap as shown in Fig. 418, and the resultant total current is never low enough to allow the arc to go out.   The purpose of the upper chamber of the glass bulb is to condense the mercury vapor so as to keep the vapor pressure down within the range of values that gives the best operation.

Single-phase glass-bulb mercury-arc rectifiers are built in sizes up to 50 amp, 65 volts and 30 amp, 320 volts, for charging storage batteries.

406. Polyphase Mercury-arc Rectifiers. The larger-size mercury-arc rectifiers are either 6-phase or 12-phase, and the vacuum chamber is a steel tank instead of a glass bulb. Three-phase rectifiers are built only in moderate sizes and may employ either a glass bulb or a steel tank. Figure 419 is a diagrammatic representation of a 6-phase rectifier. As shown in Fig. 419, the rectifier element consists of a single central mercury pool H surrounded by a circular row of vertical steel anodes. There are as many anodes as there are phases. In the detail diagram (Fig. 419b)

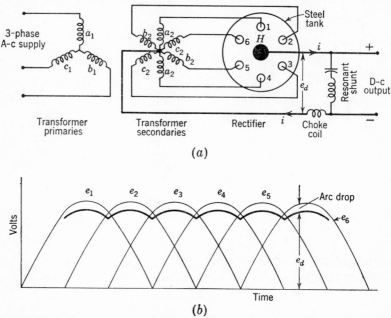

(a)

FIG. 419. Six-phase mercury-arc rectifier: **1, 2, 3, 4, 5, 6,** steel anodes; *H,* mercury pool.

the sine curves $e_1 e_2 e_3 e_4 e_5 e_6$ represent the voltages to neutral impressed on the six anodes, and they also represent the currents that would tend to flow in each anode if no other anode were present. When more than one anode is present, however, they do not share the load, but the anode that is at the highest potential takes the entire load, and the arc shifts from anode to anode, making one trip around the circle of anodes each cycle.

Since the voltage drop in the arc of a 600-volt rectifier is only about 20 volts, it follows that, except during the brief interval of transition of the arc from one anode to the next, there is never more than one anode at a time that is positive with respect to the pool, and therefore there is only one anode that can carry current.

A special type of interphase transformer (not shown) has been developed, through which the transformer secondaries pass before being joined together to form the negative d-c terminal, and this interphase transformer causes the load to be shared equally by two anodes in a 6-phase rectifier, or by four anodes in a 12-phase rectifier, thus raising both the capacity and the efficiency to some extent.

As shown in Fig. 419, the d-c output has an a-c component whose frequency is six times the supply frequency with a 6-phase rectifier, and twelve times the supply frequency with a 12-phase rectifier. This a-c component is not a pure sine wave, but contains harmonics and may cause noise in any telephone lines that come within its influence. If complaints are received from telephone companies, filter equipment is usually installed to smooth out the wave. The standard filter equipment for this purpose consists of a choke coil connected as shown in Fig. 419 and three resonant shunts made up of capacitors and inductance coils. A resonant shunt has a very low impedance at its resonant frequency and these three shunts are tuned to the three most objectionable frequencies and accordingly practically short-circuit those frequencies. The purpose of the choke coil is to offer an impedance to all a-c components and thus

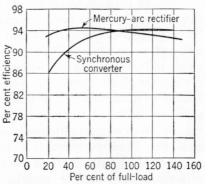

FIG. 420. Comparative efficiency curves of a mercury-arc rectifier and a rotary converter, for 3,000-kw units supplying 600 volts direct current. The a-c supply was 60 cycles.

limit the amount of current to be carried by the resonant shunts.

In addition to the main anodes there are often two small auxiliary anodes (not shown), which are connected to a small artificial load in order to maintain a hot spot on the mercury during periods of very light load. There is also an ignition electrode that can be lowered into the mercury pool and withdrawn so as to strike an arc.

A motor-driven vacuum pump is required to maintain the high degree of vacuum necessary to the successful operation of the rectifier.

Polyphase mercury-arc rectifiers are regularly supplied in sizes up to 3,125 kw, and larger ones can be built. In 600-volt ratings for street-railway service the mercury-arc rectifier is more efficient than the synchronous rotary converter for all loads up to about 90 per cent of full load, as shown in Fig. 420, but is less efficient on overload. In general, the mercury-arc rectifier is preferred to the rotary converter for 600-volt service. As the rated voltage is increased, the efficiency of the rectifier increases; and as the voltage is decreased, its efficiency decreases, while the efficiency of the converter is practically independent of the voltage. It follows that for voltages much below 600 volts the converter has the higher efficiency, but for 600 volts and upward the mercury-arc rectifier has the higher efficiency.

407. Arc-back in Mercury-arc Rectifiers. Consider a six-phase mercury-arc rectifier, as shown in Fig. 419, supplying 600 volts d-c output. At the instant when anode 1 is at its maximum positive potential, and is therefore carrying the arc, the voltage e_1 produced in the transformer secondary a_2 must be 600 volts plus the drop in the arc. The voltage drop in the arc is approximately constant at about 20 volts. Therefore $e_1 = 600 + 20 = 620$ volts. At the same instant $e_4 = -620$ volts, and the voltage between anode 1 and anode 4 is therefore 1,240 volts. Since the voltage between anode 1 and the mercury pool is only 20 volts, the voltage between anode 4 and the pool must be 1,220 volts. Thus although no anode is ever more than 20 volts positive to the pool, each anode in turn, once per cycle, becomes negative to the pool by twice the d-c voltage plus the arc drop. Normally this voltage is not nearly large enough to break down the gap between the anode and the mercury pool, with the anode negative; yet for some reason, not at all well understood, this gap does occasionally break down. Such a break-down is called an *arc-back*. This wrong-direction arc from the pool to anode 4, in conjunction with the proper arc from anode 1 to the pool, constitutes a short circuit across the complete secondary a_2a_2 of transformer a. A large current consequently flows and trips the circuit breakers. Automatic reclosing equipment is usually provided to reconnect the rectifier to the line so that it is out of service for only a second or two. A polyphase rectifier of this type may go for months without an arc-back, or it may have several in one day. Inadequate condensation of the mercury vapor and poor vacuum are conditions conducive to arc-back.

408. Ignitron. The ignitron was developed in an attempt to eliminate arc-back. The basic idea of the ignitron is to provide a separate tank and mercury pool for each anode, as shown in Fig. 421. If the rectifier is six-phase, the six mercury pools are all connected to the same bus so that they act as a single pool.

In the multianode tank of Fig. 419 an arc is always present, and it is reasonable to suppose that the great quantity of ionized mercury vapor that it produces facilitates the arc-back. When a separate tank is provided for each anode, there is no ionized vapor present at the time when the anode is at its maximum negative potential, because the chamber deionizes itself in a few microseconds once the arc is extinguished, and in each tank of a six-phase rectifier the arc remains extinguished for the major portion of each cycle. It follows however that some means must be provided to reignite the arc in each tank at the proper instant in every cycle. This makes 360 ignitions per sec for the case of a six-phase rectifier on a 60-cycle system.

The igniter, shown in Fig. 421, is a small point of silicon carbide, or other similar crystalline material that does not make a good contact with mercury. The igniter tip is permanently immersed in the mercury, and once each cycle, at the proper time in the cycle, a sudden short pulse of current is sent through the igniter; minute arcs are produced at the junction of the igniter and the mercury; electrons are emitted, and the main arc forms within a few microseconds. There are several different methods of producing the pulses of ignition current, and the

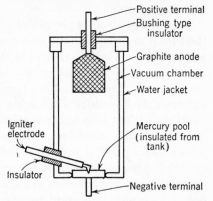

FIG. 421. Ignitron rectifier (cross section).

reader is therefore referred to the technical press for a description of these methods.[1]

FIG. 422. Twelve-phase ignitron-type mercury-arc rectifier. Note the ignitor electrode at the lower left side of each tank. (*Courtesy of Westinghouse Electric Corporation.*)

The average d-c voltage output can be reduced to any desired extent simply by retarding the time of ignition of the arc. Various methods of

[1] J. H. Cox and G. F. Jones, Ignitrons for the Transportation Industry, *Trans. AIEE*, 1939, pp. 618–624.

retarding the ignition are described in the article referred to in the foregoing paragraph.

The voltage drop in the arc of a single-anode tank is 6 or 7 volts less than for a multianode tank, the reason being that the distance from the anode to the cathode is shorter in the single-anode tank. Consequently, the efficiency of the single-anode tank is higher than that of the multianode tank. The ignitron has been very favorably received by industry, although the hoped-for elimination of arc-backs has not been completely realized. A 12-phase ignitron rectifier is shown in Fig. 422.

409. Dry-disk Rectifiers. When a semiconductor material is coated onto a metal plate, it is often found that the junction surface of the two materials possesses rectifying properties. That is, electrons pass through this surface in one direction much more easily than in the opposite direction. The most important rectifiers of this type are the selenium, germanium, and copper-oxide dry-disk rectifiers.

Selenium Rectifier. The selenium-rectifier cell is formed by coating a thin layer of selenium onto a flat disk of aluminum or nickel-plated iron and then spraying an alloy of tin and cadmium or bismuth over the selenium. This cell offers a low resistance to the flow of electrons from the metal-alloy electrode through the selenium to the iron or aluminum electrode, but offers a practically infinite resistance to flow in the opposite direction, as long as the inverse voltage does not exceed a certain limit. This limit varies from about 20 to 80 volts, peak value, depending on the forming processes used in the manufacture of the cell. However, the treatment that increases the allowable inverse voltage also increases the resistance in the conducting direction, and thus lowers the efficiency of the rectifier. Cells may be connected in series to suit any desired operating voltage. The efficiency of a selenium rectifier that is designed for an inverse peak emf of 20 volts per cell is about 85 per cent, independent of the voltage for which it is designed. Now the efficiency of a mercury-arc rectifier decreases as the operating voltage is decreased, and in consequence the selenium rectifier is preferred to the mercury-arc rectifier for all d-c voltages below 150 volts. It may also be chosen for voltages above 150 volts in some cases because of the fact that it requires less attention. There is no upper limit to the current for which low-voltage selenium rectifiers can be economically built.

Germanium Rectifier. This is the latest type of dry-disk rectifier to appear on the market. Its efficiency may be over 98%, and it can carry a much greater current density than the selenium rectifier. As a result of its high efficiency and high current-carrying capacity, the germanium rectifier is much smaller than the selenium rectifier of the same power rating. The germanium rectifier may not be any cheaper, however, because it costs much more per pound. It is competing success-fully with the selenium rectifier in current ratings above 100 amp.

Copper-oxide Rectifier. The unit cell is formed by coating copper oxide onto a flat copper disk and then clamping a lead disk against the coated side. Electrons flow easily through the cell from the copper to the lead, but a high resistance is offered to flow in the reverse direction. A single cell will withstand an inverse peak emf of only about 6 volts, but cells may be stacked up to withstand whatever voltage is required. The maximum efficiency of this type of rectifier is about 70 per cent. It has been used extensively in low-voltage applications.

410. Miscellaneous Rectifiers. There are several types of electrolytic rectifiers. These consist of a pair of plates of dissimilar materials immersed in an electrolyte. Current passes readily from one plate to the other in one direction; but when an attempt is made to reverse the current, a chemical action takes place and a very thin film of insulating material is deposited on one of the plates, thus reducing the current to a negligible quantity. This film disappears again as soon as the direction of the current is again reversed.

Commutators, rotated by small synchronous motors, are used to obtain d-c voltages of 50,000 volts and higher for use in smoke and dust precipitators.

In the vibrating-reed rectifier a mechanical contact is closed during alternate half cycles and is open during the opposite half cycles. However, the main application of this type of rectifier is as an inverter converting from direct current to alternating current, thus making it possible to operate small a-c equipment, such as automobile radios, from batteries.

Problems

*38-1. Why does a mercury-arc rectifier interrupt the circuit if the d-c load becomes too small?

*38-2. Why does the value of the voltage have an important effect on the efficiency of a thermionic rectifier?

*38-3. Why does the presence of a little gas in a thermionic tube greatly increase its current-carrying capacity?

*38-4. Show that the frequency of the ripple on the d-c voltage from a six-phase 60-cycle rectifier is 360 cycles.

39

ALTERNATING-CURRENT TRANSMISSION AND DISTRIBUTION

411. At the present time most of the electrical energy is obtained from coal-burning steam-power plants and water-power plants. In the case of the water-power plants the electrical energy must be generated wherever the waterfalls happen to be, and the electrical energy must then be transmitted to the consumer's premises, often over long distances. Steam-power plants may be located either at or near coal mines, the energy being transmitted to the consumer's premises in electrical form, or they may be located at or near the consumer's premises, in which case the energy is transported in the form of coal.

The use of small, and therefore comparatively inefficient, individual steam-power plants on the consumer's premises is not economical unless the exhaust steam can be used for heating. In general, it has been found more economical to build the steam plants in large sizes and to locate them at points which show minimum over-all costs for haulage of coal and transmission and distribution of the electrical energy, not forgetting that an abundance of water is essential for cooling the condensers. Whether the power plants are steam or water, therefore, there is an extensive system of transmission and distribution lines. This system is nearly always three-phase.

412. The Transmission and Distribution System. As explained in Art. 229, transmission of electrical energy can be carried out efficiently only at high voltages, while energy-consuming equipment, such as motors and lamps, are inherently low-voltage devices; consequently transformers play a very important part in any transmission and distribution system.

The generators in large powerhouses are designed for various voltages ranging from 6,600 to 22,000 volts, the voltage being so chosen as to give the most economical over-all design consistent with reliability of operation. Transformer banks are inserted between the generators and the transmission line to step the voltage up to whatever value appears to result in the most economical over-all operation of the line and the transformers, due consideration being given of course to reliability of operation. The optimum voltage for the operation of a transmission line and its associated transformers varies widely with the length of the line and with the amount of power to be transmitted. Transmission-line voltages have not been standardized but the preferred nominal voltages appear to be 23, 27.6, 34.5, 46, 69, 115, 138, 161, 230, 288, 330, and 380 kv.

Let us assume that the terminal station at the output end of the line is supplying electric power to a city with a population of one hundred thousand inhabitants. It would not be economical to supply each individual load directly from the terminal station. Consequently, the city is divided up into possibly five areas, each one of which is fed from a substation, which in turn is fed from the terminal station. The terminal station is generally located on the outskirts of the city in order to avoid bringing the high-voltage line into the city. The cables joining the terminal station to the substations have been quite generally 13,200 volts in the past, but the recent development of satisfactory higher-voltage cables is causing higher voltages to be used in installations where the amount of power is large.

The substation contains transformers and voltage regulators which step the voltage down to either 4,000 or 2,300 volts, depending on whether the distribution system is 4,000 volts, four-wire (Fig. 264), or 2,300 volts, three-wire. These distribution circuits radiate out from each substation and the individual loads are tapped off through transformers which step the voltage down to the proper value for the particular load in question. In the case of residence service, several residences are combined together to form a single load and are fed from the same transformer.

The foregoing description of a distribution system is a mere skeleton outline, and various modifications are met with in practice. Frequently the 4,000- or 2,300-volt lines are crisscrossed and joined together to form a network that is fed at various points by feeder cables radiating from the substations. The majority of the loads are fed from this network, but large loads are fed directly from the substations by special cables, or even directly from the terminal station.

413. Voltages Used in Practice. The voltages used on energy-consuming equipment are:

Direct Current:

115 volts for lighting, generally obtained from a 230-volt three-wire system.

115, 230, and 550 volts for motors.

600 volts for street-railway systems.

1,200 to 1,500 volts for interurban electric railways.

2,400 to 3,000 volts for trunk-line electric railways.

Alternating Current:

115 and 120 volts single-phase for lighting and for small motors.

115, 208, 230, 440, and 550 volts for polyphase motors up to 50 hp.

440, 550, and 2,200 volts for polyphase motors greater than 50 hp.

In America the standard frequency for power and lighting is 60 cycles, although there are some 50-cycle systems. Electric locomotives that are equipped with a-c series motors are provided with single-phase 25-cycle power because the operation of these motors is more satisfactory at 25 cycles than at 60 cycles.

414. Three-phase Transmission Line. A single-phase transmission-line problem was solved in Art. 272. A three-phase line consists of three

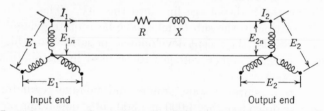

Input end   Output end

FIG. 423. Equivalent circuit of one phase of a three-phase transmission line, when the line is short enough so that its capacitance may be neglected.

single-phase lines using a common neutral return conductor. Figure 423 shows one phase of a three-phase line, and also shows the terminal transformer windings of the other two phases at each end of the line. We shall consider only the case of balanced three-phase load, in which one-third of the power is carried by each phase, and in which the sum of the three currents returning in the common neutral is zero. Since there is actually no current flowing in the neutral conductor, there will be no power loss or voltage drop in it. In fact, this conductor may not even exist. However, it clarifies the picture to draw it in.

Example. At 80 per cent power factor lagging, 15,000 kw is to be delivered at 50,000 volts 60 cycles over a 25-mile three-phase transmission line. The conductors are No. 000 copper and are spaced 72 in. Find the voltage required at the input end of the line and the power loss in the line.

The resistance and reactance of the conductor are obtained from Table 3, page 306, or from any electrical handbook, as follows:

Resistance = 0.326 ohm per mile of conductor
Reactance = 0.742 ohm per mile of conductor

This value of reactance is precise only if a cross section of the line shows the three line conductors forming the points of an equilateral triangle whose sides are

72 in. long.   If the three sides of the triangle are not equal, the equivalent spacing is given by the formula

$$\text{Equivalent spacing} = \sqrt[3]{abc}$$

where a, b, and c are the three distances between conductors.

The solution for any one phase then proceeds as follows: Let the subscript 2 denote output values, and the subscript 1 denote input values.   Then

$$\text{Power delivered} = \sqrt{3}\, E_2 I_2 \cos \phi_2 = 15,000 \times 1,000 \text{ watts}$$

Therefore
$$I_2 = \frac{15,000 \times 1,000}{\sqrt{3} \times 50,000 \times 0.8} = 217 \text{ amp}$$

Since the line is only 25 miles long, we may ignore the capacitance between conductors (Art. 415) and write

$$I_1 = I_2 = I = 217 \text{ amp}$$

E_{2n}, voltage to neutral, that is, the voltage of one phase, is

$$\frac{E_2}{\sqrt{3}} = \frac{50,000}{\sqrt{3}} = 29,000 \text{ volts}$$

R, resistance of one conductor $= 25 \times 0.326 = 8.15$ ohms
X, reactance of one conductor $= 25 \times 0.742 = 18.55$ ohms
IR drop in one conductor $= 217 \times 8.15 = 1,770$ volts
IX drop in one conductor $= 217 \times 18.55 = 4,020$ volts
$$\phi_2 = \cos^{-1} 0.80 = 36°52'$$

The vector diagram may now be drawn to scale, as follows: A horizontal line is drawn to represent the current I, Fig. 424; E_{2n} is drawn leading I by 36°52', and is

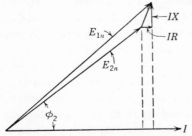

FIG. 424. Vector diagram of one phase of the three-phase transmission line of Fig. 423.

made equal to 29,000. IR is then drawn parallel to I, and IX perpendicular to I. The vector sum of E_{2n}, IR, and IX is E_{1n} and may be scaled off the vector diagram, or may be calculated as follows:

$$E_{1n} = \sqrt{(E_{2n} \cos \phi_2 + IR)^2 + (E_{2n} \sin \phi_2 + IX)^2}$$
$$= \sqrt{(29,000 \times 0.8 + 1,770)^2 + (29,000 \times 0.6 + 4,020)^2}$$
$$= 32,950 \text{ volts}$$

Input line voltage $E_1 = \sqrt{3} \times 32,950 = 57,000$ volts
Power loss in line $= 3 I^2 R$
$$= 3 \times 217^2 \times 8.15 = 1,150 \text{ kw}$$

$$\text{Efficiency of transmission} = \frac{\text{power output}}{\text{power input}}$$

$$= \frac{15,000}{15,000 + 1,150} = 92.9\%$$

415. Capacitance of Transmission Lines. The two conductors of a single-phase transmission line constitute a capacitor, and the current that flows into the line at the input end when the output current is zero is called the line-charging current. Similarly each pair of conductors in a three-phase line is a capacitor, so that a three-phase line with three conductors constitutes a set of three Δ-connected capacitors. Since the "plates" of these capacitors are merely wires, and the distance between them relatively large, the capacitance is small, and the usual practice is to ignore the line-charging currents for all voltages up to at least 50,000 volts. For example, the line-charging current of the 50,000-volt three-phase line in Art. 414 would be approximately 4 amp, which is only 2 per cent of the total current. On the other hand the line-charging current for a 220,000 volt 60-cycle three-phase line that was 200 miles long would be about 125 amp, which at 220,000 volts amounts to 48,000 kva. Obviously the charging current cannot be ignored on such a line.

Tables of charging current per mile of line are to be found in most handbooks of electrical engineering. The simplest way to take into account the line capacitance is to assume half of the capacitance concentrated at each end of the line. The calculation then becomes identical with that of power-factor correction, Art. 297. The average line current is the vector sum of the load current and one-half the line-charging current. The line-charging current of each conductor leads the voltage to neutral of that conductor by 90°.

416. Lightning Arresters. Arresters are used to protect electrical equipment from lightning discharges and from abnormally high voltages of all kinds, such, for example, as the surges resulting from switching operations. They function in much the same way as safety valves do on steam boilers. A steam safety valve allows steam to discharge to the atmosphere if the steam pressure rises above a certain fixed value, and a lightning arrester allows electricity to discharge from a conductor to the earth if the potential difference between the earth and the conductor exceeds a certain value. The ideal lightning arrester is therefore a path to earth whose resistance is infinitely great as long as the voltage is below a certain fixed value, but which becomes a good conductor if the voltage rises above the fixed limit. Also when the voltage drops below this limit again, the arrester should again become an insulator, and the change from insulator to conductor and from conductor to insulator should be practically instantaneous.

An air gap satisfies these requirements if the normal operating voltage of the line is low enough. Figure 425 shows how this type of arrester is applied to the protection of telephone lines. The gaps between the carbon blocks are adjusted to break down at about 200 volts and thus provide a good conducting path to ground. As soon as the abnormal voltage disappears, however, the arc goes out because the normal operating voltage of a telephone line is not sufficient to maintain the arc.

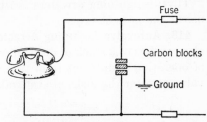

The plain air-gap type of arrester cannot be used on power lines because very much less voltage is required to maintain an arc across an ordinary air gap than is required

FIG. 425. Carbon-block lightning arrester protecting a telephone.

to start the arc; and once the abnormal voltage had started the arc, the normal operating voltage of the line would maintain it, which would, of course, interfere with the operation of the line.

417. Thyrite Lightning Arrester. This arrester, shown in Fig. 426, consists of a pile of thyrite disks connected in series with an air gap.

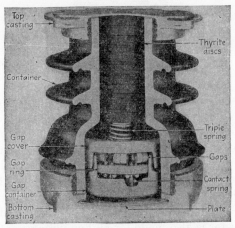

FIG. 426. Cutaway view of a thyrite lightning-arrester unit rated 11,500 volts. (*General Electric Co.*)

Thyrite is a dense, black ceramic material which has a most extraordinary resistance characteristic, and it is this characteristic that accounts for the success of this type of arrester. If 80,000 volts are impressed across the stack of disks of an 11,000-volt thyrite arrester, a current of 8,000 amp will flow, showing a resistance of $80,000/8,000 = 10$ ohms in the stack of disks; but when the voltage is reduced to 16,000 volts, the current is only 27 amp, showing a resistance of 590 ohms in the stack of disks.   Thus the arrester allows a very heavy discharge under abnormally high voltages, but, as the voltage drops to normal, the resistance of the arrester rises sharply and shuts off the current and thus extinguishes the arc across the air gap that is in series with the disks.

Thyrite lightning arresters are built for all line voltages that are in use at the present time.

418. Autovalve Lightning Arrester.   This arrester, shown in Fig. 427, also consists of a stack of disks in series with an air gap, but the principle of operation is different from that of the thyrite arrester.   In the autovalve arrester the disks are separated either by thin mica washers or by

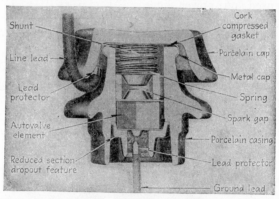

FIG. 427. Cutaway view of an autovalve lightning arrester. (*Westinghouse Electric and Manufacturing Co.*)

the irregularities of their own surfaces, so that the arrester consists of a large number of very short air gaps or air films connected in series.   Now it has been stated that in general the voltage required to maintain a discharge across an air gap is very much less than the voltage required to start that discharge, but this statement does not hold for the type of glow discharge that takes place across these thin filmlike air gaps. Abnormally high voltages cause a discharge through the arrester but the discharge is extinguished as soon as the voltage drops to normal. This type of arrester is also made for all line voltages.

A great many different types of lightning arresters have been developed, but at present the ones described above are the most popular.

419. Switches.   Switches used to rupture the currents of a-c circuits are manufactured in a wide variety of designs.   Until quite recently these switches were almost always oil switches if the circuits operated at over 550 volts.   An oil switch, or circuit breaker, is one that has its contacts immersed in oil.   The oil helps to extinguish the arc that is always formed as the contacts begin to separate.   A three-phase switch has three switch blades that open and close simultaneously. Such a switch is usually called a *three-pole* switch. If the power to be interrupted is large, a separate tank is provided for each pole, as shown in Fig. 429; otherwise all three poles are placed in the same tank, as in Fig. 428. In most designs the switch blade is horizontal in both the open

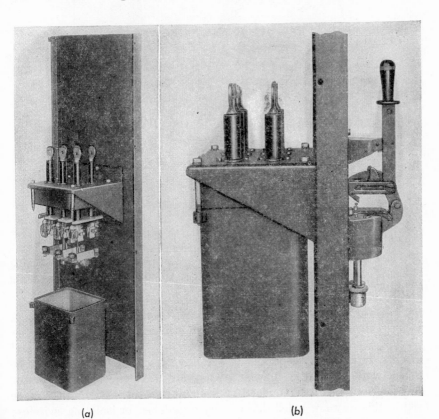

(a)   (b)

FIG. 428. Three-phase oil circuit breaker, manually operated, 5,000 volts, 600 amp. (a) Rear view, with tank lowered.   Switch open.   (b) Side view, with tank in place, showing hand-operated closing lever and trip coil.   (*General Electric* Co.)

and closed positions. It moves vertically downward when opening, thus breaking contact at both ends of the blade and forming two arcs in series. In all cases the switch is closed against the opposition of a spring and is held closed by means of a latch. This latch may be tripped by means of a solenoid, energized either automatically by one or more relays or by a small push-button switch located in any convenient place.

The larger switches are all of the remote-control type and are closed by means of a small motor or a solenoid, or by compressed air acting on a

FIG. 429. Three-phase oil circuit breaker, rated 330 kv, 1,600 amp, continuous operation. Interrupting capacity 15,000,000 kva.   Over-all height about 25 ft.   (*Courtesy General Electric Co.*)

piston.   The smaller switches may also be remote-control, or they may be closed manually by means of a system of levers.

Disconnecting Switches.   Knife switches are used at all voltages and currents, but except when the power is very small they must not be opened while current is flowing.   They are used to isolate apparatus after the circuit has been opened by a circuit breaker.   Switches that are used in this way are called disconnecting switches, or isolating switches, or simply disconnects.   In general, every important piece of equipment, such as a circuit breaker or transformer bank, has a three-pole disconnect on each side of it, so that maintenance and repairs can be carried out in safety.   The smaller disconnecting switches are opened and closed by means of a long wooden stick with a hook attached to one end, the larger ones by a motor-driven mechanism.

Air-break and Air-blast Circuit Breakers.   Small and medium-sized *air-break* circuit breakers, for voltages up to 15,000 volts, rely mainly on magnetic blowout coils to move the arc sideways into an arc chute where it is cooled and deionized by interleaved metal vanes and thus extinguished.   The principle of magnetic blowout coils was described in Art. 178.   The larger air-break circuit breakers rely mainly on a violent blast of compressed air to extinguish the arc, and are accordingly called *air-blast* circuit breakers.   These breakers require a continuously available supply of compressed air at pressures ranging up to 800 lb per sq in. This supply of compressed air is used not only to blow out the arc but also to operate the opening and closing mechanisms.

The basic principles of an air-blast circuit breaker are illustrated in Fig. 430.   The circuit breaker is opened by sending a powerful blast of air into the arc-extinction chamber.   The tubelike moving contact is blown to the left against the opposition of a spiral spring, and the arc that forms as the contacts separate is blown out through the hollow contact.   The duration of the air blast is only a fraction of a second, and at

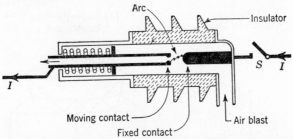

FIG. 430. The arc-extinction chamber of an air-blast circuit breaker, shown in a partially opened position.

its conclusion the spiral spring slams the contacts closed again.   In the brief interval of time during which the contacts are open a coordinated toggle mechanism opens the external disconnecting switch S, so that the reclosing of the contacts in the arc-extinction chamber does not reestablish the circuit.

The 230,000-volt air-blast circuit breakers at the Grand Coulee hydroelectric power plant have eight of these arc-extinction chambers connected in series in each of the three conductors.   Since the eight chambers operate simultaneously, it follows that with ideal operation only one-eighth of the voltage appears across each chamber.   The Grand Coulee air-blast breakers differ from earlier designs in that they do not make use of coordinated disconnects.   As soon as the arc is extinguished, the exhausts are closed and the air-blast pressure is maintained so as to hold the moving contacts open.

There is a possibility that the air-break and air-blast circuit breakers will ultimately replace the oil switches, and certainly the oil is a nuisance and a fire hazard, but at present the oil switch still dominates the scene, although the number of air-break and air-blast breakers in service is increasing rapidly.

420. Rupturing Capacity of Circuit Breakers.   The three principal factors that determine the design of a circuit breaker are (1) the voltage of the system; (2) the maximum rms current that the breaker will be required to carry continuously in normal operation; (3) the maximum current that the breaker will be required to interrupt.

At any given line voltage there is a limiting maximum value of the current that a given circuit breaker can interrupt without sustaining serious damage, either by burning or by mechanical fracture caused by

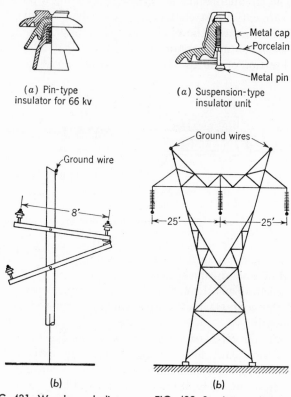

(a) Pin-type insulator for 66 kv

(a) Suspension-type insulator unit

(b)

FIG. 431. Wooden-pole line.

(b)

FIG. 432. Steel-tower line.

the explosive pressures generated in the arc. The rated rupturing capacity of a circuit breaker is expressed in kilovolt-amperes. In the case of a three-phase breaker, rupturing kva = $\sqrt{3}$ kv I, where kv = rated line kilovolts and I = maximum rms value of the current to be interrupted. In practice, the maximum current that a circuit breaker will be required to interrupt is the abnormal current that flows through it when there is an insulation failure or short circuit near the circuit breaker and on that side of the breaker that is farther from the generator. Thus the required kva rupturing capacity of a circuit breaker that connects a certain load to a distribution system is determined not by the kva rating of the load but by the nature of the distribution system. In general, therefore, the required kva rupturing capacity of the breaker is very much greater than the load kva.

421. Overhead-line Construction. For voltages up to 66,000, wooden poles with pin-type insulators are used to support the line conductors, as in Fig. 431, the conductor resting in a groove on the top of the insulator. For higher voltages, pin-type insulators become large and expensive and the stresses on the pin become excessive, so that the suspension-type of insulator is used, as shown in Fig. 432. Each conductor is suspended from the bottom of a group or string of insulator units, and there may be as many as 20 units in a single string in the case of a 220-kv line. Steel towers are generally used to support the insulators for all voltages above 110 kv, and wooden pole structures for all voltages below 110 kv, but there is no fixed dividing line between steel and wood construction.

The conductors are bare stranded cables of either copper or aluminum, but in the case of aluminum the cable is generally provided with a stranded steel core, because pure aluminum has a low tensile strength.

As a protection against lightning it is usual to run one or two steel wires the full length of the line, parallel to the power conductors. These "ground wires" are supported several feet above the power conductors and are grounded at every tower.

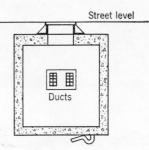

FIG. 433. Manhole.

422. Underground Construction. To carry current underground, stranded copper cable is used. The copper is insulated with paper, which is then impregnated with a compound such as resin oil, after which the cable is sheathed with lead which keeps out moisture and at the same time protects the cable against mechanical injury. The cable has to be flexible enough to bend around corners because it has to be drawn into tile ducts through manholes such as that shown in Fig. 433, and these manholes are restricted in size.

The necessary cross section of copper is generally fixed by the permissible voltage drop in the case of low-voltage cables but is always fixed by heating in high-voltage cables. A current density of 1,000 amp per sq in. of copper section can seldom be exceeded, and this requires 8.7 volts per 500 ft, which is 2.5 per cent of 350 volts, so that, if the voltage drop is limited to 2.5 per cent and the transmission distance is 500 ft, then, for voltages less than 350 volts, the current density must be less than 1,000 amp per sq in., while for voltages greater than 350 volts, the drop in the cable will be less than 2.5 per cent. Cables can now be manufactured for all voltages up to 230,000 volts.

423. Alternating-current Watthour Meter. This meter is a two-phase induction motor of special design geared to a train of recording dials. One of the two-phase coils, called the potential coil, has a very high reactance (over 2,000 ohms in a 110-volt meter) and is connected directly across the line. The current in this coil is accordingly directly proportional to the line voltage E and lags behind it by nearly 90°. The useful part of the flux produced by this coil is made to lag exactly 90° behind the line voltage by means of a small lagging coil. The other phase coil consists of only a few turns of heavy wire and is connected in series with the line so that the current in this coil is the line current. This coil is called the current coil.

When the power factor of the load is 0 per cent, the line current I is 90° behind the voltage E and therefore the fluxes produced by the two coils are in phase and no torque is developed. At 100 per cent power-factor load the two fluxes are 90° out of phase and the torque is a maximum. At any other power factor the current I can be resolved into the two components $I \sin \phi$ and $I \cos \phi$, where ϕ is the phase angle between E and I. The component $I \sin \phi$ produces a component of flux in phase with the flux from the potential coil and therefore creates no torque. The torque developed is therefore proportional to $EI \cos \phi$. That is, the torque is proportional to the power supplied to the load.

FIG. 434. A-c watthour meter.

A brake load proportional to the speed is provided by means of a thin aluminum disk and permanent magnets, as in the d-c watthour meter, Art. 233A.

The rotor of this induction motor is the same aluminum disk that provides the brake torque. At any moment one half of the disk is under the influence of the potential and current coils and the other half is under the influence of the permanent magnets. A shading coil is provided to compensate for friction. Figure 434 shows the general arrangement of the parts.

424. Meters. Meters have been devised in a great variety of forms to measure volts, amperes, ampere-hours, ohms, watts, watthours, power factor, maximum demand, etc. The types of these meters are so numerous that they can be adequately treated only in a book devoted exclusively to metering.[1]

425. Relays.   A relay is a special type of switch which operates automatically whenever the conditions of the circuit with which it is associated exceed certain limits.   For example, the no-voltage release on the motor starter of Fig. 133 disconnects the motor from the line if the voltage fails; the reverse-current relay of Fig. 164 disconnects the generator from the battery whenever the charging current reverses; and the relays *a* and *b* of the carbon-pile regulator, Fig. 183, increase the resistance in the circuit whenever the voltage across the lamps begins to rise.   These three relays are operated by the specific conditions of low voltage, reverse current, and high voltage, respectively.   Relays can equally well be designed to operate on any other conditions, normal or abnormal, and relays can be provided with as many auxiliary pairs of contacts as are desired, which can be used to operate warning signals, start or stop motors, etc.   Almost any series of operations, no matter how complicated, can be performed automatically by means of relays if it is economically advisable to do so.   A single automatic-telephone central-office building may contain over 100,000 relays.   The subject of automatic operation and protection by means of relays is a highly specialized one and cannot be taken up in a book on general principles.[2]

Problems

39-1. A three-phase 60-cycle transmission line is required to deliver 20,000 kw at 66,000 volts at a distance of 30 miles.   The power factor of the load is 85 per cent lagging.   The line conductors are No. 0000 B & S, spaced 72 in. (see page 306 for table of resistance and reactance).   Determine the input voltage to the line, the power factor at the input end, and the power loss in the line.

39-2. If the voltage available at the input end of the line in Prob. 39-1 is limited to 70,000 volts, how much must the power factor of the load be raised in order to obtain 66,000 volts at the load?   The simplest way to solve this problem is to plot a curve of input volts on a power factor of load base.

39-3. The voltage, current, and power factor at the input end of a single-phase transmission line are 2,200 volts, 30 amp, and 75 per cent, respectively.   The entire load is concentrated at the output end of the line, and the line is 7 miles long.   Calculate the voltage at the output end and the power loss in the line. The line has a resistance of 1.1 ohms per mile of wire and a reactance of 0.8 ohm per mile of wire.

39-4. A three-phase 60-cycle transmission line delivers 600 kw at 90 per cent leading power factor, and at a Δ voltage of 6,600, all measured at the receiver end. The resistance per conductor is 4.1 ohms, and the reactance per conductor is 2.5 ohms.   Assuming both the supply and receiver end to be Y-connected, determine the supply voltage and the voltage regulation of the line.

[1] "Handbook for Electrical Metermen," National Electric Light Association.
[2] See "Relay Handbook," National Electric Light Association.

40

ELECTRIC LIGHTING

426. Incandescence. Any hot body, such as the filament of an incandescent tungsten lamp, radiates energy. This radiation is apparently in the form of waves in the ether and travels in a straight line unless deflected by some external agency. If a beam of radiation from such a lamp is passed through a glass prism, as shown in Fig. 435, it is spread out into a wide band that resembles a section cut from a rainbow. Each

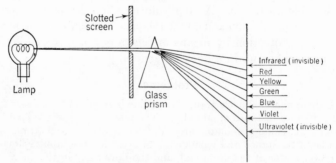

FIG. 435. Analyzing the radiation from a hot body.

shade of color is found to have a different wavelength, so that the difference between one color and another is similar to the difference between one musical note and another.

If the amount of energy being radiated per second is measured for each color over the entire band, and this radiant power is plotted against wavelength, for a tungsten incandescent lamp, the curve shown in Fig. 436 will be obtained. From this curve it appears that the tungsten lamp is an extremely inefficient light source because approximately 90 per cent of the energy being radiated is invisible.

As the voltage impressed on the lamp is increased, the temperature of the filament rises, and the ordinates of the radiant power curve of Fig. 436 increase very rapidly, while the whole curve shifts toward the left. If the temperature of the filament could be raised to the temperature of the sun, nearly 6000°C, the peak of the radiant energy curve would lie within the visible range, and the efficiency of the lamp would be high. The very low efficiency of all our incandescent lamps is due to the fact that they operate at temperatures around 2300 to 3000°C, while the human eye has been developed throughout the ages to respond most readily to the radiation from a body which is at a temperature of nearly 6000°C.

Figure 436 also shows that the incandescent lamp radiates very much more energy toward the red end of the visible range than it does near the violet end. The light from an ordinary incandescent lamp always appears quite red when compared directly with sunlight, which is one of the reasons why human eyes tire more quickly under artificial light than under sunlight.

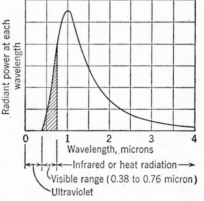

FIG. 436. Radiant power distribution of a tungsten incandescent lamp at 3000°C. The shaded area represents the power radiated as light. (1 micron = 0.001 mm.)

427. Candlepower. The candlepower of a light source, in any given direction, is the ratio of the intensity of the illumination that it produces in that direction to the intensity of the illumination that the standard candle produces in the horizontal direction.

In general, the candlepower of a lamp is different at every angle. Figure 437 shows the candlepower-distribution curve, in a vertical plane, of one type of tungsten lamp. Most electric lamps are sufficiently symmetrical about the vertical axis so that the candlepower distribution can be shown by a single graph in one plane. A complete representation of the candlepower of an unsymmetrical light source would require a three-dimensional graph.

428. Lumen. The unit of total light output is the lumen. One lumen is the amount of light that will illuminate a surface of one square foot to an average intensity of one foot-candle, one foot-candle being the intensity of illumination on a vertical plane at a point one foot distant in a horizontal direction from a standard candle. The number of lumens required to light a surface to any given illumination is found by multiplying the area of the surface in square feet by the average foot-candles that it is desired to produce. "Lumens per square foot" is often used instead of "foot-candles." They mean the same thing.

Since a foot-candle of illumination is produced by a source of 1 cp shining on a surface 1 ft distant, it follows that, if a source giving 1 cp in every direction is at the center of a hollow sphere of 1 ft radius, every point on the interior surface of the sphere will be illuminated directly from the source to an illumination of 1 ft-c. As the interior surface of a sphere of 1 ft radius has an area of 12.57 sq ft and as the 1-cp source directly illuminates this area of 12.57 sq ft to 1 ft-c, the source must produce 12.57 lumens. Consequently, a source of an intensity of 1 cp

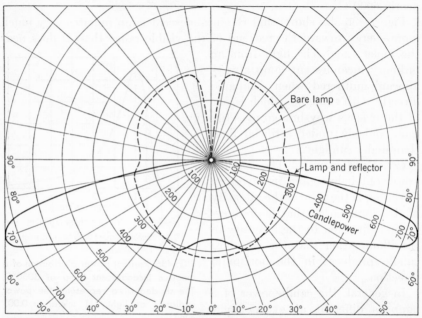

FIG. 437. Candlepower-distribution curves for a 200-watt bare tungsten lamp, and for the same lamp equipped with a street-lighting type of reflector.

in every direction, which is 1 spherical candlepower, has an output of 12.57 lumens.

429. Tungsten Incandescent Lamps. The vacuum tungsten lamp consists of a filament of tungsten enclosed in a glass bulb from which the air has been exhausted. The higher the temperature at which the filament is operated, the greater the amount of light per watt of power input, but the shorter the life. The life of the lamp is determined by the rate of evaporation of the filament, and the evaporation increases with the temperature. Raising the voltage applied to the lamp therefore decreases the power cost per lumen of light but increases the cost of the lamp renewals. This is illustrated in Fig. 438. The most economical compromise is generally considered to be the one that gives an operating life of 1,000 hr.

If the bulb is filled with an inert gas, the rate of evaporation of the filament is reduced for any given temperature, and it is therefore pos-

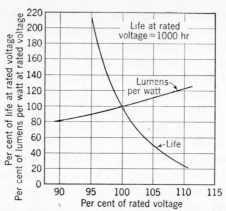

FIG. 438. Effect of varying the voltage applied to a tungsten lamp.

sible to raise the operating temperature and thus increase the light output, while still obtaining the same length of life. At the present time all tungsten incandescent lamps above 25 watts are filled with a mixture of nitrogen and argon.

The total lumens output, and the relative efficiency in lumens per watt, are given in Table 5 for various sizes of tungsten incandescent lamps.

TABLE 5. Tungsten-filament Incandescent Lamps

Size of lamp, watts	Initial total lumens	Initial lumens per watt	Filament temperature, °C
Vacuum			
15	147	9.8	
25	270	10.9	2310
Gas-filled			
40	472	11.8	2440
50	670	13.4	
60	834	13.9	
75	1,110	14.8	
100	1,640	16.4	2580
150	2,600	17.4	
200	3,650	18.3	2610
300	5,650	18.8	
500	9,850	19.7	2670
750	15,000	20.0	
1,000	21,000	21.0	2720
1,500	33,000	22.0	
5,000*	140,000	28.0	3030
10,000*	295,000	29.5	
50,000*	1,475,000	29.5	

* These lamps are designed for 100-hr life instead of the usual 1,000 hr.

Because of the positive temperature coefficient of resistance, the tungsten lamp has a much lower resistance when cold than when hot, so that, when the lamp is switched on, the initial current is much larger than the normal operating current.

430. Street Series Tungsten Lamps. The principal difference between multiple and series lamps is that multiple lamps are designed for operation on constant-voltage circuits, and series lamps on constant-current circuits.   For this reason, series lamps are made for a given current rating.   Alternating-current series circuits have been quite definitely standardized at 6.6 amp, and series lamps of low lumen rating are designed to burn either directly in the circuit or through one-to-one ratio transformers.   The high lumen-rating lamps are designed for 15- and 20-amp filament currents and are generally operated through transformers of the proper ratio.   Lamps of this type are made in sizes ranging from 600 to 25,000 lumens and are of the gas-filled type.

431. Carbon Arc Lamps. If an electric circuit is completed by bringing the ends of two carbon rods into contact, a current will flow through the circuit and, since the contact between the carbons is poor and the resistance of the contact is therefore high, the carbons at the contact will begin to glow, while a small quantity of carbon vapor passes between them.

If the carbon contacts are now separated by about a quarter of an inch, it will be found that the current still flows, because the space between the contacts is filled with carbon vapor that is conducting. The arc so formed is a powerful source of light.

An arc lamp consists of two sticks of carbon, with a mechanism which, when the voltage is applied, brings the carbons into contact and then separates them, and which also feeds the carbons together as they are consumed.

The carbon arc lamp is the oldest type of electric lamp, and it was at one time widely used for street lighting and other outdoor illumination. It is now considered obsolete in that field, but it is still used for special light-projection work where it is desired to concentrate a large amount of light into a narrow beam.   It requires a great deal of attention but its efficiency is high, about 40 to 65 lumens per watt.

432. Selective Radiation. All methods of light production may be divided into two classes: (1) incandescence; (2) luminescence.

Incandescence is the process of producing light by pure temperature radiation.   There is no chemical change in the light source and the spectrum is continuous, as indicated in Figs. 435 and 436, the colors merging into one another with no dark spaces in between.   At any temperatures attainable at present the major portion of the incandescent radiation is at wavelengths to which the human eye does not respond.

As far as illumination alone is concerned, the ideal light source would be one which would radiate energy only within the visible range, and whose spectrum over that range would be continuous and similar to that of the sun. Such a light source would give some 300 lumens of pure white light per watt, which is about fifteen times as many lumens per watt as is obtained from the largest tungsten lamps used for general illumination. With health taken into consideration it would be desirable to have some ultraviolet radiation present as well as the light.

A light source is said to give selective radiation if its distribution of radiant energy among the wavelengths differs from that of an idealized "black body" at the same temperature. (For practical purposes, carbon represents the black body sufficiently well.)

Tungsten is slightly selective but no light source has been discovered that even approaches the ideal selective radiation described above.

Luminescence embraces all methods of light production other than incandescence. It is accompanied, or caused by, chemical action and is characterized by highly selective radiation, the spectrum often consisting of only a few narrow bright lines of color, some of which may be in the ultraviolet range and therefore invisible. Such spectra suggest marvellous possibilities in the way of efficient light production. The firefly, for example, radiates all its energy in a narrow band of wavelengths at the center of the visible range. It is the most efficient light source known as far as getting the maximum vision from the minimum energy, but all objects illuminated by its light appear either yellow-green or black.

The spectrum of the mercury-vapor lamp shows narrow bands of green, yellow, blue, and violet, but no red. It is an efficient light source, but the absence of the red makes human beings appear ghastly. The red may be supplied by red neon lamps or by tungsten incandescent lamps.

433. Fluorescent Lamps. There are quite a number of minerals which when flooded with ultraviolet light will absorb this radiant energy and will reradiate a substantial proportion of it in the form of visible light. This process is called fluorescence, and it is the method of light production used in all fluorescent lamps. The most efficient known source of ultraviolet radiation is the low-pressure mercury arc. In particular, if the pressure in the arc chamber is only about 0.00001 of an atmosphere, approximately 60 per cent of the electrical energy input to the arc will be converted into ultraviolet radiation at the wavelength of 0.2537 microns, or 2,537 A. In order not to waste any of this ultraviolet radiation, the arc must be completely surrounded by fluorescent material. This is accomplished by enclosing the arc in a long glass tube, the inner walls of which are completely but thinly coated with a mixture of fluorescent powders, the mixture being chosen so as to give the desired combination of colors. The radiation from fluorescent materials is highly selective, and fluorescent lamps produce approximately twice as many lumens per watt as incandescent lamps do. Moreover, practically any color, from pure white to various vivid monochromatics, can be obtained by selecting the proper mixture of fluorescent materials.

There are three types of fluorescent lamps at present on the market. They are (1) the preheated hot-cathode type; (2) the instant-start hot-cathode type; (3) the cold-cathode type.

Preheated Hot-cathode Type. Figure 439 shows the essential features of the preheated hot-cathode type of fluorescent lamp. The lamp is

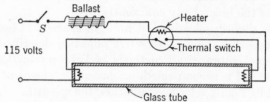

FIG. 439. Preheated hot-cathode fluorescent lamp.

switched on by closing switch S. Current then flows through the thermal switch and the two tungsten filaments in series, quickly heating the filaments to about 950°C, at which temperature they emit electrons freely. The thermal switch then opens automatically, and the resulting inductive kick from the ballast coil causes an arc to strike between the two filaments. Thereafter the filaments are kept hot by the arc itself. The ballast coil is essential to the operation of the lamp, because it is needed to limit the arc current. Without the ballast the arc would almost instantly develop into a short circuit on the line and would destroy both filaments. The circuit of Fig. 439 is only one of several arrangements for preheating the filaments.

The filaments are coated with barium and strontium oxides, which provide a copious emission of electrons. The life of the lamp is ended when this coating is used up. The bare tungsten does emit electrons but not in sufficient quantity to enable the lamp to operate at the voltage provided.

The arc current passes through zero value twice per cycle, with the result that the light output rises and falls twice per cycle. On a 60-cycle system the frequency of the flicker is almost, but not quite, high enough to be invisible. Therefore, whenever the lamps are operated in pairs, a capacitor is placed in series with one of them so that the two arc currents will be out of phase, and this normally makes the flicker completely invisible. The capacitor also raises the power factor to somewhere between 85 and 95 per cent. If no capacitor is used, the power factor is only about 50 per cent because of the inductive reactance of the ballast coil.

Instant-start Hot-cathode Type.   If a high enough voltage is impressed across the two cathodes of a fluorescent lamp, the arc will start even when the cathodes are cold.   The instant-start hot-cathode lamp is provided with an autotransformer which steps the starting voltage up to several times the voltage at which the lamp subsequently operates.   The arc strikes immediately and quickly heats the cathodes up to the proper electron-emission temperature, after which the lamp operates the same as the preheated type, except that the ballast is designed to absorb a larger proportion of the voltage than with the preheated type.

In both types of hot-cathode lamps the life of the lamp is determined more by the number of times the lamp is switched on and off than by the

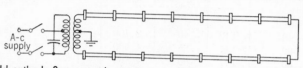

FIG. 440. Cold-cathode fluorescent lamps connected in series.   The transformer is designed to have enough leakage reactance so that it serves as a ballast coil as well as a transformer.   The purpose of the capacitor is to correct the power factor.

burning hours.   The life in practice varies from about 1,500 to 10,000 hr of operation.

Cold-cathode Type.   In the cold-cathode type of fluorescent lamp the cathodes are large, so that they never become hot enough to emit electrons.   Therefore the voltage gradient at the cathode must be steep enough to pull the electrons out of the cold metal.   This means that this type of lamp is inherently a high-voltage type.   The glass tube is usually about 8 ft long and the open-circuit voltage impressed on it at start is about 1,000 volts.   Because of the ballast, which in practice is incorporated as part of the transformer, the voltage drops to about 500 volts as soon as the arc is established.

Since the lamp, transformers, and wiring operate at voltages dangerous to human beings, they must all be kept out of reach.   That being so there would appear to be no great objection to increasing the voltage still further and thus decreasing the cost of the installation.   In practice, therefore, several lamps are usually placed end to end and connected in series, as indicated in Fig. 440.   The highest voltage used so far appears to be 15,000 volts, and this will operate about 120 ft of tubing.

The principal advantages of the series system of operation are that it requires less than one-quarter as many outlets as the multiple system, and there is much less wiring because the lamps themselves constitute the major portion of the circuit.   Cold-cathode lamps do not require any starting devices.   They have a longer life than the hot-cathode type and are not as sensitive to voltage variations; neither does frequent switching on and off reduce the life as it does with the hot-cathode type. The rated life of cold-cathode lamps is 10,000 hr, but they usually exceed that. On the other hand they are not quite so efficient as the hot-cathode type, and the high voltage tends to limit their field of application. All three types of fluorescent lamps are forging ahead, and their proper fields of application will become more definite as experience accumulates and development progresses.

TABLE 6. Typical Hot-cathode Fluorescent Lamps

Length, in.	Bulb size	Lamp, watts	Lumens		
			White	Cool white	Daylight
Preheated:					
48	T12	40	2,400	2,250	2,000
60	T17	85	4,500	4,300	3,900
60	T17	90	4,860	4,600	4,250
60	T17	100	4,600	4,350	4,000
Instant start:					
48	T12	41	2,350	2,200	1,950
64	T6	37	2,250	2,150	1,900
72	T8	37.5	2,375	2,275	2,000
72	T12	57	3,660	3,500	3,100
96	T8	49	3,250	3,100	2,750
96	T12	73	4,600	4,575	4,080

NOTE: Watts consumed by the ballast and starter, if any, must be added to obtain total watts. In general, this constitutes an addition of from 20 to 30 per cent.

The operation of fluorescent lamps is profoundly affected by any large change in the pressure of the mercury vapor, and this pressure varies with the bulb temperature, which in turn varies with the room temperature. Standard fluorescent lamps are designed to operate at room temperatures between 65°F and 100°F. Their operation becomes quite unsatisfactory if the room temperature drops below 50°F, and in fact they often will not start at all below that temperature. Special fluorescent lamps can be obtained for operation at lower temperatures.

434. Mercury-vapor Lamps. When an electric arc flows through mercury vapor at very low pressures, the radiation is chiefly ultraviolet. As the pressure is increased, the ultraviolet radiation decreases while the visible radiation increases. At atmospheric pressure, and with a suitable magnitude of electric current, 11 per cent of the watts input to the arc is radiated in the visible range, while the ultraviolet radiation is only about 1 per cent of the input watts. Such an arc is therefore an efficient light source. A ballast coil is required, and usually an autotransformer is incorporated with it. The principal objection to the mercury-vapor lamp is that its radiation contains practically no red light. On the other hand it blends well with daylight, and is a good light where red objects are not involved. Its efficiency is comparable with that of the fluorescent lamp.

435. Color. Objects are seen by means of the light that is reflected from them, and most objects possess color; that is, they reflect light of different wavelengths to widely different degrees. In order that the color may be visible, the illumination must contain some at least of the particular wavelengths that are reflected by the colored object. Therefore if a light is to be effective for the illumination of objects of all colors it must itself contain all colors. In other words it must be at least a rough approximation to daylight. The relative magnitudes of the various wavelengths can vary considerably from those of daylight without any ill effects, but if the variation is carried too far the light is either depressing or tiring to the eyes, or both. Daylight itself varies somewhat in color throughout the day and also with the weather. The "daylight" incandescent lamp is provided with a tinted glass bulb that absorbs a large proportion of the excessive red-light output of the incandescent filament, and thus gives a net output that is a fair approximation to daylight. It is never used for general illumination because it is too inefficient, but it is useful for color-comparison work. The light from the so-called "daylight" fluorescent lamp bears a superficial resemblance to daylight, but the eye is easily fooled. Actually the light from this lamp is considerably deficient in red, with the result that it gives people a rather sallow complexion. It is, however, not nearly so unflattering as the light from a mercury-vapor lamp. For color-matching work, the light from daylight fluorescent lamps should be supplemented by light from incandescent or neon lamps.

436. Glare. Glare may be defined as brightness within the field of vision of such intensity as to cause discomfort, annoyance, interference with vision, or eye fatigue. The brightness of a light source may be conveniently measured in candlepower per unit projected area. All glare may be divided into two classes: (1) direct glare; (2) reflected glare.

Direct glare is glare coming directly from a light source. It can be reduced by enclosing the light source in a globe of translucent material so as to increase the area of the light source and so decrease its brightness. It can be eliminated by placing an opaque shield or reflector between the light source and the eye.

Reflected glare is not quite so obvious, but it can be worse than direct glare. The worst conditions for reflected glare are obtained when shiny working surfaces are combined with point sources of light. There are accordingly two basic methods of reducing reflected glare. One is to replace shiny surfaces by diffuse-reflecting surfaces so far as is possible. The other is to increase the area of the light sources as much as is economically feasible. A third method is to place the light source, work, and worker, in such relative positions that the mirror or nondiffuse part of the reflection from the working surfaces misses the eyes of the worker.

437. Shadows. Shadows may be defined as differences in brightness of surfaces, and they are essential in observing objects in their three dimensions. It is, then, good practice so to design lighting installations that shadows are present, but they should be soft and luminous. It is also good practice to provide artificial illumination that will give the same relative shadows that are provided with daylight illumination.

Good lighting requires

Light of suitable quality
- Absence of direct glare
- Absence of reflected glare
- Proper color

Light in proper direction
- Shadows soft and luminous
- Uniform distribution

Light of correct amount
- Lighting for safety
- Lighting for economical production
- Proper cleaning of units

The extent to which shadows should be eliminated depends upon the nature of the work to be done and the perspective desired. It is generally considered that shadows should be eliminated as far as possible in drafting rooms and offices and that dense shadows should always be avoided.

438. Shades and Reflectors. The light distribution from a source can be completely changed by the use of a shade or reflector. Incandescent lamps are invariably equipped with shades or reflectors, and where high-grade illumination is required the ceiling is also made to function as a reflector, and sometimes the walls as well. The brightness of fluorescent lamps, measured in lumens per square inch of radiating surface, is much less than that of incandescent lamps, and therefore it is sometimes considered unnecessary to hide the lamp tube from the line of vision. The different types of fluorescent lamps, however, vary considerably in brightness, and when it is considered desirable to hide the lamp tubes, on account of glare, either diffusing glass cover plates or louvers are used, as shown on page 532, units 7 and 9, or else indirect lighting is used as with unit 10.

If the individual lamp reflectors are made to throw most of the light directly on to the working plane, the lighting is said to be "direct."

If they throw nearly all the light on to the ceiling and walls, so that the light which falls upon the working plane is practically all due to the diffuse reflection from the ceiling and walls, the lighting is said to be "indirect."

If the light falling upon the working plane is partly direct and partly indirect and at least half of the total light emitted by the lamps is thrown on to the ceiling and walls, the lighting is said to be "semi-indirect."

Direct lighting is the cheapest, and if the ceiling is dark is usually the only feasible method, but there is apt to be glare from direct lighting unless the lighting units are built into the ceiling, and the shadows tend to be rather dark.   Indirect lighting is free from glare, except for ceiling glare, and the shadows are very faint, but it is apt to be rather depressing unless it is livened up by a certain amount of decorative lighting. In large rooms with white ceilings, semi-indirect lighting is not much more expensive than direct lighting and is very much superior to it for all kinds of work.

In Table 9, page 531, are shown five typical incandescent lighting units and their corresponding candlepower distribution curves.   With reference, for example, to unit 4, the figures given in the first column, just below the description of the unit, indicate that 51 per cent of the light is projected upward from the horizontal plane passing through the center of the lamp, 21 per cent is projected downward, and the remaining 28 per cent is absorbed by the globe and is converted into heat.

439. Utilization Factors.   The total number of lumens falling on the working plane, divided by the total number of lumens emitted by the lamps, is called the utilization factor of the lighting system.   The number of lumens emitted by the lamps is obtained from the tables of total lumens output on pages 519 and 524, and the number of lumens falling upon the working plane is determined by means of a foot-candle meter. A foot-candle meter is a direct-reading meter which measures illumination intensity in foot-candles, that is, in lumens per square foot.   It is calibrated by placing it at measured distances from a light source of known candlepower.   The area of the working plane multiplied by the illumination intensity gives the total lumens falling on the working plane.

Example.   A room 25 by 36 ft is illuminated by six 200-watt lamps.   The average illumination intensity as measured by a foot-candle meter is found to be 10 lumens per sq ft.   Calculate the utilization factor.

Area of working plane = 25 × 36 = 900 sq ft
Total lumens falling on this plane = 10 × 900 = 9,000 lumens
Total lumens emitted by lamps = 6 × 3,700 = 22,200 lumens

$$\text{Utilization factor} = \frac{9,000}{22,200} = 40.5\%$$

Utilization factors have been determined in this way for a great variety of lighting installations.   These factors have been analyzed and tabulated and are now available for use in the design of new lighting installations (see Table 9).

440. Size of Room and Reflection Factor of Walls and Ceiling. The size of the room and the reflection factor of the walls and the ceiling affect the utilization factor very materially. For example, in rooms illuminated by unit 5 (Table 9) the utilization factor varies all the way from 4 per cent for a small narrow room with very dark walls and a dark ceiling to 42 per cent for a room that is very wide in proportion to its height, and whose ceiling is white.

TABLE 7. Recommended Illumination Intensities

Type of work	Foot-candles on working plane
Drafting rooms..	50
General offices:	
No close work.....................................	20
Some close work..................................	30
Bookkeeping, typing, accounting...................	50
Desk work (intermittent reading and writing)...........	30
Office corridors and stairways.......................	10
Lobbies in public buildings.........................	10
School classrooms.................................	30
Corridors in hospitals and hotels....................	5
Hotel dining rooms................................	10
Restaurants.......................................	10
Sewing:	
Light goods.......................................	30
Dark goods.......................................	200*
Factory assembling and machine-shop work:	
Rough...	20
Medium..	50
Fine...	100 to 200*

* Obtained partly by local illumination.

The size and shape of the room are taken into account by means of a factor called the *room index*. A cubical room 10 by 10 by 10 ft is arbitrarily given a room index of 1, and the room indexes of all other shapes and sizes of rooms are computed with a unit room of this character as the basis. The actual values of the room indexes have no meaning, but all rooms that have the same room index assigned to them will give approximately the same utilization factor if illuminated by the same lighting unit.

The room index for any size and shape of room may be obtained from Table 8, pages 529 to 530.

Table 9 shows utilization factors as low as 4 per cent for an indirect-lighting unit in a small room with dark walls and ceiling, but no one should seriously consider making such an installation.

441. Spacing of Lighting Units. Ceiling beams and columns divide rooms up into bays, and for the sake of appearance it is usually desirable to locate the lighting units symmetrically with respect to these structural

TABLE 8. Room Index
(For narrow and average rooms)

		Feet						
For indirect lighting use / ceiling height		9 and 9½	10 to 11½	12 to 13½	14 to 16½	17 to 20	21 to 24	25 to 30
For direct lighting use / mounting height		7 and 7½	8 and 8½	9 and 9½	10 to 11½	12 to 13½	14 to 16½	17 to 20
Room width, feet	Room length, feet	Room index						
9 (8½–9½)	8–10	1.0	0.8	0.6	0.6			
	10–14	1.0	0.8	0.8	0.6			
	14–20	1.2	1.0	0.8	0.6	0.6		
	20–30	1.2	1.2	1.0	0.8	0.6	0.6	
	30–42	1.5	1.2	1.0	0.8	0.6	0.6	0.6
	42–up	2.0	1.5	1.2	1.0	0.8	0.6	0.6
10 (9½–10½)	10–14	1.2	1.0	0.8	0.6	0.6		
	14–20	1.2	1.0	0.8	0.6	0.6	0.6	
	20–30	1.5	1.2	1.0	0.8	0.6	0.6	
	30–42	1.5	1.2	1.2	1.0	0.8	0.6	0.6
	42–60	2.0	1.5	1.2	1.0	0.8	0.6	0.6
	60–up	2.0	1.5	1.5	1.0	1.0	0.8	0.6
12 (11–12½)	10–14	1.2	1.0	0.8	0.8	0.6	0.6	
	14–20	1.5	1.2	1.0	0.8	0.6	0.6	
	20–30	1.5	1.2	1.2	1.0	0.8	0.6	0.6
	30–42	2.0	1.5	1.2	1.0	0.8	0.6	0.6
	42–60	2.0	1.5	1.5	1.2	1.0	0.8	0.6
	60–up	2.0	2.0	1.5	1.2	1.0	0.8	0.6
14 (13–15½)	14–20	1.5	1.2	1.0	1.0	0.8	0.6	0.6
	20–30	2.0	1.5	1.2	1.0	0.8	0.6	0.6
	30–42	2.0	1.5	1.5	1.2	1.0	0.8	0.6
	42–60	2.0	2.0	1.5	1.5	1.0	0.8	0.6
	60–90	2.5	2.0	2.0	1.5	1.2	1.0	0.6
	90–up	2.5	2.0	2.0	1.5	1.5	1.2	0.8
17 (16–18½)	14–20	2.0	1.5	1.2	1.0	0.8	0.6	0.6
	20–30	2.0	1.5	1.5	1.2	1.0	0.8	0.6
	30–42	2.5	2.0	1.5	1.2	1.0	1.0	0.6
	42–60	2.5	2.0	2.0	1.5	1.2	1.2	0.8
	60–110	2.5	2.0	2.0	1.5	1.2	1.2	0.8
	110–up	3.0	2.5	2.0	2.0	1.5	1.2	1.0
20 (19–21½)	20–30	2.5	2.0	1.5	1.2	1.0	0.8	0.6
	30–42	2.5	2.0	2.0	1.5	1.2	1.0	0.8
	42–60	2.5	2.5	2.0	2.0	1.5	1.2	0.8
	60–90	3.0	2.5	2.0	2.0	1.5	1.2	1.0
	90–140	3.0	2.5	2.5	2.0	1.5	1.5	1.0
	140–up	3.0	2.5	2.5	2.0	1.5	1.5	1.0
24 (22–26)	20–30	2.5	2.0	2.0	1.5	1.2	1.0	0.8
	30–42	3.0	2.5	2.0	1.5	1.2	1.2	0.8
	42–60	3.0	2.5	2.5	2.0	1.5	1.2	1.0
	60–90	3.0	2.5	2.5	2.0	1.5	1.5	1.0
	90–140	3.0	3.0	2.5	2.0	2.0	1.5	1.2
	140–up	3.0	3.0	2.5	2.0	2.0	1.5	1.2
30 (27–33)	30–42	3.0	2.5	2.5	2.0	1.5	1.2	1.0
	42–60	3.0	3.0	2.5	2.5	1.5	1.5	1.0
	60–90	4.0	3.0	3.0	2.5	2.0	1.5	1.2
	90–140	4.0	3.0	3.0	2.5	2.0	2.0	1.5
	140–180	4.0	3.0	3.0	2.5	2.0	2.0	1.5
	180–up	4.0	3.0	3.0	2.5	2.0	2.0	1.5
36 (34–39)	30–42	4.0	3.0	2.5	2.0	1.5	1.5	1.0
	42–60	4.0	3.0	3.0	2.5	2.0	1.5	1.2
	60–90	5.0	3.0	3.0	3.0	2.0	2.0	1.5
	90–140	5.0	4.0	3.0	3.0	2.5	2.0	1.5
	140–200	5.0	4.0	3.0	3.0	2.5	2.0	1.5
	200–up	5.0	4.0	3.0	3.0	2.5	2.0	1.5
40 or more	42–60	5.0	4.0	3.0	These values are given on the next page			
	60–90	5.0	4.0	4.0				
	90–140	5.0	4.0	4.0				
	140–200	5.0	5.0	4.0				
	200–up	5.0	5.0	4.0				

TABLE 8. Room Index (Continued)
(For large high rooms)

For indirect lighting use } ceiling height — Feet; For direct lighting use } mounting height — Feet; Room index

Room width, feet	Room length, feet	**Indirect (ceiling ht, Feet):** 14 to 16½ · **Direct (mounting ht, Feet):** 10 to 11½	17 to 20 · 12 to 13½	21 to 24 · 14 to 16½	25 to 30 · 17 to 20	31 to 36 · 21 to 24	37 to 50 · 25 to 30	31 to 36	37 to 50
14 (13–15½)	14–20	1.0	0.8	0.6	0.6				
	20–30	1.0	0.8	0.6	0.6				
	30–42	1.2	1.0	0.8	0.6	0.6			
	42–60	1.5	1.0	0.8	0.6	0.6	0.6		
	60–90	1.5	1.2	1.0	0.6	0.6	0.6		
	90–up	1.5	1.5	1.2	0.8	0.6	0.6		
17 (16–18½)	14–20	1.0	0.8	0.6	0.6				
	20–30	1.2	1.0	0.8	0.6				
	30–42	1.2	1.0	1.0	0.6	0.6	0.6		
	42–60	1.5	1.2	1.2	0.8	0.6	0.6	0.6	
	60–110	1.5	1.2	1.2	0.8	0.6	0.6	0.6	
	110–up	2.0	1.5	1.2	1.0	0.8	0.6	0.6	
20 (19–21½)	20–30	1.2	1.0	0.8	0.6	0.6			
	30–42	1.5	1.2	1.0	0.8	0.6	0.6		
	42–60	2.0	1.5	1.2	0.8	0 6	0.6	0.6	
	60–90	2.0	1.5	1.2	1.0	0.6	0.6	0.6	
	90–140	2.0	1.5	1.5	1.0	0.8	0.8	0.6	0.6
	140–up	2.0	1.5	1.5	1.0	1.0	0.8	0.6	0.6
24 (22–26)	20–30	1.5	1.2	1.0	0.8	0.6	0.6		
	30–42	1.5	1.2	1.2	0.8	0.6	0.6		
	42–60	2.0	1.5	1.2	1.0	0.8	0.6	0.6	
	60–90	2.0	1.5	1.5	1.0	0.8	0.6	0.6	0.6
	90–140	2.0	2.0	1.5	1.2	1.0	0.8	0.6	0.6
	140–up	2.0	2.0	1.5	1.2	1.0	0.8	0.8	0.6
30 (27–33)	30–42	2.0	1.5	1.2	1.0	0.8	0.6	0.6	
	42–60	2.5	1.5	1.5	1.0	1.0	0.8	0.6	
	60–90	2.5	2.0	1.5	1.2	1.0	0.8	0.6	0.6
	90–140	2.5	2.0	2.0	1.5	1.2	1.0	0.8	0.6
	140–180	2.5	2.0	2.0	1.5	1.2	1.0	0.8	0.6
	180–up	2.5	2.0	2.0	1.5	1.2	1.0	0.8	0.6
36 (34–39)	30–42	2.0	1.5	1.5	1.0	0.8	0.8	0.6	
	42–60	2.5	2.0	1.5	1.2	1.0	0.8	0.6	0.6
	60–90	3.0	2.0	2.0	1.5	1.0	1 0	0.6	0.6
	90–140	3.0	2.5	2.0	1.5	1.2	1.0	0.8	0.6
	140–200	3.0	2.5	2.0	1.5	1.5	1.2	1.0	0.8
	200–up	3.0	2.5	2.0	1.5	1.5	1.2	1.0	0.8
42 (40–45)	42–60	3.0	2.0	1.5	1.2	1.0	0.8	0.8	0.6
	60–90	3.0	2.5	2.0	1.5	1.2	1.0	0.8	0.6
	90–140	3.0	2.5	2.5	2.0	1.5	1.2	1.0	0.6
	140–200	3.0	2.5	2.5	2.0	1.5	1.2	1.0	0.8
	200–up	3.0	2.5	2.5	2.0	1.5	1.5	1.2	0.8
50 (46–55)	42–60	3.0	2.5	2.0	1.5	1.2	1.0	0.8	0.6
	60–90	3.0	3.0	2.5	1.5	1.5	1.2	1.0	0.6
	90–140	3.0	3.0	2.5	2.0	1.5	1.5	1.2	0.8
	140–200	3.0	3.0	2.5	2.0	2.0	1.5	1.2	0.8
	200–up	3.0	3.0	2.5	2.0	2.0	1.5	1.2	1.0
60 (56–67)	60–90	4.0	3.0	2.5	2.0	1.5	1.2	1.0	0.8
	90–140	4.0	3.0	3.0	2.5	2.0	1.5	1.2	1.0
	140–200	4.0	3.0	3.0	2.5	2 0	1.5	1.5	1.0
	200–up	4.0	3.0	3.0	2.5	2.0	2.0	1.5	1.0
75 (68–90)	60–90	5.0	4.0	3.0	2.5	2.0	1.5	1.2	0.8
	90–140	5.0	4.0	3.0	2.5	2.0	1.5	1.5	1.0
	140–200	5.0	4.0	4.0	3.0	2.5	2.0	1.5	1.2
	200–up	5.0	4.0	4.0	3.0	2.5	2.0	1.5	1.2
90 or more	60–90	5.0	4.0	3.0	2.5	2.0	1.5	1.2	1.0
	90–140	5.0	5.0	4.0	3.0	2.5	2.0	1.5	1.2
	140–200	5.0	5.0	4.0	3.0	2.5	2.0	1.5	1.2
	200–up	5.0	5.0	4.0	3.0	3.0	2.5	2.0	1.5

TABLE 9

Reflection factors }	Ceiling	Very light (70%)			Fairly light (50%)			Fairly dark (30%)	
	Walls	Fairly light (50%)	Fairly dark (30%)	Very dark (10%)	Fairly light (50%)	Fairly dark (30%)	Very dark (10%)	Fairly dark (30%)	Very dark (10%)
	Room index	Utilization factors							

Tungsten-filament Incandescent Lighting Units

1 Wide distribution ↑ 0% up ↓ 75% down MF = 65%.	0.6	.34	.29	.24	.34	.29	.24	.28	.24
	0.8	.42	.38	.34	.42	.37	.33	.37	.33
	1.0	.46	.43	.39	.45	.42	.39	.42	.39
	1.2	.50	.47	.43	.49	.46	.43	.45	.42
	1.5	.53	.50	.46	.52	.49	.46	.48	.45
	2.0	.58	.55	.51	.57	.54	.51	.53	.51
	2.5	.62	.59	.56	.61	.58	.56	.58	.56
	3.0	.64	.61	.58	.63	.60	.58	.60	.58
	4.0	.67	.65	.63	.66	.64	.62	.63	.61
	5.0	.69	.67	.65	.67	.66	.64	.65	.63
2 High bay, concentrating ↑ 0% up ↓ 72% down MF = 65%	0.6	.41	.39	.37	.40	.39	.37	.40	.37
	0.8	.49	.47	.47	.48	.47	.46	.47	.44
	1.0	.52	.52	.51	.52	.51	.50	.51	.50
	1.2	.55	.54	.54	.54	.54	.52	.54	.52
	1.5	.59	.57	.56	.57	.56	.55	.56	.54
	2.0	.61	.60	.59	.60	.60	.58	.59	.57
	2.5	.65	.63	.62	.63	.62	.61	.61	.60
	3.0	.66	.65	.63	.64	.63	.62	.62	.61
	4.0	.67	.65	.65	.65	.64	.63	.63	.62
	5.0	.69	.67	.65	.66	.65	.65	.64	.63
3 White glass enclosing globe ↑ 35% up ↓ 45% down MF = 70%	0.6	.22	.17	.14	.20	.16	.13	.14	.12
	0.8	.27	.22	.19	.25	.21	.18	.19	.17
	1.0	.31	.26	.23	.28	.24	.21	.22	.19
	1.2	.35	.30	.26	.31	.27	.24	.25	.22
	1.5	.38	.33	.29	.34	.30	.27	.27	.24
	2.0	.42	.38	.33	.38	.34	.31	.31	.28
	2.5	.46	.41	.37	.41	.37	.34	.34	.31
	3.0	.49	.45	.40	.43	.39	.36	.36	.33
	4.0	.53	.48	.44	.47	.43	.40	.38	.36
	5.0	.55	.51	.47	.49	.45	.42	.40	.38
4 Semi-indirect cased-glass bottom ↑ 51% up ↓ 21% down MF = 65%	0.6	.16	.12	.10	.13	.10	.08	.08	.07
	0.8	.20	.16	.14	.17	.14	.11	.11	.09
	1.0	.23	.19	.17	.19	.16	.14	.13	.11
	1.2	.26	.22	.19	.22	.18	.16	.14	.13
	1.5	.29	.25	.21	.24	.20	.19	.16	.14
	2.0	.32	.28	.25	.27	.23	.21	.18	.17
	2.5	.35	.31	.28	.29	.26	.24	.20	.19
	3.0	.38	.34	.31	.31	.28	.26	.22	.21
	4.0	.41	.38	.35	.34	.31	.29	.24	.23
	5.0	.43	.39	.37	.36	.33	.31	.26	.24
5 Indirect ↑ 80% up ↓ 0% down MF = 60%	0.6	.15	.12	.10	.11	.09	.07	.05	.04
	0.8	.18	.15	.13	.13	.11	.09	.07	.06
	1.0	.22	.19	.16	.15	.13	.11	.08	.07
	1.2	.25	.22	.19	.18	.15	.13	.09	.08
	1.5	.27	.24	.21	.20	.17	.15	.10	.09
	2.0	.30	.27	.25	.22	.19	.17	.11	.10
	2.5	.34	.31	.28	.24	.22	.20	.13	.12
	3.0	.36	.33	.30	.26	.24	.22	.14	.13
	4.0	.40	.37	.34	.28	.26	.24	.15	.14
	5.0	.42	.39	.37	.30	.28	.26	.17	.15

TABLE 9 (Continued)

Reflection factors }	Ceiling	75%			50%		
	Walls	50%	30%	10%	50%	30%	10%
	Room index	Utilization factors					

Fluorescent Lighting Units

6

2-lamp 100-watt — 3-lamp 40-watt, MF=0.70, 0/75

Room index	50%	30%	10%	50%	30%	10%
0.6	.35	.30	.26	.34	.30	.26
0.8	.44	.39	.36	.43	.38	.35
1.0	.48	.44	.41	.46	.44	.40
1.2	.51	.48	.45	.50	.47	.44
1.5	.54	.51	.48	.52	.50	.47
2.0	.59	.56	.53	.58	.55	.52
2.5	.63	.60	.57	.62	.59	.57
3.0	.65	.62	.59	.63	.61	.59
4.0	.68	.65	.63	.66	.64	.62
5.0	.69	.67	.65	.68	.65	.64

7

Trough with configurated glass cover, MF=0.70, 0/60

Room index	50%	30%	10%	50%	30%	10%
0.6	.30	.26	.24	.29	.26	.24
0.8	.37	.34	.32	.36	.33	.31
1.0	.40	.38	.36	.39	.37	.35
1.2	.43	.40	.39	.42	.40	.38
1.5	.45	.43	.40	.44	.42	.40
2.0	.48	.46	.44	.47	.46	.44
2.5	.52	.49	.47	.50	.49	.47
3.0	.53	.51	.49	.52	.50	.49
4.0	.55	.53	.52	.53	.52	.51
5.0	.56	.54	.53	.55	.53	.52

8

Lamps or tubes without reflector, MF=0.75, 50/50

Room index	50%	30%	10%	50%	30%	10%
0.6	.28	.22	.19	.24	.20	.17
0.8	.35	.29	.25	.30	.26	.22
1.0	.39	.33	.30	.34	.30	.26
1.2	.44	.38	.34	.38	.33	.30
1.5	.48	.42	.37	.41	.36	.32
2.0	.53	.47	.42	.46	.41	.37
2.5	.58	.52	.46	.49	.45	.41
3.0	.61	.55	.50	.52	.47	.44
4.0	.66	.61	.56	.56	.51	.48
5.0	.69	.64	.59	.59	.54	.51

9

Open grid deep louvers, MF=0.70, 42/28

Room index	50%	30%	10%	50%	30%	10%
0.6	.24	.21	.20	.21	.19	.18
0.8	.29	.26	.25	.25	.24	.22
1.0	.32	.30	.28	.28	.26	.25
1.2	.36	.33	.31	.31	.28	.27
1.5	.38	.35	.33	.32	.30	.29
2.0	.41	.38	.36	.35	.33	.31
2.5	.44	.41	.39	.37	.35	.34
3.0	.46	.43	.41	.38	.36	.35
4.0	.48	.46	.44	.40	.38	.37
5.0	.50	.48	.46	.42	.40	.38

10

Indirect, MF=0.60, 80/0

Room index	50%	30%	10%	50%	30%	10%
0.6	.16	.12	.11	.10	.09	.07
0.8	.20	.16	.14	.13	.11	.10
1.0	.23	.20	.17	.15	.13	.11
1.2	.27	.23	.20	.18	.15	.14
1.5	.29	.25	.22	.20	.17	.15
2.0	.33	.29	.26	.22	.19	.18
2.5	.36	.32	.30	.24	.22	.20
3.0	.39	.35	.32	.26	.23	.22
4.0	.43	.40	.37	.28	.26	.25
5.0	.45	.42	.39	.30	.28	.26

sections.   There are, however, quite a number of different symmetrical arrangements that can be devised for any given room, using one, two, three, or four units per bay.   Additional arrangements, which are sufficiently symmetrical, may be obtained by combining the bays into pairs and treating each pair of bays as if it were a single bay.

In no case should the spacing between units exceed 1.5 times the height of the lighting unit above the working plane.   In the case of indirect lighting the height of the lighting unit is taken as being the height of the ceiling.   In the case of the focusing unit, No. 2, the spacing between units should not exceed 0.75 times the height of the lighting unit above the working plane.

Example.   To design a lighting system for a drafting room 72 by 36 by 13 ft high having a white ceiling divided up into four bays each way as shown in Fig. 441.   There are windows along both sides.   Use lighting unit 9.

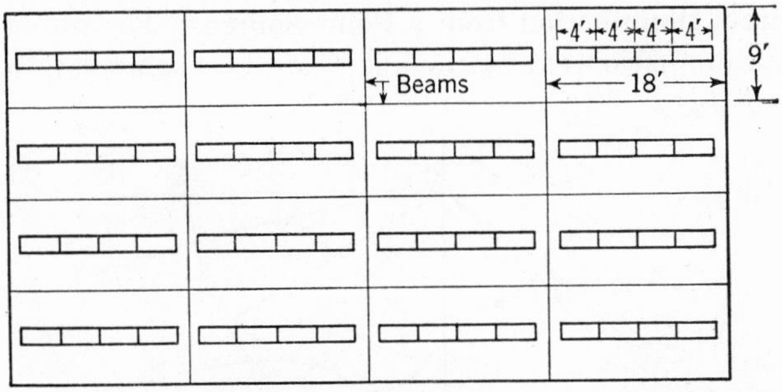

FIG. 441. Ceiling plan of drafting room, showing arrangement of lighting units.

The illumination should be about 50 lumens per sq ft, and this will be about 30 per cent less than the initial illumination, owing to dust and aging of the lamps. Therefore the initial illumination should be 50/0.70 = 71 lumens per sq ft.   The value 0.70 used in the preceding equation is called the maintenance factor.   It varies somewhat with the design of the lighting unit and is shown in Table 9 for each unit, the abbreviation being MF.

$$\text{Area of working plane} = 72 \times 36 = 2{,}592 \text{ sq ft}$$
$$\text{Lumens required on this plane} = 71 \times 2{,}592 = 184{,}000 \text{ lumens}$$
$$\text{Room index} = 3.0 \qquad \text{(Table 8)}$$

Since there are windows along the sides, the walls should be considered fairly dark (30 per cent of light reflected back into the room).   From Table 9, lighting unit 9, room index = 3.0, very light ceiling, fairly dark walls, the utilization factor is given as 43 per cent.

$$\text{Lumens emitted by lamps} = \frac{184{,}000}{0.43} = 428{,}000$$

Assuming that we use preheated, 40-watt, white fluorescent lamps,

$$\text{Output per lamp} = 2{,}400 \text{ lumens}$$
$$\text{Total lamps required} = \frac{428{,}000}{2{,}400} = 178 \text{ lamps}$$

The most obvious arrangement is to use four rows of lamps running lengthwise as in Fig. 441.   This gives a spacing of 9 ft between rows, which is approximately equal to the height of the unit above the working plane, which is an excellent spacing for semi-indirect units.

$$\text{Lamps per row} = \frac{178}{4} = 44$$

$$\text{Lamps per bay} = \frac{44}{4} = 11$$

The lamps are 4 ft long, and each bay is 18 ft long, which allows room for 4 units placed end to end in a continuous row as shown in Fig. 441.   If we place three lamps in each unit, we shall have 12 lamps per bay, which will give about 8 per cent more illumination than we assumed at the start.   Therefore the specification will call for 64 three-lamp lighting units similar to No. 9, to be arranged in groups of four, as shown on the drawing.   Another satisfactory arrangement would be to use three units per bay with four lamps per unit.

442. Direct Illumination from a Point Source.   The use of utilization factors in illumination calculations is based on the assumption that the

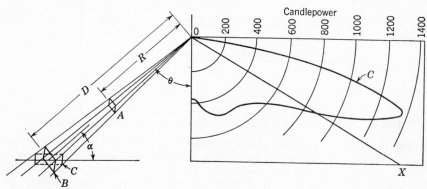

FIG. 442. Variation of light intensity with the distance from the source and with the angle of incidence.

illumination on the working plane will be fairly uniform over its entire area, so that an average value is all that is required.   In the case of outdoor illumination, however, it is often not economically feasible to provide a uniform illumination, and it then becomes necessary to compute the illumination point by point, using the candlepower distribution curve and the law of inverse squares.

In Fig. 442 the perspective drawing of the sharp pyramid with its apex at point O is intended to illustrate the principle of the law of inverse squares.   Since light travels in straight lines, it follows that the same amount of light passes through the three surfaces A, B, and C, where A and B are perpendicular to the axis of the pyramid and C is at an angle to that axis.   Therefore

$$\frac{\text{Lumens per square foot on } B}{\text{Lumens per square foot on } A} = \frac{R^2}{D^2}$$

Now the candlepower in the direction of the axis of the pyramid is, by definition, the lumens per square foot on A when $R = 1$ ft. Therefore the illumination on surface B is given by the equation

$$\text{Lumens per sq ft on } B = \frac{\text{candlepower at angle } \theta}{D^2}$$

Again $$\frac{\text{Lumens per sq ft on } C}{\text{Lumens per sq ft on } B} = \frac{\text{area } B}{\text{area } C} = \sin \alpha = \cos \theta$$

where C is the horizontal plane.

Example. Curve C, Fig. 442, is the candlepower distribution curve for a 6,000-lumen tungsten lamp equipped with a reflector for street lighting. It is required to determine the illumination at a point X, 40 ft from the lamp post, the height of the lamp being 23 ft.

Candlepower in direction $OX = 860$ (read from curve)
$OX^2 = 40^2 + 23^2 = 2,129$

Illumination at X on plane perpendicular to $OX = \dfrac{860}{2,129} = 0.404$ ft-c

Illumination on street surface $= 0.404 \times \cos \theta$

$$= 0.404 \times \frac{23}{\sqrt{2,129}} = 0.202 \text{ ft-c}$$

In general, another lamp on the other side of X will be contributing to the illumination on the horizontal surface, and the total illumination on this surface is the arithmetical sum of the illuminations produced by each lamp acting alone.

Problems

40-1. A light source has a candlepower of 50 in a given direction. What will be the illumination, in lumens per square foot, that it will produce at a point 10 ft distant in that direction, the illumination being received on a plane that is perpendicular to the direction? If the receiving plane is tilted through 30° from the perpendicular, what will be the illumination upon it?

40-2. If a light source were perfectly symmetrical and had a candlepower of 30 in all directions, what would be its total lumens output?

40-3. A 100-watt lamp operated at rated voltage has a working life of 1,000 hr. If 100-watt lamps cost 20 cts each and electrical energy costs 5 cents per kwhr, would the total cost of energy and lamp renewals, per lumen per 1,000 hr, be increased or decreased if the operating voltage were raised 2.5 per cent? (See Fig. 438.)

40-4. A skating rink, 180 ft by 80 ft, is to be lit by thirty-six 500-watt RLM dome lighting units (No. 1) spaced 20 by 20 ft and mounted 24 ft above the ice. Calculate the illumination on the ice.

*40-5. Calculate the illumination of any rooms that are conveniently accessible, and, if possible, measure the illumination with a foot-candle meter.

*40-6. It is desired to light a large machine shop in which medium-grade bench and machine work are to be done. The shop is 100 by 320 ft and the ceiling height is 20 ft. The crossbars of the roof trusses are 18 ft above floor and divide the ceiling into bays 100 by 20 ft. The color of the ceiling is medium and the walls are practically made up of windows whose reflection factor is equivalent to that of dark walls. The working plane is to be about 3 ft above the floor. Determine the type of the lighting system, and the number and size of lamps required.

NOTE: Lamps may be placed 20 ft apart if they are 16.5 ft above the floor, except in the case of a high bay or concentrating reflector.

41

THERMIONIC TUBES AND
PHOTOELECTRIC CELLS

443. Classification of Thermionic Tubes. Electron tubes generally consist of two or more electrodes enclosed in an evacuated glass or metal chamber. A thermionic tube is an electron tube in which one of the electrodes, called the cathode, is heated to a temperature at which it emits electrons freely. The nature of the electron emission from a hot filament (cathode), and the resulting electric current between the cathode and the plate, have been discussed in Art. 400. All electron tubes may be divided into two classes: (1) *high-vacuum tubes*, in which the evacuation has been carried to a point where the remaining gas molecules have no measurable effect on the operation of the tube; (2) *gas-filled tubes*, which contain a small amount of chemically inert gas introduced after thorough evacuation. Thermionic tubes may also be classified according to the number of electrodes that they contain: diode contains two electrodes; triode contains three electrodes; tetrode contains four electrodes; pentode contains five electrodes. The diode is used chiefly as a rectifier. Its operation has been discussed in Arts. 400 to 404.

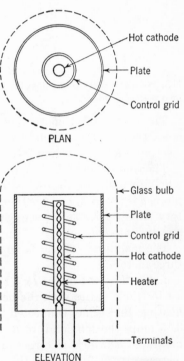

PLAN

ELEVATION

FIG. 443. Cross-sectional plan and elevation of a high-vacuum triode with an indirectly heated cathode.

444. High-vacuum Triode. Figure 443 shows the cross-sectional plan and elevation of a high-vacuum triode with an indirectly heated hot cath-

537

ode.   This cathode consists of a thin-walled metal tube which encloses an insulated tungsten electric heater.   The indirectly heated cathode has two advantages over the directly heated filament-type of cathode.   Its relatively large heat-storage capacity makes it possible to use ordinary alternating current to heat the cathode, with only a slight pulsation in the cathode temperature, while its tubular construction allows much greater precision in the geometrical spacing of the electrodes.   The outer surface of the cathode is generally coated with thorium, barium oxide, or strontium oxide, to facilitate the emission of electrons.

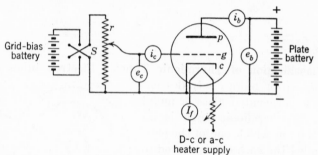

FIG. 444. Laboratory connections for determining the static or steady-state characteristics of a thermionic triode.

The control grid consists of an open spiral of fine wire.   The plate consists of a sheet of metal bent into the form of a cylinder; and all three electrodes are firmly supported so that they are coaxial.

The conventional diagrammatical representation of a high-vacuum triode with indirectly heated cathode is shown in Fig. 444, where p is the plate, g is the grid, and c is the cathode.   Figure 444 also shows a laboratory circuit suitable for the experimental determination of the static or steady-state characteristics shown in Figs. 445 to 447.

The magnitude of the plate current i_b is determined by the following three factors:

a. The Heater Current I_f.   Figure 445 shows how the plate current of a 6J5 triode varies with the heater current when the control grid is left floating, that is, not connected to anything.   At all heater currents below 0.15 amp, the temperature of the cathode is below the minimum temperature at which electrons are emitted.   The emission of electrons increases very rapidly as the heater current is increased above about 0.18 amp, and soon electrons are being emitted at a greater rate than they can be taken away by any plate voltage that can be applied to the tube without destroying it.   At the rated normal heater current of 0.3 amp the electron emission is far beyond that required, and most of the emitted electrons are repelled back into the cathode by the cloud of electrons that now surrounds it.   The plate current is said to be limited by the space charge, that is, by the cloud of electrons. Note that under normal operation the plate current is not sensitive to variations in the heater current.

b. The Plate Voltage e_b. Figure 446 shows how the plate current varies with the plate voltage. These curves would all bend over and become approximately horizontal if the plate voltage were taken to values high enough to pick up all the electrons emitted by the cathode, but modern coated filaments give such copious emission that the plate voltage

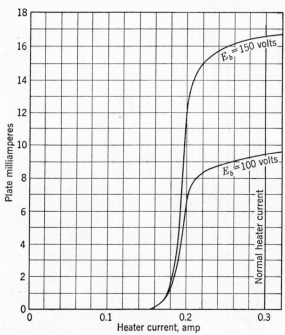

FIG. 445. Variation of plate current with heater current for a 6J5 triode, with control grid floating.

required to attain this value of plate current is far higher than the maximum plate voltage at which the tube can operate continuously without damaging the electrodes. As the electrons strike the plate, their kinetic energy is converted into heat. The energy per electron and the number of electrons striking the plate are both proportional to the plate voltage, and consequently the temperature of the plate increases rapidly with the plate voltage. This sets a limit for the allowable plate voltage. Conditions at the cathode also set an upper limit to the plate voltage, because an excessive plate voltage will destroy the coating on the cathode, presumably by positive-ion bombardment.

c. The Grid Voltage e_c. The grid voltage may be varied by moving the sliding contact on the rheostat *r*, Fig. 444, and may be reversed by means of the switch S.   If the grid is given a sufficiently large negative potential, the force of repulsion that it exerts upon the electrons will prevent any of them from passing through the open spaces between the grid wires, and the plate current will be zero.   The grid is then said to be biased to cutoff.   The grid voltage required to bias to cutoff depends on the plate voltage.   For example, from Fig. 447 it may be seen that a 6J5 triode is biased to cutoff by a grid potential of -6 volts when the plate potential is 100 volts, but a grid bias of -22 volts is required for cutoff when the plate potential is 350 volts.

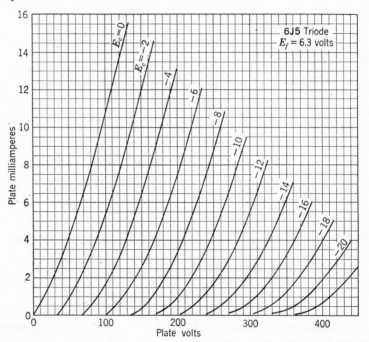

FIG. 446. Plate characteristics of a triode commonly used for voltage amplification.

445. Tube Factors.   The curves of Fig. 447 show that the plate current may be controlled over a wide range by varying the grid voltage. Moreover, the change in e_c required to produce a given change in i_b is much less than the change in e_b required to produce the same change in i_b, the reason being that the grid is nearer to the cathode.

Amplification Factor.   The ratio of the change in e_b to the change in e_c, in order that they may neutralize each other's effects on the plate current, is called the amplification factor, and is denoted by the symbol μ. Expressed in mathematical form the definition becomes

$$\mu = -\frac{de_b}{de_c}$$

to keep i_b constant.

The minus sign is inserted because the foregoing definition of μ is in terms of the *decrease* in e_b required to neutralize an increase in e_c, while the derivative of e_b with respect to e_c is the relative rate of *increase* of e_b. Alternatively the minus sign may be eliminated by defining μ as the ratio of the increase in e_b to the increase in e_c required to produce the same increase in i_b.

Example. Referring to Fig. 447, if $e_c = -10$ volts and e_b is increased from 250 to 300 volts, i_b will increase from a to b, that is, from 4.5 to 10 ma, but i_b can

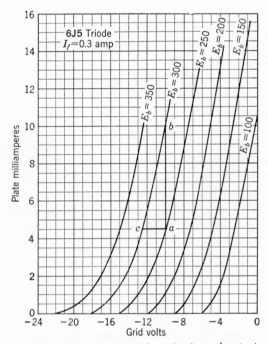

FIG. 447. Variation of plate current with grid voltage (static characteristics).

be brought back to 4.5 ma by changing e_c from a to c, that is, from -10 to -12.5 volts. Therefore the amplification factor is

$$\mu = \frac{300 - 250}{12.5 - 10} = 20$$

The amplification factor is not an absolute constant but it is reasonably constant so long as the operation is restricted to the straight portions of the curves.

Figure 447 does not show any positive values of e_c, and in practice control grids are generally negative with respect to the cathode. In the majority of practical applications alternating emfs are superimposed on the d-c voltages of both grid and plate. If the grid voltage swings positive during a portion of each cycle electrons will enter the grid and there will be a pulsating grid current, which would be measured by the milli-ammeter i_c of Fig. 444. In many applications a grid current, unless quite small, has an adverse effect on the operation of the circuit.

Plate Resistance. When a current i_b is made to flow through a tube from plate to cathode, a voltage drop e_b appears across the tube, and electrical energy is converted into heat at the rate of $e_b i_b$ watts, but this is exactly what happens when a current is made to flow through a resistance. Therefore it is convenient to regard this path through the tube as having resistance, even though the physical nature of that resistance is rather different from the resistance of a piece of wire. In practice, we are interested chiefly in the resistance that the tube offers to the a-c component of the plate current, and therefore we define the plate resistance r_p by the equation

$$r_p = \frac{de_b}{di_b} \quad \text{with } e_c \text{ constant}$$

If r_p were independent of the current, this definition would check with the Ohm's law definition, because if $e = ir$ then $de/di = r$; but r_p is not independent of current, and therefore the two definitions lead to different values of resistance. The concept of a plate resistance that is equal to de_b/di_b is very useful when dealing with variations in e_b and i_b, so long as those variations are restricted to the straight portions of the curves of i_b versus e_b, so that r_p is constant. Note that the total power loss in the plate-to-cathode portion of the circuit is not $i_b^2 r_p$ but $i_b^2 R_p$, where R_p is the true ohmic resistance of Ohm's law.

Example. Referring to Fig. 447, if E_c is constant at -10 volts, raising e_b from 250 to 300 volts increases i_b from a to b, that is, from 4.5 to 10 ma. Therefore

$$r_p = \frac{300 - 250}{0.01 - 0.0045} = 9{,}090 \text{ ohms}$$

The **transconductance or mutual conductance** of a tube may be defined as the factor by which a change in grid volts must be multiplied to obtain the resulting change in plate amperes. It is denoted by g_m, and expressed mathematically becomes

$$g_m = \frac{di_b}{de_c} \quad \text{with } e_b \text{ constant}$$

In Fig. 447,

$$g_m = \frac{ab}{ca} = \frac{0.01 - 0.0045}{12.5 - 10} = 2{,}200 \times 10^{-6} \text{ mho} = 2{,}200 \text{ } \mu\text{mhos}$$

The transconductance is not an independent factor because the amplification factor may be written

$$\mu = \frac{di_b/de_c}{di_b/de_b} = g_m r_p \tag{118}$$

446. Dynamic Characteristics of Triodes. In most practical applications of triodes an alternating emf is superimposed on the d-c grid voltage, as in Fig. 448. Moreover, in order that any use may be made of the resulting a-c component of plate current it must be passed through some sort of load. In Fig. 448 the load is the pure resistance R_L, which is the type of load generally used when the tube is functioning as a voltage amplifier.

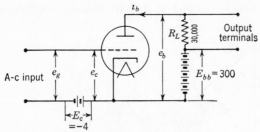

FIG. 448. Circuit illustrating dynamic operation of a triode.

In order to present a clear picture of the operation, it is essential that all symbols should be precisely defined. The following definitions will be used:

e_g = instantaneous value of a-c component of grid-to-cathode voltage

e_c = instantaneous value of total grid-to-cathode voltage

E_c = d-c component of grid-to-cathode voltage

E_g = effective value of a-c component of grid-to-cathode voltage

i_p = instantaneous value of a-c component of plate current

i_b = instantaneous value of total plate current

I_b = d-c component of plate current

I_p = effective value of a-c component of plate current

e_p = instantaneous value of a-c component of plate voltage

e_b = instantaneous value of total plate voltage

E_b = d-c component of plate voltage

E_p = effective value of a-c component of plate voltage

E_{bb} = d-c supply voltage

In Fig. 448, $E_b = E_{bb} - I_b R_L$.

The curves in Fig. 447 show the variation of plate current with grid voltage when the plate voltage is constant, and these curves are referred to as static characteristics. In Fig. 448, however, the plate voltage will not be constant, because $e_b = E_{bb} - i_b R_L$, and i_b changes as e_c changes. Thus e_c, i_b, and e_b are all three changing simultaneously. The relationship between these three varying quantities may be shown graphically, as in Fig. 449, by taking advantage of a device known as the load line.

This line is simply the graph of e_b of Fig. 448 against i_b, and its equation is $e_b = E_{bb} - i_b R_L$. Figure 449 shows the operation of the circuit of Fig. 448 when the graph of e_g is a sine curve with a peak value of 2 volts, so that e_c pulsates between the values -6 and -2 volts. The effect of the pulsations in e_c is to cause i_b to pulsate between the values 4.3 ma and 6.4 ma. Therefore the peak value of $i_p = (6.4 - 4.3)/2 = 1.05$ ma. The pulsations in i_b cause e_b to pulsate between the values $300 - (0.0043 \times 30,000)$ and $300 - (0.0064 \times 30,000)$, that is, between the values 171

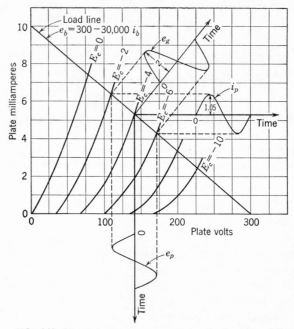

FIG. 449. Showing the operation of the circuit of Fig. 448.

and 108 volts. Therefore the peak value of $e_p = (171 - 108)/2 = 31.5$ volts. Dividing the peak values by $\sqrt{2}$ gives us the following effective values: $E_g = 1.414$ volts, $I_p = 0.743$ ma, $E_p = 22.3$ volts.

The voltage across the output terminals of Fig. 448 is made up of a d-c component and an a-c component. The d-c component is generally not wanted, and later circuits will show how it may be eliminated. Let E_0 be the effective value of the a-c component. Then $E_0 = I_p R_L = 0.000743 \times 30,000 = 22.3$ volts, which happens to be the same as E_p. Evidently in this particular circuit R_L and r_p are equal. If the circuit is being used as a voltage amplifier, then E_0 is the desired output voltage, and the voltage amplification is $E_0/E_g = 22.3/1.414 = 15.8$.

447. Distortion and Voltage Limits in Amplifiers. It is generally desired that the graph of the a-c component of the output current of an amplifier should be an exact replica of the graph of the a-c component of the input voltage to the grid. Expressed mathematically, the ideal relationship is that $i_p = ke_g$, where k is a constant. If this requirement is met, the amplifier is said to be free from distortion. Referring to Figs. 448 and 449, there will be no distortion so long as the operation is restricted to that portion of the load line over which equal intercepts are made by the static plate-current curves as shown. If in Fig. 449 the amplitude of the e_g curve is increased to 4 volts, it will be found that the negative peak of the i_p curve is about 10 per cent less than the positive peak. Therefore the wave is slightly distorted. As the amplitude of e_g is further increased, the distortion will increase rapidly. The negative peak will be depressed because the load-line intercepts referred to above become successively smaller as E_c becomes more negative, and the positive peak will be depressed because when e_c swings above the line $E_c = 0$ a grid current flows which tends to decrease e_c and therefore to decrease the plate current. Increasing the voltage E_{bb} of the plate battery makes it possible to operate over a greater length of load line for the same amount of distortion, but for every type of tube there is a limit above which the plate voltage cannot be pushed without overheating the plate. The rapidly moving electrons of the plate current possess kinetic energy that is proportional to the plate voltage, and this energy is converted into heat when the electrons hit the plate. The data provided by tube manufacturers includes the maximum allowable plate voltage and also the maximum allowable plate dissipation in watts. Tubes are available for a very wide range of plate voltages and watts output.

448. Thermionic-tube Amplifiers. Thermionic tubes are widely used in telephony and radio, and in the fields of measurement and control, as amplifiers of power, voltage, or current. It is usually required of the amplifier that its output should have the same wave form as the input, or in other words, that it should amplify without distortion.

In the great majority of cases it is power amplification that is required; a weak signal must be converted into a strong one. However, unless only a small amount of amplification is required, it must be carried out in two or more successive stages, and all the stages except the final one are voltage amplifiers, even though the final stage is a power amplifier. The output voltage of each stage is impressed on the grid of the following stage, and since the grid normally absorbs no energy, being negative to the cathode, it follows that each stage controls the following stage without transferring any energy to it, and all the energy output of the final stage comes from the plate battery, the grid merely acting as a valve to control the power output of the battery.

449. Resistance-capacitance-coupled Amplifiers. The load-line method of demonstrating the performance of a thermionic tube, as illustrated in Fig. 449, leads to a clear understanding, but so far as calculations are concerned, it is much simpler to substitute an equivalent circuit. Figure 450 shows one stage of a resistance-capacitance-coupled amplifier, and its equivalent circuit is shown in Fig. 451. The function of the coupling capacitor C_c is to keep the voltage of the plate battery from being impressed on the grid of the next tube. In other words it eliminates the d-c component from the output of the preceding tube. C_c must be large enough so that it has only a negligible effect on the flow of the a-c component. The d-c component of the grid voltage is generally called the grid bias. In Fig. 448 the grid bias E_c is produced by a battery, but in practice it is usually produced, as in Fig. 450, by the d-c component of the plate current flowing through a grid-bias resistor. The

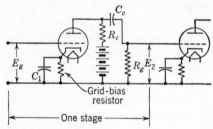

FIG. 450. Resistance-capacitance-coupled amplifier.

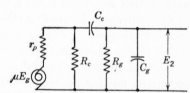

FIG. 451. Equivalent circuit of resistance-capacitance-coupled amplifier. C_g = capacitance of grid to cathode.

a-c component of the plate current is largely bypassed through the capacitor C_1. The grid leak R_g is required to provide a path through which the grid-bias voltage of the second tube can be impressed on its grid. If R_g were removed, the grid would be floating and would assume a potential not sufficiently negative for the proper or even safe operation of the tube. Since R_g is in parallel with the path through the grid, it takes part of the output of the preceding tube and thus tends to reduce the amplification. Therefore it should be made fairly large. It is usually in the range 0.1 to 1 megohm.

The equivalent circuit is based on two fundamental principles: (1) any voltage E_g impressed between the grid and the cathode can be replaced by a voltage μE_g in the plate circuit, where μ is the amplification factor, without affecting the plate current in any way; (2) the d-c components of current and voltage serve only to condition the tubes, and so long as they are present in their proper amounts they may be ignored in calculating the flow of the a-c components.

In Fig. 451, C_g is the capacitance of the grid to the cathode in the second tube. Strictly speaking it is in series with the parallel combination of the grid-bias resistor and its bypassing capacitor, but the impedance of these two parallel elements is so very much less than the impedance of

C_g that no measurable error is introduced by omitting them entirely when dealing with a-c components. The coupling capacitor C_c is made large enough so that its impedance is negligible compared with the impedance of R_g and C_g in parallel. Therefore we may reduce the impedance of C_c to zero without appreciably affecting the currents. This effectively puts R_c and R_g in parallel, and they may then be replaced by the single resistance $R = R_c R_g/(R_c + R_g)$, as in Fig. 452. Also the voltage across R is equal to E_2. Then, ignoring the very small current through C_g,

$$E_2 = \frac{R}{R + r_p} \mu E_g$$

and the voltage amplification is

$$\frac{E_2}{E_g} = \frac{\mu R}{R + r_p} \tag{119}$$

Equation (119) shows that as R is increased, which is accomplished by increasing R_c and R_g, the voltage amplification increases and approaches the limit μ. For all stages except the final stage, it is voltage amplification that is wanted, and therefore R is generally made at least five times r_p. This ratio applies only to triode amplifiers. In the final stage, it is generally maximum power output that is wanted rather than maximum voltage, and for maximum power output R should be approximately equal to r_p. The output tube is often coupled to the load through a transformer, as in Fig. 453, and the transformer ratio is then chosen to match the impedances, as will be explained in Art. 451. Also if power is required

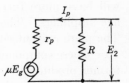

FIG. 452. Approximate equivalent circuit for a resistance-capacitance-coupled amplifier. It gives reasonably accurate results over a limited frequency range.

from the output stage, the tube for that stage is designed to have a much larger current-carrying capacity than the tubes designed for voltage-amplification stages. Figure 455 shows static plate characteristics for a power triode.

The reactance of C_c in Fig. 451 increases as f decreases, and therefore the amplification drops off at low frequencies. The magnitude of C_c is therefore determined by the lowest frequency that it is desired to amplify. Also the current taken by the capacitance C_g of the grid of the next tube is proportional to the frequency, and at very high frequencies C_g becomes equivalent to a short circuit. Therefore the amplification drops off at high frequencies. Now, when impedances are connected in parallel, the effect that any one of them has on the circuit is determined by their relative magnitudes. If R is reduced by one-half, then the frequency at which C_g begins to affect the amplification is approximately doubled.

In this way it is possible to extend the range of uniform amplification up to relatively high frequencies by using a sufficiently low value of R. However, the extended range is paid for in reduced amplification per stage over the whole range, as may be seen from Eq. (119), and therefore additional stages are required. Hence in practice the frequency range is not extended any further than is necessary, and the value of R_c is deter-

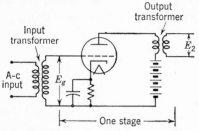

FIG. 453. Transformer-coupled amplifier.

mined by the maximum frequency that it is desired to amplify.

450. The Transformer-coupled Thermionic-tube Amplifier. Figure 453 shows one stage of a transformer-coupled amplifier. If there is a preceding stage the transformer labeled "input transformer" will of course be the output transformer of that stage. If the stage under considera-

tion is for voltage amplification, the secondaries of both transformers will have more turns than the primaries so that they also act as voltage amplifiers. The grid bias is obtained the same way as in Fig. 450. The plate current consists of a d-c component I_b and an a-c component I_p. These components flowing through the primary of the output transformer produce d-c and a-c components of mmf, but the output voltage E_2 is due solely to the a-c component of mmf, because a flux must change in order to induce an emf in a transformer winding. Thus the transformer eliminates the d-c component from the output. The d-c component of the plate current must not be allowed to saturate the iron core of the transformer. To prevent this, the core is usually built with a small air gap.

Figure 454 shows the equivalent circuit of one stage of a transformer-coupled amplifier. Consider first a voltage-amplification stage, in which case the only load connected to the secondary of the output transformer is the C_g of the next tube. C_g is so small that at low frequencies I_2 is practically zero.

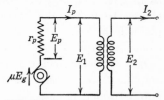

FIG. 454. Equivalent circuit of the transformer-coupled amplifier.

When $I_2 = 0$, the transformer presents a very large reactance X_1 to the primary voltage E_1. Now μE_g is the vector sum of E_p and E_1; and when the tube is a triode, E_p is very much smaller than E_1. Therefore, since the vectors E_p and E_1 are at practically 90° to each other, there will not be much error in neglecting E_p and writing $E_1 = \mu E_g$. Let n_2/n_1 be the transformer ratio. Then the voltage amplification is

$$\frac{E_2}{E_g} = \frac{n_2 E_1}{n_1 E_g} = \frac{n_2 \mu E_g}{n_1 E_g} = \mu \frac{n_2}{n_1} \qquad (120)$$

The voltage amplification will be fairly constant over a certain range of frequencies, but will drop off at both high and low frequencies. The drop at low frequencies is due to the fact that X_1 is proportional to the frequency, while r_p is independent of the frequency; and therefore as f is continuously reduced, the error resulting from neglecting E_p becomes continuously larger. The drop at high frequencies is due partly to the distributed capacitance between turns in the transformer, which takes a current proportional to the frequency, and partly to the fact that I_2 itself is proportional to the frequency and becomes less negligible as the frequency is increased. It is possible to design a transformer and associated circuit that will have a reasonably constant voltage amplification

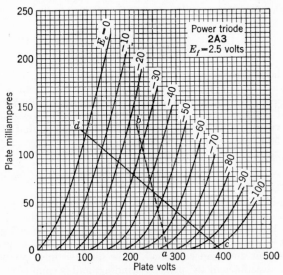

FIG. 455. Plate characteristics of a 2A3 power triode.

from about 50 to 10,000 cycles, but transformer coupling is rarely used for voltage-amplification stages. Resistance-capacitance coupling is less expensive and is capable of giving a more constant voltage amplification over a much wider range of frequencies. Moreover, its performance can be calculated with much greater precision than is possible with transformer coupling. On the other hand transformer coupling is widely used for the output stage of power amplifiers, chiefly because, by the proper choice of the transformer ratio, the impedance of the load may be matched with the plate resistance of the tube so as to obtain maximum power output, as is illustrated in Art. 451.

451. Output Stage of a Power Amplifier. Regardless of how the voltage-amplification stages are coupled, a transformer is generally used to couple the load to the final stage, as in Figs. 453 and 454.

550 PRINCIPLES AND PRACTICE OF ELECTRICAL ENGINEERING [Chap. 41

Example. In Fig. 453 let the tube be a 2A3 power triode with static characteristics as in Fig. 455. The maximum allowable plate dissipation in this tube is given as 15 watts. If we use a plate voltage of 250 volts and a grid bias of −45 volts, the quiescent (no a-c superimposed) plate current will be 60 ma and the plate dissipation will be $250 \times 0.060 = 15$ watts. For this quiescent point $r_p = de_b/di_b = 760$ ohms, obtained graphically as the slope of the curve of plate current for $E_c = -45$ volts in Fig. 455. Therefore in Fig. 454 $r_p = 760$ ohms. If the load to be supplied by E_2 is a resistance of 20 ohms, what should the ratio of the transformer be in order to obtain maximum power output to this resistance?

Neglecting for the moment the impedances of the transformer windings, we may say that a transformer with an impedance Z_L connected across its secondary can be replaced by an impedance $Z_1 = (n_1/n_2)^2 Z_L$, where n_1 and n_2 are the primary and secondary turns. In the given example Z_L is a resistance of 20 ohms. Therefore Z_1 becomes $R_1 = (n_1/n_2)^2 \times 20$. Now the power output to R_1 will be a maximum when $R_1 = r_p$; therefore

$$\frac{n_1}{n_2} = \sqrt{\frac{r_p}{20}} = \sqrt{\frac{760}{20}} = 6.15$$

In the case of large transformers, the error introduced by neglecting the resistance of the transformer windings is negligible; but in the case of a transformer designed for 5 watts, the equivalent resistance of the transformer windings referred to the primary might be anywhere from 250 to 1,000 ohms. This resistance should be added to r_p when solving for the turns ratio. Assuming that the equivalent resistance is 750 ohms, then

$$\frac{n_1}{n_2} = \sqrt{\frac{760 + 750}{20}} = 8.7$$

The matching of impedances for maximum power is not critical, and turns ratios of 8, 9, or 10 would be satisfactory for this case. Assuming that the transformer actually used has a ratio of 9 and an equivalent resistance of 750 ohms, then $R_1 = 9^2 \times 20 + 750 = 2,370$ ohms, and this is the a-c resistance presented to E_1 by the transformer and load combined. The d-c resistance presented to E_1 is simply the d-c resistance of the primary winding, and is completely independent of what may be connected to the secondary. Assuming that the d-c resistance of the primary is 500 ohms, the IR drop in the primary in the quiescent state is $0.060 \times 500 = 30$ volts, and the voltage of the plate battery must be 280 volts in order to have the assumed 250 volts on the plate. The equation of the static, or d-c, load line is $e_b = E_{bb} - 500i_b = 280 - 500i_b$. This line is the dotted line ab in Fig. 455. The dynamic, or a-c, load line for the transformer and load passes through the same quiescent point but has a slope of 2,370 ohms instead of 500 ohms, since the a-c resistance $R_1 = 2,370$ ohms. The equation of the dynamic load line is $e_b = K - 2,370i_b$, where K is determined by the fact that this load line must pass through the quiescent point, at which point $e_b = 250$ volts and $i_b = 0.060$ amp. Therefore $K = 250 + 2,370 \times 0.060 = 392$. The dynamic load line is the line cd in Fig. 455. Since the grid voltage should never swing positive, the amplitude of its a-c component should not exceed 45 volts. With this applied grid voltage, the plate current i_b will pulsate between the limits of 120 ma and 10 ma, as may be read from the dynamic load line. Since the quiescent value of i_b is 60 ma, it follows that the positive peak of the a-c component of the plate current is $120 - 60 = 60$ ma, while the negative peak is

60 − 10 = 50 ma. Therefore there is some distortion. The distortion will be less if the a-c component of the grid voltage is reduced.

452. The Push-Pull Amplifier. To increase the power output of an amplifier, and to decrease the distortion, the final stage is often made "push-pull," as shown in Fig. 456. When there is no a-c input to be amplified the two grid potentials are equal, and so are the plate currents. No flux is produced in the output transformer because the magnetomotive forces of the two d-c plate currents are in opposition. Now when the alternating current to be amplified is applied to the input terminals, alternating grid voltages E_{g1} and E_{g2} are produced in the two halves of the secondary of the input transformer. E_{g1} and E_{g2} are equal in magnitude but 180° out of phase. Therefore the resulting alternating-current components of plate current I_{p1} and I_{p2} are equal and 180° out of phase. Since they are 180° out of phase, their mmfs add in the primary of the output transformer, and therefore the output is twice as powerful as if only one tube had been used. There is no alternating current through the

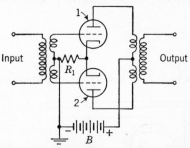

FIG. 456. Push-pull amplifier. R_1 is the grid-bias resistor.

battery B if the tubes are perfectly balanced, because then the vector sum of I_{p1} and I_{p2} is zero. The d-c component of plate current flowing through R_1 provides the proper grid bias.

One important advantage of the push-pull amplifier is that, when a d-c power supply from a rectifier is substituted for the battery B, the ripple on the voltage is not reproduced in the output, as it would be if only one tube were used; or if it is reproduced it is very feeble, being due only to the unbalance of the tubes or transformer.

453. Classification of Amplifiers. Amplifiers are generally classified according to the amount of negative grid bias applied to the tubes, as follows:

Class A. Those in which the plate carries current throughout the entire cycle of the a-c input to the grid. All the amplifiers described in this book are Class A. They have high fidelity and low efficiency.

Class B. Those in which the grid is biased to cutoff in the quiescent state so that when operated push-pull only one tube carries current at a time. This method of operation greatly reduces the power wasted as heat at the plates but results in lower fidelity.

Class C. Those in which the grid is biased beyond cutoff so that the plate carries current considerably less than half the time. This type of amplifier is used only for shock excitation of oscillating circuits.

454. The Thermionic-tube Oscillator. Since the a-c power output of an amplifier is very much greater than the a-c power input, it should be possible to obtain the required input from the output and thus have the amplifier act as an a-c generator. Figure 457 shows one method of obtaining this result. An alternating emf impressed between the grid and the cathode causes an alternating current to be superimposed upon the plate current flowing through the coil L, and the alternating current in coil L induces an alternating emf in coil A by mutual induction, and this emf is impressed on the grid.

Now the coil L and the condenser C together constitute an oscillating circuit, whose natural period of oscillation is given by the equation

$$f = \frac{1}{2\pi \sqrt{LC}} \qquad \text{(Art. 269)}$$

where L = inductance in henrys and C = capacitance in farads. And if

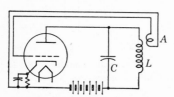

FIG. 457. Thermionic-tube oscillator.

an oscillation is once started in this circuit, it will be assisted by the tube, owing to the mutual induction between L and A, and the oscillations will increase to an amplitude that is limited only by the characteristics of the tube.

There is no difficulty about getting the oscillations started. In fact, it is usually impossible to switch on the filament current without disturbing the circuit sufficiently to start the oscillations.

Power may be abstracted from the oscillating circuit by connecting the load directly across the capacitor of the oscillating circuit, or by placing a third coil close to coil L and obtaining the power from coil L by mutual induction, or by incorporating the load as part of the oscillating circuit. If it is desired that the frequency shall be independent of the load, the oscillator is coupled to the load through a power amplifier. The frequency may be varied over a wide range by varying either L or C or both.

Thermionic-tube oscillators are used extensively in the communication field. They provide the a-c power for carrier telephony and telegraphy, and with the required modulation of their output serve as radio transmitters. They are also used to provide high-frequency power for the induction heating of conductor materials and for the dielectric heating of nonconducting materials.

The term generator is often used in referring to a thermionic-tube oscillator, but strictly speaking it is a converter rather than a generator. It converts direct current into alternating current, the plate battery supplying the direct current. In many cases the plate current is obtained from a rectifier which in turn obtains its power from an a-c line, in which case the combination of rectifier and oscillator is functioning as a frequency changer.

455. Stabilized Amplifiers; Negative Feedback. Unless the component parts of an amplifier are carefully shielded from one another, there will be a certain amount of feedback of voltage to the grids of preceding tubes by electric or magnetic induction. If this feedback opposes the a-c input, it is said to be negative; if it assists the a-c input, it is said to be positive. If positive, it may cause the amplifier to become an oscillator. To prevent this, amplifiers are often provided with a definite amount of negative feedback. The positive feedback of the oscillator in Fig. 457 may be changed to negative feedback by simply interchanging leads to coil A.

In Fig. 450, if the shunting capacitor C_1 is removed, the grid-bias resistor will carry the a-c component of plate current as well as the d-c component, and the $i_p R$ drop in the grid-bias resistor will be superimposed on the grid voltage. The phase relationship is such that this constitutes a negative feedback. If this feedback is excessive, it may be reduced by shunting a capacitor across a portion of the resistor. The negative feedback not only prevents spontaneous oscillations but also results in a very constant amount of amplification. These advantages are obtained at the expense of a substantial reduction in the amplification, with the result that when negative feedback is added to an amplifier it is generally necessary to add another stage of voltage amplification.

456. Tetrodes and Pentodes. Referring to Figs. 448 and 449, it is evident that as the potential of the grid is increased, the plate current increases, thus increasing the voltage drop in R_L, and consequently reducing the plate voltage. Conversely, when the grid voltage falls, the plate voltage rises. In other words the a-c component of plate voltage resulting from the presence of R_L in the circuit is 180° out of phase with the a-c component of grid voltage, and therefore opposes and reduces the effect that the a-c grid voltage has on the plate current. In fact, if the amplitude of e_p were equal to the amplitude of μe_g, there would be no change in the plate current. Of course e_p can never be quite so large as μe_g. It seems clear, however, that if some way can be found to prevent the pulsations in plate voltage from having any appreciable effect on the plate current the amplification factor will be greatly increased. This is readily accomplished by inserting another grid, called a screen grid, between the plate and the control grid, as indicated in Fig. 458. The potential of the screen grid is held constant so that the potential gradient between the cathode and the screen grid is almost independent of the plate voltage. It is then found that over a wide range of plate voltages the plate current is nearly independent of the plate voltage, and the amplification factor is much higher than before the introduction of the screen grid.

Since the screen grid is positive, it draws current; but it has an open mesh, and since the electrons approach it at high speed, most of them shoot through the open spaces and arrive at the plate. The plate current is normally about four times the screen-grid current.

In a tetrode the a-c component of the plate voltage is limited by the fact that the plate potential must not drop below that of the screen grid.

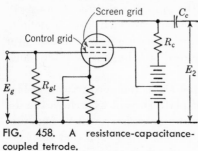

FIG. 458. A resistance-capacitance-coupled tetrode.

It has been found that as the plate potential decreases below that of the screen grid, the screen-grid current rises rapidly, while the plate current falls correspondingly. This is due to "secondary emission" of electrons at the plate. The electrons arrive at the plate with high velocity and this bombardment knocks many electrons out of the plate. Normally these dislodged electrons are drawn back into the plate and thus do not affect the magnitude of the plate current, but when the potential of the screen grid is higher than that of the plate, many of them are sucked in by the screen grid. In order to prevent the screen grid from collecting the electrons of secondary emission, a third grid, known as the suppressor grid, may be inserted between the screen grid and the plate, as shown in Fig. 459. The suppressor grid is usually kept at the same potential as the cathode. It acts as a screen to protect the electrons of secondary emission from the attraction of the screen grid. A tube that is provided with three grids, one plate, and one hot cathode is called a *pentode*. In a pentode the plate potential may be allowed to swing down to as low as one-half that of the screen grid without causing any substantial drop in the plate current.

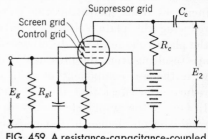

FIG. 459. A resistance-capacitance-coupled pentode.

Pentodes are used in preference to triodes for the voltage-amplification stages of the great majority of amplifiers. Figure 460 shows the plate characteristics for a pentode designed for voltage amplification. A typical quiescent point would be $E_b = 250$ volts, $E_c = -3$ volts, $I_b = 2$ ma. The analysis is the same as for the triode, but the values of r_p and μ are much larger. For example, raising the plate voltage from 100 to 500 volts increases the plate current by only about 0.1 ma, which corresponds to a plate resistance of

$$r_p = \frac{de_b}{di_b} = \frac{500 - 100}{0.0001} = 4 \text{ megohms}$$

Raising the grid voltage from -3 to -2.5 volts increases the plate current by 0.8 ma, so that the mutual conductance is

$$g_m = \frac{di_b}{de_c} = \frac{0.0008}{0.5} = 0.0016$$

Combining the two changes to obtain the amplification factor

$$\mu = \frac{di_b/de_c}{di_b/de_b} = \frac{0.0008/0.5}{0.0001/400} = 6{,}400$$

In the case of pentodes the determination of μ and r_p from the plate characteristics is inherently inaccurate, because the curve of I_b is so nearly horizontal that the slightest error in determining its slope will cause a large error in the determination of both μ and r_p. Therefore in calculating the voltage amplification of a resistance-capacitance-coupled amplifier that uses pentodes, Eq. (119) should be rearranged so as to eliminate μ. From Eq. (118), $\mu = g_m r_p$. Substituting in Eq. (119),

$$\frac{E_2}{E_g} = \frac{g_m r_p R}{R + r_p} = \frac{g_m R}{(R/r_p) + 1} \tag{121}$$

For example, if R_c is equal to 125,000 ohms and R_g of the next stage is equal to 500,000 ohms, then

$$R = \frac{125{,}000 \times 500{,}000}{625{,}000} = 100{,}000 \text{ ohms}$$

and

$$\frac{R}{r_p} = \frac{100{,}000}{4{,}000{,}000} = 0.025$$

Therefore   Voltage amplification $= \dfrac{0.0016 \times 100{,}000}{1.025} = 156$

The amplification may also be obtained by drawing the dynamic load line through the chosen quiescent point on Fig. 460. The static load resistance is $R_c = 125{,}000$ ohms. The dynamic load resistance is $R = 100{,}000$ ohms. The line cd is the dynamic load line for $R = 100{,}000$ ohms. This line intersects the I_b curve for $E_c = -2$ at $E_b = 100$ volts, and intersects the I_b curve for $E_c = -4$ volts at $E_b = 370$ volts. Therefore

$$\text{Voltage amplification} = \frac{370 - 100}{2} = 135$$

The reason why the load-line method did not check more closely with Eq. (121) is that Eq. (121) is precise only over a range of values of grid voltage for which g_m may be assumed to remain constant at its quiescent-point value. The fact that the two methods did not check indicates that there is some distortion when the amplitude of e_g is 1 volt.

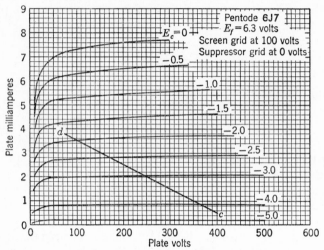

FIG. 460. Plate characteristics of a pentode.

457. Power Supply for Amplifiers and Oscillators.   In all the illustrations of thermionic-tube operation given so far the plate-voltage supply has been shown as a battery, for the sake of simplicity.   In practice, however, the required direct current is generally obtained from the usual a-c supply by means of full-wave rectification, as shown in Fig. 417.   It is necessary, however, to provide a substantial filter of capacitors and inductances in order to smooth out the pulsations.   A typical filter for this purpose is shown in Fig. 461. There is nothing critical in the design of such a filter. The larger the capacitors and inductances the smoother the direct current, but the more expensive the filter. There is no point in making the direct current any smoother than is required by the particular application under consideration.

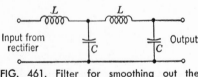

FIG. 461. Filter for smoothing out the pulsations in the d-c output of a rectifier.

458. Thyratron.   A thyratron is a hot-cathode triode or tetrode that contains an appreciable amount of gas or mercury vapor.   Whenever an anode current is flowing, gas molecules are being ionized by collision with the electrons coming from the cathode, and the presence of the positive ions so formed profoundly affects the operation of the tube.   The positive ions, in traveling toward the cathode, mingle with and largely neutralize the negative space charge of electrons that surrounds the cathode, with the result that even a small anode voltage can produce a large anode current. The presence of the positive ions also profoundly affects the ability of the grid to control the anode current.

Consider the case of a thyratron biased to cutoff by a negative grid voltage of sufficient magnitude to prevent any anode current from flowing. There will be no positive ions present and no grid current. Now let the grid voltage be gradually made less negative. At first the anode current is very small and only a few positive ions are produced. These positive ions are attracted to the negative grid, with the result that there is a small grid current. This grid current is said to be negative because it is in the opposite direction to the grid current that flows when the grid is positive. The presence of a measurable negative grid current indicates that there is gas in the tube. As the grid voltage is gradually made less negative, the anode current increases until at a certain critical grid voltage the tube suddenly fires. That is, an arc is formed in the tube and the anode current suddenly jumps to a value that is limited only by the external resistance in the anode circuit. If now an attempt is made to shut off the anode current by reapplying a negative potential to the grid, it will be found that the grid has completely lost control of the anode current, which continues to flow until the voltage is removed from the anode by some external means. The reason why the anode current cannot be shut off by applying a negative voltage to the grid is that the grid is then immediately surrounded by a cloud of positive ions that neutralize its effect in the same way that they neutralize the negative space charge around the cathode. All that the grid can do therefore is to "trigger off" an arc discharge through the tube.

The critical grid voltage, which if exceeded will permit the tube to fire, varies with the anode voltage, as shown in Fig. 462. In the case of a mercury-vapor thyratron it also varies with the temperature, because there is a small amount of liquid mercury present in the tube and therefore the vapor pressure varies rapidly with the temperature. In Fig. 462 the tube will fire with any combination of grid voltage and anode voltage that lies to the right of the curve, and will not fire for any combination that lies to the left of the curve. The temperatures shown are the temperatures of the mercury in the tube.

The thyratron has two main fields of application: (1) as an electric switch; (2) as a grid-controlled rectifier. When used as an electric switch, the circuit is open from the anode to the cathode as long as the grid is held sufficiently negative. When it is desired to close the circuit, the grid voltage is raised above the critical value and the tube fires. The thyratron switch has two great advantages over other switches: (1) It is electrically operated and requires only a minute amount of energy to close it.   (2) It closes much more rapidly than any switch with moving parts possibly could.   The main disadvantage of a thyratron switch is that it cannot open the circuit.   It can only close it.   A minor disadvantage is that when conducting it has a voltage drop across it of the order of 10 to 20 volts, which of course involves a waste of power.   A single thyratron cannot be used to pass an alternating current because it is conducting in one direction only.   It will pass only the positive half waves.   A second thyratron connected in parallel with the first but with opposite polarity may be used to pass the negative half waves.

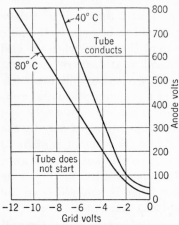

FIG. 462. Starting characteristics of a mercury-vapor thyratron.

One of the many switching applications of the thyratron is to act as a relay in conjunction with photoelectric cells.   The current from a photoelectric cell is too small to actuate most devices, but it can be used to raise the grid voltage of a thyratron and thus to trigger off as large an anode current as is desired.   The anode current is used to operate the device that the photoelectric cell is intended to control; and if the anode supply is direct current, the operation of the device must in turn remove the anode voltage from the thyratron momentarily in order that the ionization may disappear and permit the grid to regain control so as to be ready for the next operation.   The time required for deionization varies from about 10 to 1,000 μsec.

If thyratrons are substituted for the diodes in the rectifier circuit of Fig. 417, the average value of the output d-c voltage can be reduced by utilizing the grids to delay the striking of the arcs.   This is usually accomplished by applying a-c voltages to the grids as well as to the anodes and employing a phase-shifting device to retard the phase of the grid voltages by an adjustable amount.   In this way the average value of the d-c voltage output can be varied all the way down to zero.   Figure 463 shows a typical arrangement, with two thyratrons functioning as a full-wave rectifier and supplying an adjustable d-c output to the load, which in this illustration is the resistance R.   The resistances R_1 and R_2 merely serve to protect the grids against excessive currents after the tubes have fired.   The grid voltage of each tube is made up of a d-c component and an a-c component.   The a-c component is of constant amplitude and phase angle, and due to the rC phase-shifting device lags

90° behind the anode voltage. The d-c component is adjustable from $+E_{cc}$ to $-E_{cc}$ by moving the slider S from A to B. The resultant grid voltages are shown in Fig. 464a, for three positions of slider S. Each tube fires at the instant when its curve of rising grid voltage crosses the critical-grid-voltage curve. Figure 464b illustrates the case of maximum d-c output. The voltage e_R across the load is less than the voltage e_1 or e_2 from the transformer by the amount of the voltage drop in the tube.

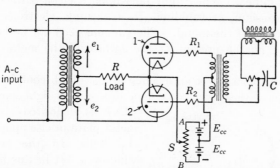

FIG. 463. Single-phase full-wave rectifier using two grid-controlled thyratrons to provide adjustable d-c power to the load R.

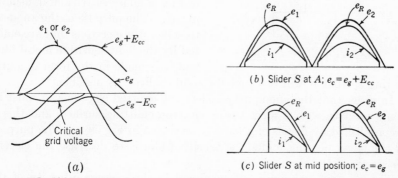

FIG. 464. Voltages and currents in the grid-controlled rectifier of Fig. 463.

In Fig. 464c the d-c output has been decreased about 33 per cent by decreasing the d-c component of grid voltage to zero.

If the armature of a separately excited d-c motor is substituted for the load resistance R in Fig. 463, the manipulation of slider S will provide a speed control that is comparable with that provided by the Ward Leonard system, except that there is no regenerative braking. In practice, dynamic braking is obtained by connecting a resistance across the brushes of the motor whenever the slider hits point B, so that the motor momentarily becomes a generator. The shapes of the current curves in Fig. 464b and c will be somewhat affected by the self-inductance of the armature, but the net result is the same.   The torque is produced in pulses which are averaged by the moment of inertia of the armature.   As the size of the motor is increased, a point is soon reached at which it is more economical to substitute ignitrons for the thyratrons, in which case it is the time of ignition that is varied instead of the grid voltage.   Further increases in power rating will cause a change from single-phase to three-phase, and then from three-phase to six-phase.

459. Phototubes.   When light falls upon a clean surface of sodium, potassium, caesium, or rubidium, in a vacuum, electrons are emitted from the surface of the metal.   The vacuum need not be very high but oxygen must not be present or the surface of the metal will become oxidized.

A phototube consists of an evacuated glass bulb containing two electrodes.   One of these electrodes is a thin film of light-sensitive metal, which is deposited either upon a metal plate or else upon the walls of the bulb.   In the latter case a window is left in this film to admit the light (see Fig. 465).   The other electrode, called the anode, is a grid or ring of nonsensitive metal, usually nickel.   The purpose of the anode is to collect the electrons that are emitted by the light-sensitive metal film, and it is made in the form of a grid

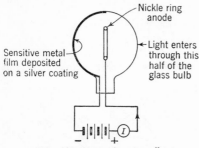

FIG. 465. Photoelectric cell.

or ring so that it will obstruct the light as little as possible.

In order that the anode may collect the emitted electrons, it must be made positive with respect to the electron-emitting surface, and this is accomplished by means of a battery as shown in Fig. 465.   The purpose of the silver coating under the sensitive film is to decrease the electric resistance of the circuit.

The electron emission is proportional to the average intensity of the illumination falling on the light-sensitive material, but varies widely with the wavelength.   Most of the light-sensitive materials respond more actively to ultraviolet light than to visible light, and some respond quite actively to infrared radiation.   A potential difference of 50 volts between the two electrodes is generally sufficient to enable the anode to collect all the emitted electrons, and any further increase in the anode voltage will not increase the current.

The electron emission from standard types of phototubes rarely exceeds $20\mu a$, except in the case of the sodium phototube, which gives up to $50\mu a$. These currents are too small to operate the usual type of relay and therefore an amplifier is generally associated with the phototube.

Figure 466 shows an arrangement in which a phototube, aided by a triode, controls the operation of a relay. The triode serves not only as an amplifier but also as a rectifier, thus making it possible to operate directly from the usual a-c supply without the complication of providing direct current. As long as no light strikes the phototube, it is nonconducting, and the grid-bias potentiometer causes the grid of the triode to swing negative each cycle as the plate swings positive, and therefore the triode also is nonconducting. Whenever light strikes the phototube, it becomes conducting, with the result that the plate and grid of the triode swing positive together. Therefore the triode acts as a half-wave rectifier, and the rectified current operates the relay, the capacitor C_r smoothing out the pulsations to some extent. The phototube also acts as a half-wave rectifier but its contribution to the relay current is negligible. If the relay is a heavy one, a gas-filled triode (thyratron) is used.

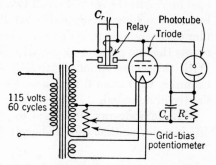

FIG. 466. Phototube controlling the operation of a relay.

The positive potential that the phototube superimposes on the grid of the triode is equal to IR_c, where I is the current through the phototube. Since I is only a few microamperes, R_c must be quite large, at least 1 megohm.

The phototube is rapidly taking the place of the human eye in a great variety of mechanical operations. Suppose, for example, that it is required to count the number of cans passing along on a belt conveyer in a canning factory. A phototube is placed on one side of the belt and a beam of light is focused upon it from the other side of the belt. Each can as it passes intercepts the beam of light and causes a substantial decrease in the current through the tube. The current pulses are used to actuate a counter. Counting is the simplest application of the phototube. It is also used extensively for timing operations where it is not feasible to provide a geared connection between successive operations so as to ensure synchronism. Cutting-off shears are often timed by means of these tubes. A phototube can read, if the message is written in a simple code, such as Morse, and the sound reproduction in the moving-picture industry is controlled by phototubes which read the special code that has been prepared for them on the edge of the photographic film.

460. Other Light-sensitive Cells. When light falls upon a copper surface that is coated with cuprous oxide, a difference of potential is developed between the oxide and the copper. A very thin sputtering of gold over the oxide serves as a conductor, without interfering too much with the light. If the copper and the gold are connected to an external circuit, as though they were the electrodes of a battery, current will flow through the external circuit. Such a cell is called a *photovoltaic cell*. Commercial cells of this type yield currents up to several hundred microamperes, and are used in illumination meters and in some control devices. They have the advantage of requiring no external source of emf. Moreover, they are light and compact. There are various other combinations of materials that exhibit the photovoltaic effect.

When light falls upon selenium, its electric resistance decreases. Since selenium is practically opaque, the action is restricted to a thin surface film. In the selenium cell two fine bare copper wires, close together but not touching, are wound in parallel to form a single-layer coil. A thin film of selenium is then deposited on the coil, in a vacuum, thus bridging across the two parallel copper wires. The coil is enclosed in a glass tube. With this construction the resistance between the two wires may, for example, vary from 6 megohms when dark to 0.75 megohms when brilliantly illuminated.

461. Cathode-ray Oscilloscope. The cathode-ray tube shown in Fig. 467 is a device that uses a sharply focused electron beam as a pencil to

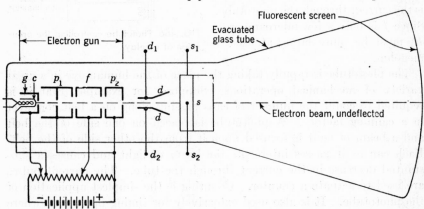

FIG. 467. Cathode-ray-tube oscilloscope: c, indirectly heated cathode; g, grid to control intensity of beam; p_1p_2, accelerating electrodes; f, focusing electrode; dd, vertical deflection plates; ss, horizontal, or sweep, deflection plates.

draw a graph of voltage on a fluorescent screen. The graph fades very quickly, but it may be photographed before it fades, or it may be rendered continuously visible by arranging to have the tube redraw the graph as many times per second as is convenient. The part of the tube that produces the electron beam is called the electron gun, the parts of which are identified in Fig. 467. In order to obtain a fine beam, it is necessary to pass it through three small apertures in succession, although this means wasting most of the electrons produced by the hot cathode. A detailed analysis of the operation of the focusing electrode f is too long and involved to be given in a book of this kind.

The voltage whose graph is to be drawn is applied to the terminals $d_1 d_2$. When d_1 is positive, the beam is deflected vertically upward; and when d_1 is negative, the beam is deflected vertically downward, the magnitude of the deflection being proportional to the instantaneous value of the voltage across $d_1 d_2$. If the ss plates were not energized, the beam would draw a vertical line on the fluorescent screen. In order to make the graph readable, it is necessary to give the beam a horizontal travel in addition to its vertical travel. This is accomplished by providing a second pair of deflecting plates ss identical with plates dd but turned through 90°. It is highly desirable that the horizontal travel should be at constant velocity so that the time scale will be linear. This can be accomplished with this particular type of tube only by applying to the terminals $s_1 s_2$ a voltage that rises at a uniform rate. Moreover, when the beam has reached the edge of the screen, this voltage should be reduced instantly to zero, so that the beam will snap back and be ready to repeat the drawing. Figure 469 shows the graph of a voltage intended for use on the ss plates of an oscilloscope. In order to center the picture on the fluorescent screen, it is necessary either to remove the d-c component of the saw-tooth voltage of Fig. 469 or else to neutralize it. It may be removed by inserting a transformer between the terminals $s_1 s_2$ and the source of the saw-tooth voltage. One method of producing the saw-tooth voltage is described in Art. 462.

In order that the successive pictures may be accurately superimposed one upon another, it is necessary that the frequency of the saw-tooth sweep voltage must either be exactly equal to the frequency of the voltage whose graph is to be drawn or else be an exact submultiple of it. Most oscilloscopes are provided with a coupling device that tends to keep the sweep circuit in synchronism with the voltage being measured once it has been adjusted.

In Fig. 467 the accelerating electrode potentials are obtained from a battery, but in practice they are generally obtained from the filtered and regulated output of a rectifier. The accelerating voltage required ranges from about 300 to 10,000 volts, depending on the nature of the graph to be obtained. Single high-speed transients require a high accelerating voltage in order to produce a graph that is vivid enough to be photographed.

The deflection sensitivity of the cathode-ray tube is relatively low, and therefore it is generally necessary to insert a voltage amplifier between the deflecting-plate terminals $d_1 d_2$ and the source of the voltage to be measured.

The oscillograph described in Art. 236 is limited to low frequencies by the mass of its moving parts. The frequency range of the cathode-ray oscilloscope is limited only by the frequency range of the amplifier associated with it, and this frequency range may be made very high by careful design.

462. Basic Electronic Timing Circuit. Figure 468 shows a circuit that, with various modifications, is widely used in electronic control. The basic idea is that the capacitor C is charged at a controlled rate through the resistor R. As the charge accumulates, the voltage across the capacitor rises, until the gas-filled cold-cathode tube breaks down, thus practically shorting the capacitor, which therefore discharges almost completely in a few microseconds. As the discharge nears completion, the current through the tube drops to such a low value that the arc extinguishes itself, whereupon the capacitor begins to charge again, and the cycle is repeated. The number

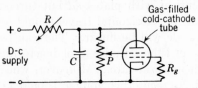

FIG. 468. Basic electronic timing circuit.

of cycles per minute can be varied over wide limits by varying R and C, while the setting of the potential-dividing grid resistor P determines the voltage at which the tube will break down.

The particular tube shown has two grids. The arc is initiated between them and then transfers to the plate and cathode. The circuit will work, however, with only one grid, or with no grid, although in the latter case the breakdown voltage will not be under control. Three typical applications of this circuit will now be given.

a. Stroboscope. The discharge of the capacitor through the tube causes the tube to emit a bright flash of light of only a few microseconds duration. These flashes come at regular intervals, which can be adjusted by means of R and C. A rotating object illuminated by such a light can be made to appear stationary by a proper adjustment of the flash frequency, or it can be made to appear to rotate slowly so that its motion can be studied. The setting of R can be calibrated to read in cycles per second, and then the stroboscope will measure speeds accurately and quickly.

b. Sweep Circuit for a Cathode-ray Oscilloscope. In Fig. 468 the voltage across the capacitor rises slowly and then drops back to zero almost instantaneously, as shown in Fig. 469. If this voltage is applied to the plates that control the horizontal travel of the spot on the fluorescent screen of an oscilloscope, and if the frequency of the timer cycle is adjusted to be equal to that of the emf to be shown on the screen, the timer will spread one cycle of the emf on the screen, and will then snap the spot back and be ready to spread the next cycle exactly over the preceding one, so that the graph appears to be continuous and motionless. In order not to distort the picture on the screen, the horizontal speed of the spot should be constant while spreading the graph on the screen. To accomplish this, the graph of capacitor voltage on a time base must be a straight line. If the gas-filled tube is set to break down at about one-third of the d-c supply voltage, as in Fig. 469, the deviation from a straight line, over the working range, is scarcely noticeable. More complicated circuits are available in which there is no measurable deviation from a straight line

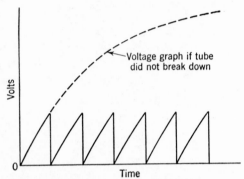

FIG. 469. Graph of capacitor voltage in the circuit of Fig. 468 when operated as the sweep circuit for a cathode-ray oscilloscope.

c. Spot-welding Timer. Spot welding is carried out at high speed by sending a large current through the contact surfaces for a short time. The time is critical. Too short a time results in a weak weld, while too long a time melts the material and ruins the work. The current is switched on by the operator, and this switching operation also applies the voltage to the electronic timer. A relay coil is inserted in the plate circuit of the gas tube, and when this tube breaks down the relay operates and trips a circuit breaker that interrupts the welding current. Electronic timers are also used in many other industrial operations.

Problems

41-1. From Fig. 446 determine the amplification factor, plate resistance, and mutual conductance of the tube at the quiescent point $E_b = 150$ volts, $E_c = -4$ volts, and check with the values obtained from Fig. 447 for the same quiescent point.

41-2. Calculate the voltage amplification at 1,000 cycles per sec and at 5 cycles per sec of one stage of a resistance-capacitance-coupled amplifier (Fig. 450) using a 6J5 triode operating with its quiescent point at $E_b = 150$ volts, $E_c = -4$ volts, and with $R_c = 100,000$ ohms, $R_g = 500,000$ ohms, $C_c = 0.05$ µf.

41-3. Calculate the voltage amplification of one stage of a resistance-capacitance-coupled amplifier (Fig. 450) using a 6J7 pentode operating with its quiescent point at $E_b = 200$ volts, $E_c = -3$ volts, and with $R_c = 250,000$ ohms, $R_g = 1$

megohm, assuming that C_c is large enough so that the voltage drop across it may be ignored.

41-4. The load impedance to be coupled to the output stage of a power amplifier is practically a pure resistance of 12 ohms. If a 2A3 power triode is used, with its quiescent point at $E_b = 200$ volts, $E_c = -30$ volts, determine the ideal transformer ratio for the coupling, assuming that the equivalent resistance of the transformer is 1,000 ohms referred to the primary side. Assuming that this ratio is actually used, draw the dynamic load line and determine the power output to the load when the a-c volts input to the grid of the power triode is a pure sine wave of peak value equal to 30 volts.

42

LABORATORY EXPERIMENTS

Control of the Current in a Circuit. In general, the simplest way to vary the current in a d-c circuit is to insert a variable resistance in series with the circuit, as in Fig. 470a. If the resistance R_c of the circuit C is large compared with that of the rheostat R, the current variation obtainable by this method will be small. In that case the potentiometer connection of Fig. 470b may be much more effective. If the sliding contact a is placed at b, then the voltage E_1 is equal to the line voltage E, and $I = E/R_c$. If contact a is placed at c, then $E_1 = 0$ and therefore $I = 0$. By moving the contact between these two points, any value of current from zero to $I = E/R_c$ may be obtained. In all cases care must be taken to see that the rheostat R is able to carry the current that will flow through it, without overheating. In particular, if the resistance R_c is small and the contact a is

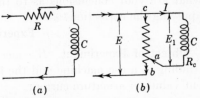

FIG. 470. Methods of controlling the current in a circuit.

moved close to b, as shown in Fig. 470b, then as contact a approaches b, the current I approaches the value E/R_c, which in many cases will be large enough to burn out the section of the rheostat between a and b. In commercial work, a fuse would be used to protect against this hazard. In experimental work, it is probably more common to rely on the watchfulness of the experimenter.

Alternating current may be controlled in the same way as direct current, but in the case of Fig. 470a a variable inductance is often substituted for the variable resistance R. This substitution reduces the power loss and also in general provides a smoother control with less maintenance.

Experiment 1

Object of Experiment. To measure a high and a low resistance by the voltmeter-ammeter method, and to investigate the magnitude of the error that results from assuming that the resistance is equal to the voltmeter reading divided by the ammeter reading.

Reference.   Article 48.

Connections.   Current control as in Fig. 470, and meter connections as in Figs. 26 and 27.

Readings.   Read the volts and the amperes for both the high and the low resistances, with the meters connected (1) as in Fig. 26 and (2) as in Fig. 27, for each resistance.   Check each measurement, using a different current.

Report.   Correct the ammeter readings of Fig. 26 for the current through the voltmeter, and the voltmeter readings of Fig. 27 for the IR drop in the ammeter.   The necessary data for the meters can usually be obtained from the manufacturer's catalogue.   If not, assume 10 ma at full scale for the voltmeter and 50 mv at full scale for the ammeter. From the corrected meter readings calculate the true value of the resistances, and also calculate the per cent error, in each of the four measurements, resulting from assuming that the resistance is equal to the voltmeter reading divided by the ammeter reading.

Question.   Assuming that the meters are accurate to one-half of 1 per cent and that the meter connection that gives minimum error is used, what are your conclusions as to the need for calculating the error and applying the correction?

Experiment 2

Object of Experiment.   To measure the resistance of the armature winding of a d-c machine and the brush-contact voltage drop for different values of armature current.

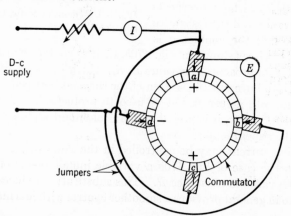

FIG. 471. Connections for measuring the resistance of the armature of a d-c machine.

Connections.   As in Fig. 471, which assumes that the machine is four-pole.   The circular jumpers are a permanent part of the machine.   The voltmeter leads should terminate in copper spikes with insulated handles. When measuring the resistance of the armature winding, the tips of the spikes should be held firmly in contact with the proper commutator bars while the voltmeter is being read. When including the brush-contact drop, the spikes should be held against the brush holders in such a way as not to alter the pressure of the brush on the commutator.

Readings. Since the temperature coefficient of resistance of copper is fairly high, a measurement of the resistance of the armature winding does not mean very much unless the temperature can be stated with reasonable accuracy. If the machine has been standing idle for several hours, it can be assumed to be at room temperature. And if the current used in making the measurement is never left on for more than 3 or 4 sec at a time—just long enough to read the meters—the rise in temperature should not be sufficient to cause a serious error.

If the armature winding is multiple, there are four paths in parallel through the winding; and if the four brushes do not make equally good contact, the current will not divide equally among the four paths, and the four voltages, a to b, a to d, b to c, and d to c, will not all be equal. To guard against this possibility, all four voltages should be measured for at least one value of current. If they are found to be equal, only one of these voltages need be measured for the other values of current. The following readings should be taken: (1) amperes, various values up to full load; (2) volts across the brushes; (3) volts across the commutator; (4) probable temperature.

Report. (1) Plot armature resistance against current. (2) Plot brush-contact voltage drop against current. Describe briefly the way in which the experiment was carried out, and answer the following questions:

1. What percentage of the output of the machine are the armature resistance loss and the brush-contact resistance loss at full load?

2. Has the pressure on the brushes much effect on the brush-contact resistance? Try the experiment. What do you imagine limits the brush pressure?

3. What range of instruments would you use to determine the resistance of the armature circuit of a 50-kw 240-volt generator if the loss in the complete armature circuit is known to be less than 4 per cent at full load?

Experiment 3

Object of Experiment. To find how the speed of a d-c shunt motor at no load varies with:

1. The exciting current, armature voltage being constant.
2. The armature voltage, exciting current being constant.

References. Articles 131, 138, and 139.

Connections. See Fig. 472.

Readings. Exciting current, armature voltage, and speed.

Curves. (1) Speed and exciting current. (2) Speed and armature voltage.

Questions. 1. Explain the shape of the curves, without formulas.

2. What would happen if, in starting up a shunt motor, a starting resistance were not placed in series with the armature circuit? How many times full-load current would flow through the armature under these conditions?

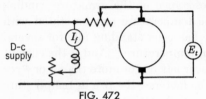

FIG. 472

3. What is the back emf of a motor and what relation has it to the applied emf?

4. What would happen if, during operation, the field-coil circuit were to open? (Do not perform this experiment.)

5. Draw a diagram of connections of any starter in the laboratory which has a no-voltage release.

Experiment 4

Object of Experiment. To find how the voltage of a d-c generator at no load varies with:

1. The exciting current, speed being constant.

2. The speed, exciting current being constant.

Reference. Article 119.

Connections. See Fig. 94, page 127.

Readings. Voltage, exciting current, and speed.

Curves. (1) Voltage and exciting current. (2) Voltage and speed.

Questions. 1. Why is there a small voltage even with no exciting current?

2. Explain the shape of the curves.

3. How would you reverse the polarity of the generator, that is, how reverse the direction of the voltage?

Experiment 5

Object of Experiment. To determine how the terminal voltage of a constant-speed generator varies with the load:

1. The generator being separately excited, I_f constant.

2. The generator being shunt excited, R_f constant.

3. The generator being compound excited.

References. Pages 127 to 132.

Connections. See Figs. 97, 98, and 99.

Readings. Terminal voltage, line current, exciting current, and speed.

Curves. (1) Terminal voltage on a line-current base. (2) Shunt-exciting current on a line-current base.

Questions. 1. Why does the terminal voltage of a separately excited generator decrease with increase of load? How much of the drop at full load is due to armature resistance?

2. Why is the voltage drop greater in a shunt than in a separately excited generator?

3. What would be the effect of shifting the brushes farther forward from the neutral position?

4. What is the principal advantage of the compound generator?

5. How would the terminal voltage of a compound generator vary with increase of load if the series-field coils were connected so as to oppose the shunt coils?

6. If the generator is overcompounded while flat compounding is desired, what can be done to fix the machine?

7. If the voltage of a shunt generator builds up when the generator rotates in a given direction, why will it not build up if the direction of rotation is reversed?

Experiment 6

Object of Experiment. To determine the efficiency and also the speed and torque characteristics of shunt, series, and compound motors, by loading the machines by means of a brake, the applied voltage being constant.

References. Chapters 18 and 20.

Connections. See Figs. 108, 113, and 117.

Readings. Applied voltage (constant), armature current, shunt-exciting current (constant), speed, brake reading.

Curves. Speed and torque on an armature-current base. Brake horsepower and total power input on an armature-current base. Efficiency on a brake-horsepower base.

Questions. 1. How would you reverse the direction of rotation of each machine?

2. For what type of service is each machine suited?

3. The field coils of a machine become hot during operation; what effect will this have on the no-load and on the full-load speed of each type of motor?

4. How can the speed of each type of motor be varied for a given load?

5. Why is the speed regulation of a shunt motor poor when the speed is controlled by a resistance in the armature circuit? Try the experiment.

6. Explain without formulas, the shapes of the speed, torque, and efficiency curves.

Experiment 7

Object of Experiment. To determine the relation between starting torque and armature current in a shunt, a series, and a compound motor.

Reference. Chapter 18.

Connections. Same as for Expt. 6, but with resistance in the armature circuit to limit the current. (Do not use a starting box for this purpose.)

Readings. Armature current and brake reading.

Curves. Torque on an armature-current base.

Questions. 1. How does the starting torque compare with the running torque, as determined in Expt. 6, for the same armature current? Does theory indicate that there should be a difference?

2. Why is the series motor preferred for heavy starting duty?

Experiment 8

Object of Experiment. To measure the mechanical and iron losses, the armature copper loss, and the excitation loss in a shunt motor, and to calculate the efficiency from these figures.

Reference. Chapter 19.

The work of this experiment should be done without instruction using either or both of the two methods described in Chap. 19. A diagram of connections should be drawn and the ranges of the necessary instruments determined before the apparatus is connected up.

Report. Describe the method of carrying out the experiment. Plot the efficiency curve on a horsepower-output base up to 25 per cent overload, and, if possible, compare this curve with that obtained by brake readings in Expt. 6; if the results show considerable difference, which would you consider to be the more reliable?

Experiment 9

Object of Experiment. To run a shunt generator in parallel with the power-supply generators, and to determine the temperature rise of the machine at full load.

References. Articles 42, 155, and 159.

Connections. See Fig. 153.

Readings. Measure the resistance of the field-coil circuit at the beginning of the test and every 10 min thereafter; take also readings of temperature of the field-coil surface at the same time. Apply thermometers to the armature core and armature winding immediately the generator is shut down. Watch them as long as the mercury continues to rise and record the highest reading attained. If it is a continuous rating that is being tested, the heat run should be continued until the temperatures are constant. If it is a short-time rating, the run should be continued for the period stated in the rating.

Curves. Observed temperature rise of field-coil surface, and also the temperature rise determined by resistance measurements, on a time base.

Questions. 1. Explain the shape of the curves.

2. Why is the temperature rise of the field coils as determined by resistance measurements greater than that determined by thermometer?

Experiment 10

Object of Experiment. To determine the voltage regulation of a three-wire system.

References. Articles 231, 232, and 233.

Connections. Use a balancer set (see Fig. 188) or a three-wire generator. If these are not available, a single-phase rotary converter with a suitable autotransformer may be connected up as shown in Fig. 473 to form a three-wire generator.

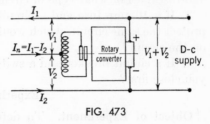

FIG. 473

Readings. Vary the loads on the two sides of the system from perfect balance, when $I_1 = I_2$ and I_n is zero, to a maximum of unbalance when the load on one side of the line is zero. Take readings of V_1, V_2, I_1, and I_2; $V_1 + V_2$ to be kept constant.

Curves. Plot V_1 and V_2 against the unbalanced current $I_1 - I_2$.

Questions. 1. Explain the action of the apparatus used.

2. What are the advantages of the three-wire over the two-wire system of distribution?

3. Explain the shapes of the curves.

Experiment 11

Object of Experiment. To determine the characteristics of fuse wire.

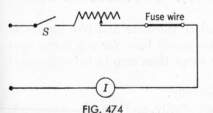

FIG. 474

Reference. Article 181.

Connections. See Fig. 474.

Readings. Length of wire between blocks, average current, time taken for fuse to melt after switch S is closed.

Curves. Plot amperes on a time base for four lengths of fuse wire and from these curves plot another set with amperes on a length base for a fusing time of 10 sec.

Questions. 1. Explain the shape of the curves.

2. If a fuse is rated at 5 amp, about what current would you expect it to carry continuously, and what current for 30 sec?

Experiment 12

Object of Experiment. To calibrate a circuit breaker.

Reference. Article 81.

Connections. Same as for fuse testing (Expt. 11).

Readings. Amperes to open, and position of plunger.

Curve. Draw a current scale that could be attached to the circuit breaker.

Questions. 1. Explain the construction and the operation of the circuit breaker used.

2. What are the advantages and disadvantages of circuit breakers and fuses? For what type of circuit is each suited?

3. If a 10-amp fuse and a circuit breaker set for 15 amp are used to protect the same circuit, which would open first in the case of an overload on the circuit?

4. If a circuit breaker and a switch are both in a circuit, which would you close first?

Experiment 13

Object of Experiment. To determine the effect of change of frequency on resistance, inductive reactance, and capacitive reactance, and

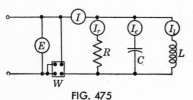

FIG. 475

to investigate the parallel operation of these three special types of load.

References. Articles 270 and 271.

Connections. As in Fig. 475.

Procedure. 1. With the frequency set at approximately the mid-point of the range available, adjust either L or C to make I_l and I_c approximately equal. Choose R to make I_r equal to or less than I_l and I_c.

2. Take a single set of readings of E, f, I_r, I_c, and I_l, and calculate R, C, and L.

3. Using these values of R, C, and L, calculate and plot curves of I_r, I_c, I_l, I, and power factor, on a frequency base, for any convenient fixed value of E, and for a frequency range from zero to twice resonant frequency.

4. Obtain the same curves experimentally.

5. When $I_l = I_c$, disconnect R momentarily, and note the magnitude of I.

Questions. 1. Explain any discrepancies between the experimental and the theoretical curves.

2. Why was I not equal to zero when I_c and I_l were equal and R was disconnected?

Experiment 14

Object of Experiment. To determine the effect of change of frequency on a circuit consisting of resistance, inductance, and capacitance in series.

Reference. Article 269.

Connections. See Fig. 476.

Procedure. 1. With the frequency set at approximately the midpoint of the range available and with E_t set at a low value, adjust either

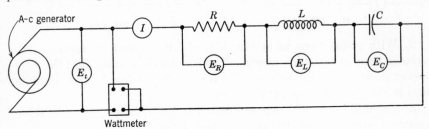

Wattmeter

FIG. 476

L or C until E_l and E_c are approximately equal. These voltages will rise rapidly as they approach equality. Take care that they do not become excessive. Choose R so that E_r is less than E_c and E_l at resonance.

2. Take a single set of readings of E_r, E_l, E_c, f, and I, and calculate R, L, and C.

3. Using these values of R, L, and C, calculate and plot curves of E_r, E_l, E_c, E_t, and power factor, on a frequency base, for any convenient fixed value of I, and for a frequency range from zero to twice resonant frequency.

4. Obtain the same curves experimentally.

Questions. 1. Explain any discrepancies between the experimental and the theoretical curves.

2. What would the voltages across the capacitor and the inductance have been at resonance if the resistance R had not been included in the circuit and the voltage E_t had been maintained at the rated voltage of the generator?

Experiment 15

Object of Experiment. To determine the efficiency and voltage regulation of a transformer.

References. Articles 306 to 314A.

Connections. Figure 477 for measuring (1) copper loss, (2) equivalent resistance, and (3) equivalent reactance. Figure 478 for measuring iron loss.

Procedure. 1. With the low-voltage winding short-circuited as in Fig. 477 measure the copper loss, equivalent resistance, and equivalent reactance, at rated frequency, with full-load currents flowing in the windings. Also vary I and obtain a curve of copper loss on a current base.

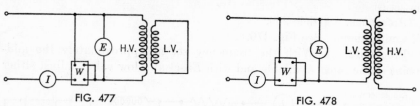

FIG. 477   FIG. 478

2. With connections as in Fig. 478, obtain a curve of iron loss on a voltage base, at rated frequency. The iron loss is so small that the wattmeter readings should be corrected for the power loss in the voltmeter and in the potential circuit of the wattmeter.

3. Calculate the efficiency at one-tenth, one-quarter, one-half, three-quarters, and full load, 100 per cent power factor.

4. Calculate the voltage regulation at 100 per cent power-factor load and at 50 per cent power-factor load. (The voltage regulation of a transformer is the rise in secondary terminal voltage when full load is thrown off the secondary, the primary voltage being kept constant. It is expressed as a per cent of full-load voltage.)

5. Obtain the voltage regulation experimentally for the same power factors.

Questions. 1. Why is the primary power factor less than that of the secondary, particularly at light loads?

2. What would the full-load efficiency of the transformer be if the power factor of the load were 50 per cent?

3. If the transformer is connected to the line for 24 hr a day but carries full load for only 6 hr a day and no load the rest of the time, what is the all-day efficiency?

Experiment 16

Object of Experiment. To predetermine the voltage characteristics (Fig. 370) of a single-phase, or three-phase, generator at 100 per cent, 80 per cent, and zero power factors, from the no-load saturation and short-circuit curves, and to compare the result at 100 per cent power factor with that found by actual load test. (A lamp bank has a power factor of approximately 100 per cent.)

References. Articles 356 to 358.

Connections. Figure 371 or 372.

Readings. 1. No-load saturation; armature volts and field current at rated speed.

2. Short circuit; armature amperes and field current at the same speed.

3. Load curve; terminal voltage and armature current with constant field excitation and the same constant speed, 100 per cent power-factor load.

4. Measure the armature resistance with direct current.

Curves. (1) No-load saturation; armature voltage on a field-current base. (2) Short circuit; armature current on a field-current base.

(3) Armature reactance determined from curves 1 and 2 plotted on a field-current base.

(4) Load curve; terminal voltage on an armature-current base, by calculation at 100 per cent, 80 per cent, and zero power factors, and by test at 100 per cent power factor, using the same field current for all four curves.

Questions.

1. Give the theory of the method used to determine the reactance of the armature of the generator.

2. Why does the voltage drop more rapidly, with increasing load, at low power factors than at high power factors?

3. Why are a-c generators rated in kilovolt-amperes and not in kilowatts?

4. How is the voltage of an a-c generator maintained constant in practice, at all loads and power factors?

Experiment 17

Object of Experiment. To determine experimentally the starting and the running characteristics of a polyphase induction motor.

References. Articles 337 to 351.

Connections. See Fig. 479.

Starting Torque. 1. With the rotor held stationary by means of a torque-measuring device, take the necessary readings to plot curves of current, torque, and power factor, at starting, on an applied voltage

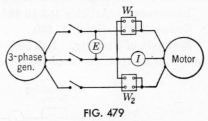

FIG. 479

base. Take care not to overheat the motor. Readings up to twice full-load current may be taken if they are taken quickly. Produce the curves to obtain the values at rated voltage.

2. If the motor is of the wound-rotor type, take the necessary readings to plot curves of current, torque, and power factor, at starting, on a rotor-resistance base, for constant applied voltage. This cannot be done at rated voltage without overheating the motor, but it may be done at one-half rated voltage if the readings are taken reasonably quickly.

Running Characteristics. With the applied voltage and the frequency both constant at the rated values, vary the brake torque and obtain curves of speed, torque, efficiency, current, and power factor, on a horsepower-output base. The speed should be obtained by measuring the slip. A stroboscopic method is best, but in the case of a wound-rotor motor the slip may be obtained by measuring the frequency of the current in the rotor. A d-c ammeter connected in the rotor circuit will oscillate at the rotor frequency, which is usually low enough to be counted.

Questions. 1. Why is the current for a given torque greater when the motor is at standstill than when running?

2. What are the advantages and disadvantages of the squirrel-cage induction motor compared with the wound-rotor induction motor?

3. Explain the shape of the power-factor curve. Why is the power factor low at light loads?

4. Explain the shape of the speed curve.

5. How would you reverse the direction of rotation of an induction motor?

6. How can the speed of an induction motor be varied for a given load? How does the induction motor compare with the d-c shunt motor for the operation of machine tools, and with the d-c series motor for the operation of cranes?

7. What effect has decrease of applied voltage on the speed of an induction motor at no load and at full load?

Experiment 18

Object of Experiment. To start up a synchronous motor, and to determine its running characteristics.

References. Articles 363 to 366.

Connections. See Fig. 480.

Methods of Starting. 1. The usual method of starting a synchronous motor is to open the field circuit and to apply reduced voltage to the

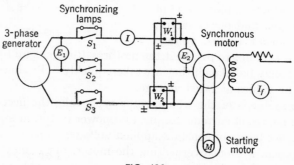

FIG. 480

armature leads. The pulling into synchronism of the motor will be indicated by the needle of the ammeter I first giving one or more swings and then suddenly dropping and becoming steady. When the motor is in or near synchronism, field current is gradually applied. If the poles have locked in with the wrong polarity, the rotor will slip back one pole pitch, which will be indicated by one large swing of the ammeter needle.

Try starting the motor with the field circuit short-circuited and with the same applied voltage.

2. Start up the synchronous motor by means of the belted d-c motor M and adjust the speed of the synchronous motor and its excitation until the voltage E_2 is equal to E_1 and the synchronizing lamps all remain dark for a second or two at a time. (If all the lamps do not become dark at the same instant, then interchange two of the motor leads.)

When all three lamps are dark at the same instant, then close the three-pole switch S_1, S_2, and S_3. The starting motor can then be disconnected by throwing the belt, and the synchronous motor loaded by means of a prony brake.

If a dynamometer is available for measuring the brake torque, it may be run as a motor to bring the synchronous motor up to speed, instead of the belted motor shown in Fig. 480.

Readings. With the applied voltage E_2, the frequency, and the brake torque all constant, take readings of the current I and the watts W_1 and W_2 for different values of the exciting current I_f. Do this for four different values of brake torque, namely, zero, one-third, two-thirds, and three-thirds of rated full-load torque.

Curves. Plot armature current and power factor on an exciting-current base for each of the four constant values of brake torque.

Questions. 1. Explain the shapes of the curves.

2. What are the advantages and disadvantages of the synchronous motor compared with the induction motor?

3. What effect has the power factor of the load on the size of the generator and on the power loss in the transmission line supplying the load?

Experiment 19

Object of Experiment. To determine the characteristics of a rotary converter.

Reference. Article 398.

Connections. On the a-c end the machine is connected in the same way as a synchronous motor (see Expt. 18), while on the d-c end it is connected in the same way as a shunt generator.

Method of Starting. The machine may be started up as a motor from the d-c end, instead of by means of a starting motor, and synchronized in the same way as a synchronous motor (see Expt. 18), or it may be started up on the a-c end as a synchronous motor (Expt. 18).

Readings. With the applied voltage E_2, the frequency, and the load resistance on the d-c side all constant, take readings of the d-c volts and amperes, the current I, and the watts W ($= W_1 + W_2$) for different values of the exciting current I_f. Take a complete set of readings for zero, one-third, two-thirds, and full-load output from the d-c side.

Curves. Plot alternating current and power factor

$$\frac{\text{Watts}}{\text{Volts} \times \text{amperes}}$$

on an exciting-current base for each load resistance.

Plot applied voltage E_2 and d-c voltage E_3 on a d-c (I_3) base.

Plot efficiency on a kilowatt-output base at 100 per cent and at some other power factor.

Questions. Why is the voltage of the d-c side independent of the field current, and how can this voltage be controlled?

Experiment 20

Object of Experiment. To determine the voltage and current relations with different transformer connections.

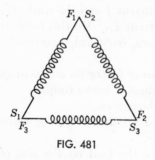

FIG. 481

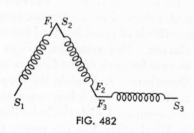

FIG. 482

Reference. Chapter 32.

Connections:

1. Y to Y, Fig. 326.
2. Y to Δ, Fig. 328.
3. Δ to Δ, Fig. 327.
4. Open Δ, Fig. 329.

Before finally closing the Δ on the secondaries of a bank of transformers, always first close the Δ through a voltmeter of range not less than twice the voltage of one phase. A potential transformer may be used to extend the range of the voltmeter if necessary. If the polarities of the transformers are correct, as in Fig. 481, the voltmeter will read zero, thus indicating that it is safe to close the Δ. If, however, the polarity of one transformer is incorrect, as in Fig. 482, the voltmeter will read twice the voltage of one phase, and closing the Δ would then be equivalent to short-circuiting the transformers.

Readings. 1. Connect the transformers Y-Y, inserting the meters necessary to measure the line volts, the volts to neutral, the line current, and the currents in the transformer windings. Record these measurements for one value of primary voltage and for any one convenient balanced load.

2. Connect the transformers Y-Δ, and proceed as with the Y-Y connection.

3. Connect the transformers Δ-Δ, and proceed as with the Y-Y connection.

4. Remove one transformer so as to leave the two remaining transformers connected open-Δ, and proceed as with the Y-Y connection.

Question. With each of the four transformer connections, how closely did the measured values of voltage and current agree with the theoretical values?

APPENDIX

TABLE 10. Conductor Materials

Material	Specific resistance, 20°C			Temperature coefficient, 20°C	Mass, g per cu cm
	μohms per cm cube	μohms per in. cube	Ohms per cir mil-ft		
Annealed copper.......	1.724	0.6788	10.37	0.00393	8.89
Hard-drawn copper....	1.79	0.695	10.77	0.00378	8.89
Annealed aluminum....	2.82	1.113	17.0	0.0039	2.7
Hard-drawn aluminum.	2.92	1.15	17.5	0.0038	2.7
Pure iron............	10.0	3.93	60.0	0.006	7.86
Steel wire............	10.7–17.5	4.2–6.9	64–106	0.006–0.0036	7.86
Cast iron............	75–100	29.5–39.4	450–600	0.001–0.00074	7.32

PRINCIPLES AND PRACTICE OF ELECTRICAL ENGINEERING

TABLE 11. Standard Annealed Solid Copper Conductors (B & S Gauge; Temperature, 20°C)

Gauge No.	Diameter, mils	Cross section, cir mils	Ohms per 1,000 ft	Pounds per 1,000 ft
0000	460.0	211,600	0.0490	640.5
000	409.6	167,800	0.0618	507.9
00	364.8	133,100	0.0779	402.8
0	324.9	105,500	0.0983	319.5
1	289.3	83,690	0.1239	253.3
2	257.6	66,370	0.1563	200.9
3	229.4	52,640	0.1970	159.3
4	204.3	41,740	0.2485	126.4
5	181.9	33,100	0.3133	100.2
6	162.0	26,250	0.3951	79.46
7	144.3	20,820	0.4982	63.02
8	128.5	16,510	0.6282	49.98
9	114.4	13,090	0.7921	39.63
10	101.9	10,380	0.9989	31.43
12	80.81	6,530	1.588	19.77
14	64.08	4,107	2.525	12.43
16	50.82	2,583	4.016	7.818
18	40.30	1,624	6.385	4.917
20	31.96	1,022	10.15	3.092
22	25.35	642.4	16.14	1.945
24	20.10	404.0	25.67	1.223
26	15.94	254.1	40.81	0.769
28	12.64	159.8	64.90	0.4837
30	10.03	100.5	103.2	0.3042
32	7.95	63.2	164.1	0.1913
34	6.305	39.75	260.9	0.1203
36	5.000	25.00	414.8	0.0757
38	3.965	15.72	659.6	0.0476
40	3.145	9.89	1,049.	0.0299

TABLE 12. Allowable Amperes Current-carrying Capacities of Insulated Copper Conductors in Cables, Conduits, and Raceways

B & S gauge No.	Type of insulation		
	Rubber, types R, RW, and RU, and thermoplastics	Rubber, type RH	Paper and varnished cambric
14	15	15	25
12	20	20	30
10	30	30	40
8	40	45	50
6	55	65	70
4	70	85	90
2	95	115	120
1	110	130	140
0	125	150	155
00	145	175	185
000	165	200	210
0000	195	230	235
Cir mils, thousands:			
250	215	255	270
500	320	380	405
750	400	475	500
1,000	455	545	585
1,500	520	625	700
2,000	560	665	775

Table 12 assumes that there are not more than three conductors in the cable, conduit, or raceway. If the number of conductors is 4, 5, or 6, the allowable amperes are 80 per cent of the values given in the table.

Single insulated conductors suspended in the air may carry anywhere from 1.3 times the values given, in the case of No. 14, to 2.0 times the values given, in the case of the 2,000,000 cir mil cable.

For more detailed and exact values, see the National Electric Code.

LIST OF VISUAL AIDS

The visual aids listed below and on the following pages can be used to supplement much of the material in this book. For the convenience of users the films have been grouped by "principles" and "practices," but it is recommended that each film be reviewed, before use, in order to determine its suitability for a particular group or unit of study.

Motion pictures and filmstrips are included in the following list, the character of each being indicated by the self-explanatory abbreviations "MP" and "FS." Immediately following this identification is the name of the producer and, if different, the distributor also. Abbreviations are used for these names and are identified in the list of sources at the end of the bibliography. Unless otherwise indicated, the motion pictures are 16-mm sound black-and-white films and the filmstrips are 35-mm black-and-white and silent. The length of motion pictures is given in minutes (min), of filmstrips in frames (fr), of accompanying disc recording in minutes.

This bibliography is a selective one, and film users should examine the latest annual editions and supplements of *Educational Film Guide* and *Filmstrip Guide*, published by the H. W. Wilson Co., New York. The *Guides*, standard reference books, are available in most college and public libraries.

Principles

Adventure in Electronics (FS, GE, 36 fr color)   Explains the essential principles of electronics.   Produced by Walt Disney and features Donald Duck having his experiences with electronics.

Basic Electricity (MP, USAF/UWF, 19 min color)   An animated cartoon explaining the fundamentals of electricity, including voltage, current, resistance, magnetic fields, induction, primary and secondary coils, series and parallel circuits.

Basic Electronics (MP, USAF/UWF, 18 min color)   An animated cartoon explaining the meaning of atoms and electrons, vacuum tube, cathode, rectifier tube, amplifier tube, grid, and bridge circuits.

Current and Electromotive Force (MP, USN/UWF, 11 min)   Explains electron theory, the arrangement of molecules, building up of current, conductors, electromotive force, resistance, and chemical and mechanical sources of electromotive force.   (Accompanying filmstrip, 38 fr, also available)

The Diode: Principles and Applications (MP, USOE/UWF, 17 min)   Principles of electron flow across a gap; basic features of the diode tube; control of electron flow in the tube; photoelectric cells; X-ray tubes; and the diode as a rectifier.   (Accompanying filmstrip, 58 fr, also available)

Electrodynamics (MP, EBF, 11 min) Explains the principles of current electricity and electromagnetism, including magnetic field of a coil, electromagnets, magnetic hypothesis, recalescence, induction by electric currents, and transformers.

The Electron: An Introduction (MP, USOE/UWF, 16 min) Nature of electrons; electron flow in solid conductors; electromotive force; types and control of electron flow; electron flow and magnetic fields; and induced electron flow. (Accompanying filmstrip, 40 fr, also available)

Electronics at Work (MP, Westinghouse, 20 min) Explains the six basic functions of electronic tubes, and how each tube is used in industrial applications.

Electrostatics (MP, EBF, 11 min) Deals with static electricity as fundamental to an understanding of modern (1952) theories of electricity. Explains positive and negative electrification; role of insulators and conductors, movement of charges in the electroscope, the Compton electrometer, and lightning as nature's display of static electricity.

Elements of Electrical Circuits (MP, EBF, 11 min) Explains the nature of electric currents and circuits, electron motions, conductors, insulators, and factors affecting resistance. Contains animated drawings and photographic demonstrations.

Magnetism (MP, EBF, 16 min) Discusses the laws of polarity, the magnetic field, and terrestrial magnetism; and shows a variety of applications of magnetism to modern civilization.

Principles of Gas-filled Tubes (MP, USOE/UWF, 15 min) Theory of ionization applied to gas-filled tubes; control of current in circuits employing gas-filled tubes; use of the gas diode as a rectifier; action of the grid in a gas triode; and application of the gas triode as a grid-controlled rectifier. (Accompanying filmstrip, 36 fr, also available)

The Triode: Amplification (MP, USOE/UWF, 14 min) Principles of the diode and triode; electric fields; a triode amplifier circuit; amplification of d-c voltage changes; alternating voltages; distortion; amplification of audio frequency signals. (Accompanying filmstrip, 36 fr, also available)

Vacuum Tubes (MP, EBF, 11 min) Explains the three functions of the vacuum tube—amplifier, rectifier, and oscillator.

Vacuum Tubes: Electron Theory and the Diode Tube (MP, USAF/UWF, 16 min) Explains electron behavior in matter, electron sources in vacuum tubes, symbols of tubes, functioning of tube in a circuit, and effect of plate voltage changes, space charge, and diode and duodiode as reflectors.

Practices

Across-the-line Starters (MP, USOE/UWF, 15 min) Theory and operation of a manually operated thermal overload switch; a magnetically operated across-the-line starter; a drum reversing switch for a three-phase motor; and a magnetic reversing switch. (Accompanying filmstrip, 37 fr, also available)

Automotive Electrical Equipment (FS series, McGraw) Fifteen filmstrips, in two sets, correlated with Crouse: *Automotive Electrical Equipment.* Titles and lengths are:

SET ONE

Electric Current Principles (37 fr)
Electric Current Measurement (33 fr)
Principles of Electromagnetism (31 fr)
Application of Electromagnetism (45 fr)

Storage Battery Principles (35 fr)
Storage Battery Operation (48 fr)
Switches, Relays, and Lights (19 fr)
Gauges and Wiring (36 fr)

SET TWO

Starting System Principles (29 fr)
Starting System Drives (29 fr)
Starting System Controls (27 fr)
Generators (30 fr)
Generator-output Regulators (54 fr)
Ignition System (38 fr)
Ignition Distributor (47 fr)

By Their Works (MP, GE, 44 min color)   Portrays the engineers and technicians at different levels of work in General Electric plants, and GE research and development practices in manufacturing new products.

D.C. Motor. Part 1: Mechanical Overhaul (MP, USOE/UWF, 20 min)   How to test for electrical and mechanical faults; dismantle d-c motor; turn the commutator; repair and replace field coils; assemble the motor; and adjust and make final tests.   (Accompanying filmstrip, 37 fr, also available)

D.C. Motor. Part 2: Rewinding (MP, USOE/UWF, 37 min)   How to dismantle and clean an armature core; determine commutator pitch; reinsulate the core; insert coils; band an armature; shape coil ends; lay in and solder leads; balance and impregnate the armature; and turn a commutator.   (Accompanying filmstrip, 43 fr, also available)

Direct Current Controllers (MP, USOE/UWF, 15 min)   Shows shunt motors and d-c controllers in operation; and by animation, a d-c faceplate controller connected to a shunt motor.   (Accompanying filmstrip, 27 fr, also available)

Industrial Electronics Course (FS series, GE)   Twelve filmstrips (each with a disc recording, $33\frac{1}{3}$ rpm, 25 min) designed to give an understanding of the fundamentals and industrial applications of electronics.   Titles of the 12 filmstrips are:

Harnessing the Electron
Electronic Tubes as Rectifiers
Grid Control of Electronic Tubes
Fundamentals of Electricity, Part 1
Fundamentals of Electricity, Part 2
Electric Relay Systems
Electronic Rectifier Equipment
Thy-mo-trol
Electronic Control of A-C Power
Electronic Frequency Changing
Photoelectric Relay Systems
Electronics—Today and Tomorrow

Reduced Voltage Starters (MP, USOE/UWF, 23 min)   Principle of the transformer; operation of a manual starting compensator; thermal overload relay, and automatic starting compensator.   (Accompanying filmstrip, 46 fr, also available)

Repulsion-Induction Motor: General Overhaul (MP, USOE/UWF, 25 min)   How to check a repulsion-induction motor for electrical and mechanical faults; dismantle it; remove a damaged coil; wind and insulate a new coil; and assemble and lubricate the motor.   (Accompanying filmstrip, 33 fr, also available)

Repulsion Motor Principles (MP, USOE/UWF, 18 min)   Explains construction of repulsion motor; rotor circuits and effect of brush position; short-circuiting and brush-lifting mechanism; and applications of repulsion motors. (Accompanying filmstrip, 40 fr, also available)

Rotating Magnetic Fields (MP, USOE/UWF, 13 min)   Explains a rotating magnetic field pattern; three-phase winding in a demonstration stator; factors that cause rotation of the magnetic field; and the construction of polyphase motors. (Accompanying filmstrip, 44 fr, also available)

Single-phase and Polyphase Circuits (MP, USOE/UWF, 17 min)   Explains a single-phase synchronous generator; the use of sine curves to illustrate flow changes; a two-phase system and three-phase system; and ways to simplify wiring. (Accompanying filmstrip, 51 fr, also available)

Squirrel-cage Rotor Principles (MP, USOE/UWF, 10 min)   Laws of magnetism and induced emf.; electron flow in squirrel-cage rotor setting up magnetic poles which create torque; construction of squirrel-cage rotors. (Accompanying filmstrip, 28 fr, also available)

Split-phase Motor Principles (MP, USOE/UWF, 17 min)   Construction of stator and rotor; comparison of winding in two-phase stator with split-phase stator; effects of winding resistances and inductive reactances; and use of capacitor to produce phase displacement. (Accompanying filmstrip, 48 fr, also available)

Split-phase Motor: Rewinding (MP, USOE/UWF, 28 min)   How to test a split-phase motor for electrical and mechanical faults; dismantle and strip the stator; rewind the stator; form and install skein windings; insulate; lace, dip, and bake the stator; and assemble, lubricate, and test the motor. (Accompanying filmstrip, 40 fr, also available)

The Story of a Storage Battery (MP, USBM, 32 min)   Explains by animation the principle of a storage battery; shows the operations in the manufacture of storage batteries; gives instructions on the care of batteries; illustrates industrial and domestic uses of batteries.

Three-phase Motor. Part 1: Preparing to Rewind (MP, USOE/UWF, 17 min)   How to interpret and record nameplate data of a three-phase motor; identify the line and finish leads; remove coils and determine coil span; use a coil winding machine; and end-tape machine-wound coils. (Accompanying filmstrip, 35 fr, also available)

Three-phase Motor. Part 2: Rewinding (MP, USOE/UWF, 17 min)   How to insert mush coils and separators or "willies"; fold, trim, and wedge slot insulation around windings; insert phase insulation; and make a delta connection. (Accompanying filmstrip, 31 fr, also available)

Using Electricity Safely (FS, McGraw, 33 fr)   Common-sense precautions in using and repairing electrical equipment—splices, soldering, taping, cords, switches, plugs, and sockets.

Wound Rotor Controllers (MP, USOE/UWF, 17 min)   Wound-rotor-motor principles; operation of a faceplate controller; drum-type nonreversing controller, drum-type reversing controller, and automatic magnetic starter for a wound-rotor motor. (Accompanying filmstrip, 40 fr, also available)

Sources of Films

EBF—Encyclopaedia Britannica Films, Wilmette, Ill.
GE—General Electric Co., 1 River Road, Schenectady 5, N.Y.

McGraw—McGraw-Hill Book Co., Text-Film Dept., 330 West 42nd St., New York 36, N.Y.

*USAF—U.S. Department of the Air Force, Washington 25, D.C.

USBM—U.S. Bureau of Mines, Pittsburgh, Pa.

*USN—U.S. Department of the Navy, Washington 25, D.C.

*USOE—U.S. Office of Education, Washington 25, D.C.

UWF—United World Films, Inc., 1445 Park Ave., New York 29, N.Y.

Westinghouse—Westinghouse Electric Corp., Pittsburgh 30, Pa.

* Films distributed by United World Films.

INDEX

A

Abampere, definition, 19
Abvolt, definition, 22
Admittance, definition, 313
Alternating voltages and currents, addition of, 268
  average value, 259
  effective value, 260
Aluminum constants, 583
Ammeter, a-c, 262
  d-c, 20, 38
Ampere, definition, 19, 28, 76
Amplidyne, 212
Amplifiers, 543–556
  classification, 551
  distortion, 544
  negative feedback, 553
  push-pull, 551
  resistance-capacitance-coupled, 545
  transformer-coupled, 548
Arc lamp, 520
Arc-welding generator, 217
Armature, a-c generator, 254, 329
  windings, 322–329
  d-c machines, 99, 105, 110
  laminations, 106
  windings, 97–104
Armature copper loss, 165
Armature reaction, a-c generators, 438
  d-c generators, 121
  d-c motors, 143
Atom, structure of, 2
Automobile, battery charging, 239
  engine ignition, 95
Autotransformer, 382

B

Balancer sets, three-wire, 248
Barlow's wheel, 18

B (cont.)

Batteries, primary, dry cells, 220
  Weston standard cell, 222
  storage, 222–241
  Edison, 230–235
  lead, 222–230
  operation, 236–241
Blow-out coil, 187
Boosters, 134, 239
Brake, electromagnetic, 85
Braking, dynamic, 202, 473
  regenerative, 182, 202, 433
British thermal unit (Btu), 46
Brushes, commutator, 111, 119
  shifting of, 118, 122

C

Cable, underground, 513
Calorie, 46
Candlepower, 517
Capacitive reactance, 291
Capacitor, 286–293
Carbon-pile battery regulator, 239
Carbon-pile rheostat, 54
Cast-iron grid resistance, 53
Cathode-ray oscilloscope, 562
Circuit breakers, air-blast, 510
  air-break, 81, 187, 510
  oil, 509
  rupturing capacity, 511
Circuits, a-c, single-phase, 271–316
  resonant, 297–302
  solution by complex numbers, 307
  three-phase, 331–351
  equivalent Y and Δ loads, 346
  power measurement, 340–346
  parallel, 33, 299–304, 314
Circular mil, 29
Clutches, electromagnetic, 84
Commutating poles, 111, 117, 124

Generator, d-c, 97–114, 126–134
  arc welding, 217
  armature reaction, 121
  commutation, 115
  compound-excited, 131
  construction, 109
  efficiency, 169
  emf equation, 106
  excitation, 112
  heating, 171
  limits of output, 172
  losses, 165–169
  parallel operation, 204
  rating, 172
  series-excited, 133
  shunt-excited, 127–131
  third-brush, 216
  three-wire, 249
  voltage characteristics, 129, 131–133
  windings, 97–105
Gilbert, definition, 61
Glare, 525
Gram-calorie, 46
Gramme-ring winding, 97
Growth of current, 93

H

Heat and electric energy, 46
Heater elements, 56
Henry, definition, 76, 90, 91
Horn gaps, 189
Horsepower and watts, 46
Hunting of synchronous machines, 463
Hysteresis, 70, 165, 369

I

Ignitron, 498
Illumination, 516–535
  calculations, 527–535
  room index, 529
  utilization factors, 527, 531, 532
Impedance, 271, 280, 297, 312
Incandescence, 516
Inductance, mutual, 90
  self-, 91
Induction, electromagnetic, 22, 88
  mutual, 88
  self-, 90
Induction furnace, 385
Induction motors (see Motors, three-phase, induction)

Inductive reactance, 274
Instrument transformers, 400
Insulating materials, 172
  permissible temperatures, 172
Insulators, 4, 245, 512
International units, 28
Interpoles (commutating poles), 112, 117, 124
Ions, 6
Iron, constants, 583
  laminations, 106, 351, 370
  loss, 165, 369
  magnetic properties, 62, 63

J

Joule, 46, 76

K

Kilogram, 76
Kilovolt-amperes (kva), 346, 447
Kilowatt, 46
Kilowatthour, 46
Kirchhoff's laws, 32, 297
Knife switches, 186

L

Lamination, of armature cores, 106, 166, 351
  of transformer cores, 370
Lamps, arc, 520
  fluorescent, 521
  lumens output tables, 519, 524
  mercury-vapor, 524
  tungsten, gas-filled, 518
    series street, 520
    vacuum, 518
Lenz's law, 89
Lightning arresters, autovalve, 508
  carbon-block, 507
  thyrite, 507
Loading-back tests, 206
Lumen, definition, 517
Lumens output of lamps, 519, 524

M

Magnetic brake, 84
Magnetic circuits, 58–71
Magnetic clutch, 84